AERODYNAMICS FOR ENGINEERING STUDENTS

AERODYNAMICS
for Engineering Students

E. L. HOUGHTON, B.Sc. (Eng.), A.F.R.Ae.S., A.M.I.Mech.E.

Senior Lecturer in Aeronautical Engineering
Northampton College of Advanced Technology, London

and

A. E. BROCK, M.Sc. (Eng.), A.F.R.Ae.S.

Lecturer in Aeronautical Engineering,
Northampton College of Advanced Technology, London

LONDON
EDWARD ARNOLD (PUBLISHERS) LTD.

Printed in Great Britain by
Butler & Tanner Ltd., Frome and London

PREFACE

This volume is intended for all students of Aeronautical Engineering in the earlier years of their specialist course studies. In particular, students taking the University of London B.Sc.(Eng.) Degree, Parts I and II, and the first three years of the Hives Council Diploma of Technology have been kept in mind. The standard, however, is well suited to the A1 and A2 levels of the Higher National Certificate and Diploma Courses.

The early chapters define the units and dimensions of the physical quantities used in aeronautics. Hydro- and aerostatics are considered next, with their allied topics of manometry and atmospheric stability respectively. 'Air in motion' forms the theme of Chapter 4, where we seek to relate the fundamental laws of aerodynamics in a concise sequence, unhindered by the detailed exposition of potential flow theory, which is considered separately in Chapters 10 and 11. In Chapter 5, definitions of wing and aerofoil geometry are introduced in readiness for the discussion, in Chapter 6, of the forces and pressure systems which are the core of applied aerodynamics. The chapter on propulsion permits a reappraisal before progressing to aircraft performance in Chapters 8 and 9. These chapters treat the behaviour of aircraft as stable machines experiencing certain aerodynamic and other force systems. The aerofoil theories (first introduced in Chapter 6) are treated in full in Chapters 12 and 13, and the last chapter, though using basic ideas developed in the preceding chapters, stands by itself as a treatment of the static stability of aircraft in longitudinal, lateral and directional modes.

Although experimental data have been quoted, no attempt has been made to describe techniques or apparatus, as we feel that Experimental Aerodynamics demands a separate treatment.

In most schemes of study in Aeronautics, the theory of viscous flow and boundary layer problems are omitted from the elementary stages and, beyond very brief qualitative references, this book does not include these topics. For a similar reason it is felt that quantitative treatment of high-speed aerodynamics must largely be deferred to a later volume.

In accordance with these aims, then, this text is considered sufficiently comprehensive to bring a student to the threshold of advanced aerodynamics.

During the writing and preparation of this work we have had the help and encouragement of our colleagues in the Aeronautical Engineering Department of the Northampton College of Advanced Technology and, although they knew it not, the assistance of many students of that College. To all we offer our thanks but must add that the responsibility for all that appears is ours alone.

The abbreviations of U. of L. and N.C.A.T. refer to the University of

London and the Northampton College of Advanced Technology, London, and we are indebted to the Senate of the former and the Governing Body of the latter for kindly giving permission for the use of past examination questions.

This foreword would be incomplete without reference to the many authors of classical and popular texts whose works have formed the framework and guided the acquisition of our own incomplete knowledge of our science. A selection of these, on whom we draw freely in our work, is given in the bibliography, and we apologize if due recognition of a source has been inadvertently omitted in any particular in this book.

Surrey   E. L. HOUGHTON
1960   A. E. BROCK

CONTENTS

vii

CHAPTER 1

UNITS AND DIMENSIONS

A study in any science must include measurement and calculation, which presupposes an agreed system of units in terms of which quantities can be measured and expressed. There is no single system as yet universally accepted, and each branch of science or engineering selects a system convenient for its own requirements. The units employed in aerodynamics in particular are detailed in this chapter.

It is essential to distinguish between the terms 'dimension' and 'unit'. For example, the dimension 'length' expresses the *qualitative* concept of linear displacement, or distance between two points, as an abstract idea, without reference to actual quantitative measurement. The term 'unit' indicates a specified amount of the quantity. Thus a foot is a unit of length, being an actual 'amount' of linear displacement, and so also is a metre. The foot and metre are different *units*, since each contains a different *amount* of length, but both describe length and therefore are identical *dimensions*.*

Expressing this in symbolic form:

x ft $= [L]$ (a quantity of x ft has the dimension of length).

x metres $= [L]$ (a quantity of x metres has the dimension of length).

x ft $\neq x$ metres (x ft and x metres are unequal quantities of length).

$[x$ ft$] = [x$ metres$]$ (the dimension of x metres is the same as the dimension of x ft).

1.1. The fundamental dimensions and units.

There are four fundamental *dimensions* in terms of which the dimensions of all other physical quantities may be expressed. They are mass $[M]$, length $[L]$, time $[T]$ and temperature $[\theta]$.† A consistent set of *units* is formed by specifying units of particular value for each of these dimensions. In aeronautical engineering the accepted units are respectively the slug, the foot, the second and the degree Centigrade (or Kelvin—see below).

The foot and the second are identical with the units of the same names in common use.

The slug, the aeronautical unit of mass, is defined as 'that mass which, when acted on by a force of one pound weight, has an acceleration of one foot per second per second'. This compares with the pound mass which,

---

* Quite often 'dimension' appears in the form 'a dimension of 8 feet' and thus means a specified length. This meaning of the word is thus closely related to the engineer's 'unit', and implies linear extension only. Another common example of its use is in 'three-dimensional geometry', implying three linear extensions in different directions. References to three-dimensional aerofoils and two-dimensional flow in later chapters illustrate this. The original meaning must not be confused with either of these uses.

† Some authorities express temperature in terms of length and time. This introduces complications which are briefly considered in § 2.8.

1

when acted on by a force of one pound weight, has an acceleration of 32·18 feet per second per second. By comparison of these two definitions it is seen that one slug is equivalent to 32·18 pounds mass. The slug is, in fact, a comparatively large, 'sluggish' mass, whence the name is derived. This fact provides a useful mnemonic for the size of the slug.

It must be remembered that, in the present subject, all masses are measured in slugs and all forces in pounds weight; it is, strictly, incorrect to talk of a force of so many pounds. Since, however, there is no danger of confusion between the unit of mass and the unit of force, such as may arise when mass is in pounds and force in pounds weight, the word 'weight' is rarely used in this context.

The degree Centigrade is one one-hundredth part of the temperature rise involved when pure water at freezing temperature is heated to boiling temperature at standard pressure. In the Centigrade scale, pure water at standard pressure freezes at 0°C and boils at 100°C.

The degree Kelvin (°K) is identical in size with the degree Centigrade (°C), but the Kelvin scale of temperature is measured from the absolute zero of temperature, which is approximately −273°C. Thus a temperature in °K is equal to the temperature in °C plus 273 (approximately).

1.2. The units of other physical quantities. Having defined the four fundamental dimensions and their units, it is possible to establish units of all other physical quantities (see Table 1.1).

Speed, for example, is defined as the distance travelled in unit time; it therefore has the dimension LT^{-1} and is measured in feet per second (ft/sec). It is sometimes desirable and permissible to use 'miles per hour' or 'knots' as units of speed and care must then be exercised to avoid errors caused by inconsistency.

To find the dimensions and units of more complex quantities, appeal is made to the principle of '*dimensional homogeneity*'. This means simply that, in any valid physical equation, the dimensions of both sides must be the same. Thus if, for example, (mass)^n appears on the left-hand side of the equation, (mass)^n must also appear on the right-hand side, and similarly this applies to length, time and temperature.*

Thus, to find the dimensions of *force*, use is made of the equation

$$\text{Force} = \text{mass} \times \text{acceleration}$$

while acceleration is speed ÷ time.

Expressed dimensionally, this is

$$\text{Force} = [M] \times \left[\frac{L}{T} \div T \right] = [MLT^{-2}]$$

Writing in the appropriate units, it is seen that a force is measured in units of slug ft/sec². Since, however, the unit of force is given the name pound weight (contracted usually to pound), it follows that

$$1 \text{ lb} = 1 \text{ slug ft/sec}^2.$$

* This is considered in more detail in Chapter 2, where the wider applications of dimensional analysis are also discussed (see also 6.2 and 7.2).

TABLE 1.1
Units and Dimensions

Quantity	Dimension	Unit
Length	L	foot (ft)
Mass	M	slug
Time	T	second (sec)
Temperature	θ	degrees Centigrade (°C)
		degrees Kelvin (°K)
Area	L^2	ft²
Volume	L^3	ft³
Speed	LT^{-1}	ft/sec
Acceleration	LT^{-2}	ft/sec²
Angle	1	radian or degree(°)
		[The radian is expressed
		as a ratio and is therefore
		dimensionless]
Angular velocity . . .	T^{-1}	1/sec
Angular acceleration . .	T^{-2}	1/sec²
Frequency	T^{-1}	1/sec
Density	ML^{-3}	slug/ft³
Force	MLT^{-2}	pound weight (lb)
Stress	$ML^{-1}T^{-2}$	lb/ft²
Strain	1	(None, expressed as %)
Pressure	$ML^{-1}T^{-2}$	lb/ft²
Energy	ML^2T^{-2}	ft lb
Power	ML^2T^{-3}	ft lb/sec
		[One horse-power (H.P.)
		= 550 ft lb/sec]
Moment	ML^2T^{-2}	lb ft
Absolute viscosity . . .	$ML^{-1}T^{-1}$	slug/ft sec
Kinematic viscosity . .	L^2T^{-1}	ft²/sec
Bulk elasticity	$ML^{-1}T^{-2}$	lb/ft²

EXERCISES

1. Verify the dimensions and units given in Table 1.1.

2. The Constant of Gravitation G is defined by $F = G\dfrac{mM}{r^2}$, where F is the gravitational force between two masses m and M whose centres of mass are distance r apart. Find the dimensions of G, and its units in the slug-foot-second system. (*Ans.* MT^2L^{-3}, slug sec²/ft³)

CHAPTER 2

THE RELEVANT PROPERTIES OF A FLUID

2.1. The forms of matter.   Matter may exist in three principal forms, solid, liquid or gas, corresponding in that order to decreasing rigidity of the bonds between the molecules of which the matter is composed. A special form of a gas, known as a *plasma*, has properties different from those of a normal gas and, although belonging to the third group, can be regarded justifiably as a separate, distinct form of matter.

In a solid the intermolecular bonds are very rigid, maintaining the molecules in what is virtually a fixed spatial relationship. Thus a solid has a fixed volume and shape. This is seen particularly clearly in crystals, in which the molecules or atoms are arranged in a definite, uniform pattern, giving all crystals of that substance the same geometric shape.

A liquid has weaker bonds between the molecules. The distances between the molecules are fairly rigidly controlled but the arrangement in space is free. A liquid, therefore, has a closely defined volume but no definite shape, and may accommodate itself to the shape of its container within the limits imposed by its volume.

A gas has very weak bonding between the molecules and therefore has neither a definite shape nor a definite volume, but will always fill the whole of the vessel containing it.

A plasma is a special form of gas in which the atoms are ionized, that is, they have lost one or more electrons and therefore have a nett positive electrical charge. The electrons which have been stripped from the atoms are wandering free within the gas and have a negative electrical charge. If the numbers of ionized atoms and free electrons are such that the total positive and negative charges are approximately equal, so that the gas as a whole has little or no charge, it is termed a plasma. In aeronautics the plasma is usually met as a jet of ionized gas produced by passing a stream of normal gas through an electric arc. It is of particular interest in problems of the re-entry of rockets and satellites into the atmosphere.

2.2. Fluids.   The basic feature of a fluid is that it can flow, and this is the essence of any definition of it. This feature, however, applies to substances which are not true fluids, e.g., a fine powder piled on a sloping surface will also flow. Fine powder, such as flour, poured in a column on to a flat surface will form a roughly conical pile, with a large angle of repose, whereas water—a true fluid—poured on to a fully wetted surface will spread uniformly over the whole surface. Equally a powder may be heaped in a spoon or bowl, whereas a liquid will always form a level surface. A definition of a fluid must allow for these facts. Thus a fluid may be defined as 'matter capable of flowing and either finding its own level (if liquid) or filling the whole of its container (if a gas)'.

4

Experiment shows that an extremely fine powder, in which the particles are not much larger than molecular size, will also find its own level and may thus come under the common definition of a liquid. Also a phenomenon well known in the transport of sands, gravels, etc. is that they will find their own level if they are agitated by vibration, or the passage of air jets through the particles. These, however, are special cases and do not detract from the authority of the definition of a fluid as a substance that flows or (tautologically) that possesses fluidity.

2.3. Pressure. At any point in a fluid, which can be either liquid or gas, there is a pressure. If a body is placed in a fluid, its surface is bombarded by a large number of molecules moving at random. Under normal conditions the collisions on a small area of surface are so frequent that they cannot be distinguished as individual impacts. They appear as a steady force on the area. The *intensity* of this 'molecular bombardment' force is the *static pressure*.

For large bodies moving or at rest in the fluid (air, say) the pressure is not uniform over the surface and this gives rise to *aerodynamic force* or *aerostatic force* respectively (see § 3.2).

Since a pressure is intensity of force, it has the *dimensions*

$$[\text{Force}] \div [\text{area}] = [MLT^{-2}] \div [L^2] = [ML^{-1}T^{-2}]$$

and is expressed in the *units* of pounds per square foot (lb/ft²).

2.4. Temperature. In any form of matter the molecules are in motion relative to each other. In gases the motion is random movement of appreciable amplitude ranging from about 3×10^{-6} inches under normal conditions to several inches at very low pressures. The distance of free movement of a molecule of gas is the distance it can travel before colliding with another molecule or the walls of the container. The mean value of this distance for all the molecules in a gas is called the 'mean molecular free path'.

By virtue of this motion the molecules possess kinetic energy, and this energy is sensed as *temperature* of the solid, liquid or gas. In the case of a gas in motion it is called the 'static temperature'.

Temperature has the *dimension* $[\theta]$ and the *units* °C or °K (Chap. 1). In practically all calculations in aerodynamics, temperature is measured in °K, i.e., from absolute zero.

2.5. Density. The density of a material is a measure of the amount of the material contained in a given volume. In a fluid the density may vary from point to point. Consider the fluid contained within a small spherical region of volume δV centred at some point in the fluid, and let the mass of fluid within this spherical region be δm. Then the density of the fluid at the point on which the sphere is centred is defined by

$$\text{Density } \rho = \lim_{\delta V \to 0} \frac{\delta m}{\delta V} . \qquad . \qquad . \qquad . \qquad (2.1)$$

The *dimensions* of density are thus ML^{-3}, and it is measured in units of slugs per cubic foot (slug/ft³).

At standard temperature and pressure (288°K, 2116 lb/ft²) the density of dry air is 0·002378 slug/ft³.

Difficulties arise in applying the above definition rigorously to a real fluid composed of discrete molecules since the sphere, when taken to the limit, either will or will not contain part of a molecule. If it does contain a molecule the value obtained for the density will be fictitiously high. If it does not contain a molecule the resultant value for the density will be zero. This difficulty can be avoided in two ways over the range of temperatures and pressures normally encountered in aerodynamics:

(i) The molecular nature of a gas may for many purposes be ignored and the assumption made that the fluid is a continuum, i.e., does not consist of discrete particles, or

(ii) the decrease in size of the imaginary sphere may be supposed to be carried to a limiting minimum size. This limiting size is such that, although the sphere is small compared with the dimensions of any physical body, such as an aeroplane, placed in the fluid, it is large compared with the fluid molecules, and therefore contains a reasonable number of whole molecules.

2.6. Viscosity. This is often regarded as the 'stickiness' of a fluid and is its tendency to resist sliding between layers or, more rigorously, a rate of change of shear strain.

There is very little resistance to the movement of a knife-blade edge-on through air, but to produce the same motion through thick oil needs much more effort. This is because the viscosity of oil is high compared with that of air.

2.6.1. Absolute coefficient of viscosity is a direct measure of the viscosity of a fluid. Consider two parallel flat plates placed a distance h apart, the space between them being filled with fluid. One plate is held fixed and the other is moved in its own plane at a speed V (see Fig. 2.1).

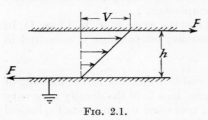

The fluid immediately adjacent to each plate will move with that plate (i.e., there is no slip). Thus the fluid in contact with the lower plate will be at rest while that in contact with the upper plate will be moving with speed V. Between the plates the speed of the fluid will vary linearly as shown in Fig. 2.1, in the

FIG. 2.1.

absence of other influences. As a direct result of viscosity a force F has to be applied to each plate to maintain the motion, the fluid tending to retard the moving plate and to drag the fixed plate to the right.

If the area of fluid in contact with each plate is A, the shear stress is F/A. The rate of slide of the upper plate over the lower is V/h.

These quantities are connected by Maxwell's Equation, which serves to define the 'Absolute Coefficient of Viscosity' μ. This equation is

$$\frac{F}{A} = \mu\left(\frac{V}{h}\right) \qquad . \qquad . \qquad . \qquad . \qquad (2.2)$$

Hence $\qquad [ML^{-1}T^{-2}] = [\mu][LT^{-1}L^{-1}] = [\mu][T^{-1}]$

Thus $\qquad\qquad [\mu] = [ML^{-1}T^{-1}]$

and the units of μ are therefore slugs/ft sec.

At 0°C (273°K) the absolute coefficient of viscosity for dry air is $3·58 \times 10^{-7}$ slug/ft sec.

2.6.2. Kinematic coefficient of viscosity.
This is a convenient form in which the viscosity of a fluid may be expressed. It is formed by combining the density ρ and the absolute coefficient of viscosity μ according to the equation

$$\nu = \frac{\mu}{\rho}$$

and has the dimensions L^2T^{-1} and the units ft²/sec.

It may be regarded as a measure of the relative magnitudes of viscosity and inertia of the fluid and has the practical advantage, in calculations, of replacing two numbers representing μ and ρ by a single number.

2.7. Bulk elasticity.
This is a measure of how easily the fluid may be compressed, and is defined as the ratio of a change in pressure to the volumetric strain produced thereby.

If a certain bulk of fluid, under a pressure p, has a volume V and the pressure is then increased to $p + \delta p$, the volume will decrease to $V - \delta V$.

The volumetric strain produced by the pressure increase δp is $\delta V/V$, and so the modulus of bulk elasticity is given by

$$K = \delta p / \delta V / V \qquad . \qquad . \qquad . \qquad . \qquad (2.3)$$

Since $\delta V/V$ is the ratio of two volumes it is non-dimensional and thus the dimensions of K are identical with those of pressure, namely $ML^{-1}T^{-2}$, and it is measured in units of lb/ft².

2.8. Heat properties.
For present purposes, heat may be regarded as a form of energy.* This is implicit in the First Law of Thermodynamics: 'heat and mechanical energy are equivalent in a constant proportion'. Consequently, heat has the same dimensions as energy, namely ML^2T^{-2} and can be measured in units of ft lb. It has been convenient to measure heat by the quantity needed to perform some specified heating operation.

On this basis the Aerodynamic Heat Unit (A.H.U.) is 'one one-hundredth part of the heat needed to raise one slug of pure (liquid) water

---

* For a fuller discussion on heat, not appropriate here, see *Engineering Thermodynamics* by Rogers and Mayhew (Longmans).

from freezing temperature to boiling temperature (i.e., from 0°C to 100°C)' at standard atmospheric pressure.*

The fundamental heat unit which has been redefined, but which has not gained general currency in aerodynamics, is the joule, defined as 10^7 ergs.† The joule is equal to $1\cdot64 \times 10^{-5}$ A.H.U. and is thus an inconveniently small unit.

Joule's constant J. This is the constant of proportionality in the First Law of Thermodynamics. It has the numerical value of 45,050 ft lb/A.H.U., and is non-dimensional, being the ratio of two quantities of energy.

2.8.1. Specific heat.

The specific heat of a material is the amount of heat necessary to raise the temperature of unit mass of the material by one degree. Thus it has the dimensions $L^2 T^{-2} \theta^{-1}$ and is measured in units of A.H.U./slug °C, or ft lb/slug °C.

With a gas there are two distinct ways in which the heating operation may be performed: at constant volume and at constant pressure.

Specific heat at constant volume. If unit mass of the gas is enclosed in a cylinder sealed by a piston, and the piston is locked in position, the volume of the gas cannot change, and any heat added is used solely to raise the temperature of the gas. (It is assumed that the cylinder and piston do not receive any of the heat.) The specific heat of the gas under these conditions is the specific heat at constant volume, c_v.

For dry air at normal aerodynamic temperatures, $c_v = 0\cdot1715$ A.H.U./ slug °C.

Specific heat at constant pressure. Assume that the piston referred to above is now freed and acted on by a constant force. The pressure of the gas is that necessary to resist the force and is therefore constant. The application of heat to the gas causes its temperature to rise, which leads to an increase in the volume of the gas, in order to maintain the constant pressure. Thus the gas does mechanical work against the force. It is therefore necessary to supply the heat required to increase the temperature of the gas (as in the case at constant volume) and in addition the amount of heat equivalent to the mechanical work done against the force. This total amount of heat is called the 'specific heat at constant pressure', c_p, and is defined as 'that amount of heat required to raise the temperature of unit mass of the gas by one degree, the pressure of the gas being kept constant while heating'. In view of the foregoing it will be realized that c_p is always greater than c_v. For dry air at normal aerodynamic temperatures, $c_p = 0\cdot24$ A.H.U./slug °C.

* Sometimes the Centigrade Heat Unit (C.H.U.) is used, the definition of which differs from that of the A.H.U. only in that the mass of pure water is one pound, instead of one slug. The introduction of the pound mass means that the C.H.U. is not consistent with the accepted system of units. Its use is, therefore, not recommended. 1 C.H.U. = 1/32·18 A.H.U.

† Units of heat are now *defined* [9th General Conference of Weights & Measures, 1948] in terms of work units. This avoids the anomaly of having two sets of absolute standards. Temperature has the dimensions $L^2 . T^{-2}$ and specific heats are dimensionless.

2.8.2. The ratio of specific heats. This is a property important in high-speed flows and is defined by the equation

$$\gamma = \frac{c_p}{c_v} \qquad \qquad (2.4)$$

The value of γ depends on the number of atoms in each molecule of the gas. Since c_p is greater than c_v, it follows that γ is always greater than unity. For dry air $\gamma = 1.403$, often used as the approximate value 1·4.

2.8.3. The gas constant, R. This is the amount of mechanical work which is obtained by heating unit mass of the gas through unit temperature rise at constant pressure. It is derived from the definitions of c_p and c_v:

$$c_p - c_v = \frac{R}{J} \qquad \qquad (2.5)$$

It follows that R is measured in the units of ft lb per slug degree Centigrade (ft lb/slug °C). For air over the range of temperatures and pressures normally encountered in aerodynamics it has the value 3092 ft lb/slug °C.

From eqns. (2.4) and (2.5), the following relationships can be derived:

$$c_p = \frac{\gamma}{\gamma - 1} \frac{R}{J} \qquad \qquad (2.6.1)$$

and

$$c_v = \frac{1}{\gamma - 1} \frac{R}{J} \qquad \qquad (2.6.2)$$

2.9. Dimensional analysis. The theory of dimensional homogeneity has additional uses to that described in Chapter 1. By predicting how one variable may depend on a number of others, it may be used to direct the course of an experiment or the analysis of experimental results. For example, when fluid flows past a circular cylinder whose axis is perpendicular to the stream, eddies are formed behind the cylinder at a frequency which depends on a number of factors, such as the size of the cylinder, the speed of the stream, etc.

In an experiment to investigate the variation of eddy frequency the obvious procedure is to take several sizes of cylinder, place them in streams of various fluids at a number of different speeds and count the frequency of the eddies in each case. No matter how detailed, the results apply directly only to the cases tested, and it is necessary to find some pattern underlying the results; a theoretical guide is helpful in achieving this end, and it is in this direction that 'dimensional analysis' is of use.

In the above problem the frequency of the eddies, n per second, will depend primarily on:

    (i) the size of the cylinder, represented by its diameter, d ft,

    (ii) the speed of the stream, V ft/sec,

    (iii) the density of the fluid, ρ slugs/ft³, and

    (iv) the viscosity of the fluid, ν ft²/sec,

noting that either μ or ν may be used to represent the viscosity of the fluid.

B

The factors should also include the geometric shape of the body. Since the problem here is concerned only with long circular cylinders with their axes perpendicular to the stream, this factor will be common to all readings and may be ignored in this analysis. It is also assumed that the speed is low compared to the speed of sound in the fluid, so that compressibility (represented by the modulus of bulk elasticity) may be ignored; also gravitational effects are excluded.

Then
$$n = f(d, V, \rho, \nu)$$

and, assuming that this function $f(\ldots)$ may be put in the form

$$n = Cd^a V^b \rho^e \nu^f \quad . \quad . \quad . \quad . \quad (2.7)$$

where C is a constant and a, b, e and f are some unknown indices, not necessarily rational or real, putting eqn. (2.7) in dimensional form leads to

$$[T^{-1}] = [L^a(LT^{-1})^b(ML^{-3})^e(L^2T^{-1})^f] \quad . \quad . \quad (2.8)$$

where each factor has been replaced by its dimensions. Now the dimensions of both sides must be the same and therefore the indices of M, L and T on the two sides of the equation may be equated as follows:

Mass (M) $\qquad\qquad 0 = e \qquad . \qquad . \qquad . \qquad . \qquad (2.9.1)$

Length (L) $\qquad\qquad 0 = a + b - 3e + 2f \qquad . \qquad . \qquad (2.9.2)$

Time (T) $\qquad\qquad -1 = -b - f \qquad . \qquad . \qquad . \qquad (2.9.3)$

Here are three equations in four unknowns. One unknown must therefore be left undetermined; f, the index of ν, is selected for this role, and the equations are solved for a, b and e in terms of f.

The solution is, in fact,

$$b = 1 - f \quad . \quad . \quad . \quad . \quad (2.9.4)$$

$$e = 0 \quad . \quad . \quad . \quad . \quad (2.9.5)$$

$$a = -1 - f \quad . \quad . \quad . \quad . \quad (2.9.6)$$

Substituting these values in eqn. (2.7),

$$n = Cd^{-1-f} V^{1-f} \rho^0 \nu^f \quad . \quad . \quad . \quad (2.10)$$

Rearranging eqn. (2.10), it becomes

$$n = C\frac{V}{d} \cdot \left(\frac{Vd}{\nu}\right)^{-f} . \quad . \quad . \quad . \quad (2.11)$$

or, alternatively,

$$\frac{nd}{V} = g\left(\frac{Vd}{\nu}\right) \quad . \quad . \quad . \quad . \quad (2.12)$$

where 'g' represents some function which, as it includes the undetermined constant C and index f, is unknown from the present analysis.

Although it may not appear so at first sight, eqn. (2.12) is extremely valuable, as it shows that the values of nd/V should depend only on the corresponding value of Vd/ν, regardless of the actual values of the original variables. This means that if, for each observation, the values of nd/V and Vd/ν are calculated and plotted as a graph, all the results should lie on a single curve, this curve representing the unknown function 'g'. This curve can now be published, and a person wishing to estimate the eddy frequency for some given cylinder, fluid and speed need only calculate the value of Vd/v, read from the curve the corresponding value of nd/V and convert this to eddy frequency n. Thus the results of the series of observations are now in a usable form.

Consider for a moment the two compound variables derived above.

(a) nd/V. The dimensions of this are given by

$$\frac{nd}{V} = [T^{-1} \times L \times (LT^{-1})^{-1}] = 1$$

(b) Vd/v. The dimensions of this are given by

$$\frac{Vd}{v} = [(LT^{-1}) \times L \times (L^2 T^{-1})^{-1}] = 1$$

Thus the above analysis has collapsed the four original variables d, V, ρ and v into two compound variables, both of which are non-dimensional. This has a great advantage, namely that the values obtained for these two quantities are independent of the consistent system of units used. Thus two persons, one working in, say, the slug-foot-second system and the other in the gramme-metre-second system will obtain the same values for nd/V and Vd/v for the same test, and so the 'language' problem has been overcome.

There are certain problems (e.g., the frequency of vibration of a stretched string) in which all the indices may be determined, leaving only the constant C undetermined. It is, however, usual to have more indices than equations, requiring one or more index to be left undetermined as above.

It must be noted that, while dimensional analysis will show which factors are not relevant to a given problem, the method cannot indicate which relevant factors, if any, have been left out. It is, therefore, advisable to include all factors likely to have any bearing on a given problem, leaving out only those factors which, on *a priori* considerations, may be shown to have little or no relevance.

EXERCISES

1. Assuming the period of oscillation of a simple pendulum to depend on the mass of the bob, the length of the pendulum and the acceleration due to gravity g, use the theory of dimensional analysis to show that the mass of the bob is not, in fact, relevant and find a suitable expression for the period of oscillation in terms of the other variables.   (*Ans.* $t = c\sqrt{l/g}$)

2. A thin flat disc of diameter D is rotated about a spindle through its centre at a speed of ω radians per second, in a fluid of density ρ and kinematic viscosity v. Show that the power P needed to rotate the disc may be expressed as either

(a) $$P = \rho \omega^3 D^5 f\left(\frac{v}{\omega D^2}\right), \text{ or}$$

(b) $$P = \frac{\rho v^3}{D} h\left(\frac{\omega D^2}{v}\right)$$

(Note: for (a) solve in terms of the index of ν and for (b) in terms of the index of ω.)

Further, show that $\omega D^2/\nu$, $PD/\rho\nu^3$ and $P/\rho\omega^3 D^5$ are all non-dimensional quantities.   (N.C.A.T.)

3. Spheres of various diameters D and densities σ are allowed to fall freely under gravity through various fluids (represented by their densities ρ and kinematic viscosities ν) and their terminal velocities V are measured.

Find a rational expression connecting V with the other variables, and hence suggest a suitable form of graph in which the results could be presented.

(Note: there will be 5 unknown indices, and therefore 2 must remain undetermined, which will give 2 unknown functions on the right-hand side. Make the unknown indices those of σ and ν.)

$$\left(Ans. \ V = \sqrt{Dg}\, f\!\left(\frac{\sigma}{\rho}\right) h\!\left(\frac{D}{\nu}\sqrt{Dg}\right).\right.$$

Therefore plot curves of $\dfrac{V}{\sqrt{Dg}}$ against $\dfrac{D}{\nu}\sqrt{Dg}$ for various values of σ/ρ)

CHAPTER 3

HYDROSTATICS AND AEROSTATICS; THE ATMOSPHERE

3.1. Pressure in fluid at rest.

Consider a small cubic element containing fluid at rest in a larger bulk of fluid also at rest. The faces of the cube, assumed to be made of some thin flexible material, are subject to continual bombardment by the molecules of the fluid, and thus experience a *force* (see § 2.3). The force on any face may be resolved into two components, one acting perpendicular to the face and the other along it, i.e., tangential to it. Consider for the moment the tangential components only; there are three significantly different arrangements possible (Fig. 3.1).

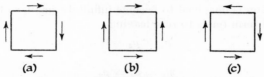

(a)   (b)   (c)

Fig. 3.1.—Fictitious systems of tangential forces in static fluid.

The system at (a) would cause the element to rotate and thus the fluid would not be at rest.

System (b) would cause the element to move (upwards and to the right for the case shown) and once more, the fluid would not be at rest. Since a fluid cannot resist shear stress, but only rate of change of shear strain (§ 2.6) the system (c) would cause the element to distort, the degree of distortion increasing with time, and the fluid would not remain at rest.

The conclusion is that a fluid at rest cannot sustain tangential pressures, or conversely, that in a fluid at rest the pressure on a surface must act in the direction perpendicular to that surface.

3.1.1. Pascal's Law.

Consider the right prism of width δy and cross-section ABC, the angle ABC being a right-angle (Fig. 3.2). The prism is constructed of material of the same density as a bulk of fluid in which the prism floats at rest with the face $BCC'B'$ horizontal.

Pressures p_1, p_2 and p_3 act on the faces shown and, as proved above, these pressures act in the direction perpendicular to the respective face. Other pressures act on the end faces of the prism but are ignored in the

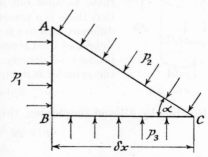

Fig. 3.2.—The prism for Pascal's Law.

present problem. In addition to these pressures, the weight W of the prism acts vertically downwards. Consider the forces acting on the wedge which is in equilibrium and at rest.

Resolving forces horizontally,

$$p_1(\delta x \tan \alpha)\, \delta y - p_2(\delta x \sec \alpha)\, \delta y \sin \alpha = 0$$

Dividing by $\delta x\, \delta y \tan \alpha$, this becomes

$$p_1 - p_2 = 0$$

i.e.,
$$p_1 = p_2 \qquad . \qquad . \qquad . \qquad (3.1)$$

Resolving forces vertically,

$$p_3\, \delta x\, \delta y - p_2(\delta x \sec \alpha)\, \delta y \cos \alpha - W = 0 \qquad . \qquad (3.2)$$

Now
$$W = \rho g \tfrac{1}{2}(\delta x)^2 \tan \alpha . \delta y$$

therefore, substituting this in eqn. (3.2) and dividing by $\delta x\, \delta y$

$$p_3 - p_2 - \tfrac{1}{2}\rho g \tan \alpha . \delta x = 0$$

If now the prism is imagined to become infinitely small, so that $\delta x \rightarrow 0$, then the third term tends to zero leaving

$$p_3 - p_2 = 0$$

Thus finally,

$$p_1 = p_2 = p_3 \qquad . \qquad . \qquad . \qquad (3.3)$$

Having become infinitely small, the prism is in effect a point and thus the above analysis shows that, at a point, the three pressures considered are equal. In addition, the angle α is purely arbitrary and can take any value in all the four quadrants, while the whole prism could be rotated through a complete circle about a vertical axis without affecting the result. Consequently it may be concluded that the pressure acting at a point in a fluid at rest is the same in all directions.

3.2. The buoyancy equation.

Consider a large volume of fluid at rest and in equilibrium and imagine a small right cylinder of the fluid, of cross-sectional area δA and height δh centred at some point (Fig. 3.3). The forces acting on the cylinder are as shown. There are also pressures acting on the vertical surface but these balance out and may be ignored. It will be seen that there is a pressure p acting on the lower face and a different pressure $p + \delta p$ acting on the upper face. The weight of fluid contained in the cylinder is equal to the product of density, volume and g, i.e., $\rho \delta A\, \delta h g$. Since the cylinder is in equilibrium,

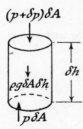

$(p + \delta p)\delta A$

δh

$\rho g \delta A \delta h$

$p \delta A$

FIG. 3.3.

$$(p + \delta p)\, \delta A + \rho \delta A\, \delta h g - p\, \delta A = 0$$

Dividing by δA and simplifying, this becomes

$$\delta p + \rho g\, \delta h = 0$$

or
$$\frac{\delta p}{\delta h} = -\rho g \qquad . \qquad . \qquad . \qquad (3.4)$$

Taking the limit as δh tends to zero this becomes

$$\frac{dp}{dh} = -\rho g \qquad . \qquad . \qquad . \qquad . \qquad (3.5)$$

which shows how the pressure varies with height in a bulk of fluid at rest.

3.2.1. Measurement of pressures.
Eqn. (3.5) may be rearranged as

$$dp = -\rho g \, dh$$

To compare the pressures p_1 and p_2 at two points in the fluid at heights h_1 and h_2 respectively, this equation may be integrated between condition 1 and condition 2 as

$$\int_1^2 dp = -\int_1^2 \rho g \, dh$$

In the special case where ρ and g are constant this may be integrated as

$$p_2 - p_1 = -\rho g (h_2 - h_1)$$

or
$$p_1 - p_2 = \rho g (h_2 - h_1) \qquad . \qquad . \qquad . \qquad (3.6)$$

If $h_2 - h_1$ is positive (point 2 above point 1), $p_1 - p_2$ is also positive ($p_2 < p_1$). Thus pressure decreases with height. Also note that $\rho g(h_2 - h_1)$ is the weight of a column of fluid of unit area and height $h_2 - h_1$. It may thus be deduced that the pressure at any point in a fluid at rest is equal to the weight of all the fluid contained in a column of unit area above that point. It should be noted here that most liquids have a density which may be regarded as constant.

This suggests methods for measuring a pressure difference between two points. A pressure difference may be used to support a column of liquid of known density, and can be measured by the height of that column. The mercury barometer is a well-known example of this, and it is common to talk of a pressure difference of, say, 2·21 in. of mercury, which in aerodynamic units is a pressure difference of 156 lb/ft². A practical application of this principle is the U-tube, which forms the basis of several pressure-measuring instruments.* The simplest form is a tube bent into the form of a U and partly filled with liquid (Fig. 3.4). The two limbs are connected to the two points between which the pressure difference is to be measured. Eqn. (3.6) states

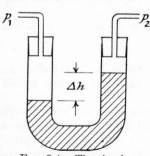

FIG. 3.4.—The simple U-tube.

$$p_1 - p_2 = \rho g (h_2 - h_1) \qquad . \qquad (3.6)$$

or
$$\Delta p = \rho g \, \Delta h \qquad . \qquad . \qquad (3.7)$$

Then by measuring Δh and using the known value of ρ it is possible to calculate the pressure difference Δp, taking care to use consistent units.

* Any pressure measuring instrument is called a manometer.

Example 3.1. On a certain day the barometric pressure is found to be 29 in. of mercury. A U-tube, filled with alcohol of specific gravity 0·82, has one limb connected to a point on a model wing in a wind-tunnel and the other limb is open to the atmosphere. The liquid level in the first limb is 1·0 in. higher than that in the second limb.

Calculate (a) the pressure difference between the point on the model and the atmosphere and (b) the absolute pressure at that point. The specific gravity of mercury is 13·6 and the density of water is 1·94 slugs/ft³.

(a) The pressure difference supports a column of 1 in. or $\frac{1}{12}$ ft of the liquid. The pressure difference is therefore

$$\Delta p = \rho g \, \Delta h = (0{\cdot}82 \times 1{\cdot}94) \times 32{\cdot}2 \times \tfrac{1}{12}$$
$$= 4{\cdot}26 \text{ lb/ft}^2.$$

(Note the conversion of the column height to feet.)

Since the liquid has been drawn higher in the limb connected to the mode the air pressure in that limb must be lower than atmospheric pressure.

(b)   Barometric pressure $= (13{\cdot}6 \times 1{\cdot}94) \times 32{\cdot}2 \times \tfrac{29}{12}$.
$$= 2055 \text{ lb/ft}^2.$$

Therefore the absolute pressure at the point on the model is
$$2055 - 4{\cdot}26 = 2051 \text{ lb/ft}^2.$$

In aeronautics it is often necessary to measure pressure differences corresponding to $\frac{1}{100}$ in. of water or less. For such small pressure differences the simple U-tube is not sufficiently sensitive and various other forms of manometer have been developed to measure these small differences. Most of these are based on the U-tube and differ only in the method used to give the increased sensitivity. Two principal methods are,

(i) making the fluid displacement to be measured greater than the displacement in a simple U-tube. A common example of this in aeronautics is the inclined tube manometer. The fluid displacement is increased by the factor cosec θ, θ being the angle of slope to the horizontal;

(ii) using some optical arrangement to magnify the actual measurement. Examples include the Casella and Betz manometers.

Other instruments, such as the Chattock tilting manometer, employ a combination of these two methods.

3.3. The Atmosphere. Since the atmosphere may be regarded as an expanse of fluid (air) substantially at rest, hydrostatic theory may be used to calculate its properties.

The atmosphere is a mixture of gases of which oxygen and nitrogen are the main constituents, but it also contains small amounts of other gases including hydrogen and helium and the rare inert gases argon, krypton, neon, etc. Over the range of altitudes involved in aerodynamics the proportion of the constituents varies little, and the atmosphere may be regarded as a homogeneous gas of uniform composition.

Investigation has shown that the atmosphere may conveniently be divided into two distinct contiguous regions. The lower of these regions is called the *troposphere* and it is found that the temperature within the troposphere decreases approximately linearly with height. The upper region is the *stratosphere* wherein the temperature remains almost constant with height. The supposed boundary between the two regions is termed the *tropopause*. The sharp distinction between the two, implied above, does not exist in reality, but one merges gradually into the other. Nevertheless, this distinction represents a useful convention for the purposes of calculation.

3.3.1. The International Standard Atmosphere.

The performance of an aeroplane is very dependent on the physical properties (e.g., density and temperature) of the air in which it flies. It is therefore desirable that comparisons between aircraft should be based on similar atmospheric conditions. To assist aircraft designers and operators in this, agreement has been reached on an International Standard Atmosphere (I.S.A.) intended to approximate to the atmospheric conditions prevailing for most of the year in temperate latitudes, such as Europe and North America. The I.S.A. is defined by the pressure and temperature at mean sea-level, and the variation of temperature with altitude. These values are shown in Fig. 3.5, which also shows the characteristics of two other agreed 'Standard Atmospheres' intended to represent the most extreme conditions likely to be encountered on this planet. With this model of the atmosphere it is possible to find the required physical characteristics at any altitude.

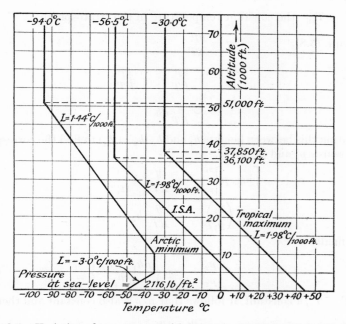

F ig. 3.5.—Variation of temperature with height in the International Standard, tropical maximum and arctic minimum atmospheres.

3.3.2. Calculations on the stratosphere.   For this purpose the buoyancy equation

$$\frac{dp}{dh} = -\rho g \qquad . \qquad . \qquad . \qquad (3.5)$$

is used, and also the fact that, in the stratosphere, the temperature does not vary with height.

A further equation is necessary, namely

$$\frac{p}{\rho} = RT \qquad . \qquad . \qquad . \qquad (3.8)$$

where p, ρ and T are the pressure, density and absolute temperature of a gas, and R is the appropriate gas constant (§ 2.8.3).

This equation is the aerodynamicist's form of the Gas Equation of State, familiar as

$$PV = wRT$$

with w/V replaced by ρ.

Thus there are now three equations:

$$\frac{dp}{dh} = -\rho g \text{ (eqn. (3.5))}$$

$$\frac{p}{\rho} = RT \text{ (eqn. (3.8))}$$

and $T = T_s$,   the constant temperature in the stratosphere .   (3.9)

From eqn. (3.8), $\rho g = \dfrac{gp}{RT}$

whence $\dfrac{dp}{dh} = -\dfrac{gp}{RT} = -\dfrac{gp}{RT_s}$

or $\dfrac{dp}{\cdot p} = -\dfrac{g}{RT_s} dh$

Integrating this between heights h_1 and h_2 ($h_2 > h_1$) to find the corresponding pressures p_1 and p_2, gives,

$$\left[\log_e p \right]_{p_1}^{p_2} = -\frac{g}{RT_s}\left[h\right]_{h_1}^{h_2}$$

or $\log_e\left(\dfrac{p_2}{p_1}\right) = -\dfrac{g}{RT_s}(h_2 - h_1)$

giving finally

$$\frac{p_2}{p_1} = \exp\left\{\frac{g(h_1 - h_2)}{RT_s}\right\} \qquad . \qquad . \qquad (3.10)$$

Since $T = T_s$, a constant, it follows that p/ρ is also constant and therefore

$$\frac{p_1}{p_2} = \frac{\rho_1}{\rho_2} \qquad . \qquad . \qquad . \qquad (3.11)$$

Therefore the variation of pressure and density in the stratosphere obeys the law

$$\frac{p_2}{p_1} = \frac{\rho_2}{\rho_1} = \exp\left\{\frac{g(h_1 - h_2)}{RT_s}\right\} \quad . \qquad . \qquad . \quad (3.12)$$

Some worked examples on this are given later.

3.3.3. Calculations on the troposphere.

These calculations also use eqns. (3.5) and (3.8) and in addition an equation stating the variation of temperature with altitude, namely

$$T = T_0 - Lh \quad . \qquad . \qquad . \qquad . \quad (3.13)$$

where T_0 is the absolute temperature at mean sea-level and L is the 'lapse rate', or the rate of decrease of temperature with altitude in °C per foot.

As before eqns. (3.5) and (3.8) may be used to give

$$\frac{dp}{p} = -\frac{g}{RT}dh$$

Substituting in this for T (from eqn. (3.13)) gives

$$\frac{dp}{p} = -\frac{g}{R}\frac{dh}{T_0 - Lh}$$

Integrating this between h_1 and h_2, p_1 and p_2, gives

$$\left[\log_e p\right]_{p_1}^{p_2} = \frac{g}{LR}\left[\log_e (T_0 - Lh)\right]_{h_1}^{h_2} \quad . \qquad . \quad (3.14)$$

Now since $T_0 - Lh = T$, eqn. (3.14) may be written as

$$\log_e\left(\frac{p_2}{p_1}\right) = \frac{g}{LR}\log_e\left(\frac{T_2}{T_1}\right)$$

or

$$\frac{p_2}{p_1} = \left(\frac{T_2}{T_1}\right)^{\frac{g}{LR}} \quad . \qquad . \qquad . \qquad . \quad (3.15)$$

an equation which gives the variation of pressure with temperature and hence altitude.

Also $\quad \dfrac{p_2/\rho_2}{p_1/\rho_1} = \dfrac{T_2}{T_1}$ from eqn. (3.8) and therefore

$$\frac{\rho_2}{\rho_1} = \left(\frac{p_2}{p_1}\right)\left(\frac{T_1}{T_2}\right) = \left(\frac{T_2}{T_1}\right)^{\frac{g}{LR}}\left(\frac{T_1}{T_2}\right) = \left(\frac{T_2}{T_1}\right)^{\frac{g}{LR}-1}$$

$$= \left(\frac{T_2}{T_1}\right)^{\frac{g-LR}{LR}} \quad . \qquad . \qquad . \qquad . \qquad . \quad (3.16)$$

Comparing eqns. (3.15) and (3.16), it follows that

$$\frac{p_2}{p_1} = \left(\frac{\rho_2}{\rho_1}\right)^{\frac{g}{g-LR}} \quad . \qquad . \qquad . \qquad . \quad (3.17)$$

Since the conditions represented by 1 and 2 were selected quite arbitrarily and are therefore quite general it further follows that eqn. (3.17) may be written as

$$p = k\rho^{\frac{g}{g-LR}} \qquad \qquad (3.18)$$

where k is a constant.

Now for the International Standard Atmosphere the value of L is $0.00198°C/\text{ft}$. With this value for the lapse rate and using the value 3092 ft lb/slug $°C$ for R the above equations become:

$$\frac{p_2}{p_1} = \left(\frac{T_2}{T_1}\right)^{5.256} \qquad \qquad (3.19)$$

$$\frac{\rho_2}{\rho_1} = \left(\frac{T_2}{T_1}\right)^{4.256} \qquad \qquad (3.20)$$

and

$$p = k\rho^{1.235} \qquad \qquad (3.21)$$

Example 3.2. Calculate the pressure and density at 30,000 ft and 60,000 ft in the I.S.A. The pressure at sea-level is 2116 lb/ft², the sea-level temperature is 288°K and the lapse rate is 0.00198°C per ft.

(a) *30,000 feet.*

$$\text{Temperature} = 288 - 30{,}000 \times 0.00198 = 228.6°K.$$

Therefore

$$\frac{2116}{p_{30}} = \left(\frac{288}{228.6}\right)^{5.256} = \left(1 + \frac{59.4}{228.6}\right)^{5.256}$$

$$= (1.2595)^{5.256}$$

$$= 3.36$$

$$\therefore\ p_{30} = \frac{2116}{3.36} = \underline{630\ \text{lb/ft}^2}.$$

The density will not be found from eqn. (3.20) but from eqn. (3.8) as follows

$$\rho_{30} = \frac{p_{30}}{RT_{30}} = \frac{630}{3092 \times 228.6}$$

$$= \underline{0.00089\ \text{slug/ft}^3}.$$

(b) *60,000 feet.* This is a more complicated case since the change in characteristics between the troposphere and the stratosphere must be taken into account. It is therefore necessary to calculate conditions at the tropopause using the troposphere equations and then proceed using the equations for the stratosphere.

At the tropopause, temperature $T = 216.5°K = T_s$

$$\therefore\ \frac{2116}{p_{36}} = \left(\frac{288}{216.5}\right)^{5.256} = 4.50$$

whence

$$p_{36} = \frac{2116}{4.50} = 470\ \text{lb/ft}^2.$$

In the stratosphere,

$$\frac{p_{36}}{p_{60}} = \exp\left\{\frac{(60{,}000 - 36{,}100).32.18}{3092 \times 216.5}\right\}$$

$$= \exp(1.15) = 3.155$$

$$\therefore\ p_{60} = \frac{470}{3.155} = \underline{149\ \text{lb/ft}^2}.$$

Using eqn. (3.8),

$$\rho_{60} = \frac{149}{3092 \times 216 \cdot 5}$$

$$= 0 \cdot 000228 \text{ slug/ft}^3.$$

3.3.4. Relative density.

A quantity which is very important in aero-dynamics is the *relative density* (σ). This is defined by:

$$\text{relative density} = \frac{\text{density at the relevant altitude}}{\text{density at sea-level in the I.S.A.}} \cdot \quad (3.22)$$

The value of density at sea-level in the I.S.A., or 'standard density', as it is often called, may be found from eqn. (3.8) to be

$$\rho_0 = \frac{p_0}{RT_0} = \frac{2116}{3092 \times 288}$$

$$= 0 \cdot 002378 \text{ slug/ft}^3 \quad . \quad . \quad . \quad (3.23)$$

Eqn. (3.22) may be written in the symbolic form

$$\sigma = \frac{\rho}{\rho_0}. \quad . \quad . \quad . \quad (3.22a)$$

It is useful to remember that $\rho_0 = 0 \cdot 002378 = 1/420 \cdot 5$ slug/ft^3. Then $\frac{1}{2}\rho_0 = 1/841$ slug/ft^3 and $\sqrt{\frac{1}{2}\rho_0} = 1/29$.

3.3.5. Variation of viscosity.

The viscosity of air under particular atmospheric conditions may be calculated from *Rayleigh's Formula*, which is

$$\frac{\mu_2}{\mu_1} = \left(\frac{T_2}{T_1}\right)^{\frac{3}{4}} \quad . \quad . \quad . \quad (3.24)$$

where μ_1 and μ_2 are the absolute coefficients of viscosity at absolute temperatures T_1 and T_2 respectively. This formula is a good approximation over the range of pressures and temperatures usually met in aerodynamics. It will be noted that pressure does not appear in the formula and viscosity is virtually independent of pressure over the normal aerodynamic range.[*] At 0°C, 273°K, the value of μ for air is $3 \cdot 58 \times 10^{-7}$ slug/ft sec.

Example 3.3. Calculate μ and v at 60,000 ft in the I.S.A.

$$\frac{\mu_0}{\mu_{60}} = \left(\frac{273}{216 \cdot 5}\right)^{\frac{3}{4}} = \left(1 + \frac{56 \cdot 5}{216 \cdot 5}\right)^{\frac{3}{4}}$$

$$= (1 \cdot 251)^{\frac{3}{4}} = 1 \cdot 183$$

$$\therefore \mu_{60} = \frac{3 \cdot 58}{1 \cdot 183} \times 10^{-7} = 3 \cdot 02 \times 10^{-7} \text{ slug/ft sec.}$$

Note that since the temperature in the stratosphere is constant the value of μ is also constant there.

$$v = \frac{\mu}{\rho} = \frac{3 \cdot 02 \times 10^{-7}}{0 \cdot 000228}$$

$$= 0 \cdot 00133 \text{ ft}^2/\text{sec.}$$

[*] See, e.g., Piercy, Aerodynamics, pp. 26–32.

A table of the properties of the International Standard Atmosphere is given in Appendix 2. The values in the table are given as relative values, i.e., as multiples of the values at sea-level, which are themselves given separately at the head of the table.

3.3.6. The stability of the atmosphere.

The atmosphere is not normally given to the violent up and down currents which result from gross instability. It is, however, not hard to visualize conditions under which large vertical currents might exist and, indeed, such currents are occasionally detected by aircraft as bumps and rough air.

Consider the atmosphere at rest and a small element of it to be suddenly displaced a short distance upwards (Fig. 3.6). Three possibilities exist:

(i) the displaced section may remain in its new position

(ii) it may tend to return to its original position or

(iii) it may continue upwards.

These three cases correspond respectively to neutral stability, positive stability and instability of the atmosphere.

$$p_2 \; \rho_2 \; T_2 \; \text{— — — —} \left(\frac{p_2' \; \rho_2'}{T_2'} \right) \! - h_2$$

Displaced mass

Atmosphere

$$p_1 \; \rho_1 \; T_1 \; \text{— — — —} \left(\frac{p_1' \; \rho_1'}{T_1'} \right) \! - h_1$$

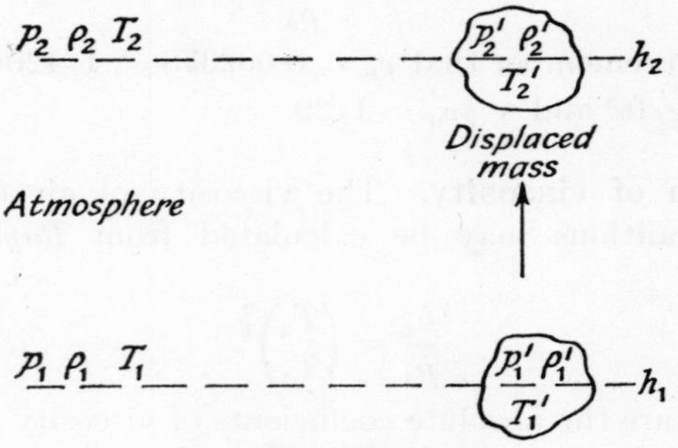

Fig. 3.6.

Suppose the element, initially at a height h_1, is displaced suddenly to a higher level h_2. The conditions of the atmosphere at large at h_1 are p_1, T_1 and ρ_1, while at h_2 these conditions are p_2, T_2 and ρ_2. The conditions of the displaced mass, when at h_1 are p_1', T_1' and ρ_1' becoming, after displacement, h_2, p_2', T_2' and ρ_2'.

Now it has been shown that the atmosphere obeys a law of the form $p = k\rho^n$ (eqn. (3.18)), where $n = 1\cdot235$ in the I.S.A. troposphere and $n = 1\cdot0$ in the stratosphere.

Then
$$\frac{p_2/\rho_2}{p_1/\rho_1} = \frac{T_2}{T_1} \quad \text{(eqn. (3.8) rearranged)}$$

or
$$\frac{T_2}{T_1} = \left(\frac{p_2}{p_1} \right)\!\left(\frac{\rho_1}{\rho_2} \right)$$

Rearranging eqn. (3.18) in its modified form,

$$\frac{\rho_1}{\rho_2} = \left(\frac{p_1}{p_2} \right)^{\frac{1}{n}}$$

Then
$$\frac{T_2}{T_1} = \left(\frac{p_2}{p_1}\right)\left(\frac{p_1}{p_2}\right)^{\frac{1}{n}} = \left(\frac{p_2}{p_1}\right)^{\frac{n-1}{n}} \qquad . \qquad . \qquad . \quad (3.25)$$

If the displaced mass is moved quickly enough it will have no time to lose or gain heat, and will therefore expand adiabatically, according to the law

$$p = c\rho^\gamma \qquad . \qquad . \qquad . \qquad . \quad (3.26)$$

where γ is the ratio of specific heats. Then from eqns. (3.8) and (3.26),

$$\frac{T_2'}{T_1'} = \left(\frac{p_2'}{p_1'}\right)^{\frac{\gamma-1}{\gamma}} \qquad . \qquad . \qquad . \quad (3.27)$$

It is assumed that the displaced section of air was initially a genuine sample of the air at h_1. This implies that $p_1' = p_1$; $T_1' = T_1$; and $\rho_1' = \rho_1$. A further assumption is that the pressure of the displaced mass is always the same as that of the atmosphere then surrounding it; in particular $p_2' = p_2$.

Then
$$\frac{T_2'}{T_2} = \frac{T_2'}{T_1'} \cdot \frac{T_1'}{T_1} \cdot \frac{T_1}{T_2} \qquad . \qquad . \qquad . \quad (3.28)$$

Now $T_1' = T_1$; while the other factors on the right-hand side of eqn. (3.28) are given in eqns. (3.25) and (3.27), whence

$$\frac{T_2'}{T_2} = \left(\frac{p_2}{p_1}\right)^{\frac{\gamma-1}{\gamma}} \cdot \left(\frac{p_1}{p_2}\right)^{\frac{n-1}{n}} = \left(\frac{p_2}{p_1}\right)^{\frac{\gamma-1}{\gamma} - \frac{n-1}{n}} = \left(\frac{p_2}{p_1}\right)^{\frac{\gamma-n}{\gamma n}}$$

Also since $p/\rho = RT$ and $p_2' = p_2$ this becomes

$$\frac{\rho_2'}{\rho_2} = \frac{p_2'}{T_2'} \cdot \frac{T_2}{p_2} = \frac{T_2}{T_2'}$$

$$= \left(\frac{p_1}{p_2}\right)^{\frac{\gamma-n}{\gamma n}} \qquad . \qquad . \qquad . \quad (3.29)$$

There are three possibilities which determine the stability, namely $\gamma > n$, $\gamma = n$ and $\gamma < n$. Considering each of these in turn:

(i) $n < \gamma \quad \dfrac{\gamma - n}{\gamma n}$ is positive, $= + a$, say.

Then, since $p_1 > p_2$,

$$\frac{\rho_2'}{\rho_2} = \left(\frac{p_1}{p_2}\right)^{+a} > 1$$

Thus the density of the mass of air after displacement is greater than that of the atmosphere then surrounding it, and it will therefore tend to sink back to its original level. The atmosphere is therefore stable.

(ii) $n = \gamma \quad \dfrac{\gamma - n}{\gamma n} = 0$ and therefore

$$\frac{\rho_2'}{\rho_2} = \left(\frac{p_1}{p_2}\right)^0 = 1$$

The density of the displaced mass is therefore at all times equal to that of the atmosphere at the same level, and will neither tend to sink nor to rise, but will remain in its displaced position. The atmosphere is therefore neutrally stable.

(iii) $n > \gamma$ $\quad \dfrac{\gamma - n}{\gamma n}$ is negative, $= -b$, say, when

$$\frac{\rho_2'}{\rho_2} = \left(\frac{p_1}{p_2}\right)^{-b} = \left(\frac{p_2}{p_1}\right)^{+b} < 1$$

Thus after displacement, the density of the small mass is less than that of the surrounding atmosphere, and the mass will tend to rise further. The atmosphere is then unstable.

Thus the three cases, $n < \gamma$, $n = \gamma$ and $n > \gamma$ correspond respectively to stable, neutrally stable and unstable atmospheres.

It is at once apparent that the troposphere in the International Standard Atmosphere, for which $n = 1.235$, is stable. Also since, for the stratosphere $n = 1.0$, the stratosphere is very stable.

It will be recalled that the index n is related to the lapse rate L from eqn. (3.18) by

$$n = \frac{g}{g - LR}$$

Since $n = \gamma = 1.4$ is the critical value corresponding to neutral stability, it is of interest to calculate the corresponding value of the lapse rate L. Then

$$1.4 = \frac{32.18}{32.18 - 3092L}$$

whence

$$L = \frac{0.4 \times 32.18}{1.4 \times 3092}$$

$$= 0.00298°\text{C/ft or } 2.98°\text{C per thousand feet.}$$

This is termed the 'adiabatic lapse rate'. If the lapse rate exceeds this critical value, i.e., is 'super-adiabatic', the atmosphere is unstable.

Example 3.4. If the sea-level pressure and temperature are 2110 lb/ft^2 and 20°C respectively, while at some unknown altitude the pressure is 1500 lb/ft^2 and the temperature is $-10°$C, is the atmosphere between those altitudes stable or unstable? Estimate the height at which the second pair of readings were taken. Assume a linear variation of temperature with height.

Now

$$\frac{p_1}{p_2} = \left(\frac{T_1}{T_2}\right)^{\frac{g}{LR}}$$

i.e.,

$$\frac{2110}{1500} = \left(\frac{273 + 20}{273 - 10}\right)^{\frac{g}{LR}} = (1.114)^{\frac{g}{LR}}$$

i.e.,

$$1.407 = (1.114)^{\frac{g}{LR}}$$

$$\frac{g}{LR} = 3.163$$

giving

$$L = 0.0033°\text{C/ft} = 3.3°\text{C/thousand feet.}$$

Since this is greater than the adiabatic lapse rate (2·98°C/thousand feet) the atmosphere is unstable.

The altitude for the second pair of readings is calculated from

$$\text{altitude} = \frac{\text{temperature change}}{\text{lapse rate}}$$

$$= \frac{30}{3\cdot3} \times 1000 \text{ ft}$$

$$= 9090 \text{ ft.}$$

3.4. The aircraft altimeter. All aircraft are required by law to be fitted with one or more altimeters to indicate the altitude at which the aircraft is flying.

Fig. 3.7 is a cut-away diagram of a Smith's Sensitive Altimeter. An

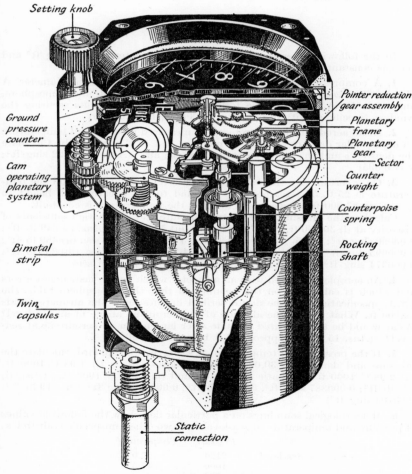

FIG. 3.7.—Sensitive altimeter.

(By courtesy of Smith's Aircraft Instruments Ltd.)

C

altimeter consists essentially of an evacuated aneroid capsule fixed by one side to the instrument casing, the other side of the capsule being free to move as the capsule expands or contracts. The movement of the free side of the capsule is communicated by a gearing system to two or three needles which move over a circular scale calibrated in feet or metres. Atmospheric static pressure is applied to the interior of the instrument case through a static tube mounted on the exterior of the aircraft. The equilibrium distension of the capsule is determined by the pressure difference between the instrument case and the evacuated capsule, and thus is directly related to the atmospheric pressure. Therefore the altitude indicated on the scale by the needles is related to the *pressure* of the atmosphere in which the aircraft is flying.

EXERCISES

In the following exercises take the density of water as 1·94 slug/ft³ and the gas constant for air as 3092 ft lb/slug °C.

1. A compressed air tank is fitted with a window of 6 in. diameter. A U-tube filled with mercury is connected between the tank and atmosphere, and reads 73 in. Calculate the total load acting on the bolts securing the window. Specific gravity of mercury = 13·6. (*Ans.* 1018 lb)

2. At an aerodrome in the tropics, the measured pressure and temperature on a particular day are 29·00 in. of mercury and 40°C respectively. Calculate the density ρ and the relative density σ of the air. (*Ans.* 0·002122 slug/ft³; $\sigma = 0·895$)

3. On a certain day the pressure at sea-level is 2120 lb/ft² and the temperature is 25°C. The temperature is found to fall linearly with height to −55°C at 37,000 ft, above which altitude the temperature is constant.

Calculate the pressure, density and absolute and kinematic coefficients of viscosity at (i) 30,000 ft, (ii) 37,000 ft and (iii) 50,000 ft. (*Ans.* (i) 649 lb/ft²; 0·00090 slug/ft³; 3·165 × 10⁻⁷ slug/ft sec, 3·52 × 10⁻⁴ ft²/sec. (ii) 469 lb/ft²; 0·000695 slug/ft³; 3·03 × 10⁻⁷ slug/ft sec, 4·35 × 10⁻⁴ ft²/sec. (iii) 252 lb/ft²; 0·000374 slug/ft³; 3·03 × 10⁻⁷ slug/ft sec, 8·10 × 10⁻⁴ ft²/sec)

4. An aeroplane is fitted with an altimeter which has no instrument errors and which is calibrated on the assumption that the atmosphere fulfils the I.S.A. specification. On the day described in question 3 the altimeter reads 15,000 ft. What is the true altitude of the aeroplane above mean sea-level? What would be the indicated altitude after landing on an aerodrome at sea-level? (*Ans.* 15,550 ft; approx. 52 ft below sea-level)

5. If the pressure and temperature at sea-level are standard, calculate the pressure and density at 30,000 ft, if the lapse rate is (i) 1·98°C/1000 ft, (ii) 2·98°C/1000 ft (adiabatic lapse rate) and (iii) 3·98°C/1000 ft. (*Ans.* (i) 628 lb/ft²; 0·000887 slug/ft³. (ii) 576 lb/ft²; 0·000940 slug/ft³. (iii) 519 lb/ft²; 0·00103 slug/ft³)

6. Meteorological soundings on a particular day show the following values of pressure and temperature at sea-level and two other, unspecified, altitudes:

	Pressure	Temperature
Sea-level	2120	+17·0
	1000	−47·5
	650	−68·0

the pressures being in lb/ft² and the temperatures in °C.

Investigate the stability of the atmosphere between these altitudes and, in addition, estimate the two unspecified heights, assuming a linear variation of temperature with altitude between each pair of readings. (*Ans.* Lower band unstable, $n = 1\cdot505$. Upper band stable, $n = 1\cdot280$. Altitudes 18,500 ft and 27,400 ft)

CHAPTER 4

AIR FLOW

Aerodynamics is based on Newtonian mechanics as described in the three classical Laws of Motion. One consequence of the laws is that if two observers, in uniform motion relative to each other, observe an 'event' (e.g., a mass being accelerated by a force) they may use the same mathematical equations and physical ideas to describe and study the event. This finds the following application in aerodynamics.

Consider an aeroplane in steady flight. To an observer on the ground the aeroplane is flying into a mass of air substantially at rest (assuming no wind) and any movement of the air is caused directly by the motion of the aeroplane through it. The pilot of the aeroplane, on the other hand, could consider that he is stationary, and that a stream of air is flowing past him and that the aeroplane modifies the motion of the air. In fact both viewpoints are mathematically and physically correct. Both observers may use the same equations to study the mutual effects of the air and the aeroplane and they will both arrive at the same answers for, say, the forces exerted by the air on the aeroplane. However, the pilot will find that certain terms in the equations become, from his viewpoint, zero. He will therefore find that his equations are easier to solve than will the ground-based observer. Because of this it is convenient to regard most problems in aerodynamics as cases of the flow of a stream of fluid past a body at rest, with consequent simplification of the mathematics.

As an illustration of this convention, consider an aeroplane flying from right to left at speed V through air at rest (Fig. 4.1).

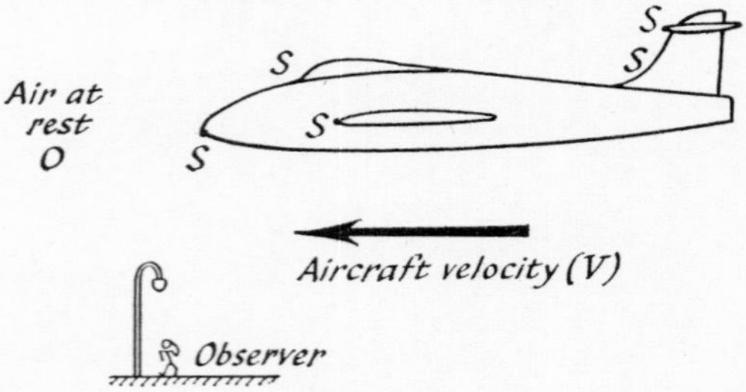

Fig. 4.1.

At any stagnation point S the air is brought to rest relative to the aircraft. The observer on the ground would interpret this as follows: the point S on the aeroplane is moving at speed V, and the air at that point is moving with it. Thus a particle of air, initially at rest well ahead of the aeroplane, gradually accelerates in the direction of flight SO until, when the aircraft catches up with it, the speed of the particle is V. This acceleration would be caused by the pressure at S being greater than at O.

28

The pilot would have a different interpretation. He would say that a particle of air at O was approaching him at a speed V along the path OS. As the particle came nearer it decelerated until, by the time it had reached S, it had come to rest. The deceleration would be caused by the pressure at S being greater than that at O.

Both the observer and the pilot would find the same value for the pressure difference between O and S, though their estimates of the speed of the air particle would always differ by the constant speed V.

The aircraft causes the direction and speed of the air flowing round it to differ from what they would be were it not present. These changes are termed 'perturbations' and lead to a change in the pressure on the surface of the aircraft. The overall effect of these pressure changes is to produce a force and a moment acting on the aircraft.

4.1. Types of flow. The flow round a body may be steady or unsteady. A steady flow is one in which the flow parameters (speed, direction, pressure, etc.) may vary from point to point in the flow but at any point are constant with respect to time, i.e., measurements of the flow parameters at a given point in the flow at various times remain the same.

In an unsteady flow the flow parameters at any point vary with time.

4.1.1. A comparison of steady and unsteady flow. Fig. 4.2 (a) shows a section of a stationary wing with air flowing past. The velocity of the air a long way from the wing is constant at V ft/sec as shown. The flow parameters are measured at some point fixed relative to the wing, say at $P(x, y)$. The flow perturbations produced at P by the body will be the same at all times, i.e., the flow is steady relative to a set of axes fixed in the body.

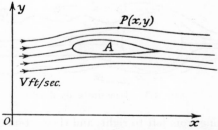

FIG. 4.2 (a).—Air moves at speed V past axes fixed relative to aerofoil.

Fig. 4.2 (b) represents the same wing moving at the same speed (V ft/sec) through air which, a long way from the body, is at rest. The flow parameters are measured at a point $P'(x', y')$ fixed relative to the stationary air; the wing thus moves past P'. At time t_1, when the wing is at A_1, P' is a fairly large distance ahead of the wing, and the perturbations at P' are small. Later, at time t_2, the wing is at A_2, directly beneath P', and the perturbations are much larger. Later still, at time t_3, P' is far behind the wing, which is now at A_3, and the perturbations are again small. Thus the perturbation at P' has started from a small value, increased to a maximum, and finally decreased back to a small value. The perturbation at the fixed point P' is therefore not constant with respect

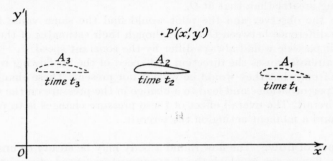

FIG. 4.2 (b).—Aerofoil moves at speed V through air initially at rest. Axes Ox', Oy', fixed relative to undisturbed air.

to time, and so the flow, referred to axes fixed in the fluid, is not steady. Thus, changing the axes of reference from a set fixed relative to the wind, to a different set fixed relative to the body, changes the flow from unsteady to steady. This produces the mathematical simplification mentioned earlier by eliminating time from the equations. Since the flow relative to the wind axes can, by a change of axes, be made steady, it is sometimes known as 'quasi-steady'.

4.1.2. True unsteady flow.   An example of true unsteady flow is in the wake behind a bluff body, e.g., a circular cylinder (Fig. 4.3).

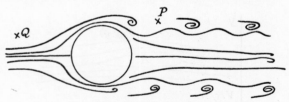

FIG. 4.3.—True unsteady flow.

The air is flowing from left to right, and the system of eddies or whirlpools behind the cylinder is moving in the same direction at a somewhat lower speed. This region of slower moving fluid is the 'wake'. Now consider a point P, fixed relative to the cylinder, in the wake. Sometimes the point will be immersed in an eddy and sometimes not. Thus the flow parameters will be changing rapidly at P, and the flow there is unsteady. Moreover it is impossible to find a set of axes relative to which the flow is steady. At a point Q well outside the wake the fluctuations are so small that they may be ignored and the flow at Q may, with little error, be regarded as steady. Thus, even though the flow in some region may be unsteady, there may be some other region where the unsteadiness is negligibly small, so that the flow there may be regarded as steady with sufficient accuracy for all practical purposes.

Three concepts which are useful in describing fluid flows are:

(i) *A streamline.* A streamline is defined as 'an imaginary line drawn in the fluid such that there is no flow across it at any point'. Since this is identical to the condition at a solid boundary it follows that:

  (a) any streamline may be replaced by a solid boundary without modifying the flow, and

  (b) any solid boundary is itself a streamline of the flow around it.

Both ideas are of great use in the more advanced theory discussed in § 10.2.

(ii) *A filament (or streak) line.* This is the line taken up by successive particles of fluid passing through some given point. A fine filament of smoke injected into the flow through a nozzle traces out a filament line. The lines shown in Fig. 4.3 and Fig. 6.11 are examples of this.

(iii) *A path line or particle path.* This is the path traced out by any one particle of the fluid in motion.

In unsteady flow, these three are in general different, while in steady flow all three are identical.

4.2. The boundary layer.

Consider a long, wide, flat plate with a stream flowing past it from left to right at a speed of V ft/sec. In § 2.6 it was shown that the molecules actually in contact with the plate are at rest relative to it and yet the speed of flow past the plate is V ft/sec. These two statements can be reconciled by postulating the existence of the 'boundary layer'.

In Fig. 4.4, AB represents one surface of the flat plate some distance

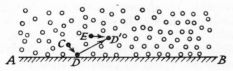

FIG. 4.4.—The mechanism of viscosity.

from its leading edge. The particles of the gas have a general streaming motion from left to right, but superimposed on this, each particle has an individual velocity, random in speed and direction. As a result, each particle is moving at a speed and in a direction which differs from those for all the other particles. The general streaming motion is, in fact, merely the statistical mean of all the different velocities of the various particles. The exceptions to this are where particles are at any instant in contact with the surface and at rest. Consider the particle C. Its individual velocity is such that it moves towards the plate striking particle D, knocking D off the surface and back into the stream, while C adheres to the plate in its stead. Thus C has lost all its momentum. Some of this has been imparted to D

and the remainder is lost when C adheres to the plate. This loss of momentum by C is felt by the plate as a small impulse from left to right. Particle D has been returned to the stream as shown at D' but has a very low speed, and is overtaken and struck by particle E. As a result of this collision D is speeded up and E slowed down. E in turn may move outwards from the plate at its now low speed, being struck by a faster moving particle in the next 'layer'. This elementary argument has considered only a few particles. When this type of behaviour applies to the millions of particles present in the gas, producing a few million collisions per second, it is easy to see that the overall effect produces:

(a) a speed of flow which increases from zero at the surface of the plate, to the full streaming speed away from the plate, and

(b) a summation of a very large number of small impulses on the surface of the plate per unit time, or in other words, an apparently steady force acting on the plate in the direction of flow. This force is called the 'surface friction drag'.

The region of reduced speed is called the 'boundary layer', and it is seen that it is a direct result of viscosity. If the fluid had no viscosity, i.e., were 'inviscid', there would be no boundary layer.

Theoretically, it would seem from the above argument that the boundary layer extends to an infinite distance from the plate. Prandtl laid the foundations of modern aerodynamics by suggesting that the flow round a body could be treated as two distinct parts. One part, that close to the body surface, is the region in which the effects of viscosity are relatively large, and it is this region which is in practice called the boundary layer. The second part consists of the flow outside this restricted boundary layer. In this second region the velocity gradients across the flow are so small that the effects of viscosity are negligible and the flow may be regarded as that of an inviscid fluid.

In accordance with this suggestion, the boundary layer is normally defined as that region of the flow in which the speed is less than (usually) 99% of the velocity which would exist in inviscid flow. The thickness of this region, usually measured in inches, is called the '0·99 thickness', sometimes abbreviated to 'the thickness', and is denoted by Δ.

It is found that the boundary layer may exist in two forms: laminar and turbulent. In the laminar boundary layer, the flow is smooth and regular, behaving much like laminae sliding over each other, hence its name. In contrast to this, the flow in the turbulent boundary layer is chaotic, the boundary layer consisting of a very large number of small eddies of various strengths and sizes. In general the boundary layer at the front of a body is laminar, and degenerates into the turbulent form some distance along the surface. The phenomenon of change from a laminar to a turbulent boundary layer is known as 'boundary layer transition'.

4.2.1. Velocity distribution and surface friction.
Fig. 4.5 shows how the fluid speed varies through the boundary for typical laminar and turbulent boundary layers. A graph of this form is termed 'a boundary layer

velocity profile'. In this Figure, u represents the speed parallel to the surface at a distance y from the surface, U is the speed which would exist in the absence of viscosity, and Δ is the 0·99 thickness.

Maxwell's definition of viscosity states that the skin-friction force on a plate is given by

$$\frac{F}{A} = \mu\left(\frac{V}{h}\right) \quad \text{(eqn. (2.2))}$$

Applying this definition to the boundary layer, h is made very small and given the value δy. Similarly, V is replaced by δu while F/A, the force per unit area, is denoted by τ, the intensity of shear friction.

Taking the limiting case as $\delta y \longrightarrow 0$, this becomes

$$\tau = \mu\left(\frac{\partial u}{\partial y}\right) .$$

This gives the intensity of shear force at any point in the boundary layer. To find the intensity of surface friction on the plate, the value of $\partial u/\partial y$ at the surface, i.e., at $y = 0$, is used,

i.e., $$\tau_0 = \mu\left(\frac{\partial u}{\partial y}\right)_{y=0} \qquad . \qquad . \qquad . \qquad (4.1)$$

Inspection of Fig. 4.5 shows immediately that the velocity gradient at the surface is higher for the turbulent boundary layer than for the laminar, with the result that the skin friction of the turbulent boundary layer is greater than that of the laminar boundary layer. Also the thickness of the turbulent boundary layer at any point on a body is greater than that of the laminar boundary layer which would exist at the same point. It is for this reason that much effort is directed towards maintaining the maximum possible extent of laminar boundary layer over an aeroplane.

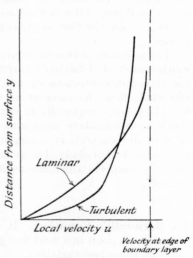

FIG. 4.5.—Typical boundary layer velocity profiles.

To give some idea of proportion, boundary layer thickness will range from almost zero at the front edge to roughly 0·07 in. 3 ft from the front edge of a plate in a stream of 200 ft/sec at sea-level, if the boundary layer remains laminar. The corresponding thickness of a turbulent boundary layer would be roughly 0·7 in.

It was shown that τ is proportional to $\partial u/\partial y$, and it is seen from Fig. 4.5 that for $y < \Delta$, this may be appreciable while for $y > \Delta$, $\partial u/\partial y$ is negligibly small, and so therefore are the effects of viscosity. This justifies Prandtl's suggestion described earlier.

4.2.2. The influences of the boundary layer in aeronautics. Theories are available (Chaps. 10 and 11) which permit calculation of the flow round a body in an inviscid fluid. In such an ideal case, at subsonic speeds, there is no resistance to motion. The viscosity of real fluids results in a modification of the flow round the body which produces a force tending to resist the motion. Part of this force is the 'surface friction drag' referred to in the earlier parts of § 4.2, the remainder arises from the modification of the flow pattern round the body by the 'displacement thickness' of the boundary layer, and hence a change in the pressure distribution, discussed more fully in § 6.6.6. Because of the reduced flow speeds in the boundary layer, the mass flow within the boundary layer is less than would occur in the corresponding region of an inviscid flow. As a result the streamlines of the flow are displaced outwards compared to those of the ideal flow by an amount equal to the displacement thickness of the boundary layer. This leads to the major simplification in aerodynamics due to Prandtl. He postulated that the flow of a fluid of small viscosity around a slim body could be treated as inviscid outside the narrow region where the viscous stresses are high, i.e., outside the boundary layer. The effect of the boundary layer on the outside flow is to increase the effective size and to change the effective shape of the body very slightly. Since the boundary layer is always very thin it may, for a first approximation, be neglected in practical aeronautics, where the flow of air is treated as inviscid, thus simplifying the theory.

The influence of this boundary layer in other respects is enormous and much complicated due to its variation along the length of a body, including the almost discontinuous change at transition to turbulence. In general, the whole flow character at all speeds is intimately dependent on the boundary layer, especially in critical flow regimes such as the stall and shock wave-boundary layer interaction, and the study of the boundary layer in all its aspects is so complex and broad in scope that it is virtually a separate field of study. The very brief survey given above has introduced only those aspects which are needed for a full understanding of the following text.

4.3. Bernoulli's Equation. It was stated earlier that the velocity and pressure at a point in a fluid flow are interdependent. Bernoulli's Equation connects these two variables.

Consider a fluid in steady flow, and take any small stream-tube as in Fig. 4.6. (A stream-tube is an imaginary tube formed of adjacent streamlines.)

s is distance measured along the axis of the stream-tube from some arbitrary origin,

A is the cross-sectional area of the stream-tube at distance s from the arbitrary origin,

p, ρ, and v represent pressure, density and speed of fluid respectively.

A, p, ρ, and v vary with s, i.e., with position along the stream-tube, but not with time since the motion is steady.

Now consider a small 'slice' of the fluid in the stream-tube, shown shaded.

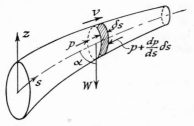

FIG. 4.6.—The stream-tube and element for Bernoulli's Equation.

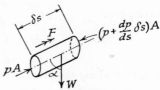

FIG. 4.7.—The forces on the element.

The first condition to be satisfied is of continuity (i.e., that matter cannot be created or destroyed) (§ 10.1.2). This means that the same mass of fluid must cross each section of the stream-tube in unit time. This may be expressed as

$$\rho A v = \text{constant} \quad . \qquad . \qquad . \qquad . \qquad (4.2)$$

Here Av is the volumetric flow per second, and the mass flow is $\rho A v$ slugs per sec.

Now consider the small element of fluid shown in Fig. 4.7, which is immersed in fluid of varying pressure. The element is a right cylinder of area A and length δs.

The pressure acting on one face of the element is p, and on the other face is $p + \dfrac{dp}{ds}\delta s$. In addition the weight W of the fluid in the element acts vertically as shown.

As a result of these pressures and the weight there is a resultant force F acting along the axis of the cylinder where F is given by

$$F = pA - \left(p + \frac{dp}{ds}\delta s\right)A - W \cos \alpha \quad . \qquad . \qquad (4.3)$$

where α is the angle between the axis of the stream-tube and the vertical.

From eqn. (4.3) it is seen that

$$F = -\frac{dp}{ds}A \ \delta s - \rho g A (\delta s) \cos \alpha \ . \qquad . \qquad . \qquad (4.4)$$

since the weight of fluid in the element is $\rho g A \ \delta s$ (volume × density).

Now by Newton's Second Law of Motion (force = mass × acceleration), applied to the element of Fig. 4.7,

$$- \rho g A \ \delta s \cos \alpha - \frac{dp}{ds}A \ \delta s = \rho A \ \delta s . \frac{dv}{dt} \quad . \qquad . \qquad (4.5)$$

where t represents time.

Dividing by $A\ \delta s$ this becomes

$$- \rho g \cos \alpha - \frac{dp}{ds} = \rho \frac{dv}{dt}$$

But

$$\frac{dv}{dt} = \frac{dv}{ds} \cdot \frac{ds}{dt} = v \frac{dv}{ds}$$

and therefore

$$\rho v \frac{dv}{ds} + \frac{dp}{ds} + \rho g \cos \alpha = 0$$

or

$$v \frac{dv}{ds} + \frac{1}{\rho} \frac{dp}{ds} + g \cos \alpha = 0$$

Integrating along the stream-tube, this becomes

$$\int \frac{dp}{\rho} + \int v\, dv + g \int \cos \alpha . ds = \text{constant}$$

but since $\int \cos \alpha\, ds =$ increase in vertical co-ordinate z

and $\int v\, dv = \frac{1}{2} v^2$

then $\int \frac{dp}{\rho} + \frac{1}{2} v^2 + gz = \text{constant}$.   .   .   .   .   (4.6)

4.3.1. Bernoulli's Equation for an incompressible fluid. Provided
velocity and pressure changes are small density changes will be very small,
and it is permissible to assume that the density ρ is constant throughout
the flow.

With this assumption, eqn. (4.6) may be integrated as

$$\int dp + \frac{1}{2} \rho v^2 + \rho g z = \text{constant}$$

Performing this integration between two conditions represented by suffices
1 and 2 gives

$$(p_2 - p_1) + \frac{1}{2} \rho (v_2^2 - v_1^2) + \rho g (z_2 - z_1) = 0$$

i.e., $p_1 + \frac{1}{2} \rho v_1^2 + \rho g z_1 = p_2 + \frac{1}{2} \rho v_2^2 + \rho g z_2$

In the foregoing analysis 1 and 2 were completely arbitrary choices,
and therefore the same equation must apply to conditions at any other
point.

Thus finally $p + \frac{1}{2} \rho v^2 + \rho g z = \text{constant}$.   .   .   (4.7)

This is Bernoulli's Equation for an incompressible fluid, i.e., a fluid
which cannot be compressed or expanded, and for which the density is
invariable.

4.3.2. Bernoulli's Equation for a compressible fluid. At high speeds
the assumption of constant density becomes invalid, and allowance has to
be made for the variation of density when solving eqn. (4.6).

To suggest a suitable form for this allowance, consider a wing of 6 ft chord in a wind stream of 600 ft/sec. A given particle of air flows over the whole chord in a time of approximately 0·01 sec. Since air is a poor conductor and radiator of heat it follows that there is practically no heat interchange between the different regions of the air. The air thus undergoes a compression and rarefaction process in which heat is neither lost nor gained, in other words an adiabatic process which obeys the law

$$p = k\rho^{\gamma} \quad . \quad . \quad . \quad . \quad (4.8)$$

where k is a constant for a particular airstream, and γ is the ratio of specific heats (§ 2.8.2). Eqn. (4.6) may be evaluated using this relationship between p and ρ as follows.
From eqn. (4.8),

$$\rho = (p/k)^{\frac{1}{\gamma}} \quad . \quad . \quad . \quad . \quad (4.9)$$

Substituting this in eqn. (4.6) gives

$$k^{\frac{1}{\gamma}} \int p^{-\frac{1}{\gamma}} dp + \tfrac{1}{2}v^2 + gz = \text{const.}$$

Integrating between limits representing conditions 1 and 2 this becomes

$$k^{\frac{1}{\gamma}} \left[\frac{1}{1 - 1/\gamma} p^{1 - \frac{1}{\gamma}} \right]_{p_1}^{p_2} + \tfrac{1}{2}(v_2^2 - v_1^2) + g(z_2 - z_1) = 0$$

or $\quad \dfrac{\gamma}{\gamma - 1} k^{\frac{1}{\gamma}} \left[p_2^{\frac{\gamma-1}{\gamma}} - p_1^{\frac{\gamma-1}{\gamma}} \right] + \tfrac{1}{2}(v_2^2 - v_1^2) + g(z_2 - z_1) = 0 \quad (4.10)$

Now from eqn. (4.8) $\qquad k^{\frac{1}{\gamma}} = \dfrac{p_1^{\frac{1}{\gamma}}}{\rho_1} = \dfrac{p_2^{\frac{1}{\gamma}}}{\rho_2} \quad . \quad . \quad . \quad (4.11)$

Substituting this in eqn. (4.10) gives

$$\frac{\gamma}{\gamma - 1} \left[\frac{p_2^{\frac{1}{\gamma}}}{\rho_2} p_2^{1 - \frac{1}{\gamma}} - \frac{p_1^{\frac{1}{\gamma}}}{\rho_1} p_1^{1 - \frac{1}{\gamma}} \right] + \tfrac{1}{2}(v_2^2 - v_1^2) + g(z_2 - z_1) = 0$$

or $\qquad \dfrac{\gamma}{\gamma - 1} \left[\dfrac{p_2}{\rho_2} - \dfrac{p_1}{\rho_1} \right] + \tfrac{1}{2}(v_2^2 - v_1^2) + g(z_2 - z_1) = 0$

Since subscripts 1 and 2 denote arbitrarily chosen conditions, this equation may be written as

$$\frac{\gamma}{\gamma - 1} \cdot \frac{p}{\rho} + \frac{v^2}{2} + gz = \text{const.} \quad . \quad . \quad . \quad (4.12)$$

Putting, for air, $\gamma = 1\cdot4 = 7/5$, this becomes

$$\frac{p}{\rho} + \frac{1}{7}v^2 + 9\cdot2z = \text{const.} \quad . \quad . \quad . \quad (4.13)$$

while if, as is usual in aerodynamics, the term involving height (z) is ignored

$$\frac{p}{\rho} + \frac{1}{7}v^2 = \text{const.} \qquad . \qquad . \qquad . \qquad . \qquad (4.14)$$

Now, the speed of sound in a gas is given by

$$a = \sqrt{\frac{\gamma p}{\rho}} = \sqrt{\gamma RT} = \sqrt{\frac{K}{\rho}} * \qquad . \qquad . \qquad (4.15)$$

Substituting this in eqn. (4.12), it is found that, if the term z be ignored

$$\frac{a^2}{\gamma - 1} + \frac{v^2}{2} = \text{const.} \qquad . \qquad . \qquad . \qquad (4.16)$$

Again putting $\gamma = 7/5$ this becomes, for air,

$$5a^2 + v^2 = \text{const.} \qquad . \qquad . \qquad . \qquad (4.17)$$

giving a relationship between the air speed and the speed of sound at a point in the adiabatic flow.

Pressure, density and temperature ratios along a streamline. From eqn. (4.11),

$$k^{\frac{1}{\gamma}} = \frac{p_1^{\frac{1}{\gamma}}}{\rho_1} = \frac{p_1}{\rho_1}p_1^{\frac{1}{\gamma}-1} = \frac{p_1}{\rho_1}p_1^{-\left(\frac{\gamma-1}{\gamma}\right)} \qquad . \qquad . \qquad (4.18)$$

Substituting this in eqn. (4.10) leads to

$$\frac{1}{\gamma - 1}\left(\frac{\gamma p_1}{\rho_1}\right)\left[\left(\frac{p_2}{p_1}\right)^{\frac{\gamma-1}{\gamma}} - 1\right] + \tfrac{1}{2}(v_2^2 - v_1^2) + g(z_2 - z_1) = 0$$

Now using $\dfrac{\gamma p_1}{\rho_1} = a_1^2$, the equation above gives

$$\frac{a_1^2}{\gamma - 1}\left[\left(\frac{p_2}{p_1}\right)^{\frac{\gamma-1}{\gamma}} - 1\right] + \tfrac{1}{2}(v_2^2 - v_1^2) + g(z_2 - z_1) = 0$$

which may be rearranged to give

$$\frac{p_2}{p_1} = \left[1 - \frac{\gamma - 1}{2}\frac{v_2^2 - v_1^2}{a_1^2}\right]^{\frac{\gamma}{\gamma-1}} \qquad . \qquad . \qquad (4.19)$$

if the term in z is ignored. This equation connects the pressure p_2 and the speed v_2 along the stream-tube, given the conditions p_1, v_1 and a_1.

Now $\qquad \dfrac{p_1}{\rho_1^\gamma} = \dfrac{p_2}{\rho_2^\gamma}; \quad \dfrac{p_1}{\rho_1} = RT_1 \quad$ and $\quad \dfrac{p_2}{\rho_2} = RT_2$

where T represents absolute temperature, °K.

Then $\qquad\qquad\qquad\qquad \dfrac{\rho_2}{\rho_1} = \left(\dfrac{p_2}{p_1}\right)^{\frac{1}{\gamma}}$

---

* See, e.g., Milne-Thompson, *Theoretical Aerodynamics*, p. 14, and/or Piercy, *Aerodynamics*, p. 22.

which, with eqn. (4.19), gives

$$\frac{p_2}{p_1} = \left[1 - \frac{\gamma - 1}{2} \frac{v_2^2 - v_1^2}{a_1^2}\right]^{\frac{1}{\gamma-1}} \qquad . \qquad . \qquad (4.20)$$

Further,

$$\frac{p_2/\rho_2}{p_1/\rho_1} = \frac{T_2}{T_1}$$

i.e.,

$$\frac{T_2}{T_1} = \left(\frac{p_2}{p_1}\right)\left(\frac{\rho_1}{\rho_2}\right) = \left(\frac{p_2}{p_1}\right)\left(\frac{p_1}{p_2}\right)^{\frac{1}{\gamma}} = \left(\frac{p_2}{p_1}\right)^{1 - \frac{1}{\gamma}} = \left(\frac{p_2}{p_1}\right)^{\frac{\gamma-1}{\gamma}}$$

This, in conjunction with eqn. (4.19), gives

$$\frac{T_2}{T_1} = \left[1 - \frac{\gamma - 1}{2} \frac{v_2^2 - v_1^2}{a_1^2}\right] \qquad . \qquad . \qquad (4.21)$$

Putting in the value of γ for air as 1·4, these ratios become

$$\frac{p_2}{p_1} = \left[1 - \frac{1}{5} \frac{v_2^2 - v_1^2}{a_1^2}\right]^{3.5} \qquad . \qquad . \qquad (4.19.1)$$

$$\frac{\rho_2}{\rho_1} = \left[1 - \frac{1}{5} \frac{v_2^2 - v_1^2}{a_1^2}\right]^{2.5} \qquad . \qquad . \qquad (4.20.1)$$

and

$$\frac{T_2}{T_1} = \left[1 - \frac{1}{5} \frac{v_2^2 - v_1^2}{a_1^2}\right] \qquad . \qquad . \qquad (4.21.1)$$

A special case of these equations is obtained by putting $v_2 = 0$, i.e., by assuming conditions 2 to represent air at rest. Then the term inside the square brackets in the above three equations becomes

$$1 - \frac{1}{5} \frac{0^2 - v_1^2}{a_1^2} = 1 + \frac{1}{5} \frac{v_1^2}{a_1^2} = 1 + \frac{1}{5} M_1^2$$

where M_1 is the local Mach number at the point 1.

The Mach number, named after the Austrian physicist Ernst Mach, is defined as the ratio of the flow speed to the speed of sound at a point in a fluid. (The Mach number of an aeroplane in flight is the ratio of the flight speed to the speed of sound in the surrounding atmosphere.)

The pressure of the air at rest is denoted by the symbol p_s and is called the *total pressure*. Since a *stagnation point* is defined as a point relative to a body where the air is brought to rest on the surface of the body, it follows that the pressure there is equal to the total head of the airstream immediately surrounding the stagnation point. This pressure is then known as the *stagnation pressure*.

Thus

$$\frac{p_s}{p} = [1 + \tfrac{1}{5}M^2]^{3.5} \qquad . \qquad . \qquad (4.19.2)$$

$$\frac{\rho_s}{\rho} = [1 + \tfrac{1}{5}M^2]^{2.5} \qquad . \qquad . \qquad (4.20.2)$$

and

$$\frac{T_s}{T} = [1 + \tfrac{1}{5}M^2] \qquad . \qquad . \qquad . \qquad (4.21.2)$$

T_s is the temperature of the air at rest and is called the *total temperature* or, at a stagnation point, the *stagnation temperature*. The quantities p, ρ and T represent the static pressure, the density and the static temperature at the point in the flow where the local Mach number has the value M. It is important to realize that, provided no shock waves exist, at no point in a flow can the pressure, density or temperature exceed p_s, ρ_s and T_s respectively, unless some source of heat, such as a heated wing or a flame, be present.

4.3.3. Comments on Bernoulli's Equations.   Referring back to eqn. (4.6),

$$\int dp/\rho + \tfrac{1}{2}v^2 + gz = \text{const.}$$

the first term is the internal energy of unit mass of the air, $\tfrac{1}{2}v^2$ is the kinetic energy of unit mass and gz is the potential energy of unit mass. Thus Bernoulli's equation in this form is really a statement of the principle of Conservation of Energy. As a corollary, it applies only to flows where there is no mechanism for the dissipation of energy into some form not included in the above three terms. In aerodynamics the most common other form of energy is that associated with vorticity. Thus Bernoulli's Equation cannot be applied to a flow with appreciable vorticity, such as that in a boundary layer.

There is one consequence of Bernoulli's Equation which often causes difficulty at first sight. It is that the equations derived above require a low velocity to be associated with a high pressure, and vice versa, whereas there is an instinctive feeling that a high velocity should correspond with a high pressure. Perhaps the best way to clear this up is to consider a reservoir of compressed air with a tapping leading to another reservoir of variable pressure. Then it is surely obvious that the lower the pressure in the second reservoir (i.e., the greater the pressure difference between the two reservoirs) the greater the speed of flow. In other words, for air initially at rest at some pressure, the higher the speed to which the air is accelerated the lower the corresponding pressure must be. The incorrect 'instinctive' feeling is really the result of thinking the wrong way round.

4.4. The measurement of air speed; the incompressibility assumption.   Consider an instrument of the form sketched in Fig. 4.8, called a Pitôt-static tube.

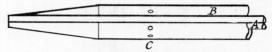

FIG. 4.8.—The simple pitôt-static tube.

It consists of two concentric tubes A and B. The mouth of A is open and faces directly into the airstream, while the end of B is closed on to A, causing B to be sealed off. Some very fine holes are drilled in the wall of B, as at C, allowing B to communicate with the surrounding air. The right-hand ends of A and B are connected to opposite sides of a manometer. The instrument is placed into a stream of air, with the mouth of A pointing directly upstream, the stream being of speed V ft/sec and of static pressure p lb/ft². The air flowing past the holes at C will be moving at a speed very little different from V; its pressure will therefore be equal to p, and this pressure will be communicated to the interior of tube B through the holes C. The pressure in B is therefore the static pressure of the stream.

Air entering the mouth of A will, on the other hand, be brought to rest (in the ultimate analysis by the fluid in the manometer). Its pressure will therefore be equal to the total head of the stream. As a result a pressure difference exists between the air in A and that in B, and this may be measured on the manometer. Denote the pressure in A by p_A, that in B by p_B, and the difference between them by Δp.

Then
$$\Delta p = p_A - p_B . \qquad . \qquad . \qquad . \qquad (4.22)$$
But, by Bernoulli's Equation for incompressible flow
$$p_A + \tfrac{1}{2}\rho(0)^2 = p_B + \tfrac{1}{2}\rho V^2$$
and therefore
$$p_A - p_B = \tfrac{1}{2}\rho V^2 \qquad . \qquad . \qquad . \qquad (4.23)$$
or
$$\Delta p = \tfrac{1}{2}\rho V^2$$
whence
$$V = \sqrt{\frac{2\Delta p}{\rho}} \qquad . \qquad . \qquad . \qquad (4.24)$$

The value of ρ (constant in incompressible flow) may be calculated from the pressure and the temperature. This, together with the measured value of Δp, permits calculation of the speed V ft/sec.

The quantity $\tfrac{1}{2}\rho V^2$ is the *dynamic pressure* of the stream. Since p_A = total pressure = p_s and p_B = static pressure = p, then
$$p_s - p = \tfrac{1}{2}\rho V^2 \qquad . \qquad . \qquad . \qquad (4.25)$$
which may be expressed in words as

total pressure — static pressure = dynamic pressure

It should be noted that this equation applies at all speeds, but the dynamic pressure is equal to $\tfrac{1}{2}\rho V^2$ only in incompressible flow.

Note also that $\quad \tfrac{1}{2}\rho V^2 = [ML^{-3}.L^2T^{-2}] = [ML^{-1}T^{-2}]$
$$= \text{pressure}$$
as is of course essential.

Defining the *stagnation pressure coefficient* as
$$C_{p\,s} = \frac{p_s - p}{\tfrac{1}{2}\rho V^2} \qquad . \qquad . \qquad . \qquad (4.26)$$
it follows immediately from eqn. (4.25) that for incompressible flow,
$$C_{p\,s} = 1 \quad \text{(always)} \qquad . \qquad . \qquad . \qquad (4.27)$$

D

As a first step in calculating the stagnation pressure coefficient in compressible flow,

$$\frac{1}{2}\rho V^2 = \frac{1}{2}\left(\frac{\rho}{\gamma p}\right)\gamma p V^2 = \frac{1}{2}\gamma p \frac{V^2}{a^2}$$

$$= \tfrac{1}{2}\gamma p M^2 \quad . \qquad . \qquad . \qquad . \qquad (4.28)$$

$$= 0.7 p M^2 \quad \text{for } \gamma = 1.4 \ . \qquad . \qquad . \quad (4.28.1)$$

This relation is very useful in high-speed, and particularly supersonic, aerodynamics.

The stagnation pressure coefficient becomes

$$C_{p\,s} = \frac{p_s - p}{0.7 p M^2} = \frac{1}{0.7 M^2}\left(\frac{p_s}{p} - 1\right) \quad . \qquad . \quad (4.29)$$

Now

$$\frac{p_s}{p} = [1 + \tfrac{1}{5}M^2]^{\frac{7}{2}} \quad (\text{eqn. (4.19.2)})$$

Expanding this by the Binomial Theorem gives

$$\frac{p_s}{p} = 1 + \frac{7}{2}\left(\frac{1}{5}M^2\right) + \frac{7}{2}\frac{5}{2}\frac{1}{2!}\left(\frac{1}{5}M^2\right)^2 + \frac{7}{2}\frac{5}{2}\frac{3}{2}\frac{1}{3!}\left(\frac{1}{5}M^2\right)^3$$

$$+ \frac{7}{2}\frac{5}{2}\frac{3}{2}\frac{1}{2}\frac{1}{4!}\left(\frac{1}{5}M^2\right)^4 + \cdots$$

$$= 1 + \frac{7M^2}{10} + \frac{7M^4}{40} + \frac{7M^6}{400} + \frac{7M^8}{16,000} + \cdots$$

Then

$$C_{p\,s} = \frac{10}{7M^2}\left(\frac{p_s}{p} - 1\right)$$

$$= \frac{10}{7M^2}\left[\frac{7M^2}{10} + \frac{7M^4}{40} + \frac{7M^6}{400} + \frac{7M^8}{16,000} + \cdots\right]$$

$$= 1 + \frac{M^2}{4} + \frac{M^4}{40} + \frac{M^6}{1600} + \cdots \quad . \qquad . \qquad . \quad (4.30)$$

It is seen that this becomes unity, the incompressible value, at $M = 0$. This is the practical meaning of the incompressibility assumption, namely that any velocity changes are small compared with the speed of sound in the fluid. The result given in eqn. (4.30) is the correct one which applies at all Mach numbers less than unity. At supersonic speeds shock waves may be formed in which case the physics of the flow is completely altered.

Table 4.1 shows the variation of $C_{p\,s}$ with Mach number. It is seen that

TABLE 4.1

Variation of stagnation pressure coefficient with Mach number,
for Mach numbers less than unity

M . . .	0	0·2	0·4	0·6	0·7	0·8	0·9	1·0
$C_{p\,s}$ . . .	1	1·01	1·04	1·09	1·13	1·16	1·217	1·276

the error in assuming $C_{p\,s} = 1$ is only 2% at $M = 0\cdot3$ but rises rapidly at higher Mach numbers, being almost 10% at $M = 0\cdot5$ and $27\cdot6\%$ at $M = 1\cdot0$.

4.4.1. The air-speed indicator; indicated and equivalent air speeds.

A Pitôt-static tube can be used to measure air speed and such an instrument is in fact used for speed measurement on aircraft. There are, however, slight differences between the systems used in aircraft and in the laboratory, the chief difference being in the manometer used. In the laboratory liquid manometers are normally employed. Such manometers with their liquids are, however, quite unsuitable for an aircraft and normally an aneroid barometric capsule is used (Fig. 4.9). This consists of a corrugated capsule, with static pressure applied to the casing surrounding the capsule, and the total pressure from the Pitôt tube is admitted to the interior of the capsule. The pressure difference causes the capsule to expand, and this expansion is transmitted by a mechanism to the pointer on the air-speed indicator dial. The dial is calibrated 'indicated air speed'.

When converting the observed pressure difference into air speed, the correct value for the air density can be calculated and used in eqn. (4.24). This is easy enough in the laboratory but it is hardly reasonable to expect a simple instrument such as the air-speed indicator to do this. The instrument is therefore calibrated on the assumption that the air density is always that appropriate to standard (i.e., sea-level I.S.A.) conditions.

Suppose the aircraft is flying at a true speed relative to the air of V ft/sec under conditions in which the ambient (surrounding) air density is ρ. Assuming that V is low enough for the flow to be regarded as incompressible, the corresponding dynamic pressure, which is the pressure difference applied to the aneroid capsule is

$$\Delta p = \tfrac{1}{2}\rho V^2 \qquad . \qquad . \qquad . \qquad (4.31)$$

Now suppose that the air-speed indicator is perfectly made, so that this pressure difference is detected and converted into needle movement without error. The air-speed indicator reading will then be some speed V_E ft/sec, calculated on the assumption that the air density is $\rho_0 = 0\cdot002378$ slug/ft³. This means that

$$\Delta p = \tfrac{1}{2}\rho_0 V_E^2 \qquad . \qquad . \qquad . \qquad (4.32)$$

But these two values of Δp (eqns. (4.31) and (4.32)) are one and the same pressure difference and therefore

$$\tfrac{1}{2}\rho_0 V_E^2 = \tfrac{1}{2}\rho V^2 \qquad . \qquad . \qquad . \qquad (4.33)$$

or

$$V_E = V\sqrt{\frac{\rho}{\rho_0}} \qquad . \qquad . \qquad . \qquad (4.34)$$

Now ρ/ρ_0 is the relative density σ introduced in § 3.3.4 and therefore

$$V_E = V\sqrt{\sigma} \qquad . \qquad . \qquad . \qquad (4.35)$$

This speed V_E, indicated by an error-free air-speed indicator, is called the 'equivalent air speed', abbreviated to E.A.S. The 'indicated air speed',

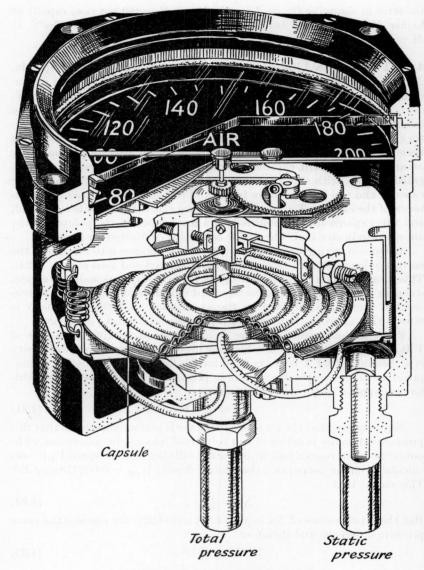

Capsule

Total
pressure

Static
pressure

FIG. 4.9.—Simple air-speed indicator.
(*By courtesy of Smith's Aircraft Instruments Ltd.*)

I.A.S. shown by a particular instrument will in general differ from the
equivalent air speed, due to errors in sensing the total and static pressures,
and to errors and inaccuracies in the mechanism and calibration of the
instrument.

The following definitions may therefore be stated:

Indicated air speed is that speed shown by an air-speed indicator.
Equivalent air speed is the speed which would be shown by an error-free
air speed indicator.
True air speed, T.A.S., is the actual speed of an aircraft relative to
the air.

Only when $\sigma = 1$ will true air speed and equivalent air speed be equal;
the E.A.S. is normally, but not always, less than the T.A.S.

It might be thought that this systematic difference due to density
changes between indicated air speed and true air speed would be a great
disadvantage. Certainly the navigator of an aeroplane needs to know the
true air speed. The pilot is, broadly speaking, quite indifferent to the true
air speed; as far as flying the aircraft is concerned the relevant speed is the
E.A.S. to which the indicated air speed is a good approximation depending
on the quality of the instruments.

Air-speed indicators are, as stated above, usually calibrated on the
assumption that $\rho_0 = 0.002378$ slug/ft^3. In addition the calibration usually
assumes incompressible flow, although some more modern instruments
make an approximate correction for compressibility.

In the following examples use will be made of the eqn. (4.15)

$$a = \sqrt{\gamma R T}$$

For air, with $\gamma = 1.4$ and $R = 3092$ ft lb/slug °C, this becomes

$$a = 65.9\sqrt{T} \text{ ft/sec} \qquad . \qquad . \qquad . \quad (4.15.1)$$

where T is the temperature in °K.

Example 4.1. The air-speed indicator fitted to a particular aeroplane has
no instrument errors and is calibrated assuming incompressible flow in
standard conditions. While flying at sea-level in the I.S.A. the indicated air
speed is 600 miles per hour. What is the true air speed?

600 m.p.h = 880 ft/sec, and this is the speed corresponding to the
pressure difference applied to the instrument based on the stated calibration.
This pressure difference can therefore be calculated by

$$p_s - p = \Delta p = \tfrac{1}{2}\rho_0 V_E^2$$

and therefore

$$p_s - p = \frac{1}{841}(880)^2 = 920 \text{ lb/ft}^2$$

Now

$$\frac{p_s}{p} = \left[1 + \frac{1}{5}M^2\right]^{3.5}$$

In standard conditions $p = 2116$ lb/ft^2 and therefore

$$\frac{p_s}{p} = \frac{920}{2116} + 1 = 1.435$$

Therefore

$$1 + \tfrac{1}{5}M^2 = (1.435)^{\frac{2}{7}} = 1.109$$

$$\therefore \tfrac{1}{5}M^2 = 0.109$$

$$M^2 = 0.545$$

$$M = 0.737$$

The speed of sound at standard conditions is

$$a = 65\cdot9(288)^{\frac{1}{2}} = 1117 \text{ ft/sec}$$
$$\therefore \text{ true air speed} = Ma = 0\cdot737 \times 1117$$
$$= 823 \text{ ft/sec} = \underline{560 \text{ m.p.h.}}$$

In this example, $\sigma = 1$ and therefore there is no effect due to density; the difference is due entirely to compressibility. Thus it is seen that neglecting compressibility in the calibration has led the air-speed indicator to over-estimate the true air speed by 40 m.p.h.

Example 4.2. The aeroplane above is flying at an altitude where the ambient pressure is 628 lb/ft^2 and the temperature is $-44\cdot4°$C. Its true air speed is 614 m.p.h. Calculate the indicated air speed and compare the result with that obtained by neglecting compressibility.

$$\text{T.A.S.} = 614 \text{ m.p.h} = 900 \text{ ft/sec}$$
$$\text{Speed of sound } a = 65\cdot9(273 - 44\cdot4)^{\frac{1}{2}} = 995 \text{ ft/sec}$$
$$\therefore \text{ Mach number } M = \frac{900}{995} = 0\cdot905$$

Therefore
$$\frac{p_s}{p} = \left[1 + \frac{1}{5}M^2\right]^{3\cdot5} = \left[1 + \frac{(0\cdot905)^2}{5}\right]^{3\cdot5}$$
$$= 1\cdot70$$

Then
$$p_s - p = p\left(\frac{p_s}{p} - 1\right) = 628(1\cdot70 - 1)$$
$$= 440 \text{ lb/ft}^2$$

Now the air-speed indicator senses this pressure difference and converts it to speed V_E according to the law

$$p_s - p = \tfrac{1}{2}\rho_0 V_E^{\,2}$$

i.e.,
$$440 = \frac{1}{841}V_E^{\,2} \quad \text{which leads to}$$
$$V_E = (440 \times 841)^{\frac{1}{2}} = 29(440)^{\frac{1}{2}}$$
$$= 609 \text{ ft/sec} = \underline{415 \text{ m.p.h.}}$$

Now, from eqn. (3.8),

$$\rho = \frac{p}{RT}$$

whence relative density
$$\sigma = \frac{\rho}{\rho_0} = \frac{p}{p_0}\cdot\frac{T_0}{T}$$

i.e., in this case
$$\sigma = \frac{628}{2116} \times \frac{288}{273 - 44\cdot4} = 0\cdot374$$

whence
$$\sqrt{\sigma} = 0\cdot610$$

Therefore, without correction for compressibility

$$\text{I.A.S.} = \text{T.A.S.} \times \sqrt{\sigma}$$
$$= 614(0\cdot610) = \underline{374 \text{ m.p.h.}}$$

To summarize these results

T.A.S.   = 614 m.p.h.
I.A.S. (no correction for compressibility) = 374 m.p.h.
I.A.S. (corrected for compressibility)   = 415 m.p.h.

The last of these results is that which would actually be shown by an air-speed indicator, while the second is fictitious and would be obtained were air truly incompressible. The simplified calibration of the instrument has caused it to underestimate the aircraft speed by 200 m.p.h. It almost seems fair to say of the air-speed indicator that the last thing it does is to indicate air speed.

If the aircraft in the previous examples is assumed to fly at the altitude of Example 4.2, but at an indicated air speed of 150 m.p.h, the true air speeds, calculated with and without correction for compressibility, are 241·5 m.p.h and 246 m.p.h respectively. As would be expected the lower Mach number in this case results in the compressibility correction being much reduced, 4 m.p.h as against 40 m.p.h. in the previous examples.

It should perhaps be emphasized that the best estimate of the true T.A.S. is that resulting from allowance for compressibility effects.

4.5. Variation of stream-tube area with flow speed. For incompressible flow,

$$V_1 A_1 = V_2 A_2 \qquad . \qquad . \qquad . \qquad (4.36)$$

Taking V_1 and A_1 as 'reference' values of velocity and stream-tube area, it follows that if $A_2 < A_1$, then $V_2 > V_1$; i.e., the speed V is inversely proportional to the duct area. The smaller the duct area the faster must be the flow in order to pass the same mass in unit time.

Now the incompressibility assumption applies only at low speeds. It is therefore to be expected that the simple inverse relationship between area and speed will similarly only hold at low speeds; at higher speeds the change in density will modify this simple rule. To work out the more accurate rule, the continuity (or constant mass flow) condition can be written as

$$\rho_1 A_1 V_1 = \rho_2 A_2 V_2 . \qquad . \qquad . \qquad . \qquad (4.37)$$

Consider the case of air initially at rest at a pressure p_s, density ρ_s and temperature T_s, expanding to two different Mach numbers M_1 and M_2. The stream-tube areas A_1 and A_2 necessary to pass a mass flow of $\dot{m}$ slug/sec are given by

$$\dot{m} = \rho_1 A_1 V_1 = \rho_2 A_2 V_2 \qquad . \qquad . \qquad . \qquad (4.38)$$

whence

$$\frac{A_1}{A_2} = \frac{\rho_2 V_2}{\rho_1 V_1} \qquad . \qquad . \qquad . \qquad . \qquad (4.39)$$

From eqn. (4.20.2),

$$\rho_s = \rho_1 [1 + \tfrac{1}{5} M_1^2]^{2 \cdot 5} = \rho_2 [1 + \tfrac{1}{5} M_2^2]^{2 \cdot 5}$$

while from eqn. (4.21.2),

$$T_s = T_1 [1 + \tfrac{1}{5} M_1^2] = T_2 [1 + \tfrac{1}{5} M_2^2]$$

where T_1 and T_2 are the relevant static temperatures, (°K).

Also, $$a_1 = 65 \cdot 9 (T_1)^{\frac{1}{2}}$$

and $$a_2 = 65 \cdot 9 (T_2)^{\frac{1}{2}}$$

while, from the definition of Mach number

$$V_1 = M_1 a_1 \quad \text{and} \quad V_2 = M_2 a_2$$

From the above relationships it is found that

$$\frac{\rho_2}{\rho_1} = \left(\frac{5 + M_1^2}{5 + M_2^2}\right)^{2 \cdot 5} \qquad . \qquad . \qquad . \qquad (4.40)$$

and

$$\frac{V_2}{V_1} = \frac{M_2 a_2}{M_1 a_1} = \frac{M_2}{M_1}\left(\frac{T_2}{T_1}\right)^{0 \cdot 5}$$

$$= \frac{M_2}{M_1}\left(\frac{5 + M_1^2}{5 + M_2^2}\right)^{0 \cdot 5} \qquad . \qquad . \qquad (4.41)$$

Substituting from eqns. (4.40) and (4.41) in eqn. (4.39) gives

$$\frac{A_1}{A_2} = \frac{M_2}{M_1}\left(\frac{5 + M_1^2}{5 + M_2^2}\right)^{3} \qquad . \qquad . \qquad (4.42)$$

Suppose we have conditions where the local Mach number is unity, i.e., $M_1 = 1$, and denote the corresponding area by A^*

$$\frac{A^*}{A_2} = \frac{M_2}{1}\left(\frac{5 + 1}{5 + M_2^2}\right)^{3} = M_2\left(\frac{6}{5 + M_2^2}\right)^{3} \quad . \qquad (4.43)$$

or, in a more usual form

$$\frac{A}{A^*} = \frac{1}{M}\left(\frac{5 + M^2}{6}\right)^{3} \qquad . \qquad . \qquad (4.44)$$

The subscript 2 has been dropped as it is no longer necessary.

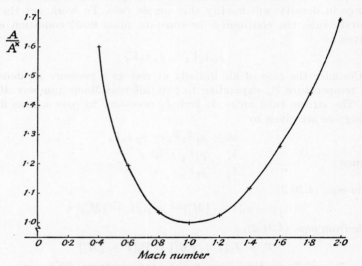

Fig. 4.10.—Variation of stream-tube area with Mach number.

Fig. 4.10 shows the variation of A/A^* with Mach number for the range $0 \cdot 4 \leqslant M \leqslant 2 \cdot 0$. This graph shows one very important point: that the minimum value of A/A^* is unity and occurs when the local Mach number is itself unity. Thus for any other Mach number, whether greater or less than unity, the stream-tube area is greater than for $M = 1$.

Thus suppose a stream of air is accelerating from rest to some supersonic speed. Then initially the channel must contract, i.e., in the same sense, but to a different degree, to that required for incompressible flow. This contraction must continue until the local Mach number becomes unity. Thereafter the channel must expand if the flow is to accelerate further. Thus an accelerating supersonic stream is associated with an expanding duct. The physical explanation of this is that, at supersonic speeds, the air density decreases more rapidly than the speed increases, thus requiring a greater cross-sectional area to pass a given mass flow.

In digesting these facts it is useful to remember that for present purposes a duct with solid walls and a stream-tube are equivalent.

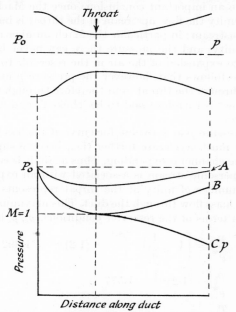

Fig. 4.11.—Variation of pressure along a convergent-divergent duct.

The conclusion regarding the shape of a duct for supersonic flow can also be derived by a purely qualitative argument, as follows.

Fig. 4.11 shows a convergent-divergent duct, and the variation of pressure along its length. Suppose the upstream end of the duct is connected to a reservoir containing compressed air whose total pressure p_s and temperature T_s are maintained constant. The downstream end is connected to another tank in which the pressure p may be varied at will. If no pressure difference exists along the duct there is no flow. If now, p is made slightly less than p_s there is a low-speed flow, and the pressure distribution is as curve A, the air leaving the downstream end of the duct with a small velocity. Gradual lowering of the pressure p will lead to larger flow speeds until the local Mach number at the throat becomes unity (curve B).

Now suppose the pressure p to be gradually decreased further to some particular value (curve C). One very important point now enters the argument. The speed of sound is the speed of propagation of small pressure disturbances. Thus the change in the pressure p from value (B) to value (C) will pass upstream at the local speed of sound. When this pressure change reaches the throat the flow will be travelling downstream as fast as the pressure wave is travelling upstream, the pressure disturbance is unable to make headway upstream and is therefore unable to pass through the throat. The flow upstream of the throat is therefore 'unaware' of the change in pressure at the downstream end and cannot accommodate itself to the new conditions.

This leads to an important conclusion: once the Mach number in the throat reaches unity the flow upstream of the throat is independent of the conditions downstream; in particular the Mach number in the throat can never exceed unity, and the pressure there can never be less than that corresponding to expansion of the air in the reservoir to a Mach number of unity. It also follows that, however the pressure p may be decreased, the mass flow through the throat (and therefore through the duct) cannot increase. The duct is therefore said to be 'choked', and it cannot pass air at a greater rate.

Since the pressure p at its value for curve (C) is less than that at the throat the flow must accelerate further (i.e., become supersonic) despite the fact that the channel is expanding. Thus again it is concluded that an accelerating supersonic stream is associated with an expanding channel.

The Mach number of unity at the throat represents a limiting case, with maximum mass flow through the duct. This maximum mass flow may be calculated in terms of the reservoir conditions, p_s, ρ_s and T_s.

$$\frac{p_s}{p^*} = \left[1 + \frac{1}{5}(1)^2\right]^{3 \cdot 5} = (1 \cdot 2)^{3 \cdot 5} = 1 \cdot 892 \ . \qquad . \qquad (4.45)$$

$$\frac{\rho_s}{\rho^*} = (1 \cdot 2)^{2 \cdot 5} = 1 \cdot 577 \ . \qquad . \qquad . \qquad . \qquad (4.46)$$

$$\frac{T_s}{T^*} = 1 \cdot 2 \ . \qquad . \qquad . \qquad . \qquad . \qquad . \qquad (4.47)$$

where p^*, ρ^* and T^* are the pressure, density and temperature at the throat.

Maximum speed at throat = speed of sound at throat when local Mach number is unity,

$$\therefore \ V^* = a^* = 65 \cdot 9\sqrt{T^*} = 65 \cdot 9\sqrt{\frac{T_s}{1 \cdot 2}}$$

$$= 60 \cdot 1\sqrt{T_s} \ \text{ft/sec} \ . \qquad . \qquad . \qquad (4.48)$$

Therefore,   maximum mass flow $= \rho^* A^* V^*$

$$= \frac{\rho_s}{1 \cdot 577}A^* \times 60 \cdot 1\sqrt{T_s}$$

i.e., max. mass flow $= 38 \cdot 2 \rho_s A^* \sqrt{T_s}$ slug/sec

But since $\rho_s = \dfrac{p_s}{RT_s}$ (by eqn. (3.8))

max. mass flow $= 38 \cdot 2A^* \dfrac{p_s}{3092T_s} \sqrt{T_s}$

$$= 0 \cdot 01237A^* \dfrac{p_s}{\sqrt{T_s}} \text{ slug/sec} \qquad . \qquad (4.49)$$

4.6. Pressure coefficient. In Chapter 2 it was seen that it is often convenient to express variables in a non-dimensional form. Such an artifice is commonly applied to aerodynamic pressures.

The stagnation pressure coefficient has already been defined as

$$C_{ps} = \dfrac{p_s - p}{\frac{1}{2}\rho V^2}$$

This is a special case of the general 'pressure coefficient' defined by

$$\text{pressure coefficient } C_p = \dfrac{p - p_0}{\frac{1}{2}\rho V^2} \qquad . \qquad . \qquad (4.50)$$

where C_p = pressure coefficient
p = static pressure at some point in the flow
p_0 = static pressure of the undisturbed stream
ρ = density of the undisturbed stream
V = speed of the undisturbed stream

Now, in incompressible flow,

$$p + \tfrac{1}{2}\rho q^2 = p_0 + \tfrac{1}{2}\rho V^2$$

where q = speed of flow at the point where p is measured

Then $p - p_0 = \tfrac{1}{2}\rho(V^2 - q^2)$

and therefore $C_p = 1 - \left(\dfrac{q}{V}\right)^2 \qquad . \qquad . \qquad . \qquad (4.51)$

Then:

    (i) if C_p is positive $p > p_0$ and $q < V$
    (ii) if C_p is zero $p = p_0$ and $q = V$
    (iii) if C_p is negative $p < p_0$ and $q > V$

Note also that, as shown in eqn. (4.28.1),

$$\tfrac{1}{2}\rho V^2 = 0 \cdot 7p_0 M^2$$

Using this, eqn. (4.50) becomes

$$C_p = \dfrac{p - p_0}{0 \cdot 7p_0 M^2} = \dfrac{1}{0 \cdot 7M^2}\left(\dfrac{p}{p_0} - 1\right) \qquad . \qquad . \qquad (4.52)$$

One point to be noted in connection with this equation is that although $\frac{1}{2}\rho V^2$ $(= 0 \cdot 7p_0 M^2)$ is not the dynamic pressure in compressible flow, no recognition of this is made in the definition of C_p, which remains as given in eqns. (4.50) and (4.52). However, eqn. (4.51) applies only in incompressible flow since it was derived using Bernoulli's Equation in the incompressible form.

Example 4.3. A wind-tunnel has a smallest section measuring 4 ft × 3 ft 3 in., and a largest section of 13 ft square. The smallest is vented, so that it is at atmospheric pressure. A pressure tapping at the largest section is connected to an inclined tube manometer, sloped at 30° to the horizontal. The manometer reservoir is vented to the atmosphere, and the manometer liquid has a specific gravity of 0·85. What will be the manometer reading when the speed at the smallest section is (i) 260 ft/sec and (ii) 780 ft/sec?

Denote conditions at the smallest section by suffix 2, and the largest section by suffix 1.

Since both the smallest section and the reservoir are vented to the same pressure, the reservoir may be regarded as being connected directly to the smallest section.

$$\text{Area of smallest section} = 4 \times 3\tfrac{1}{4}$$
$$= 13 \text{ ft}^2$$
$$\text{Area of largest section} = 13 \times 13$$
$$= 169 \text{ ft}^2$$

(i) Since the maximum speed is 260 ft/sec the flow may be regarded as incompressible.

Then
$$V_1 A_1 = V_2 A_2$$
i.e.,
$$V_1 \times 169 = 260 \times 13$$
whence
$$V_1 = \tfrac{260}{13} = 20 \text{ ft/sec}.$$

By Bernoulli's Equation, and assuming standard temperature and pressure;

$$p_1 + \tfrac{1}{2}\rho V_1^2 = p_2 + \tfrac{1}{2}\rho V_2^2$$
Then
$$p_1 - p_2 = \tfrac{1}{2}\rho(V_2^2 - V_1^2) = \tfrac{1}{841}(260^2 - 20^2)$$
$$= \tfrac{1}{841}(280)(240)$$
$$= 80 \text{ lb/ft}^2.$$

This is the pressure across the manometer, and therefore
$$\Delta p = \rho_m g \Delta h \qquad \qquad \qquad \qquad (3.7)$$
where Δh is the head of liquid in feet and ρ_m the manometric fluid density,

i.e.,
$$80 = (1\cdot 94 \times 0\cdot 85) \times 32\cdot 18 \times \Delta h$$
This gives
$$\Delta h = 1\cdot 505 \text{ ft}$$
But
$$\Delta h = r \sin \theta$$
where r is the manometer reading and θ is the manometer slope.

Then
$$1\cdot 505 = r \sin 30° = \tfrac{1}{2} r$$
and therefore
$$r = 2 \times 1\cdot 505 = 3\cdot 01 \text{ ft}$$
$$= \underline{36\cdot 12 \text{ in.}}$$

(ii) In this case the speed is well into the range where compressibility becomes important, and it will be seen how much more complicated the solution becomes. To simplify the arithmetic it will be assumed that the temperature at the smallest section is −42°C, which makes the speed of sound there a convenient 1000 ft/sec. In such a case the density will not have the standard value.

From the equation of continuity

$$\rho_1 A_1 V_1 = \rho_2 A_2 V_2$$

i.e.,

$$\frac{\rho_1}{\rho_2} = \frac{A_2 V_2}{A_1 V_1}$$

Also, by Bernoulli's Equation for compressible flow,

$$\frac{\rho_1}{\rho_0} = \left\{ 1 - \frac{1}{5} \frac{V_1^2 - V_2^2}{a_2^2} \right\}^{2\cdot5}$$

Equating these expressions for ρ_1/ρ_2, and putting in the known values for A_1, A_2, V_2 and a_2

$$\frac{13 \times 780}{169 V_1} = \left[1 - \frac{1}{5} \frac{V_1^2 - (780)^2}{(1000)^2} \right]^{2\cdot5}$$

or

$$\frac{60}{V_1} = \left[1 - \frac{1}{5} \left\{ \left(\frac{V_1}{1000} \right)^2 - 0\cdot6084 \right\} \right]^{2\cdot5}$$

This equation in V_1 cannot be solved directly; the best procedure is to solve by trial and error. Doing so gives

$$V_1 = 45 \text{ ft/sec approximately}$$

and

$$\frac{\rho_1}{\rho_2} = \frac{60}{45} = 1\cdot333.$$

But

$$\frac{p_1}{p_2} = \left(\frac{\rho_1}{\rho_2} \right)^{\gamma} = (1\cdot333)^{1\cdot4} = 1\cdot495$$

Therefore $p_1 - p_2 = p_2 \left(\frac{p_1}{p_2} - 1 \right) = 2116 \times 0\cdot495 = 1048 \text{ lb/ft}^2.$

Then the reading of the manometer, r, is given by

$$r = \frac{\Delta p}{\rho_m g \sin \theta}$$

$$= \frac{1048 \times 2}{1\cdot94 \times 0\cdot85 \times 32\cdot18}$$

$$= \underline{39\cdot5 \text{ ft.}}$$

The main complication lies in the equation for V_1, which is rather unpleasant.

The result of 39 ft for the manometer reading shows that for speeds of this order a manometer using a low-density liquid is unsuitable. In practice it is probable that mercury would be used, when the reading would be reduced to $39\cdot5 \times 0\cdot85/13\cdot6 = 2\cdot46$ ft, a far more manageable figure.

Example 4.4. The reading of the manometer in Example 4.3 at a certain tunnel speed is 28 in. Another manometer tube is connected at its free end to a point on an aerofoil model in the smallest section of the tunnel, while a third tube is connected to the total pressure tube of a Pitôt-static tube. If the liquid in the second tube is 3 in. above the zero level, calculate the pressure coefficient and the speed of flow at that point on the model in terms of the flow parameters at the smallest section. Calculate also the reading, including sense, of the third tube.

(i) To find speed of flow at smallest section.

Manometer reading $= 28$ in.

∴ pressure difference $= 1\cdot94 \times 0\cdot85 \times 32\cdot18 \times \frac{28}{12} \times \frac{1}{2}$

$$= 62 \text{ lb/ft}^2$$

$$\therefore p_1 - p_2 = 62 = \tfrac{1}{841}(V_2^2 - V_1^2)$$

But $\quad V_2 = 13V_1$, giving $V_2^2 = 169V_1^2$

whence $\qquad\qquad 62 = \dfrac{1}{841}\left(V_2^2 - \dfrac{V_2^2}{169}\right) = \dfrac{V_2^2}{841} \times \dfrac{168}{169}$

whence $\qquad\qquad V_2^2 = 52{,}500 \text{ (ft/sec)}^2$

$$V_2 = 229 \text{ ft/sec,}$$

and therefore dynamic pressure at smallest section $= (229)^2/841 = 62\cdot4 \text{ lb/ft}^2$

(ii) *Pressure coefficient.*

Since static pressure at smallest section = atmospheric pressure, then pressure difference between aerofoil and tunnel stream = pressure difference between aerofoil and atmosphere. This pressure difference is 3 in. on the manometer, or

$$\Delta p = 1\cdot94 \times 0\cdot85 \times 32\cdot18 \times \tfrac{3}{12} \times \tfrac{1}{2} = 6\cdot64 \text{ lb/ft}^2$$

Now the manometer liquid has been drawn upwards from the zero level, showing that the pressure on the aerofoil is less than that of the undisturbed tunnel stream, and therefore the pressure coefficient will be negative.

$$\therefore \; C_p = \frac{p - p_0}{\frac{1}{2}\rho V^2} = \frac{-6\cdot64}{62\cdot4} = -\underline{0\cdot1065}.$$

Now $\qquad\qquad C_p = 1 - \left(\dfrac{q}{V}\right)^2$

$$\therefore \; -0\cdot1065 = 1 - \left(\frac{q}{V_2}\right)^2$$

Hence, $\qquad q = V_2(1 - C_p)^{\frac{1}{2}} = 229(1\cdot1065)^{\frac{1}{2}}$

$$= \underline{240 \text{ ft/sec.}}$$

(iii) The total pressure is equal to stream static pressure plus the dynamic pressure, and therefore pressure difference corresponding to the reading of the third tube is $(p_0 + \frac{1}{2}\rho V_2^2) - p_0$, i.e., is equal to $\frac{1}{2}\rho V_2^2$.
Therefore, if the reading is r_3

$$\tfrac{1}{2}\rho V_2^2 = \rho_m g r_3 \sin\theta$$

i.e., $\qquad 62\cdot4 = 1\cdot94 \times 0\cdot85 \times 32\cdot18 \times r_3 \times \tfrac{1}{2}$

whence $\qquad r_3 = 2\cdot36 \text{ ft} = \underline{28\cdot3 \text{ in.}}$

Since the total head is greater than the stream static pressure, and therefore greater than atmospheric pressure, the liquid in the third tube will be depressed below the zero level, i.e., the reading will be $-28\cdot3$ in.

Example 4.5. An aircraft is flying at 20,000 ft, where the pressure, temperature and relative density are 972 lb/ft², $-24\cdot6°C$, and 0·533 respectively. The wing is vented so that its internal pressure is uniform and equal to the ambient pressure. On the upper surface of the wing is an inspection panel 6 in. square.

Calculate the load tending to lift the inspection panel and the air speed over the panel under the following conditions:

(i) Mach number = 0·2, mean C_p over panel = $-0\cdot8$, and
(ii) Mach number = 0·85, mean C_p over panel = $-0\cdot5$.

(i) Since the Mach number of 0·2 is small, it is a fair assumption that, although the speed over the panel will be higher than the flight speed, it will still be small enough for compressibility to be ignored. Then, since

$$C_p = \frac{p - p_0}{0\cdot7p_0 M^2}$$

$$p - p_0 = 0\cdot7p_0 M^2 C_p = 0\cdot7 \times 972 \times (0\cdot2)^2 \times (-0\cdot8)$$

$$= -21\cdot75 \text{ lb/ft}^2$$

The load on the panel = pressure difference × area
$$= 21 \cdot 75 \times (\tfrac{1}{2})^2$$
$$= \underline{5 \cdot 45 \text{ lb.}}$$

Also
$$C_p = 1 - \left(\frac{q}{V}\right)^2$$

i.e.,
$$- 0 \cdot 8 = 1 - \left(\frac{q}{V}\right)^2$$

whence
$$\left(\frac{q}{V}\right)^2 = 1 \cdot 8, \quad \frac{q}{V} = 1 \cdot 34.$$

Now   speed of sound $= 65 \cdot 9(273 - 24 \cdot 6)^{\frac{1}{2}} = 1040$ ft/sec
$$\therefore \text{ true flight speed} = 0 \cdot 2 \times 1040 = 208 \text{ ft/sec}$$
$$\therefore \text{ air speed over panel, } q = 208 \times 1 \cdot 34 = \underline{279 \text{ ft/sec.}}$$

(ii) Here the flow is definitely compressible.

As before
$$C_p = \frac{p - p_0}{0 \cdot 7 p_0 M^2}$$

and therefore
$$p - p_0 = 0 \cdot 7 \times 972 \times (0 \cdot 85)^2 \times (- 0 \cdot 5)$$
$$= - 246 \text{ lb/ft}^2$$
$$\therefore \text{ load on panel} = 246 \times (\tfrac{1}{2})^2 = \underline{61 \cdot 5 \text{ lb.}}$$

There are two ways of calculating the speed of flow over the panel:

(a)
$$\frac{p_1}{p_0} = \left[1 - \frac{1}{5}\frac{q^2 - V^2}{a^2}\right]^{3 \cdot 5}$$

where a is the speed of sound in the free stream.

i.e.,
$$\frac{p_1}{p_0} = \left[1 - \frac{1}{5}\left\{\left(\frac{q}{a}\right)^2 - M^2\right\}\right]^{3 \cdot 5}$$

Now $p_1 - p_0 = - 246$ lb/ft^2
and therefore $p_1 = 972 - 246 = 726$ lb/ft^2.

Thus substituting in the above equation the known values $p_0 = 972$, $p_1 = 726$ and $M = 0 \cdot 85$ leads to
$$\left(\frac{q}{a}\right)^2 = 1 \cdot 123, \quad \frac{q}{a} = 1 \cdot 06$$
$$\therefore q = 1 \cdot 06a = 1 \cdot 06 \times 1040 = \underline{1100 \text{ ft/sec.}}$$

It is also possible to calculate the Mach number of the flow over the panel, as follows. The local temperature T_1 is found from
$$\frac{T_1}{T_0} = \left(\frac{p_1}{p_0}\right)^{1/3 \cdot 5} = \left(\frac{726}{972}\right)^{1/3 \cdot 5} = 0 \cdot 920$$

whence $T_1 = 0 \cdot 920 T_0$
and $a_1 = a_0(0 \cdot 920)^{\frac{1}{2}} = 1040(0 \cdot 920)^{\frac{1}{2}} = 997$ ft/sec
Therefore   Mach number over panel $= \frac{1100}{997} = \underline{1 \cdot 103}$.

(b) The alternative method of solution is as follows, with the total pressure of the flow denoted by p_s.
$$\frac{p_s}{p_0} = \left[1 + \frac{1}{5}M^2\right]^{3 \cdot 5} = \left[1 + \frac{(0 \cdot 85)^2}{5}\right]^{3 \cdot 5}$$
$$= (1 \cdot 1445)^{3 \cdot 5} = 1 \cdot 605$$

Therefore $p_s = 972 \times 1 \cdot 605 = 1560$ lb/ft^2

As found in method (a), $p_1 - p_0 = -246 \text{ lb/ft}^2$

and $p_1 = 726 \text{ lb/ft}^2$

Then $\dfrac{p_s}{p_1} = \dfrac{1560}{726} = 2\cdot15 = \left[1 + \dfrac{1}{5}M_1^2\right]^{3\cdot5}$

whence $M_1^2 = 1\cdot22, \quad \underline{M_1 = 1\cdot103}$

which agrees with the result found in method (a).

The total temperature T_s is given by

$$\frac{T_s}{T_0} = \left(\frac{p}{p_0}\right)^{1/3\cdot5} = 1\cdot1445$$

$$\therefore \ T_s = 1\cdot1445 \times 248\cdot6 = 284°\text{K}$$

Then $\dfrac{T_s}{T_1} = (2\cdot15)^{1/3\cdot5} = 1\cdot244$

giving $T_1 = \dfrac{284}{1\cdot244} = 228°\text{K}$

and the local speed of sound over the panel, a_1 is

$$a_1 = 65\cdot9(228)^{\frac{1}{2}} = 993 \text{ ft/sec}$$

$\therefore$ flow speed over the panel, $q = 993 \times 1\cdot103 = \underline{1095 \text{ ft/sec}}$

which agrees with the answer obtained by method (a).

One interesting feature of this example is that, although the flight speed is subsonic ($M = 0\cdot85$), the flow over the panel is supersonic. This fact was used in the 'wing-flow' method of transonic research. The method dates from about 1940, when transonic wind-tunnels were unsatisfactory. A small model was mounted on the upper surface of the wing of an aeroplane, which then dived at near maximum speed. As a result the model experienced a flow which was supersonic locally. The method, though not very satisfactory, was an improvement on other methods available at that time.

Example 4.6. A high-speed wind-tunnel consists of a reservoir of compressed air which discharges through a convergent-divergent nozzle. The temperature and pressure in the reservoir are 200°C and 300 lb/in.² gauge respectively. In the test section the Mach number is to be 2·5.

If the test section area is to be 24 in.², what should be the throat area? Calculate also the mass flow, and the pressure, temperature, speed, μ and ν in the test section.

$$\frac{A}{A^*} = \frac{1}{M}\left(\frac{5 + M^2}{6}\right)^3 = \frac{1}{2\cdot5}\left(\frac{5 + 6\cdot25}{6}\right)^3 = 2\cdot64$$

$$\therefore \ \text{throat area} = \frac{24}{2\cdot64} = \underline{9\cdot1 \text{ in.}^2}$$

Since the throat is choked, the mass flow may be calculated from eqn. (4.49).

i.e.,   mass flow $= 0\cdot01237(p_s/\sqrt{T_s})A^*$

Now the reservoir pressure is 300 lb/in.² gauge, or

$(300 \times 144) + 2116 \text{ lb/ft}^2 \text{ absolute} = 45,316 \text{ lb/ft}^2$,

while the reservoir temperature is 200°C $= 473°\text{K}$.

$$\therefore \text{ mass flow } = 0\cdot01237 \times \frac{45{,}316}{(473)^{\frac{1}{2}}} \times \frac{9\cdot1}{144} = \underline{1\cdot63 \text{ slug/sec.}}$$

In the test section,

$$1 + \frac{1}{5}M^2 = 1 + \frac{6\cdot25}{5} = 2\cdot25$$

$$\therefore \frac{p_s}{p} = (2\cdot25)^{3\cdot5} = 17\cdot1$$

$$\therefore \text{ pressure in test section } = \frac{45{,}316}{17\cdot1} = \underline{2650 \text{ lb/ft}^2}$$

Also

$$\frac{T_s}{T} = 2\cdot25$$

$$\therefore \text{ temperature in test section } = \frac{473}{2\cdot25} = 210°\text{K} = \underline{-\ 63°\text{C}}$$

$$\text{Density in test section } = \frac{2650}{3092 \times 210}$$

$$= \underline{0\cdot00409 \text{ slug/ft}^3}$$

$$\text{speed of sound in test section } = 65\cdot9(210)^{\frac{1}{2}} = 955 \text{ ft/sec}$$

$$\therefore \text{ air speed in test section } = 2\cdot5 \times 955 = \underline{2385 \text{ ft/sec}}$$

By Rayleigh's Law,

$$\mu = 3\cdot58 \times 10^{-7}\Big(\frac{210}{273}\Big)^{\frac{3}{4}}$$

$$= 2\cdot94 \times 10^{-7} \text{ slug/ft sec}$$

$$\nu = \frac{\mu}{\rho} = \frac{2\cdot94 \times 10^{-7}}{4\cdot09 \times 10^{-3}}$$

$$= 0\cdot72 \times 10^{-4} = 7\cdot2 \times 10^{-5} \text{ ft}^2/\text{sec}$$

As a check, the mass flow may be calculated from the above results. This gives

$$\text{Mass flow } = \rho A V = 0\cdot00409 \times \tfrac{24}{144} \times 2385$$

$$= \underline{1\cdot626 \text{ slug/sec}}$$

Example 4.7. A long flat wall is bent sharply downwards at B as shown in Fig. 4.12. Over the portion AB the stream Mach number is 1·50, while over the portion BC it has increased to 2·00. Regarding the flow over AB as the undisturbed stream, find the pressure coefficient over the face BC.

The continuous streamline DEF is such that DE is parallel to, and 1 in. from, AB. Calculate the distance x on the sketch.

It may be assumed that there is no loss of total pressure at the corner B, and that boundary layer effects may be ignored.

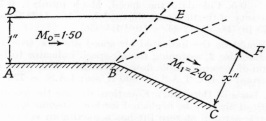

FIG. 4.12.—The flow for Example 4.7.

E

(i) $$C_p = \frac{p_1 - p_0}{0 \cdot 7 p_0 M_0^2} = \frac{1}{0 \cdot 7 M_0^2}\left[\frac{p_1}{p_0} - 1\right]$$

Since there is no loss of total pressure at the corner, with p_s for the total pressure,

$$\frac{p_s}{p_0} = \left[1 + \frac{1}{5}(1 \cdot 5)^2\right]^{3 \cdot 5} = (1 \cdot 45)^{3 \cdot 5}$$

and $$\frac{p_s}{p_1} = \left[1 + \frac{1}{5}(2 \cdot 00)^2\right]^{3 \cdot 5} = (1 \cdot 8)^{3 \cdot 5}$$

$$\therefore \frac{p_1}{p_0} = \frac{p_s}{p_0} \times \frac{p_1}{p_s} = \left(\frac{1 \cdot 45}{1 \cdot 80}\right)^{3 \cdot 5} = 0 \cdot 470$$

$$\therefore C_p = \frac{1}{0 \cdot 7(1 \cdot 5)^2}(0 \cdot 470 - 1) = -\underline{0 \cdot 336}.$$

$$\frac{A_1}{A_0} = \frac{M_0}{M_1}\left(\frac{1 + \frac{1}{5}M_1^2}{1 + \frac{1}{5}M_0^2}\right)^3$$

Considering unit width of the flow,

$$\frac{x}{1} = \frac{1 \cdot 500}{2 \cdot 000}\left(\frac{1 \cdot 80}{1 \cdot 45}\right)^3 = 0 \cdot 75(1 \cdot 911) = 1 \cdot 43$$

$$\therefore x = 1 \cdot 43 \text{ in.}$$

Note that, since the left-hand side is the ratio of two areas, it is not necessary to convert from inches to feet, the factor $\frac{1}{12}$ cancelling from numerator and denominator.

EXERCISES

1. A convergent-divergent duct has a maximum diameter of 6 in. and a Pitôt-static tube is placed in the throat of the duct. Neglecting the effect of the Pitôt-static tube on the flow, estimate the throat diameter under the following conditions:

(i) air at the maximum section is of standard pressure and density, pressure difference across Pitôt-static ≡ 5 in. water;

(ii) pressure and temperature in the maximum section are 2116 lb/ft² and 100°C respectively, pressure difference across Pitôt-static tube ≡ 5 in. mercury. (*Ans.* (i) 4·93 in.; (ii) 2·66 in.)

2. In the 'wing-flow' method of transonic research an aeroplane dives at a Mach number of 0·87 at 20,000 ft, where the pressure and temperature are 972 lb/ft² and −24·6°C respectively. At the position of the model the pressure coefficient is −0·5. Calculate the speed, Mach number, $0 \cdot 7 p M^2$, and the kinematic viscosity of the flow past the model. (*Ans.* 1128 ft/sec; $M = 1 \cdot 133$; $0 \cdot 7 p M^2 = 645$ lb/ft²; $\nu = 2 \cdot 84 \times 10^{-4}$ ft²/sec)

3. What would be the indicated air speed and the true air speed of the aeroplane in Exercise 2, assuming the air-speed indicator to be calibrated on the assumption of incompressible flow in standard conditions, and to have no instrument errors? (*Ans.* T.A.S. = 900 ft/sec; I.A.S. = 720 ft/sec)

4. On the basis of Bernoulli's Equation, discuss the assumption that the compressibility of air may be neglected for low subsonic speeds.

A symmetric aerofoil at zero lift has a maximum velocity which is 10% greater than the free stream velocity. This maximum increases at the rate of

7% of the free stream velocity for each degree of incidence. What is the free stream velocity at which compressibility effects become important on the aerofoil surface when the incidence is 5 deg.? (*Ans.* Approx. 210 ft/sec)
(U. of L.)

5. A return type wind-tunnel of large contraction ratio has air at standard conditions of temperature and pressure in the settling chamber upstream of the contraction to the working section. Assuming isentropic compressible flow in the tunnel estimate the speed in the working section where the Mach number is 0·75. Take the ratio of specific heats for air as $\gamma = 1·4$. (*Ans.* 796 ft/sec)
(U. of L.)

CHAPTER 5

WING AND AEROFOIL SECTION GEOMETRY

5.1. Planform geometry. The *planform* of a wing is the shape of the wing seen on a plan view of the aircraft. Fig. 5.1 illustrates this and includes the names or symbols of the various parameters of the planform geometry. Note that the root ends of the leading and trailing edges have been connected across the fuselage by straight lines. An alternative to this convention is that the leading and trailing edges, if straight, are produced to the aircraft centre-line.

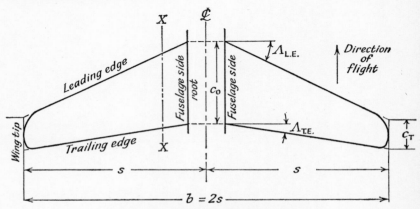

Fig. 5.1.—Wing planform geometry.

5.1.1. Wing span. The wing span is the dimension b, the distance between the extreme wing-tips. The dimension from each tip to the centre-line s is the wing semi-span.

5.1.2. Chords. The two dimensions c_T and c_0 are the tip and root chords respectively (with the alternative convention, the root chord is the distance between the intersections with the fuselage centre-line of the leading and trailing edges produced).

The ratio c_T/c_0 is the taper ratio λ. Sometimes the reciprocal of this, namely c_0/c_T, is taken as the taper ratio. For most wings $c_T/c_0 < 1$.

5.1.3. Wing area. The plan-area of the wing including the continuation within the fuselage is the 'gross wing area' S_G. The unqualified term 'wing area' S is usually intended to mean this gross wing area.

The plan-area of the exposed wing (i.e., excluding the continuation within the fuselage) is the 'nett wing area' S_N.

60

5.1.4. Mean chords. A useful parameter, the 'standard mean chord' or the 'geometric mean chord' is denoted by $\bar{c}$, defined by $\bar{c} = \dfrac{S_G \text{ or } S_N}{b}$; it should be stated whether S_G or S_N is used.

This definition may also be written as

$$\bar{c} = \frac{\displaystyle\int_{-s}^{+s} c\,dy}{\displaystyle\int_{-s}^{+s} dy}$$

where y is distance measured from the centre-line towards the starboard (right-hand to the pilot) tip. This standard mean chord is often abbreviated to S.M.C.

Another mean chord is the 'aerodynamic mean chord' (A.M.C.), denoted by $\bar{c}_A$ or $\bar{\bar{c}}$, and is defined by

$$\bar{c}_A = \frac{\displaystyle\int_{-s}^{+s} c^2\,dy}{\displaystyle\int_{-s}^{+s} c\,dy}$$

5.1.5. Aspect ratio. The aspect ratio is a measure of the narrowness of the wing planform. It is denoted by A, or sometimes by $Æ$, and is given by

$$A = \frac{\text{span}}{\text{S.M.C.}} = \frac{b}{\bar{c}}$$

If both top and bottom of this expression are multiplied by the wing span, b, it becomes:

$$A = \frac{b^2}{b\bar{c}} = \frac{(\text{span})^2}{\text{area}}$$

a form which is often more convenient than the original.

5.1.6. Sweep-back. The sweep-back angle of a wing is the angle between a line drawn along the span at a constant fraction of the chord from the leading edge, and a line perpendicular to the centre-line. It is usually denoted by either Λ or ϕ. Sweep-back is commonly measured on the leading edge ($\Lambda_{L.E.}$ or $\phi_{L.E.}$), on the quarter-chord line, i.e., the line $\frac{1}{4}$ of the chord behind the leading edge ($\Lambda_{\frac{1}{4}}$ or $\phi_{\frac{1}{4}}$), or on the trailing edge ($\Lambda_{T.E.}$ or $\phi_{T.E.}$).

5.2. Aerofoil section geometry. If a horizontal wing is cut by a vertical plane parallel to the centre-line, such as X–X in Fig. 5.1, the shape of the resulting section is usually of a type shown in Fig. 5.2 (c). This is an 'aerofoil section'.

For subsonic use, the aerofoil section has a rounded leading edge. The depth increases smoothly to a maximum which usually occurs between $\frac{1}{4}$

and $\frac{1}{2}$ way along the profile, and thereafter tapers off towards the rear of the section.

If the leading edge is rounded it has a definite radius of curvature. It is therefore possible to draw a circle of this radius which coincides with a very short arc of the section where the curvature is greatest. The trailing edge may be sharp or it, too, may have a radius of curvature, though this is normally much smaller than for the leading edge. Thus a small circle

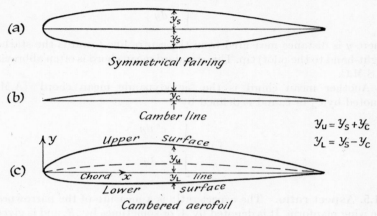

FIG. 5.2.—Wing section geometry.

may be drawn to coincide with the arc of maximum curvature of the trailing edge, and a line may be drawn passing through the centres of maximum curvature of the leading and trailing edges. This line, when produced to intersect the section at each end, is called the 'chord line'. The length of the chord line is the 'aerofoil chord', denoted by c.

The point where the chord line intersects the front (or nose) of the section is used as the origin of a pair of axes, the x-axis being the chord line and the y-axis being perpendicular to the chord line, positive in the upwards direction. The shape of the section is then usually given as a table of values of x and the corresponding values of y. These 'section ordinates' are usually expressed as percentages of the chord, $\dfrac{100x}{c}\%$ and $\dfrac{100y}{c}\%$.

5.2.1. The camber line; camber.

At any distance along the chord from the nose, a point may be marked mid-way between the upper and lower surfaces. The locus of all such points, usually curved, is the median line of the section, usually called the 'camber line'.

The maximum height of the camber line above the chord line is denoted by δ and the quantity $\dfrac{100\delta}{c}\%$ is called the 'percentage camber' of the section. Aerofoil sections have cambers which are usually in the range from zero (a symmetrical section) to 5%, though much larger cambers are used in cascades (e.g., turbine blading).

It is seldom that a camber line can be expressed in simple geometric or algebraic forms, though a few simple curves, such as circular arcs or parabolas, have been used.

5.2.2. The symmetrical fairing.

Having found the median, or camber, line, the distances from this line to the upper and lower surfaces may be measured at any value of x. These are, by the definition of the camber line, equal. These distances may be measured at all points along the chord and then plotted against x from a straight line. The result is a symmetrical shape, called the 'symmetrical fairing' or 'thickness distribution'.

An important parameter of the thickness distribution is the maximum thickness, or depth, t. This, when expressed as a fraction of the chord, is called the thickness/chord ratio. It is commonly expressed as a percentage $\dfrac{100t}{c}\%$. Current values in use range from 13% to 18% for civil aircraft down to 3% or so for supersonic aircraft.

The position along the chord at which this maximum thickness occurs is another important parameter of the symmetrical fairing. Values usually lie between 30% and 60% of the chord from the leading edge. Some older sections had the maximum thickness at about 25% chord, while some more extreme sections have the maximum thickness more than 60% of the chord behind the leading edge.

It will be realized that any aerofoil section may be regarded as a symmetrical fairing plotted round a camber line. American and British conventions differ in the exact method of derivation of an aerofoil section from a given camber line and fairing. In the British convention, the camber line is plotted, and the thickness ordinates are then plotted from this, perpendicular to the chord line. Thus the fairing is, in effect, 'sheared' until its median line, initially straight, has been distorted to coincide with the given camber line. The American convention is that the thickness ordinates are plotted perpendicular to the curved camber line. The fairing is, therefore, regarded as being bent until its median line coincides with the given camber line.

Since the camber line curvature is generally very small the difference in aerofoil section shape given by these two conventions is very small.

5.3. Dihedral angle.

If an aeroplane is looked at from directly ahead, it is seen that the wings are not, in general, in a single plane (in the geometric sense), but are instead inclined to each other at a small angle. Imagine lines drawn on the wings along the locus of the intersections between the chord lines and the section noses, as in Fig. 5.3. Then the angle $2\varGamma$ is the 'dihedral angle' of the wings. If the wings are inclined upwards, they are said to have 'dihedral', if inclined downwards they have 'anhedral'.

Fig. 5.3.—Illustrating the dihedral angle.

5.4. Incidence; twist; wash-out and wash-in.

When an aeroplane is in flight the chord lines of the various wing sections are not normally parallel to the direction of flight. The angle between the chord line of a given aerofoil section and the direction of flight (or of the undisturbed stream) is called the 'geometric angle of incidence', α.

Carrying this concept of incidence to the twist of a wing, it may be said that, if the geometric angles of incidence of all sections are not the same, the wing is twisted. If the incidence increases towards the tip, the wing has 'wash-in', while if the incidence decreases towards the tip the wing has 'wash-out'.

CHAPTER 6

AERODYNAMIC FORCE

Air flowing past an aeroplane, or any other body, must be diverted from its original path, and such deflections lead to changes in the speed of the air. Bernoulli's Equation shows that the pressure exerted by the air on the aeroplane is altered from that of the undisturbed stream. Also the viscosity of the air leads to the existence of frictional forces tending to resist its flow. As a result of these processes, the aeroplane experiences a resultant aerodynamic force and moment.

6.1. Force and moment components. It is conventional and convenient to separate this aerodynamic force and moment into three components each, as follows.

6.1.1. The lift, L $(-Z)$. This is the component of force acting upwards, perpendicular to the direction of flight or of the undisturbed stream. The word 'upwards' is used in the same sense that the pilot's head is above his feet. Fig. 6.1 illustrates the meaning in various attitudes of flight. The arrow V represents the direction of flight, the arrow L represents the lift acting 'upwards' and the arrow W the weight of the aircraft, and shows

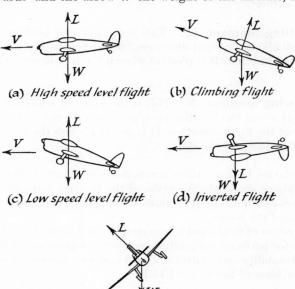

(a) *High speed level flight*   (b) *Climbing flight*

(c) *Low speed level flight*   (d) *Inverted flight*

(e) *Banked circling flight*

FIG. 6.1.—The direction of the lift force.

the downward vertical. Comparison of (a), (c) and (d) shows that this 'upwards' is not fixed relative to the aircraft, while (a), (b), (d) and (e) show that the meaning is not fixed relative to the earth. As a general rule, if it is remembered that the lift is always a component perpendicular to the flight direction, the exact direction in which the lift acts will be obvious, particularly after reference to Fig. 6.1. This may not apply to certain guided missiles which have no obvious 'top' or 'bottom', and the exact meaning of 'up' must then be defined with care.

6.1.2. The drag, D $(-X)$.   This is the component of force acting in the opposite direction to the line of flight, or in the same direction as the motion of the undisturbed stream. It is the force which resists the motion of the aircraft. There is no ambiguity regarding its direction or sense.

6.1.3. Cross-wind force, Y.   This is the component of force mutually perpendicular to the lift and the drag, i.e., in a spanwise direction. It is reckoned positive when acting towards the starboard (right-hand to the pilot) wing-tip.

6.1.4. Pitching moment, M.   This is the moment acting in the plane containing the lift and the drag, i.e., in the vertical plane when the aircraft is flying horizontally. It is positive when it tends to increase the incidence, or raise the nose of the aircraft 'upwards' (using this word in the sense discussed earlier).

6.1.5. Rolling moment, L_R.   This is the moment tending to make the aircraft roll about the flight direction, i.e., tending to depress one wing-tip and to raise the other. It is positive when it tends to depress the starboard wing-tip.

6.1.6. Yawing moment, N.   This is the moment which tends to rotate the aircraft about the lift direction, i.e., to swing the nose to one side or the other of the flight direction. It is positive when the nose is swung, or tends to be swung, to the right.

The relation between these components is shown in Fig. 6.2. In each case the arrow shows the direction of the positive force or moment. All three forces are mutually perpendicular, and each moment acts about the line of one of the forces.

The system of forces and moments described above is that conventionally used for performance analysis and other simple problems. For more advanced stability and control studies it is more convenient to use a slightly different system of forces, see § 14.1.

6.2. Dimensional theory.   In discussing aerodynamic force it is necessary to know how the dependent variables, aerodynamic force and moment, vary with independent variables thought to be relevant.

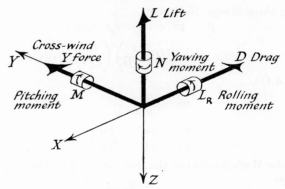

FIG. 6.2.—The systems of force and moment components.

The broad arrows represent the forces used in elementary work. The line arrows represent the system used in control and stability studies, chap. 14. The moments are common to both systems.

Assume, then, that the aerodynamic force, or one of its components, is denoted by F and depends on the following quantities: fluid density ρ, fluid kinematic viscosity ν, stream speed V and fluid bulk elasticity K. The force and moment will also depend on the shape and size of the body and its orientation to the stream. If, however, attention is confined to geometrically similar bodies (e.g., spheres, or models of a given aeroplane to different scales) the effects of shape as such will be eliminated, and the size of the body can be represented by a single typical dimension (e.g., the sphere diameter, or the wing span of the model aeroplane), denoted by D. Then, following the method of § 2.9,

$$F = \mathrm{f}(V,\, D,\, \rho,\, \nu,\, K)$$
$$= C \cdot V^a D^b \rho^c \nu^d K^e \qquad . \qquad . \qquad . \qquad (6.1)$$

In dimensional form this becomes

$$\left[\frac{ML}{T^2}\right] = \left[\left(\frac{L}{T}\right)^a (L)^b \left(\frac{M}{L^3}\right)^c \left(\frac{L^2}{T}\right)^d \left(\frac{M}{LT^2}\right)^e\right]$$

Equating indices of mass, length and time separately leads to the three equations:

(Mass)	$1 = c + e$	(6.2.1)
(Length)	$1 = a + b - 3c + 2d - e$ . .	(6.2.2)
(Time)	$-2 = -a - d - 2e$	(6.2.3)

With five unknowns and three equations it is impossible to determine completely all unknowns, and two must be left undetermined. These will be d and e.

The eqns. (6.2) may then be solved for a, b and c in terms of d and e, giving

$$a = 2 - d - 2e$$
$$b = 2 - d$$

and

$$c = 1 - e$$

Substituting these in eqn. (6.1) gives

$$F = V^{2-d-2e}D^{2-d}\rho^{1-e}\nu^d K^e$$

$$= \rho V^2 D^2 \left(\frac{\nu}{VD}\right)^d \left(\frac{K}{\rho V^2}\right)^e \quad . \qquad . \qquad . \qquad (6.3)$$

From eqn. (4.15),

$$a^2 = \frac{\gamma p}{\rho} = \frac{K}{\rho}$$

Then

$$\frac{K}{\rho V^2} = \frac{\rho a^2}{\rho V^2} = \left(\frac{a}{V}\right)^2$$

and V/a is the Mach number of the free stream. Therefore eqn. (6.3) may be written as

$$F = \rho V^2 D^2 . g\left(\frac{VD}{\nu}\right) . h(M) \quad . \qquad . \qquad . \qquad (6.4)$$

where $g(VD/\nu)$ and $h(M)$ are some undetermined functions of the stated compound variables.

Thus it can be concluded that the aerodynamic forces acting on a family of geometrically similar bodies (the similarity including the orientation to the stream), obey the law

$$\frac{F}{\rho V^2 D^2} = \text{function}\left\{\frac{VD}{\nu}; M\right\} . \qquad . \qquad . \qquad (6.5)$$

This relationship is usually known as Rayleigh's Equation.

The term VD/ν may also be written, from the definition of ν, as $\rho VD/\mu$, and was met previously in § 2.9, in the problem relating to the eddy frequency in the flow behind a circular cylinder. It is a very important parameter in fluid flows, and is called the *Reynolds Number*.

Now consider any parameter representing the geometry of the flow round the bodies at any point relative to the bodies. If this parameter is expressed in a suitable non-dimensional form it can easily be shown by dimensional analysis that this non-dimensional parameter is a function of the Reynolds number and the Mach number only. If, therefore, the values of R (a common symbol for Reynolds number) and M of a number of flows round geometrically similar bodies are each the same for all the flows, it follows that all the flows are geometrically similar in all respects, differing only in geometric scale and/or speed. This is true even though some of the fluids may be gaseous and the others liquid. Flows which obey these conditions are said to be 'dynamically similar', and the concept of 'dynamic similarity' is essential in wind-tunnel experiment.

It has been found, for most bodies of aeronautical interest, that the effects of compressibility are negligible for stream Mach numbers less than 0·5 or so, and in cases where this limit is not exceeded, Reynolds number may be used as the only criterion of dynamic similarity.

Example 6.1. An aircraft and some scale models of it are tested under various conditions, given below. Which cases are dynamically similar to the aircraft in flight, given as case A?

	(A)	(B)	(C)	(D)	(E)	(F)
Span (ft) . . .	50	10	10	5	5	10
Rel. density . . .	0·533	1	3	1	10	10
Temp. (°C)	−24·6	+15	+15	+15	+15	+15
Speed, T.A.S. (ft/sec) .	300	300	300	250	180	180

Case (A) represents the full-size aircraft flying at 20,000 ft. The other cases represent models under test in various types of wind-tunnel. Cases (C), (E) and (F) where the relative density is greater than unity represent a special type of tunnel, the compressed-air tunnel or C.A.T., which may be operated at static pressures in excess of atmospheric.

From the figures given above the Reynolds number $VD\rho/\mu$ may be calculated for each case. These are found to be

Case A,	$R = 5·7 \times 10^7$	Case D,	$R = 8 \times 10^6$
Case B,	$R = 1·9 \times 10^7$	Case E,	$R = 5·74 \times 10^7$
Case C,	$R = 5·75 \times 10^7$	Case F,	$R = 1·15 \times 10^8$

It is seen that the values of R for cases (C) and (E) are very close to that for the full-size aircraft. Cases (A), (C) and (E) are therefore dynamically similar, and the flow patterns in these three cases will be geometrically similar. In addition the ratios of the local velocity to the free stream velocity at any point on the three bodies will be the same for these three cases. Hence, from Bernoulli's Equation, the pressure coefficients will similarly be the same in these three cases, and thus the forces on the bodies will be simply and directly related.

Cases (B) and (D) have Reynolds Numbers considerably less than (A), and are therefore said to represent a 'smaller aerodynamic scale'. The flows round these models, and the forces acting on them, will not be simply or directly related to the force or flow pattern on the full-size aircraft.

In case (F) the value of R is larger than that of any other case, and this case has the largest aerodynamic scale of the six.

Example 6.2. An aeroplane weighs 15,000 lb. At approach incidence with flaps out its E.A.S. in straight and level flight at 5000 ft ($\sigma = 0·862$, temperature = 5·1°C) is 70 m.p.h. Determine the scale and lift of a model suitable for obtaining the drag at this incidence in a compressed-air tunnel which works at 100 ft/sec and 22 atmospheres pressure at 15°C.

To ensure that the results of the wind-tunnel test shall be directly applicable to the full-size aircraft, it is necessary that the flows shall be dynamically similar which, at low speeds, mean that the Reynolds numbers must be equal.

Let μ_0 be the absolute viscosity of air at 0°C, and ρ_0 be sea-level standard density. Let B_f be some characteristic length (e.g., the wing span) of the full-size aircraft and B_m the corresponding length on the model.

(i) Full-size aircraft in flight.

$$\mu = \mu_0\left(1 + \frac{5·1}{273}\right)^{\frac{3}{4}} \text{ by Rayleigh's Law}$$

$$= 1·014\mu_0$$

Flight speed $V = 70 \times \frac{88}{60} = 102·7$ ft/sec, E.A.S.

$$= 102·7(0·862)^{-\frac{1}{2}} = 110·5 \text{ ft/sec, T.A.S.}$$

$$\text{Reynolds number R} = \frac{VB}{\nu} = \frac{VB\rho}{\mu}$$

$$= \frac{110 \cdot 5 B_f \; 0 \cdot 862 \rho_0}{1 \cdot 014 \mu_0}$$

$$= 93 \cdot 9 B_f \frac{\rho_0}{\mu_0}$$

(ii) Model under test.

$$\mu = \mu_0 (1 + \tfrac{15}{273})^{\frac{3}{2}} = 1 \cdot 0412 \mu_0$$

Since the pressure in the tunnel is 22 atmospheres while the temperature is 15°C, i.e., standard, it follows that the density will also be 22 times the sea-level standard value.

Thus $$\text{R} = \frac{100 B_m \; 22 \rho_0}{1 \cdot 0412 \mu_0} = 2110 B_m \frac{\rho_0}{\mu_0}$$

For dynamic similarity, these two values of the Reynolds number must be equal, i.e.,

$$93 \cdot 9 B_f = 2110 B_m$$

$$\therefore \frac{B_f}{B_m} = \frac{2110}{93 \cdot 9} = 22 \cdot 5$$

Thus the model scale should be $1/22 \cdot 5$ of full size.

For low speeds, eqn. (6.4) becomes:

$$F = \rho V^2 B^2 g(\text{R})$$

By ensuring equality of the Reynolds numbers, R, it is automatically ensured that the function $g(\text{R})$ has the same value for both model and full-size aircraft. Then, if L_f is the lift of the aircraft and L_m the lift of the model,

$$\frac{L_m}{L_f} = \frac{\rho_m}{\rho_f} \left(\frac{V_m}{V_f} \right)^2 \left(\frac{B_m}{B_f} \right)^2$$

$$= \frac{22}{0 \cdot 862} (1 \cdot 105)^2 \left(\frac{1}{22 \cdot 5} \right)^2 = 0 \cdot 0616$$

Since $$L_f = 15{,}000 \text{ lb}, \quad L_m = 15{,}000 \times 0 \cdot 0616$$

$$= \underline{925 \text{ lb.}}$$

It should be noted that the model sustains $0 \cdot 0616$ of the lift of the full-sized aircraft, but its wing area is only $(1/22 \cdot 5)^2$ of that of the aircraft. Thus the intensity of loading on the model is $0 \cdot 0616 \times (22 \cdot 5)^2$, i.e., $31 \cdot 2$ times that on the aircraft in flight. This points the need for models used in compressed-air tunnels to be very strong and rigid, to prevent excessive bending which might invalidate the geometric similarity between the aircraft and the scale model.

Example 6.3. An aeroplane approaches to land at a speed of 90 m.p.h. at sea-level. A 1/5th scale model is tested under dynamically similar conditions in a C.A.T. working at 10 atmospheres pressure and 15°C. It is found that the load on the tailplane is subject to impulsive fluctuations at a frequency of 20 cycles/sec, due to eddies being shed from the wing-fuselage junction. If the natural frequency of flexural vibration of the tailplane is $8 \cdot 5$ cycles/sec, could this represent a dangerous condition?

For dynamic similarity, the Reynolds numbers must be equal. Since the temperature of the atmosphere equals that in the tunnel, 15°C, the value of μ is the same in both model and full-scale cases. Thus,

$$V_f d_f \rho_f = V_m d_m \rho_m$$

In this case, then, since

$$V_f = 90 \times \tfrac{88}{60} = 132 \text{ ft/sec}$$

$$132 \times 1 \times 1 = V_m \times \tfrac{1}{5} \times 10 = 2V_m$$

whence $\qquad\qquad V_m = 66 \text{ ft/sec}$

Now eqn. (2.12) covers this case of eddy shedding, and is

$$\frac{nd}{V} = g(R)$$

$$\therefore \frac{n_f 1}{132} = \frac{20 \times \tfrac{1}{5}}{66}$$

whence $\qquad\qquad n_f = \tfrac{132}{66} \times \tfrac{20}{5} = \underline{8 \text{ cycles/sec}}$

This is very close to the given natural frequency of the tailplane, and there is thus a considerable danger that the eddies might excite sympathetic vibration of the tailplane, possibly leading to structural failure of that component. Thus the shedding of eddies at this frequency is very dangerous to the aircraft.

Example 6.4. An aircraft flies at a Mach number of 0·85 at 60,000 ft where the pressure is 150 lb/ft² and the temperature is −56·5°C. A model of 1/10th scale is to be tested in a high-speed wind-tunnel. Calculate the total pressure of the tunnel stream necessary to give dynamic similarity, if the total temperature is 50°C.

(i) Full-scale aircraft.

$$M = 0·85 \quad a = 65·9(273 - 56·5)^{\frac{1}{2}} = 968 \text{ ft/sec}$$

$$\therefore V = 0·85 \times 968 = 823 \text{ ft/sec, T.A.S.}$$

$$\rho = \frac{p}{RT} = \frac{150}{3092 \times 216·5} = 0.000224 \text{ slug/ft}^3$$

$$\frac{\mu_0}{\mu} = \left(\frac{273}{216·5}\right)^{\frac{3}{4}} = 1·19$$

$$\therefore \mu = \frac{3·58}{1·19} \times 10^{-7} = 3·12 \times 10^{-7} \text{ slug/ft sec}$$

Consider a dimension which, on the aircraft, has a length of 10 ft. Then, basing the Reynolds number on this dimension,

$$R_f = \frac{Vd\rho}{\mu} = \frac{823 \times 10 \times 2·24 \times 10^{-4}}{3·12 \times 10^{-7}}$$

$$= 5·91 \times 10^6$$

(ii) Model.

$$\text{Total temperature } T_s = 273 + 50 = 323°\text{K}$$

$\therefore$ at $M = 0·85$,

$$\frac{T_s}{T} = 1 + \tfrac{1}{5}(0·85)^2 = 1·1445$$

whence $\qquad\qquad T = 282°\text{K}$

$$\therefore a = 65·9(282)^{\frac{1}{2}} = 1107 \text{ ft/sec}$$

$$\therefore V = 0·85 \times 1107 = 940 \text{ ft/sec}$$

$$\frac{\mu}{\mu_0} = \frac{(282)^{\frac{3}{4}}}{(273)} = 1·0246$$

$$\therefore \mu = 3·58 \times 1·0246 \times 10^{-7} = 3·67 \times 10^{-7} \text{ slug/ft sec}$$

For dynamic similarity the Reynolds numbers must be equal, i.e.,

$$\frac{940 \times 1 \times \rho}{3\cdot67 \times 10^{-7}} = 5\cdot91 \times 10^6$$

leading to $\qquad\qquad\qquad \rho = 0\cdot00231$ slug/ft^3

Thus the static pressure required in the test section, p, is

$$p = \rho RT = 2\cdot31 \times 10^{-3} \times 3\cdot092 \times 10^3 \times 282$$
$$= 2014 \text{ lb/ft}^2$$

The total pressure p_s is given by

$$\frac{p_s}{p} = \{1 + \tfrac{1}{5}M^2\}^{3\cdot5} = (1\cdot1445)^{3\cdot5} = 1\cdot605$$

giving $\qquad\qquad p_s = 2014 \times 1\cdot605 = \underline{3230 \text{ lb/ft}^2}.$

If the total pressure available in the tunnel is less than this value, it is not possible to achieve equality of both the Mach and Reynolds numbers. Either the Mach number may be achieved at a lower value of R or, alternatively, R may be made equal at a lower Mach number. In such a case it is normally preferable to make the Mach number correct since, provided the Reynolds number in the tunnel is not too low, the effects of compressibility are more important than the effects of aerodynamic scale at Mach numbers of this order. Moreover, techniques are available which can alleviate the errors due to unequal aerodynamic scales.

6.3. Force and moment coefficients. The quantity $F/\rho V^2 D^2$ of eqn. (6.5) is a non-dimensional quantity of the type often developed and used in aerodynamics. It is not, however, used in quite this form. In place of ρV^2 it is conventional to use $\tfrac{1}{2}\rho V^2$, the dynamic pressure of the stream (if incompressible). Moreover D^2 is in the form of an area, and it is usually preferable to use, in place of the square of a single length D, an actual physical area of the body, such as the plan-area of the wing, or the maximum cross-sectional area of a fuselage.

Using S to denote such an area it is usual to write

$$C_F = \frac{F}{\tfrac{1}{2}\rho V^2 S} \qquad . \qquad . \qquad . \qquad . \qquad (6.6)$$

in which C_F is the 'aerodynamic force coefficient' and is non-dimensional.

The two most important force coefficients are the lift and drag coefficients, defined by:

lift coefficient $C_L = \text{lift}/\tfrac{1}{2}\rho V^2 S \qquad . \qquad . \qquad (6.6.1)$

and $\qquad\qquad$ drag coefficient $C_D = \text{drag}/\tfrac{1}{2}\rho V^2 S \qquad . \qquad . \qquad (6.6.2)$

When the body in question is a wing the area S is almost invariably the planform area as defined in § 5.1.3. For the drag of a body such as a fuselage, sphere or cylinder the area S is usually the projected frontal area, the maximum cross-sectional area or the (volume)$^{2/3}$. The area used for definition of the lift and drag coefficients of such a body is thus seen to be variable from case to case, and therefore needs to be stated for each case.

The impression is sometimes formed that lift and drag coefficients cannot exceed unity. This is not true; with modern developments some wings can produce lift coefficients based on their plan-area of 10 or more.

Aerodynamic moments can also be expressed in the form of non-dimensional coefficients. Since a moment is the product of a force and a length it follows that a non-dimensional form for a moment is $Q/\rho V^2 D^3$, where Q is any aerodynamic moment. Here again it is conventional to replace ρV^2 by $\frac{1}{2}\rho V^2$. The term D^3 has the dimensions of a volume, but to use, say, the volume of a wing would be of very little use. The 'volume' is therefore taken as the product of an area and a length. In the case of the pitching moment of a wing the area is the plan-area S and the length is the wing chord $\bar{c}$ or $\bar{c}_A$ (see § 5.1.4).

Then the pitching moment coefficient C_M is defined by

$$C_M = \frac{M}{\frac{1}{2}\rho V^2 S \bar{c}} \quad . \quad . \quad . \quad . \quad (6.7)$$

or

$$= \frac{M}{\frac{1}{2}\rho V^2 S \bar{c}_A}$$

For a fuselage the area used in defining the pitching moment coefficient is usually that used for the drag coefficient, and the length $\bar{c}$ is normally taken to be the overall length.

6.4. Pressure distribution on an aerofoil.

The pressure on the surface of an aerofoil in flight is not uniform. Fig. 6.3 shows some typical pressure distributions for a given section at various angles of incidence.

Looking at the sketch for zero incidence ($\alpha = 0$) it is seen that there are small regions at the nose and tail where C_p is positive but that over most of the section C_p is negative. At the trailing edge the pressure coefficient comes close to $+1$ but does not actually reach this value. More will be said on this point later. The reduced pressure on the upper surface is tending to draw the section upwards while that on the lower surface has the opposite effect. With the pressure distribution as sketched, the effect on the upper surface is the larger, and there is a resultant upwards force on the section, which is the lift.

As incidence is increased from zero the following points are noted:

(i) the pressure reduction on the upper surface increases both in intensity and extent until, at large incidence, it actually encroaches on a small part of the front lower surface;

(ii) the stagnation point moves progressively further back on the lower surface, and the increased pressure on the lower surface covers a greater proportion of the surface. The pressure reduction on the lower surface is simultaneously decreased in both intensity and extent.

The large negative values of C_p reached on the upper surface at large incidences (e.g., 15 degrees) are also noteworthy. In some cases values of -6 or -7 are found; by eqn. (4.51) this corresponds to local flow speeds of nearly three times the speed of the undisturbed stream.

F

(a) *Incidence = 0°*

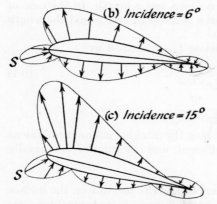

(b) *Incidence = 6°*

Length of arrows $\propto C_p$

S denotes C_p at stagnation where
   $C_{ps} = $ unity

Direction of arrows indicates $+$ve or
   $-$ve C_p

(c) *Incidence = 15°*

Fig. 6.3.—Typical pressure distributions
on an aerofoil section.

From the foregoing, the following conclusions may be drawn:

(i) at low incidence the lift arises from the difference between the pressure reductions on the upper and lower surfaces;

(ii) at higher incidences the lift is partly due to pressure reduction on the upper surface and partly due to pressure increase on the lower surface.

At angles of incidence around 18° or 20° the pressure reduction on the upper surface suddenly collapses and such little lift as remains is due principally to the pressure increase on the lower surface.

A picture drawn for one small negative incidence (for this aerofoil section, about $-4°$) would show equal 'suction' effects on the upper and lower surfaces, and the section would give no lift. At more negative incidences the lift would be negative.

The relationship between the pressure distribution and the drag of an aerofoil section is discussed later, in § 6.6.6.

6.5. Relation between the pitching moment at various points along the chord.

The pitching moment on a wing may be estimated experimentally by two principal methods; direct measurement on a balance, or by pressure plotting, as described in § 6.7. In either case, the pitching moment coefficient is measured about some definite point on the aerofoil chord, while for some particular purpose it may be desirable to know the pitching moment coefficient about some other point on the chord. To convert from one reference point to the other is a simple application of statics.

Suppose, for example, the lift and drag are known, as also is the pitching moment M_a about a point distance a from the leading edge, and it is desired to find the pitching moment M_x about a different point, distance x behind the leading edge. The situation is then as shown in Fig. 6.4. The left-hand picture represents the known conditions, and the right-hand picture represents the unknown conditions. These represent two alternative ways of looking at the same physical system, and must therefore give identical effects on the aerofoil.

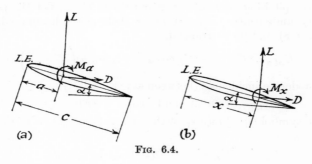

(a) (b)

FIG. 6.4.

Obviously, then,

$$L = L$$

and

$$D = D$$

Taking moments in each case about the leading edge,

$$M_{\text{LE}} = M_a - La \cos \alpha - Da \sin \alpha = M_x - Lx \cos \alpha - Dx \sin \alpha$$

whence

$$M_x = M_a - (L \cos \alpha + D \sin \alpha)(a - x)$$

Converting to coefficient form by dividing by $\frac{1}{2}\rho V^2 S c$ gives

$$C_{M\,x} = C_{M\,a} - (C_L \cos \alpha + C_D \sin \alpha)\left(\frac{a}{c} - \frac{x}{c}\right) \qquad . \qquad (6.8)$$

With this equation it is easy to calculate $C_{M\,x}$ for any value of x/c. As a particular case, if the known pitching moment coefficient is that about the leading edge, $C_{M\,\text{LE}}$, then $a = 0$, and eqn. (6.8) becomes

$$C_{M\,x} = C_{M\,\text{LE}} + \frac{x}{c}(C_L \cos \alpha + C_D \sin \alpha) \qquad . \qquad (6.9)$$

6.5.1. Aerodynamic centre. If the pitching moment coefficient at each point along the chord is calculated for each of several values of C_L one very special point is found for which C_M is virtually constant, independent of the lift coefficient. This point is the 'aerodynamic centre'. For incidences up to 10 degrees or so it is a fixed point close to, but not in general on, the chord line, between 23% and 25% of the chord behind the leading edge.

For a flat or curved plate in inviscid, incompressible flow the aerodynamic centre is theoretically exactly one quarter of the chord behind the leading edge, but thickness of the section, and viscosity of the fluid, tend to place it a few per cent further forward as indicated above, while compressibility tends to move it backwards. For a thin aerofoil of infinite aspect ratio in supersonic flow the aerodynamic centre is theoretically at 50% chord.

Knowledge of how the pitching moment coefficient about a point distance a behind the leading edge varies with C_L may be used to find the position of the aerodynamic centre behind the leading edge, and also the value of the pitching moment coefficient there, $C_{M\,ac}$. Let the position of the aerodynamic centre be a distance x_{ac} behind the leading edge. Then, with eqn. (6.8) slightly rearranged,

$$C_{M\,a} = C_{M\,ac} - (C_L \cos \alpha + C_D \sin \alpha)\left(\frac{x_{ac}}{c} - \frac{a}{c}\right)$$

Now at moderate incidences (between say $3°$ and $7°$)

$$C_L = O[20C_D] \quad \text{and} \quad \cos \alpha = O[10 \sin \alpha]$$

where the symbol $O[\quad]$ means 'of the order of', i.e., C_L is of the order of 20 times C_D.

Then
$$C_L \cos \alpha = O[200 \, C_D \sin \alpha]$$

and therefore $C_D \sin \alpha$ can be neglected compared with $C_L \cos \alpha$. With this approximation and the further approximation $\cos \alpha = 1$,

$$C_{M\,a} = C_{M\,ac} - C_L\left(\frac{x_{ac}}{c} - \frac{a}{c}\right) \qquad . \qquad . \qquad (6.10)$$

Differentiating eqn. (6.10) with respect to C_L gives

$$\frac{d}{dC_L}(C_{M\,a}) = \frac{d}{dC_L}(C_{M\,ac}) - \left(\frac{x_{ac}}{c} - \frac{a}{c}\right)$$

But the aerodynamic centre is, by definition, that point about which C_M is independent of C_L, and therefore the first term on the right-hand side is identically zero, and therefore

$$\frac{d}{dC_L}(C_{M\,a}) = 0 - \left(\frac{x_{ac}}{c} - \frac{a}{c}\right) = \frac{a}{c} - \frac{x_{ac}}{c} \qquad . \qquad . \qquad (6.11)$$

$$\therefore \frac{x_{ac}}{c} = \frac{a}{c} - \frac{d}{dC_L}(C_{M\,a}) \qquad . \qquad . \qquad . \qquad (6.12)$$

If, then, $C_{M\,a}$ is plotted against C_L, and the slope of the resulting line is measured, subtraction of this value from a/c gives the aerodynamic centre position x_{ac}/c.

In addition if, in eqn. (6.10), C_L is made zero, that equation becomes

$$C_{M\,a} = C_{M\,ac} \qquad . \qquad . \qquad . \qquad . \qquad (6.13)$$

i.e., the pitching moment coefficient about the balance spindle (or any other point) at zero lift is equal to the constant pitching moment coefficient about the aerodynamic centre. Because of this association with zero lift, $C_{M\,ac}$ is often denoted by C_{M_0}.

Example 6.5. For a particular aerofoil section the pitching moment coefficient about a spindle $1/3$ chord behind the leading edge varies with the lift coefficient in the following manner:

C_L . .	0·2	0·4	0·6	0·8
C_M . .	−0·02	0·00	+0·02	+0·04

Find the aerodynamic centre and the value of C_{M_0}.

It is seen that C_M varies linearly with C_L, the value of dC_M/dC_L being

$$\frac{0\cdot04 - (-0\cdot02)}{0\cdot80 - 0\cdot20} = +\frac{0\cdot06}{0\cdot60} = +0\cdot10$$

Therefore, from eqn. (6.12), with $a/c = 1/3$

$$\frac{x_{ac}}{c} = \frac{1}{3} - 0\cdot10 = \underline{0\cdot233}$$

The aerodynamic centre is therefore at 23·3% chord behind the leading edge.

Plotting C_M against C_L gives the value of C_{M_0}, the value of C_M when $C_L = 0$, as − 0·04.

A particular case is that when the known values of C_M are those about the leading edge, namely $C_{M\,LE}$. In this case $a = 0$ and therefore

$$\frac{x_{ac}}{c} = -\frac{d}{dC_L}(C_{M\,LE}) \qquad . \qquad . \qquad . \qquad (6.14)$$

Taking this equation with the statement made earlier about the normal position of the aerodynamic centre implies that, for all aerofoils at low Mach numbers,

$$\frac{d}{dC_L}(C_{M\,LE}) \simeq -\frac{1}{4} \qquad . \qquad . \qquad . \qquad (6.15)$$

6.5.2. Centre of pressure.

The aerodynamic forces on an aerofoil section may be represented by a lift, a drag, and a pitching moment. Now at each value of the lift coefficient there will be found to be one particular point about which the pitching moment coefficient is zero, and the aerodynamic effects on the aerofoil section may be represented by the lift and the drag alone acting at that point. This special point is termed the 'centre of pressure'.

Whereas the aerodynamic centre is a fixed point which always lies within the profile of a normal aerofoil section, the centre of pressure moves with change of lift coefficient and is not necessarily within the aerofoil profile. Fig. 6.5 shows the forces on the aerofoil regarded as either

(i) lift, drag and moment acting at the aerodynamic centre, or

(ii) lift and drag only acting at the centre of pressure, a fraction k_{cp} of the chord behind the leading edge.

FIG. 6.5.—Determination of the centre of pressure position.

Then, taking moments about the leading edge,

$$M_{\text{LE}} = M_{\text{ac}} - (L \cos \alpha + D \sin \alpha)x_{\text{ac}} = - (L \cos \alpha + D \sin \alpha)k_{cp}c$$

Dividing this by $\frac{1}{2}\rho V^2 Sc$, it becomes

$$C_{M\,\text{ac}} - (C_L \cos \alpha + C_D \sin \alpha)\frac{x_{\text{ac}}}{c} = - (C_L \cos \alpha + C_D \sin \alpha)k_{pc}$$

whence

$$k_{cp} = \frac{x_{\text{ac}}}{c} - \frac{C_{M\,\text{ac}}}{C_L \cos \alpha + C_D \sin \alpha} \qquad . \qquad . \qquad (6.16)$$

Again making the approximation that $C_D \sin \alpha$ can be ignored, the eqn. (6.16), above, becomes

$$k_{cp} \simeq \frac{x_{\text{ac}}}{c} - \frac{C_{M\,\text{ac}}}{C_L} \qquad . \qquad . \qquad . \qquad (6.17)$$

At first sight this would suggest that k_{cp} is always less than x_{ac}. However $C_{M\,\text{ac}}$ is almost invariably negative, so that in fact k_{cp} is numerically greater than x_{ac}, and the centre of pressure is behind the aerodynamic centre.

Example 6.6. For the aerofoil section of Example 6.5, plot a curve showing the approximate variation of centre of pressure position with lift coefficient, for lift coefficients between zero and unity.

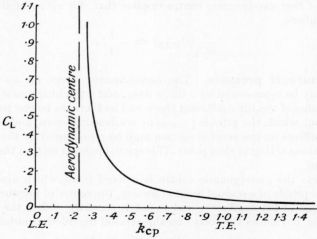

FIG. 6.6.—Centre of pressure position for Example 6.6.

For this case, $$k_{cp} \simeq 0.233 - \frac{-0.04}{C_L}$$

$$\simeq 0.233 + \frac{0.04}{C_L}$$

The corresponding curve is shown as Fig. 6.6. It shows that k_{cp} tends asymptotically to x_{ac} as C_L increases, and tends to infinity behind the aerofoil as C_L tends to zero. For values of C_L less than 0·05 the centre of pressure is actually behind the aerofoil.

For a symmetrical section (zero camber) and for some special camber lines (see § 12.4), the pitching moment coefficient about the aerodynamic centre is zero. It then follows, from eqn. (6.17) that $k_{cp} = x_{ac}$, i.e., the centre of pressure and the aerodynamic centre coincide, and that for moderate incidences the centre of pressure is therefore stationary at about the quarter-chord point.

6.6. Types of drag.
In the following sections, the terms and definitions used follow *A.R.C. Current Paper* No. 369, also published in the *Journal of the Royal Aeronautical Society*, November 1958, q.v. These definitions and terms represent significant departures from previous conventions. Since the older terms may remain in currency for a time, and also appear in the literature published prior to A.R.C. C.P. 369, on the first occasion each term is introduced the nearest terms from the earlier conventions will be given in parenthesis.

6.6.1. Total drag.
This is formally defined as

'the force corresponding to the rate of decrease of momentum, in a direction parallel to the undisturbed stream, of the external flow around the body, this decrease being calculated between stations at infinite distances upstream and downstream of the body'.

It is thus the total force tending to drag the body in the direction of the undisturbed stream, or to resist the motion of the body through a bulk of fluid.

Total drag may be separated into a number of items each contributing to the total. As a first step it may be divided into 'normal pressure drag' or 'pressure drag' and 'surface friction drag' or 'friction drag'.

6.6.2. Surface friction drag.
This is 'the drag arising from the resolved components of the tangential stresses on the surface of the body'.

At all points on the surface of a body past which a viscous fluid is flowing there is a traction along the surface in the direction of flow. This traction is due directly to viscosity. The traction at each point has a component acting in the direction of the undisturbed stream (or in the direction opposite to the direction of flight). The total effect of these components, taken over the whole of the exposed surface of the body, is the surface friction drag (hitherto *skin-friction* drag).

Surface friction drag cannot exist in an inviscid fluid.

6.6.3. Normal pressure drag. This is 'the drag arising from the resolved components of the normal pressure on the boundary under consideration'.

This normal pressure drag may itself be considered as the sum of several distinct items, namely:

 (i) boundary layer normal-pressure drag, or boundary layer pressure drag (hitherto known as *form* drag);

 (ii) trailing vortex drag, or vortex drag (hitherto known as *induced* drag);

 (iii) wave drag.

6.6.4. Trailing vortex drag (Induced drag). This is discussed in more detail in §§ 6.8.7 and 13.3. For the present it may be noted that the trailing vortex drag depends on lift and could exist in an inviscid fluid.

6.6.5. Wave drag. This is the drag associated with the formation of shock waves in high-speed flight.

6.6.6. Boundary layer normal-pressure drag (Form drag). This is defined, in A.R.C. C.P. No. 369, as 'the difference between the boundary layer drag and the surface friction drag', where the boundary layer drag is defined as 'the drag associated with losses of total pressure and total temperature in the boundary layers. It is the sum of the boundary layer normal-pressure drag and the surface friction drag.'

The above definitions are somewhat unhelpful in giving a clear idea of the nature and mechanism of the boundary layer normal-pressure drag, and a simple explanation is attempted below.

The pressure distribution on a body in a viscous fluid is different to that obtaining in an inviscid fluid (see § 4.2.2). Consider the trailing edge Fig. 6.7. If the fluid is inviscid it can be shown that the fluid speed there is zero, and therefore the pressure coefficient is $+1$. Now the body plus displacement thickness has a finite width at the trailing edge and at all positions downstream and, as a result, the velocity does not fall to zero, and therefore the pressure coefficient is less than $+1$.

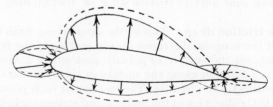

FIG. 6.7.—Pressure distribution on an aerofoil section in viscous flow (dotted line) and inviscid flow (full line).

The increased pressures near the nose tend to push the section backwards. The decreased pressures ahead of the maximum thickness tend to pull the section forwards. The decreased pressures behind the maximum thickness tend to pull the section backwards, while the increased pressures near the tail push the section forwards. In an inviscid fluid, the forward and backward forces cancel out exactly for all shapes, giving zero overall drag. Now it will be seen that in a viscous fluid the situation is very different. The pressures ahead of the maximum thickness are little altered, but the backward force due to the decreased pressures behind the maximum thickness is somewhat increased, while the forward push due to the increased pressures near the tail is much reduced. Thus the exact balance of the forces is upset, and there is an overall rearwards force. This force is the boundary layer normal-pressure drag (form drag).

6.6.7. It is again emphasized that both boundary layer normal-pressure drag and surface friction drag depend essentially on viscosity for their formation, and cannot exist in an inviscid fluid.

6.6.8. Boundary layer drag (Profile drag). The boundary layer drag is the sum of the surface friction drag and the boundary layer normal-pressure drag.

6.6.9. Drag comparison on four different bodies.
Normal flat plate, Fig. 6.8. This is a flat plate set broadside in a stream. In this case the drag is entirely boundary layer normal-pressure drag, coming mostly from the large negative pressure coefficients over the rear face. Although viscous tractions exist, they act along the surface of the plate, and therefore have no rearwards component to produce surface friction drag.

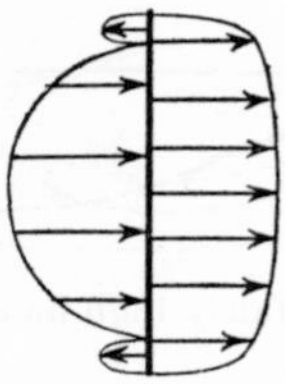

FIG. 6.8.—Pressure on a normal flat plate.

FIG. 6.9.—Viscous tractions on a tangential flat plate.

Parallel flat plate, Fig. 6.9. In this case the drag is entirely surface friction drag. Whatever the distribution of normal pressure may be it can have no rearward component, and therefore the boundary layer normal-pressure drag must be zero.

Circular cylinder, Fig. 6.10. Fig. 6.10 is a sketch of the distribution of normal pressure round a circular cylinder in inviscid flow (solid lines) (see § 10.2.12) and in a viscous fluid (dotted lines). The perfect symmetry in the inviscid case shows that there is no resultant force on the cylinder. The drastic modification of the pressure distribution due to viscosity is apparent, the result being a large boundary layer normal-pressure drag. In this case, some 5% of the drag is surface friction drag, the remaining 95% being boundary layer normal-pressure drag, though these proportions depend on the Reynolds number.

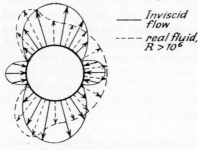

FIG. 6.10.—Pressure on a circular cylinder with its axis normal to the stream (see also Fig. 10.32).

Aerofoil or streamline strut. The pressure distributions for this case are given in Fig. 6.7. The effect of viscosity on the pressure distribution is much less than for the circular cylinder, and the boundary layer normal-pressure drag is much lower as a result. The percentage of the total drag represented by surface friction drag depends on the Reynolds number, the thickness/chord ratio, and a number of other factors, but between 40% and 80% is a fairly typical range.

6.6.10. The wake.　Behind any body moving in air is a wake, just as there is a wake behind a ship. Though this wake in air is not normally visible it may be felt, as when, for example, a 'bus passes by. The total drag of a body appears as a loss of momentum and increase of energy in this wake. The loss of momentum appears as a reduction of average fluid speed, while the increase of energy is seen as violent eddying (or vorticity)

(a)

Normal flat plate. In this case the wake oscillates up and down at several cycles per second. Half a cycle later the picture would be reversed, with the upper filaments curving back as do the lower filaments in this sketch.

(b)

Flat plate at fairly high incidence.

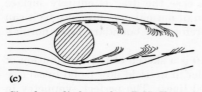

(c)

Circular cylinder at low R.N. For pattern at higher R.N. see Fig. 4.3.

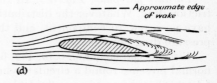

(d)

Aerofoil section at moderate incidence and low R.N.

FIG. 6.11.—The behaviour of smoke filaments in the flows past various bodies, showing the wakes.

in the wake. The size and intensity of the wake is therefore an indication of the profile drag of the body. Fig. 6.11 gives an indication of the comparative widths of the wakes behind a few bodies.

6.7. Estimation of the lift, drag and pitching moment coefficients from the pressure distribution.

Let Fig. 6.12 represent a section of an aerofoil at an incidence α to the fluid stream, which is assumed to be

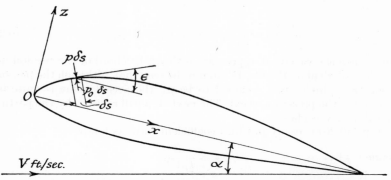

FIG. 6.12.—Normal pressure force on an element of aerofoil surface.

from left to right at a speed of V ft/sec. Through the nose of the aerofoil are drawn axes Ox and Oz parallel and perpendicular to the chord line respectively. The chord of the aerofoil is denoted by c. The ordinates of the highest and lowest points of the section are z_2 and z_1 respectively.

The aerofoil may or may not be solid. In either case its surface is regarded as a thin sheet of material, perfectly rigid, with the pressure inside uniform at p_0, the static pressure of the undisturbed stream. This is permissible, since the pressures are to be integrated round the surface, and the integral of a uniform pressure over a closed surface is zero, whatever its magnitude.

Taking a slice of the aerofoil of unit spanwise length, consider the forces acting on a small element, of length δs, of the surface. The normal force on the element is composed of $p\,\delta s$ inwards, and $p_0\,\delta s$ outwards, leaving a nett inwards force of $(p - p_0)\delta s$. This force may be resolved into components δZ and δX acting parallel to the Oz and Ox axes respectively. Then

$$\delta Z = -(p - p_0)\,\delta s \cos \varepsilon \quad . \qquad . \qquad . \qquad (6.18)$$

Now, from the geometry of the element,

$$\delta s \cos \varepsilon = \delta x \quad . \qquad . \qquad . \qquad . \qquad . \qquad . \qquad (6.19)$$

whence $\qquad\qquad \delta Z = -(p - p_0)\,\delta x$ per unit span

This is for an element on the upper surface. For an element on the lower surface it becomes

$$\delta Z = (p - p_0)\,\delta x \text{ per unit span}$$

If this is now integrated with respect to x between the limits $x = 0$ and $x = c$, the integral of δZ becomes the total force Z, whence

$$Z = \int_0^c - (p - p_0)\, dx + \int_0^c (p - p_0)\, dx$$

upper surface   lower surface

Using subscripts u and l for the upper and lower surfaces respectively, this becomes

$$Z = - \int_0^c [(p - p_0)_u - (p - p_0)_l]\, dx \quad . \qquad . \qquad (6.20)$$

Thus given the variation of pressure p along the chord of the aerofoil it is possible to calculate the lift. It can now be seen that, although the pressure inside the cylinder was assumed to be p_0, the actual value is quite immaterial in the present context. The next step will reveal why the particular value p_0 was chosen.

Eqn. (6.20) is easily put into coefficient form as follows.

Define C_Z by
$$C_Z = \frac{Z}{\frac{1}{2}\rho V^2 S}$$

Now in the present case the area S is the product of chord and unit span, namely c.

Therefore

$$C_Z = \frac{Z}{\frac{1}{2}\rho V^2 c}$$

$$= - \frac{1}{\frac{1}{2}\rho V^2 c} \int_0^c [(p - p_0)_u - (p - p_0)_l]\, dx$$

Dividing by $\frac{1}{2}\rho V^2$ inside the square bracket, and remembering that

$$\frac{1}{c}(dx) = d\left(\frac{x}{c}\right)$$

$$C_Z = - \int_0^1 (C_{p\,u} - C_{p\,l})\, d\left(\frac{x}{c}\right) \quad . \qquad . \qquad (6.21)$$

since
$$\frac{p - p_0}{\frac{1}{2}\rho V^2} = C_p \text{ by definition}$$

A similar argument may be used to give the following relations.

$$\delta X = - (p - p_0)\, \delta s \sin \varepsilon$$

$$\delta s \sin \varepsilon = \delta z$$

leading finally to

$$C_X = \int_{z_1/c}^{z_2/c} C_p\, d\left(\frac{z}{c}\right) \qquad . \qquad . \qquad . \qquad (6.22)$$

This coefficient is based on the plan-area of the aerofoil.

The pitching moment may also be calculated from the pressure distribution. For simplicity it will be found about the origin of the Ox and Oz axes.

$$\delta Z = - \, [(p - p_0)_u - (p - p_0)_l] \, \delta x \text{ per unit span}$$

and therefore the contribution to the pitching moment due to this element of Z-force is

$$\delta M = + \, [(p - p_0)_u - (p - p_0)_l] x \, . \, \delta x$$

whence the total pitching moment due to Z is

$$C_{MZ} = + \int_0^c [C_{p\,u} - C_{p\,l}] \left(\frac{x}{c}\right) d\left(\frac{x}{c}\right) = - \int_0^c \Delta C_p \left(\frac{x}{c}\right) d\left(\frac{x}{c}\right) \qquad . \qquad (6.23)$$

since

$$C_M = \frac{M}{\tfrac{1}{2}\rho V^2 Sc} = \frac{M}{\tfrac{1}{2}\rho V^2 c^2} \quad \text{and} \quad S = c \text{ in this case}$$

Similarly, the contribution to C_M due to the X-force may be obtained as

$$C_{MX} = \int_{z_1/c}^{z_2/c} \Delta C_p \left(\frac{z}{c}\right) d\left(\frac{z}{c}\right) \qquad . \qquad . \qquad . \qquad (6.24)$$

The integrations given above are normally performed graphically.

The force coefficients C_X and C_Z are parallel and perpendicular to the chord line, whereas the more usual coefficients C_L and C_D are referred to the air direction. The conversion from one pair to the other may be performed by reference to Fig. 6.13, in which C_R, the coefficient of the resultant aerodynamic force, acts at an angle γ to C_Z. C_R is the resultant both of C_X and C_Z, and of C_L and C_D, and therefore, from Fig. 6.13,

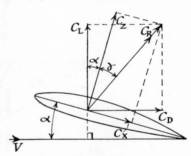

FIG. 6.13.

$$C_L = C_R \cos(\gamma + \alpha) = C_R \cos \gamma \cos \alpha - C_R \sin \alpha \sin \gamma$$

Now

$$C_R \cos \gamma = C_Z \quad \text{and} \quad C_R \sin \gamma = C_X$$

whence

$$C_L = C_Z \cos \alpha - C_X \sin \alpha \, . \qquad . \qquad . \qquad (6.25)$$

Similarly

$$C_D = C_R \sin(\alpha + \gamma)$$
$$= C_Z \sin \alpha + C_X \cos \alpha \, . \qquad . \qquad . \qquad (6.26)$$

The total pitching moment coefficient is

$$C_M = C_{MZ} + C_{MX} \qquad . \qquad . \qquad . \qquad (6.27)$$

In Fig. 6.14 are shown the graphs necessary for the evaluation of the aerodynamic coefficients for the mid-section of a three-dimensional wing of the ellipto-Zhukovsky profile of § 11.5 at a geometric incidence of 6°.

6.8. The vortex theory of lift. This section is concerned with the more elementary aspects of this theory. A fuller development is given in Chapter 13.

Ellipto-Zhukovsky section at the mid-section of a three-dimensional wing.

Geometric incidence $= 6°$

Reynolds number $= 4{\cdot}8 \times 10^5$

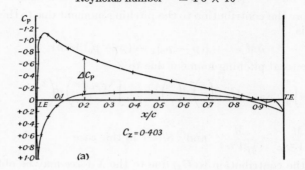

(a)

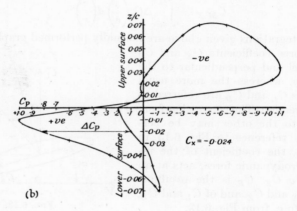

(b)

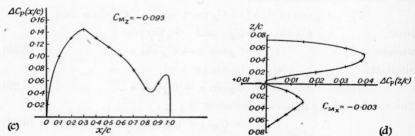

(c)

(d)

$$C_L = C_Z \cos \alpha - C_X \sin \alpha = + 0{\cdot}402$$
$$C_D = C_Z \sin \alpha + C_X \cos \alpha = + 0{\cdot}0182$$
$$C_{M_{LE}} = C_{M_X} + C_{M_Z} = - 0{\cdot}096$$

Fig. 6.14.—Pressure distribution on an aerofoil section.

Figs. 6.3 and 6.14 show how the pressure coefficient varies along the chord of a typical aerofoil section. Remembering that

$$C_p = 1 - \left(\frac{q}{V}\right)^2 \text{ from eqn. (4.51)}$$

it is easy to convert the values of C_p into values of q/V which, when plotted against x/c, gives a result typified by Fig. 6.15.

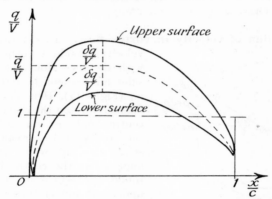

FIG. 6.15.—Velocity distribution on an aerofoil section.

The dotted line is drawn exactly half-way between the curves for the upper and lower surfaces, and is denoted by $\bar{q}/V$. This curve of $\bar{q}/V$ against x/c is the variation of velocity round the symmetrical fairing of the aerofoil section, at zero lift. The differences $\delta q/V$ represent the changes in velocity over the upper and lower surfaces due to the combined effects of camber and incidence. It is seen that, relative to the no-lift case, the air is speeded up over the upper surface and slowed down over the lower surface. Thus the flow over the aerofoil can be regarded as the combination of two different types of flow. One of these is the normal flow round the symmetrical fairing at zero incidence (Fig. 6.16 (a)), and the other is a flow in which the air circulates around the aerofoil, backwards over the upper surface and forwards over the lower surface (Fig. 6.16 (b)).

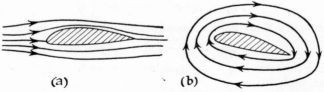

(a) (b)

FIG. 6.16.—The flow round a lifting aerofoil section, separated into two elemental flows (see also Fig. 10.47).

The lift of the aerofoil due to camber and incidence must therefore be associated with this circulatory flow. A special type of flow which is similar to that of Fig. 6.16 (b) is that due to a vortex. A vortex is a 'core' of fluid rotating as though it were solid, and around which air flows in concentric circles. Although an element of 'outside' air is flowing in circles the element itself does not rotate (see § 10.2.10). This is not easy to visualize, but a good analogy is with a car on a fairground 'Big Wheel'. Although the car 'circulates' round the axis of the wheel, the car does not rotate about its own axis. The 'top' of the car is always at the top and the passengers are never upside down. The elements of air in the flow outside a vortex core behave in a very similar way.

6.8.1. Variation of velocity in vortex flow.

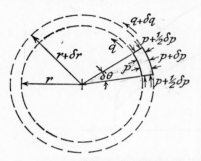

FIG. 6.17.—Motion of an element outside a vortex core.

To determine how the velocity outside a vortex core varies with distance from the centre consider an element in a thin shell of air (Fig. 6.17). Here, flow conditions depend only on the distance from the centre, and are constant all round the vortex at any given radius. The small element, which subtends the angle $\delta\theta$ at the centre, is circulating round the centre in steady motion under the influence of the force due to the radial pressure gradient.

Considering unit axial length, the inwards force due to the pressures is:

$$(p + \delta p)(r + \delta r)\,\delta\theta - pr\,\delta\theta - 2(p + \tfrac{1}{2}\delta p)\,\delta r.\tfrac{1}{2}\delta\theta$$

which reduces to $\delta p(r - \tfrac{1}{2}\delta r)\,\delta\theta$. Ignoring $\tfrac{1}{2}\delta r$ in comparison with r, this becomes $r\,\delta p\,\delta\theta$.

The volume of unit length of the element is $r\,\delta r\,\delta\theta$ and therefore its mass is $\rho r\,\delta r\,\delta\theta$. Its centripetal acceleration is (velocity)^2/radius, and the force required to produce this acceleration is:

$$\text{mass}.\frac{(\text{velocity})^2}{\text{radius}} = \rho r\,\delta r\,\delta\theta.\frac{q^2}{r} = \rho q^2\,\delta r\,\delta\theta$$

Equating this to the force produced by the pressure gradient leads to

$$r\,\delta p = \rho q^2\,\delta r \quad \text{since} \quad \delta\theta \neq 0 \qquad . \qquad . \qquad (6.28)$$

Now Bernoulli's Equation for incompressible flow gives, in this case,

$$p + \tfrac{1}{2}\rho q^2 = (p + \delta p) + \tfrac{1}{2}\rho(q + \delta q)^2$$

Expanding the term in $q + \delta q$, ignoring terms such as $(\delta q)^2$ as small, and cancelling, leads to:

$$\delta p + \rho q\,\delta q = 0$$

i.e.,
$$\delta p = -\rho q\,\delta q \qquad . \qquad . \qquad . \qquad (6.29)$$

Substituting this value for δp in eqn. (6.28) gives

$$\rho q^2\,\delta r + \rho q r\,\delta q = 0$$

which when divided by ρq becomes

$$q \, \delta r + r \, \delta q = 0$$

But the left-hand side of this equation is $\delta(qr)$. Thus

$$\delta(qr) = 0$$

or $\qquad\qquad\qquad qr = \text{constant} \qquad . \qquad . \qquad . \qquad (6.30)$

This shows that, in the flow round a vortex core, the velocity is inversely proportional to the radius (see also § 10.2.10).

When the core is small, or assumed concentrated on a line axis, it is apparent from eqn. (6.30) that when r is small q can be very large. However, within the core the air behaves as though it were a solid cylinder and rotates at a uniform angular velocity. Fig. 6.18 shows the variation of velocity with radius for a typical vortex. The solid line represents the idealized case, but in reality the boundary is not so distinct, and the velocity peak is rounded off, after the style of the dotted lines.

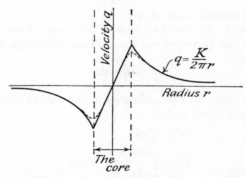

FIG. 6.18.—Velocity distribution in a real vortex with a core.

6.8.2. Circulation and vortex strength (see also § 10.5).

A quantity called the circulation, K, is defined as 'the line integral of the tangential velocity component round any closed circuit in the fluid'. Fig. 6.19 shows an imaginary closed circuit drawn in the fluid. At some point as shown the velocity is of magnitude q, and makes an angle α with the tangent to the circuit at that point.

FIG. 6.19.—The definition of circulation, K.

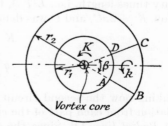

FIG. 6.20.—Two circuits in the flow around a point vortex.

G

Then the tangential velocity component is ($q \cos \alpha$) and so the circulation K is given by

$$K = \oint q \cos \alpha \, ds \qquad . \qquad . \qquad . \qquad (6.31)$$

where s is distance round the circuit and the symbol $\oint$ denotes integration once around the complete circuit in the anti-clockwise sense.

This definition of circulation will now be applied to two particular circuits outside the core of a vortex (Fig. 6.20). One of these is a circle, of radius r_1, centred at the centre of the vortex. The second circuit is $ABCD$, composed of two circular arcs of radii r_1 and r_2 and two radial lines subtending the angle β at the centre of the vortex.

For the concentric circuit, the velocity is constant at the value

$$q = \frac{C}{r_1}$$

where C is the constant value of (qr).

Since the flow is, by the definition of a vortex, along the circle, α is everywhere zero and therefore $\cos \alpha = 1$. Then, from eqn. (6.31)

$$K = \oint \frac{C}{r_1} \, ds$$

Now suppose an angle θ to be measured in the anti-clockwise sense from some arbitrary axis, such as OP.

Then $$ds = r_1 \, d\theta$$

whence $$K = \int_0^{2\pi} \frac{C}{r_1} r_1 \, d\theta = 2\pi C \qquad . \qquad . \qquad . \qquad (6.32)$$

Since C is a constant, it follows that K is also a constant, independent of the radius. It can be shown that, provided the circuit encloses the centre of the vortex, the circulation round it is equal to K, whatever the shape of the circuit.

The circulation K round a circuit enclosing the centre of a vortex is called the 'strength' of the vortex.

The dimensions of circulation and vortex strength are, from eqn. (6.31), velocity times length, i.e., L^2T^{-1}, ft²/sec.

Now $K = 2\pi C$, and C was defined as (qr); hence

$$K = 2\pi qr$$

and $$q = \frac{K}{2\pi r} \qquad . \qquad . \qquad . \qquad . \qquad (6.33)$$

Taking now the second circuit $ABCD$, the contribution towards the circulation from each part of the circuit is calculated as follows:

(i) *Radial line AB*. Since the flow around a vortex is in concentric circles, the velocity vector is everywhere perpendicular to the radial line, i.e., $\alpha = 90°$, $\cos \alpha = 0$. Thus the tangential velocity component is zero along AB, and there is therefore no contribution to the circulation.

(ii) *Circular arc BC.* Here $\alpha = 0$, $\cos \alpha = 1$.

$$\therefore \; \delta k = \int_{BC} q \cos \alpha \, ds = \int_0^\beta q \, r_2 \, d\theta$$

But, by eqn. (6.33),

$$q = \frac{K}{2\pi r_2}$$

$$\therefore \; \delta k = \int_0^\beta \frac{K}{2\pi r_2} r_2 \, d\theta = \frac{\beta K}{2\pi}$$

(iii) *Radial line CD.* As for AB, there is no contribution to the circulation from this part of the circuit.

(iv) *Circular arc DA.* Here the path of integration is from D to A, while the direction of velocity is from A to D. Therefore $\alpha = 180°$, $\cos \alpha = -1$.
Then

$$\delta k = \int_0^\beta \frac{K}{2\pi r_1}(-1)r_1 \, d\theta = -\frac{\beta K}{2\pi}$$

Therefore the total circulation round the complete circuit $ABCD$ is k where

$$k = 0 + \frac{\beta K}{2\pi} + 0 - \frac{\beta K}{2\pi} = 0 \qquad . \qquad . \qquad (6.34)$$

Thus the total circulation round this circuit, which does not enclose the core of the vortex, is zero. Now any circuit can be split into infinitely short circular arcs joined by infinitely short radial lines. Applying the above process to such a circuit would lead to the result that the circulation round a circuit of any shape which does not enclose the core of a vortex is zero.

6.8.3. The pressure in a vortex flow.

Suppose that an expanse of air is initially at rest with pressure p_0, and then a vortex of strength K and core radius a is created within the fluid, and consider conditions when the flow has developed fully. At a very large (infinite) radius the velocity of flow will be vanishingly small, and the pressure remains at p_0. At all other radii the pressure will be less than p_0. To study the exact variation of pressure it is necessary to consider the two parts of the vortex separately.

(i) *Flow outside the core.* Here, Bernoulli's Equation applies, and also eqn. (6.33), namely

$$q = \frac{K}{2\pi r}$$

Therefore if the pressure at a radius r ($\geqslant a$) is p_r, then

$$p_r + \tfrac{1}{2}\rho\left(\frac{K}{2\pi r}\right)^2 = p_0$$

$$\therefore \; p_r = p_0 - \frac{\rho K^2}{8\pi^2 r^2} \qquad . \qquad . \qquad . \qquad (6.35)$$

In particular at the surface of the core, where $r = a$

$$p_a = p_0 - \frac{\rho K^2}{8\pi^2 a^2} \ . \qquad . \qquad . \qquad (6.36)$$

(ii) *Inside the core.* The air circulating in the core must be held to its circular path by the effect of a radial pressure gradient. The pressure must therefore be a minimum at the centre, increasing outwards. At the same time, the velocity at the centre is zero, increasing outwards and therefore,

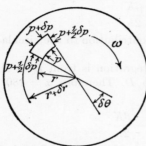

if the air in the core obeyed Bernoulli's Equation the pressure would decrease outwards, in direct contradiction to the earlier requirement. It follows that Bernoulli's Equation cannot apply in the core. It is therefore necessary to consider the equilibrium of an element. Consider the element in Fig. 6.21, which depicts a vortex core rotating at an angular velocity of ω rads/sec.

FIG. 6.21.—Motion of an element in a vortex core.

Volume of element $= r\,\delta r\,\delta\theta$ per unit length

$\therefore$ inwards force on the element due to the radial pressure gradient is, by the same method as § 6.8.1,

$$r\,\delta p\,\delta\theta = r\,\delta\theta\!\left(\frac{dp}{dr}\right)\delta r$$

This is the force required to hold the element in its circular path, i.e., to give it a centripetal acceleration of $r\omega^2$.

Since the mass of the element is $\rho r\,\delta r\,\delta\theta$ per unit length

$$r\,\delta r\,\delta\theta\!\left(\frac{dp}{dr}\right) = \rho r\,\delta r\,\delta\theta(r\omega^2)$$

i.e., $$\frac{dp}{dr} = \rho\omega^2 r$$

$$dp = \rho\omega^2 r\,dr$$

whence $$p = \tfrac{1}{2}\rho\omega^2 r^2 + C \qquad . \qquad . \qquad . \qquad (6.37)$$

Knowing the pressure at the surface of the core, from eqn. (6.36) the constant of integration can be determined. That is, when $r = a$,

$$p_a = \tfrac{1}{2}\rho\omega^2 a^2 + C = p_0 - \frac{\rho K^2}{8\pi^2 a^2}$$

whence

$$C = p_0 - \frac{\rho K^2}{8\pi^2 a^2} - \tfrac{1}{2}\rho\omega^2 a^2$$

and therefore, inside the core

$$p = p_0 - \frac{\rho K^2}{8\pi^2 a^2} - \tfrac{1}{2}\rho\omega^2(a^2 - r^2) \qquad . \qquad . \qquad (6.38)$$

Now the circulation round the vortex $= K = 2\pi rq$ on or outside the vortex core. Evaluating K on the core surface from the flow conditions within the core gives

$$K = 2\pi a(\omega a) = 2\pi\omega a^2$$

whence

$$\omega = \frac{K}{2\pi a^2}$$

Substituting this in eqn. (6.38) leads to

$$p = p_0 - \frac{\rho K^2}{8\pi^2 a^2} - \tfrac{1}{2}\rho\frac{K^2}{4\pi^2 a^4}(a^2 - r^2)$$

which easily simplifies to

$$p = p_0 - \frac{\rho K^2}{8\pi^2 a^2}\left[2 - \left(\frac{r}{a}\right)^2\right] \qquad . \qquad . \qquad (6.39)$$

In particular the minimum pressure in a vortex occurs at the centre when $r = 0$ and

$$p_{\min} = p_0 - \frac{\rho K^2}{4\pi^2 a^2} \qquad . \qquad . \qquad . \qquad (6.40)$$

By comparing eqns. (6.36), (6.39) and (6.40) it is seen that, of the pressure drop between infinity and the centre of a vortex, half occurs from infinity to the core surface, and the other half occurs in the core itself.

6.8.4. The vortex in a uniform stream.

Suppose a vortex is in a stream of air, and that some restraint is applied to the vortex to prevent it being blown downstream. Then the streamlines of the flow outside the core are as sketched in Fig. 6.22. The point S is of interest. It is a stagnation point out in the stream, and the direction of the flow passing through S is shown by the arrows. The air which passes through S splits into two, some going over the top of the vortex and some going below it. That part of the streamline through S which passes over the vortex forms a closed loop and the air within this loop does not pass downstream, but circulates continually round the vortex core.

It is obvious from the sketch that the flow is not symmetrical; that below the vortex differs from that above. In fact the air above the vortex is speeded up, and that below the vortex is slowed down. (The velocity at any point is the vector sum of the velocity of the uniform stream and the velocity

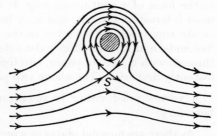

FIG. 6.22.—Flow around a vortex core rotating in a uniform stream.

due to the vortex in isolation.) As a result of these velocity differences between the flow above and below the vortex, there are pressure differences. These pressure differences cause a force on the vortex of magnitude

$$l = \rho V K \text{ per unit length}$$

which acts perpendicular to the direction of the stream at infinity. There is no drag, the force on the vortex being a pure lift in an ideal fluid.

This relationship is very important, and is known as the 'Kutta–Zhukovsky' relationship (see § 10.2.13).

6.8.5. The wing replaced by a vortex.

The flow round an aerofoil section can be idealized into a uniform stream, a distortion of the stream due to aerofoil thickness, and a flow similar to a vortex, and it has now been stated that a vortex in a uniform stream experiences a lift. Here, then, is a second way in which lift may be explained. Assuming, for the time being, that the lift is uniform over the span it seems that, if the effects of thickness are ignored, a wing can be replaced by a vortex of suitable strength along the locus of the centres of pressure (Fig. 6.23).

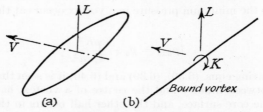

FIG. 6.23.—A wing with uniform lift replaced by a line vortex.

In fact, the arrangement of Fig. 6.23 (b) is physically impossible. To appreciate this, it must be remembered that the pressure in a vortex core is less than that of the free-stream. If a vortex were to exist as in Fig. 6.23 (b) with free ends, air would be drawn into the core and immediately destroy it.

There are two ways whereby this difficulty can be overcome. The ends of the vortex can be sealed by large solid plates, so that air cannot be drawn in. Alternatively a vortex which has no free ends may be imagined, in the form of a continuous ring. It is this latter possibility which is of most interest at present, and may be demonstrated by a smoke ring. A smoke ring is simply a vortex in the shape of a ring and as such has no free ends, and can therefore exist safely. If, however, a smoke ring is cut through with a piece of paper, two free ends are created, and the vortex is instantly destroyed. The above two possibilities are formally stated as:

'a vortex must either be re-entrant, or abut at each end on a solid boundary'.

As there are no solid plates at wing-tips, the vortex must be re-entrant.

The pressure on the upper surface of a lifting wing is lower than that of the surrounding atmosphere, while the pressure on the lower surface is greater than that on the upper surface, and may be greater than that of the surrounding atmosphere (Fig. 6.3). Thus, over the upper surface, air will tend to flow inwards towards the root from the tips, being replaced by air which was originally outboard of the tips. Similarly, on the under-surface air will either tend to flow inwards to a lesser extent, or may tend to flow outwards. Where these two streams combine at the trailing edge,

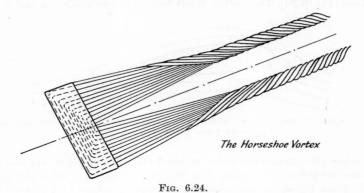

The Horseshoe Vortex

FIG. 6.24.

the difference in spanwise velocity will cause the air to roll up into a number of small streamwise vortices, distributed along the whole span. These small vortices roll up into two large vortices just inboard of the wing-tips. This is illustrated in Fig. 6.24. The strength of each of these two vortices will equal the strength of the vortex replacing the wing itself.

So far, then, it is possible to represent the uniformly loaded wing by a vortex system forming three sides of a rectangle. To make the vortex

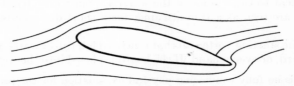

FIG. 6.25.—Streamlines of the flow around an aerofoil with zero circulation, stagnation point on the rear upper surface.

re-entrant it is necessary to complete the fourth side of the rectangle by a suitable vortex. When a wing is accelerated from rest the circulation round it, and therefore the lift, is not produced instantaneously. Instead, at the instant of starting the streamlines over the rear part of the wing section are as shown in Fig. 6.25, with a stagnation point occurring on the rear upper surface. At the sharp trailing edge the air is required to change direction suddenly while still moving at high speed. This high speed calls for extremely high accelerations and produces very large viscous tractions, and the air is unable to turn round the trailing edge to the stagnation point. Instead it leaves the surface and produces a vortex just above the trailing edge. The stagnation point moves towards the trailing edge, the circulation round the wing, and therefore its lift, increasing progressively as the stagnation point moves back. When the stagnation point reaches the trailing edge the air is no longer required to flow round the trailing edge. Instead it decelerates gradually along the aerofoil surface, comes to rest at the trailing edge, and then accelerates from rest in a different direction (Fig. 6.26). The vortex is left behind at the point reached by the

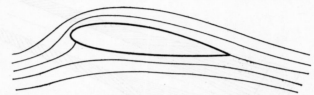

Fig. 6.26.—Streamlines of the flow around an aerofoil with full circulation, stagnation point at the trailing edge.

wing when the stagnation point reached the trailing edge. Its reaction, the circulation round the wing, has become stabilized at the value necessary to place the stagnation point at the trailing edge (see § 11.4).*

The vortex which has been left behind is equal in strength and opposite in sense to the circulation round the wing and is called the 'starting vortex' or 'initial eddy'.

The complete simplified wing vortex system is seen to be a rectangular re-entrant vortex, and is therefore physically possible.

The existence of the trailing and starting vortices may easily be verified visually. When a fast aeroplane pulls out of a dive in humid air the reduction of pressure and temperature at the centres of the trailing vortices is often sufficient to cause some of the water vapour to condense into droplets, which are seen as a thin streamer for a short distance behind each wing-tip.

To see the starting vortex all that is needed is a tub of water and a small piece of board, or even a hand. If the board is placed into the water cutting

* There is no fully convincing physical explanation for the production of the starting vortex and the generation of the circulation around the aerofoil.

Various incomplete explanations will be found in the references quoted in the bibliography. The most usual explanation is based on the large viscous tractions associated with the high velocities round the trailing edge, from which it is inferred that circulation cannot be generated, and aerodynamic lift produced, in an inviscid fluid. It may be, however, that local flow acceleration is equally important and that this is sufficiently high to account for the failure of the flow to follow round the sharp trailing edge, without invoking viscosity. As a corollary, it is possible that circulation and aerodynamic lift can be generated in an inviscid fluid. This opens up interesting possibilities for further research into a fundamental but commonplace aerodynamic concept.

In practical aeronautics, fluid is not inviscid and the complete explanation of this phenomenon must take account of viscosity and the consequent growth of the boundary layer as well as high local velocities as the motion is generated.

the surface and then suddenly moved through the water at a moderate incidence, an eddy will be seen to leave the rear, and move forwards and away from the 'wing'. This is the starting vortex, and its movement is induced by the circulation round the plate.

6.8.6. The simplified 'horseshoe' vortex. The starting vortex is left behind at the point where the aircraft took off or, more accurately, where the circulation round the wing was last changed. It is therefore usually so far behind the wing that its effect on the wing may be ignored, and the trailing vortices may, with negligible error, be regarded as extending for an infinite distance behind the wing. In such a case the wing vortex system may be regarded as shown in Fig. 6.27. This is called the 'simplified horseshoe vortex' (see also § 13.1.2).

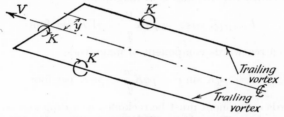

FIG. 6.27.—The simplified horseshoe vortex system.

This simplified picture of the vortex system may be used to explain several phenomena, of which the most important is trailing vortex drag.

6.8.7. Trailing vortex drag (see also § 13.3.2). Consider what is happening at some point y along the wing span (Fig. 6.27). Each of the trailing vortices produces a downwards component of velocity, w, at y, known as the 'downwash' or 'induced velocity' (see § 13.3.1). This causes the flow over that section of the wing to be inclined slightly downwards from the direction of the undisturbed stream V (Fig. 6.28) by the angle ε, the 'induced angle of incidence' or 'downwash angle'. The local flow is also at a slightly different speed, q.

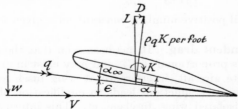

FIG. 6.28.—Flow conditions and forces at a section of a three-dimensional lifting wing.

If the angle between the aerofoil chord line and the direction of the undisturbed stream, the geometric angle of incidence, is α, it is seen that the angle between the chord line and the actual flow at that section of the wing is equal to $\alpha - \varepsilon$, and is called the 'effective incidence' α_∞. It is this effective incidence which determines the lift coefficient at that section of the wing, and thus the wing is lifting less strongly than the geometric incidence would suggest. Since K, and therefore w and ε increase with lift coefficient, it follows that the lift of a three-dimensional wing increases less rapidly with incidence than does that for a two-dimensional wing, which has no trailing vortices.

Now the circulation round this section of the wing will have a value K appropriate to α_∞, and the 'lift' force on this circulation will be $\rho q K$ per foot, acting perpendicular to the direction of q as shown, i.e., inclined backwards from the vertical by the angle ε. This force therefore has a component perpendicular to the undisturbed stream V, which, by definition, is called the lift, and is of magnitude

$$l = \rho q K \cos \varepsilon = \rho q K \frac{V}{q} = \rho V K \text{ per foot}$$

There is also a rearwards component of magnitude

$$d = \rho q K \sin \varepsilon = \rho q K \frac{w}{q} = \rho w K \text{ per foot}$$

This rearwards component must be reckoned as a drag and is, in fact, the trailing vortex drag. Thus the trailing vortex drag arises essentially from the downwards velocity induced over the wing by the wing-tip vortices.

The further apart the wing-tip vortices the less will be their effectiveness in producing induced incidence and drag. It is therefore to be expected that these induced quantities will depend on the wing aspect ratio, $\mathcal{R}$. Some results which will be obtained in Chapter 13 are:

$$\frac{dC_L}{d\alpha} = a = \frac{a_\infty}{1 + a_\infty/\pi\mathcal{R}} \text{ (eqn. (13.59))}$$

where a_∞ is the lift curve slope for the two-dimensional wing, and the trailing vortex drag coefficient C_{Dv} is given by

$$C_{Dv} = \frac{D_v}{\frac{1}{2}\rho V^2 S} = \frac{C_L^2}{\pi\mathcal{R}}(1 + \delta) \text{ (eqn. (13.44))}$$

where δ is a small positive number, constant for a given wing.

6.8.8. Lift-dependent drag.

It has been seen that the trailing vortex drag coefficient is proportional to C_L^2, and may exist in an inviscid fluid.

On a complete aircraft, interference at wing/fuselage, wing/engine-nacelle, and such other junctions leads to modification of the boundary layers over the isolated wing, fuselage, etc. This interference, which is actually part of the boundary layer drag, usually varies with the lift coefficient in such a manner that it may be treated as of the form $(a + bC_L^2)$. The part of this boundary layer drag coefficient which is represented by the term (bC_L^2) may be added to the trailing vortex drag.

The sum so obtained is known as the lift-dependent drag coefficient. The lift-dependent drag is actually defined as

'the difference between the drag at a given lift coefficient and the drag at some datum lift coefficient'.

If this datum lift coefficient is taken to be zero, the total drag coefficient of a complete aeroplane may be taken, to a good approximation in most cases, as

$$C_D = C_{D0} + kC_L^2$$

where C_{D0} is the drag coefficient at zero lift, and kC_L^2 is the lift-dependent drag coefficient, denoted by $C_{D\,L}$.

6.9. Aerofoil characteristics—Lift coefficient versus incidence.

This variation is illustrated in Fig. 6.29 for a two-dimensional (infinite span) wing.

Considering first the full curve (a) which is for a moderately thick (13%) section of zero camber, it is seen to consist of a straight line passing through the origin, curving over at the higher values of C_L, reaching a maximum value of $C_{L\,max}$ at an incidence of α_s, known as the stalling point. After the stalling point, the lift coefficient decreases, tending to level off at some lower value for higher incidences. The slope of the straight portion of the curve is called the

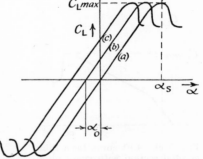

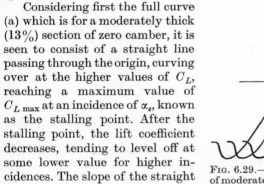

Fig. 6.29.—Typical lift-curves for sections of moderate thickness and various cambers.

'two-dimensional lift curve slope', $(dC_L/d\alpha)_\infty$ or a_∞. Its theoretical value for a 'thin' section (strictly a curved or flat plate) is 2π per radian (see § 11.4). For a section of finite thickness in air, a more accurate empirical value is

$$\left(\frac{dC_L}{d\alpha}\right)_\infty = 1\cdot8\pi\left(1 + 0\cdot8\frac{t}{c}\right) \qquad . \qquad . \qquad . \qquad (6.41)$$

The value of $C_{L\,max}$ is a very important characteristic of the aerofoil since it determines the minimum speed at which an aeroplane can fly (see § 8.1.1). A typical value for the type of aerofoil section mentioned is about 1·5. The corresponding value of α_s would be around 18°.

Curves (b) and (c) in Fig. 6.29 are for sections which have the same symmetrical fairing but which are cambered, (c) being more cambered than (b). The effect of camber is merely to reduce the incidence at which a given lift coefficient is produced, i.e., to shift the whole lift curve somewhat to the left, with negligible change in the value of the lift curve slope, or in the shape of the curve. This shift of the curve is measured by the incidence at which the lift coefficient is zero. This is the 'no-lift incidence', denoted by α_0, and a typical value is $-3°$. The same reduction occurs in α_s. Thus a cambered section has the same value of $C_{L\,max}$ as does its symmetrical fairing, but this occurs at a smaller incidence.

Modern, thin, sharp-nosed sections display a slightly different characteristic to the above, as shown in Fig. 6.30.

In this case the lift curve has two approximately straight portions, of different slopes. The slope of the lower portion is almost the same as that for a thicker section but, at a moderate incidence, the slope takes a different, smaller value, leading to a smaller value of $C_{L\,max}$, typically of the order of unity. This change in the lift curve slope is due to a change in the type of flow near the nose of the aerofoil.

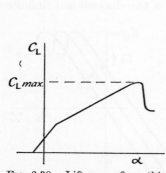

FIG. 6.30.—Lift curve for a thin aerofoil section with small nose radius of curvature.

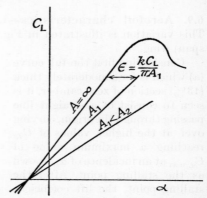

FIG. 6.31.—Influence of wing aspect ratio on the lift curve.

6.9.1. Effect of aspect ratio on the C_L: α curve.

The induced angle of incidence ε is given by

$$\varepsilon = \frac{kC_L}{\pi A}$$

and thus

$$\alpha_\infty = \alpha - \frac{kC_L}{\pi A}$$

Considering a number of wings of the same symmetrical section but of different aspect ratios, the above expression leads to a family of C_L, α curves, as in Fig. 6.31, since the actual lift coefficient at a given section of the wing is equal to the lift coefficient for a two-dimensional wing at an incidence of α_∞.

For highly swept wings of very low aspect ratio (less than 3 or so), the lift curve slope becomes very small, leading to values of $C_{L\,max}$ of about $1 \cdot 0$, occurring at stalling incidences of around $45°$. This is reflected in the extreme nose-up landing attitudes of many aircraft fitted with wings of this description.

6.9.2. Drag coefficient versus lift coefficient. For a two-dimensional wing at low Mach numbers the drag contains no trailing vortex or wave drag, and the drag coefficient is C_{D0}. There are two distinct forms of variation of C_D with C_L, both illustrated in Fig. 6.32.

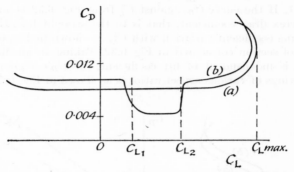

FIG. 6.32.—Typical variation of sectional drag coefficient with lift coefficient.

Curve (a) represents a typical conventional aerofoil with C_{D0} fairly constant over the working range of lift coefficient, increasing rapidly towards the two extreme values of C_L. Curve (b) represents the type of variation found for 'low-drag' aerofoil sections. Over much of the C_L range the drag coefficient is rather larger than for the conventional type of aerofoil, but within a restricted range of lift coefficient (C_{L1} to C_{L2}) the profile drag coefficient is considerably less. This range of C_L is known as the 'favourable range' for the section, and the low drag coefficient is due to the design of the aerofoil section, which permits a comparatively large extent of laminar boundary layer. It is for this reason that aerofoils of this type are also known as 'laminar flow' sections. The width and depth of this 'favourable range' or, more graphically, 'low-drag bucket' is determined by the shape of the symmetrical fairing. The central value of the lift coefficient is known as the 'optimum' or 'ideal' lift coefficient, $C_{L\,opt}$ or $C_{L\,i}$. Its value is decided by the shape of the camber-line, and the degree of camber, and thus the position of the favourable range may be placed where desired by suitable design of the camber line. The favourable range may be placed to cover the most common range of lift coefficient for a particular aeroplane (e.g., C_{L2} may be slightly larger than the lift coefficient used on the climb, and C_{L1} may be slightly less than the cruising lift coefficient). In such a case the aeroplane will have the benefit of a low value of the boundary layer drag coefficient for the wing throughout most of the flight, with obvious benefits in performance and economy.

The effect of a finite aspect ratio is to give rise to trailing vortex drag and this drag coefficient is proportional to C_L^2, and must be added to the curves of Fig. 6.32.

6.9.3. Drag coefficient versus (lift coefficient)². Since

$$C_{Dv} = \frac{C_L^2}{\pi A}(1 + \delta)$$

it follows that a curve of C_{Dv} against C_L^2 will be a straight line of slope $(1 + \delta)/\pi A$. If the curve C_{D0} against C_L^2 from Fig. 6.32 is added to the trailing vortex drag coefficient, that is to the straight line, the result is the total drag coefficient variation with C_L^2, as shown in Fig. 6.33 for the two types of section considered in Fig. 6.32. Taking an idealized case in which C_{D0} is independent of lift coefficient, the $C_D v (C_L)^2$ curve for a family of wings of various aspect ratios is as shown in Fig. 6.34.

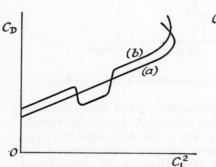

FIG. 6.33.—Variation of total wing drag coefficient with (lift coefficient)².

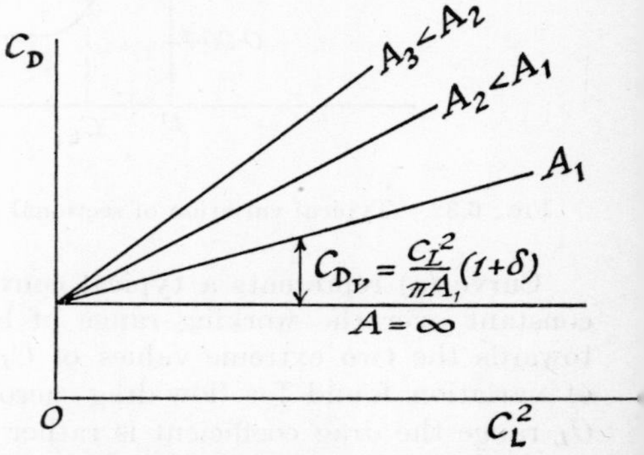

FIG. 6.34.—Idealized variation of total wing drag coefficient with (lift coefficient)² for a family of three-dimensional wings of various aspect ratios.

6.9.4. Pitching moment coefficient. In § 6.5.1 it was shown that

$$\frac{dC_M}{dC_L} = \text{constant}$$

the value of the constant depending on the point of the aerofoil section about which C_M is measured. Thus a curve of $C_M v C_L$ is theoretically as shown in Fig. 6.35.

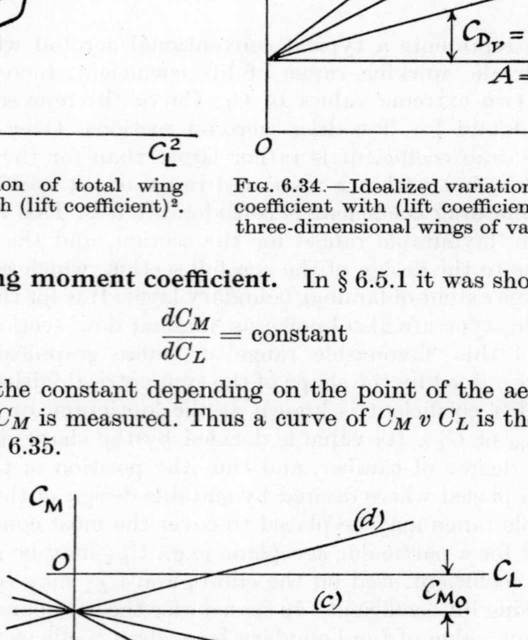

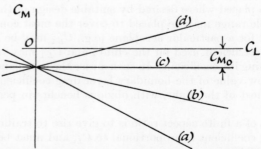

FIG. 6.35.—Variation of C_M with C_L for an aerofoil section, for four different reference points.

Line (a) for which $dC_M/dC_L \simeq -\frac{1}{4}$ is for C_M measured about the leading edge. Line (c), for which the slope is zero, is for the case where C_M is measured about the aerodynamic centre. Line (b) would be obtained if C_M were measured about a point between the leading edge and the aerodynamic centre, while for (d) the reference point is behind the aerodynamic centre. These curves are straight only for moderate values of C_L. As the lift coefficient approaches $C_{L\,max}$, the $C_M\,v\,C_L$ curve departs from the straight line. The two possibilities are sketched in Fig. 6.36.

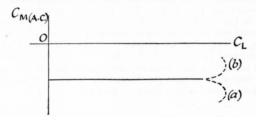

Fig. 6.36.—The behaviour of the pitching moment coefficient in the region of the stalling point, showing stable and unstable breaks.

For curve (a) the pitching moment coefficient becomes more negative near the stall, thus tending to decrease the incidence, and unstall the wing. This is known as a 'stable break'. Curve (b), on the other hand, shows that, near the stall, the pitching moment coefficient becomes less negative. The tendency then is for the incidence to increase, aggravating the stall. Such a characteristic is an 'unstable break'. This type of characteristic is commonly found with highly swept wings, though measures can be taken to counteract this undesirable behaviour.

EXERCISES

1. An aeroplane of 5·36 tons all-up-weight and having wings of aspect ratio 8, loaded to 41·75 lb/ft², is required to operate normally at 44,000 ft altitude, where the relative density may be taken as 0·2. The drag is to be measured on a model of 6 in. chord in a compressed-air tunnel running at 100 ft/sec at 15°C. Calculate (i) the compression required for the test if the full-scale flight speed is 180 m.p.h. E.A.S. and (ii) the wing loading on the model during the test. (*Ans.* 17·6: 105·5 lb/ft²)   (N.C.A.T.)

2. An aeroplane weighs 15,000 lb and has a wing span of 55 ft. A 1/10th scale model is tested, flaps down, in a compressed-air tunnel at 15 atmospheres pressure and 15°C at various speeds. The maximum lift on the model is measured at the various speeds, with the results as given below:

Speed (ft/sec)	65	70	75	80	85
Max. lift (lb)	740	865	1000	1145	1300

Estimate the minimum flying speed of the aircraft at sea-level, i.e., the speed at which the maximum lift of the aircraft is equal to its weight. (*Ans.* 112·5 ft/sec)

3. The pressure distribution over a section of a two-dimensional wing at 4° incidence may be approximated as follows:

Upper surface; C_p constant at -0.8 from the leading edge to 60% chord, then increasing linearly to $+0.1$ at the trailing edge.

Lower surface; C_p constant at -0.4 from the L.E. to 60% chord, then increasing linearly to $+0.1$ at the T.E.

Estimate the lift coefficient and the pitching moment coefficient about the leading edge due to lift. (*Ans.* 0.3192; and -0.13)

4. The static pressure is measured at a number of points on the surface of a long circular cylinder of 6 in. diameter with its axis perpendicular to a stream of standard density at 100 ft/sec. The pressure points are defined by the angle θ, which is the angle subtended at the centre by the arc between the pressure point and the front stagnation point. In the table below values are given of $p - p_0$, where p is the pressure on the surface of the cylinder and p_0 is the undisturbed pressure of the free stream, for various angles θ, all pressures being in lb/ft². The readings are identical for the upper and lower halves of the cylinder. Estimate the boundary layer normal pressure drag per foot run, and the corresponding drag coefficient.

θ . .	0	10	20	30	40	50	60
$p - p_0$	$+11.9$	$+10.5$	$+6.3$	-1.19	-8.2	-12.5	-15.1

θ	70	80	90	100	110	120
$p - p_0$ . . .	-15.2	-14.8	-13.8	-13.1	-12.3	-11.9

For values of θ between 120° and 180°, $p - p_0$ is constant at -11.9 lb/ft². (*Ans.* $C_D = 0.875$, $D = 5.2$ lb/ft run)

5. A sailplane has a wing of 60 ft span and aspect ratio of 16. The fuselage is 2 ft wide at the wing root, and the wing taper ratio is 0.3 with square-cut wing-tips. At a true air speed of 72 m.p.h. at an altitude where the relative density is 0.7 the lift and drag are 800 lb and 32 lb respectively. The wing pitching moment coefficient about the $\frac{1}{4}$ chord point is -0.03 based on the gross wing area and the aerodynamic mean chord. Calculate the lift and drag coefficients based on the gross wing area, and the pitching moment about the $\frac{1}{4}$ chord point. (*Ans.* $C_L = 0.384$, $C_D = 0.0153$, $M = -260$ lb/ft since $\bar{c}_A = 4.15$ ft)

6. To tow a certain body through the atmosphere at sea-level requires a power P_0. Calculate the power necessary to tow the same body under dynamically similar conditions at the base of the stratosphere. (*Ans.* $5.97P_0$)

7. Describe qualitatively the results expected from the pressure plotting of a conventional symmetrical low-speed two-dimensional aerofoil. Indicate the changes expected with incidence and discuss the processes for determining the resultant forces. Are any further tests needed to complete the determination of the overall forces of lift and drag? Include in the discussion the order of magnitude expected for the various distributions and forces described. (U. of L.)

8. Show that for geometrically similar aerodynamic systems the non-dimensional force coefficients of lift and drag depend on Reynolds number and Mach number only.

Discuss briefly the importance of this theorem in wind-tunnel testing and simple performance theory. (U. of L.)

CHAPTER 7

AIRSCREWS AND PROPULSION

The forward propulsive force, or thrust, in aeronautics is invariably obtained by increasing the rearward momentum of a quantity of gas. Aircraft propulsion systems may be divided into two classes:

 (I) those systems where the gas worked on is wholly or principally atmospheric air;

 (II) other propulsive systems, in which the gas does not contain atmospheric air in any appreciable quantity.

The first class includes turbo-jets, ram-jets and all systems using airscrews or helicopter rotors. It also includes ornithopters (and birds).

The only example of the second class currently used in aviation is the rocket.

7.1. Froude's momentum theory of propulsion.

This theory applies to propulsive systems of Class I. In this class, work is done on air from the atmosphere and its energy increased. This increase in energy is used to increase the rearward momentum of the air, the reaction to which appears as a thrust on the engine or airscrew.

The theory is based on the concept of the 'ideal actuator disc' or 'pure energy supplier'. This is an infinitely thin disc of area S which offers no resistance to air passing through it. Air passing through the disc receives energy in the form of pressure energy from the disc, the energy being added uniformly over the whole area of the disc. It is assumed that the velocity of the air through the disc is constant over the whole area and that all the power supplied to the disc is transferred to the air.

Consider the system shown in Fig. 7.1.

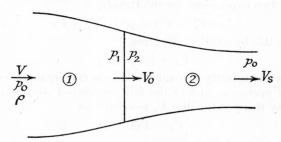

FIG. 7.1.—The ideal actuator disc, and flow in the slipstream.

This represents an actuator disc at rest in a fluid which, a long way ahead of the disc, is moving uniformly with a speed of V ft/sec and has a pressure of p_0 lb/ft². The outer curved lines represent the streamlines which separate the fluid which passes through the disc from that which does not. As the fluid between these streamlines approaches the disc it accelerates to a speed V_0, its pressure decreasing to p_1. At the disc the pressure is increased to p_2 but continuity prohibits a sudden change in speed. Behind the disc the air expands and accelerates until, well behind the disc, its pressure has returned to p_0, when its speed is V_s. The flow between the bounding streamlines behind the disc is known as the *slip-stream*.

In unit time,
mass of fluid passing through disc

$$= \rho S V_0 \text{ slugs} \qquad . \qquad . \qquad . \qquad . \qquad (7.1)$$

increase of rearward momentum of this mass of fluid

$$= \rho S V_0 (V_s - V) \qquad . \qquad . \qquad . \qquad (7.2)$$

and this is the thrust on the disc.

Thus
$$T = \rho S V_0 (V_s - V) \qquad . \qquad . \qquad . \qquad (7.3)$$

The thrust can also be calculated from the pressures on the two sides of the disc as

$$T = S(p_2 - p_1) \qquad . \qquad . \qquad . \qquad . \qquad (7.4)$$

The flow is seen to be divided into two regions 1 and 2, and Bernoulli's Equation may be applied within each of these regions. Since the fluid receives energy at the disc Bernoulli's Equation may *not* be applied through the disc. Then

$$p_0 + \tfrac{1}{2}\rho V^2 = p_1 + \tfrac{1}{2}\rho V_0^2 \qquad . \qquad . \qquad . \qquad (7.5)$$

and
$$p_2 + \tfrac{1}{2}\rho V_0^2 = p_0 + \tfrac{1}{2}\rho V_s^2 \qquad . \qquad . \qquad . \qquad (7.6)$$

From eqns. (7.5) and (7.6)

$$(p_2 + \tfrac{1}{2}\rho V_0^2) - (p_1 + \tfrac{1}{2}\rho V_0^2) = (p_0 + \tfrac{1}{2}\rho V_s^2) - (p_0 + \tfrac{1}{2}\rho V^2)$$

i.e.,
$$p_2 - p_1 = \tfrac{1}{2}\rho(V_s^2 - V^2) \qquad . \qquad . \qquad . \qquad (7.7)$$

Substituting this in eqn. (7.4) and equating the result to eqn. (7.3) (i.e., equating the two expressions for the thrust),

$$\tfrac{1}{2}\rho S(V_s^2 - V^2) = \rho S V_0 (V_s - V)$$

and dividing this by $\rho S(V_s - V)$ gives

$$V_0 = \tfrac{1}{2}(V_s + V) \qquad . \qquad . \qquad . \qquad (7.8)$$

showing that the velocity through the disc is the arithmetic mean of the velocity well upstream, and in the fully developed slipstream. Further, if the velocity through the disc V_0 is written as

$$V_0 = V(1 + a) \qquad . \qquad . \qquad . \qquad (7.9)$$

it follows from eqn. (7.8) that

$$V_s + V = 2V_0 = 2V(1 + a)$$

whence
$$V_s = V(1 + 2a) \qquad . \qquad . \qquad . \qquad (7.10)$$

The quantity a is termed the 'inflow factor'.

Now unit mass of the fluid upstream of the disc has kinetic energy of $\frac{1}{2}V^2$ and a pressure energy appropriate to the pressure p_0, while the same mass well behind the disc has, after passing through the disc, kinetic energy of $\frac{1}{2}V_s^2$ and pressure energy appropriate to the pressure p_0. Thus unit mass of the fluid receives an energy increase of $\frac{1}{2}(V_s^2 - V^2)$ on passing through the disc. Thus the rate of increase of energy of the fluid in the system, dE/dt, is given by

$$\frac{dE}{dt} = \rho S V_0 \cdot \frac{1}{2}(V_s^2 - V^2)$$

$$= \frac{1}{2}\rho S V_0(V_s^2 - V^2) \quad . \quad . \quad . \quad (7.11)$$

This rate of increase of energy of the fluid is, in fact, the power supplied to the actuator disc.

If it is now imagined that the disc is moving from right to left at speed V into initially stationary fluid, useful work is done at the rate TV. Thus the efficiency of the disc as a propulsive system is

$$\eta_i = \frac{TV}{\frac{1}{2}\rho S V_0(V_s^2 - V^2)}$$

Substituting for T from eqn. (7.3) gives

$$\eta_i = \frac{\rho S V_0(V_s - V)V}{\frac{1}{2}\rho S V_0(V_s^2 - V^2)}$$

$$= \frac{V}{\frac{1}{2}(V_s + V)} \quad . \quad . \quad . \quad (7.12)$$

This is the 'ideal propulsive efficiency' or the 'Froude efficiency' of the propulsive system.

In practice the part of the ideal actuator disc would be played by the airscrew or jet engine, which will violate some or all of the assumptions made. Each departure from the ideal assumed will lead to a reduction in efficiency, and thus the efficiency of a practical propulsive system will always be less than the Froude efficiency as calculated for an ideal disc of the same area producing the same thrust under the same conditions.

Eqn. (7.12) may be treated to give several different expressions for the efficiency, each of which has its own merit and use. Thus

$$\eta_i = \frac{V}{\frac{1}{2}(V_s + V)}$$

$$= \frac{2}{1 + (V_s/V)} \quad . \quad . \quad . \quad (7.12.1)$$

$$= \frac{V}{V_0} \quad . \quad . \quad . \quad . \quad (7.12.2)$$

$$= \frac{1}{1 + a} \quad . \quad . \quad . \quad . \quad (7.12.3)$$

Also, since useful power $= TV$, and the efficiency is V/V_0, the power supplied is

$$P = \frac{TV}{V/V_0} = TV_0 \qquad . \qquad . \qquad . \qquad (7.13)$$

Of particular interest is eqn. (7.12.1). This shows that, for a given flight speed V, the efficiency decreases with increasing V_s. Now the thrust is obtained by accelerating a mass of air. Consider two extreme cases. In the first a large mass of air is affected (i.e., the diameter of the disc is large). Then the required increase in speed of the air is small, so V_s/V differs little from unity, and the efficiency is relatively high. In the second case a disc of small diameter affects a small mass of air, requiring a large increase in speed to give the same thrust. Thus V_s/V is large, leading to a low efficiency. Therefore to achieve a given thrust at a high efficiency it is necessary to use the largest practicable actuator disc.

An airscrew does, in fact, affect a relatively large mass of air, and therefore has a high propulsive efficiency. A simple turbo-jet or ram-jet, on the other hand, is closer to the second extreme considered above, and consequently has a poor propulsive efficiency. However, at high forward speeds compressibility causes a marked reduction in the efficiency of a practical airscrew, when the advantage shifts to the jet engine. It was to improve the propulsive efficiency of the turbo-jet engine that the by-pass or turbo-fan type of engine was introduced. In this form of engine only part of the air taken is fully compressed and passed through the combustion chambers and turbines. The remainder is slightly compressed and ducted round the combustion chambers. It is then exhausted at a relatively low speed, producing thrust at a fairly high propulsive efficiency. The air which passed through the combustion chambers is ejected at high speed, producing thrust at a comparatively low efficiency. The overall propulsive efficiency is thus slightly greater than that of a simple turbo-jet engine giving the same thrust. The turbo-prop engine is, in effect, an extreme form of by-pass engine in which nearly all the thrust is obtained at high efficiency.

Another very useful equation in this theory may be obtained by expressing eqn. (7.3) in a different form.

Since $\qquad V_0 = V(1 + a) \quad$ and $\quad V_s = V(1 + 2a)$

then $\qquad T = \rho S V_0 (V_s - V) = \rho S V (1 + a)[V(1 + 2a) - V]$

$$= 2\rho S V^2 a(1 + a) \qquad . \qquad . \qquad . \qquad . \qquad . \qquad . \qquad (7.14)$$

Example 7.1. An airscrew is required to produce a thrust of 1000 lb at a flight speed of 400 ft/sec at sea-level. If the diameter is 8 ft, estimate the minimum power which must be supplied, on the basis of Froude's theory.

$$T = 2\rho S V^2 a(1 + a)$$

i.e., $\qquad\qquad a + a^2 = \dfrac{T}{2\rho S V^2}.$

Now $T = 1000$ lb, $V = 400$ ft/sec and $S = \dfrac{\pi}{4}(8^2) = 16\pi$ ft^2.

Thus $\qquad\qquad a + a^2 = \dfrac{1000 \times 420\cdot5}{32\pi \times 160{,}000} = 0\cdot0262$

whence $\qquad\qquad\qquad a = 0\cdot0256$

Then the ideal efficiency is

$$\eta_i = \frac{1}{1\cdot0256}$$

$$\text{useful power} = \frac{TV}{550} = 728 \text{ T.H.P.}$$

Therefore minimum power supplied, P, is given by

$$P = 728 \times 1\cdot0256 = \underline{745 \text{ B.H.P.}}$$

The actual power required by a practical airscrew would probably be about 15% greater than this, i.e., about 850 B.H.P.

Example 7.2. A pair of airscrews are placed in tandem, at a streamwise spacing sufficient to eliminate mutual interference. The rear airscrew is of such a diameter that it just fills the slipstream of the front airscrew. Using the simple momentum theory calculate

(i) the efficiency of the combination and
(ii) the efficiency of the rear airscrew

if the front airscrew has a Froude efficiency of 90%, and if both airscrews deliver the same thrust. (U. of L.)

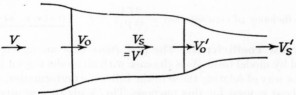

FIG. 7.2.—Actuator discs in tandem.

For the front airscrew, $\quad \eta_i = 0\cdot90 = \frac{9}{10}$

$$\therefore \quad \frac{1}{1+a} = \tfrac{9}{10}; \quad 1+a = \tfrac{10}{9}; \quad a = \tfrac{1}{9}$$

Thus $\qquad\qquad V_0 = V(1+a) = \tfrac{10}{9}V$

and $\qquad\qquad V_s = V(1+2a) = \tfrac{11}{9}V$

The thrust of the front airscrew is

$$T = \rho S_1 V_0(V_s - V) = \rho S_1(\tfrac{10}{9}V)(\tfrac{2}{9}V)$$
$$= \tfrac{20}{81}\rho S_1 V^2$$

The second airscrew is working entirely in the slipstream of the first. Therefore the speed of the approaching flow is V_s, namely $\tfrac{11}{9}V$.

The thrust is

$$T = \rho S_2 V_0'(V_s' - V') = \rho S_2 V_0'(V_s' - V_s)$$

Now, by continuity,

$$\rho S_2 V_0' = \rho S_1 V_0$$

and also the thrusts from the two airscrews are equal. Therefore

$$T = \rho S_1 V_0(V_s - V) = \rho S_2 V_0'(V_s' - V')$$
$$= \rho S_1 V_0(V_s' - V_s)$$

whence $V_s - V = V_s' - V_s$

i.e., $V_s' = 2V_s - V = (\frac{22}{9} - 1)V = \frac{13}{9}V$

Then, if the rate of mass flow through the discs is $\dot{m}$ slug/sec,

thrust of rear airscrew $= \dot{m}(V_s' - V_s) = \dot{m}(\frac{13}{9} - \frac{11}{9})V = \frac{2}{9}\dot{m}V$

The useful power given by the second airscrew is TV, not TV_s, and therefore:

useful power from 2nd airscrew $= \frac{2}{9}\dot{m}V^2$

Kinetic energy added per second by the second airscrew, which is the power supplied by (and to) the second disc, is

$$\frac{dE}{dt} = P = \tfrac{1}{2}\dot{m}(V_s'^2 - V_s^2) = \tfrac{1}{2}\dot{m}(\tfrac{169}{81} - \tfrac{121}{81})V^2 = \tfrac{8}{27}\dot{m}V^2$$

Thus the efficiency of the rear component is

$$= \frac{\frac{2}{9}\dot{m}V^2}{\frac{8}{27}\dot{m}V^2} = 0.75, \text{ or } 75\%.$$

$$\text{power input to front airscrew} = \frac{TV}{0.90}$$

$$\text{power input to rear airscrew} = \frac{TV}{0.75}$$

Therefore

the total power input $= (\frac{10}{9} + \frac{4}{3})TV = \frac{22}{9}TV.$

total useful power output $= 2TV$

Therefore

$$\text{efficiency of combination} = \frac{2TV}{\frac{22}{9}TV} = \tfrac{9}{11} = \underline{0.818, \text{ or } 81.8\%.}$$

7.2. Airscrew coefficients.

The performance of an airscrew may be determined by model tests. As is the case with all model tests it is necessary to find some way of relating these to the full-scale performance, and dimensional analysis is used for this purpose. This leads to a number of coefficients, analogous to the lift and drag coefficients of a body. These coefficients also serve as a very convenient way of presenting airscrew performance data, which may be calculated by blade element theory (§ 7.4), for use in aircraft design.

7.2.1. Thrust coefficient.

Consider an airscrew of diameter D ft revolving at n revolutions per second, driven by a torque Q lb ft, and giving a thrust of T lb. The characteristics of the fluid are defined by its density, ρ slug/ft³, its viscosity ν ft²/sec, and its modulus of bulk elasticity, K lb/ft². The forward speed of the airscrew is V ft/sec. It is then assumed that

$$T = h(D; n; \rho; \nu; K; V)$$
$$= CD^a n^b \rho^c \nu^d K^e V^f \quad . \quad . \quad . \quad (7.15)$$

Then, putting this in dimensional form,

$$[MLT^{-2}] = [(L)^a(T)^{-b}(ML^{-3})^c(L^2T^{-1})^d(ML^{-1}T^{-2})^e(LT^{-1})^f]$$

Separating this into the three fundamental equations gives

(M)	$1 = c + e$
(L)	$1 = a - 3c + 2d - e + f$
(T)	$2 = b + d + 2e + f$

Solving these three equations for a, b and c in terms of d, e and f gives

$$a = 4 - 2e - 2d - f$$
$$b = 2 - d - 2e - f$$
$$c = 1 - e$$

Substituting these in eqn. (7.15) gives

$$T = C . D^{4-2e-2d-f} n^{2-d-2e-f} \rho^{1-e} \nu^d K^e V^f$$

$$= C . \rho n^2 D^4 \left\{ \left(\frac{\nu}{D^2 n} \right)^d \left(\frac{K}{\rho D^2 n^2} \right)^e \left(\frac{V}{nD} \right) \right\}^f \qquad . \qquad . \qquad (7.16)$$

Consider the three factors within the vinculae.

(i) $\dfrac{\nu}{D^2 n}$. The product Dn is a multiple of the rotational component of the blade tip speed, and thus the complete factor is of the form $\dfrac{\nu}{\text{length} \times \text{velocity}}$, and is therefore of the form of the reciprocal of a Reynolds number. Thus ensuring equality of Reynolds numbers as between model and full scale will take care of this term.

(ii) $\dfrac{K}{\rho D^2 n^2}$. $\dfrac{K}{\rho} = a^2$, where a is the speed of sound in the fluid. As noted above, Dn is related to the blade tipspeed and therefore the complete factor is related to (speed of sound/velocity)^2, i.e., it is related to the tip Mach number. Therefore care in matching the tip Mach number in model test and full-scale flight will allow for this factor.

(iii) $\dfrac{V}{nD}$. V is the forward speed of the airscrew, and therefore V/n is the distance advanced per revolution. Then V/nD is this advance per revolution expressed as a multiple of the airscrew diameter, and is known as the 'advance ratio', denoted by J.

Thus eqn. (7.16) may be written as

$$T = C . \rho n^2 D^4 \, \text{h}(\text{R}; M; J) \qquad . \qquad . \qquad . \qquad (7.17)$$

The constant C and the factor $\text{h}(\text{R}; M; J)$ are usually collected together, and denoted by k_T, the thrust coefficient. Thus finally,

$$T = k_T \rho n^2 D^4 \qquad . \qquad . \qquad . \qquad . \qquad (7.18)$$

k_T being a dimensionless quantity dependent on the airscrew design, and on R, M and J. This dependence may be found experimentally, or by the more advanced blade element theory.

7.2.2. Torque coefficient. The torque Q is a force multiplied by a length, and it follows that a rational expression for the torque is

$$Q = k_Q \rho n^2 D^5 \qquad . \qquad . \qquad . \qquad . \qquad (7.19)$$

k_Q being the torque coefficient which, like k_T, depends on the airscrew design and on R, M and J.

7.2.3. Efficiency. The power supplied to an airscrew is P_{in} where

$$P_{\text{in}} = 2\pi n Q$$

while the useful power output is P_{out} where

$$P_{\text{out}} = TV$$

Therefore the airscrew efficiency, η, is given by

$$\eta = \frac{TV}{2\pi n Q} = \frac{k_T \rho n^2 D^4 V}{k_Q \rho n^2 D^5 . 2\pi n}$$

$$= \frac{1}{2\pi}\frac{k_T}{k_Q}\frac{V}{nD} = \frac{1}{2\pi}\frac{k_T}{k_Q}J \qquad . \qquad . \qquad . \qquad (7.20)$$

7.2.4. Power coefficient. The power required to drive an airscrew is

$$P = 2\pi n Q = 2\pi n(k_Q \rho n^2 D^5) \text{ ft lb/sec}$$

$$= \tfrac{1}{550}(2\pi k_Q \rho n^3 D^5) \text{ B.H.P.} \qquad . \qquad . \qquad . \qquad (7.21)$$

The power coefficient, C_p, is then defined by

$$P = \tfrac{1}{550} C_p \rho n^3 D^5 \qquad . \qquad . \qquad . \qquad (7.22)$$

i.e.,

$$C_p = \frac{550P}{\rho n^3 D^5} . \qquad . \qquad . \qquad . \qquad (7.22.1)$$

By comparison of eqns. (7.21) and (7.22) it is seen that

$$C_p = 2\pi k_Q \qquad . \qquad . \qquad . \qquad . \qquad (7.22.2)$$

Then, from eqn. (7.20), the efficiency of the airscrew is

$$\eta = J\left(\frac{k_T}{C_p}\right) \qquad . \qquad . \qquad . \qquad (7.23)$$

7.2.5. Activity factor. This is a measure of the power-absorbing capacity of the airscrew, which, for optimum performance, must be accurately matched to the power produced by the engine.

Consider an airscrew of diameter D ft rotating at n revs/sec with zero forward speed, and consider in particular an element of the blade at a radius of r ft, the chord of the element being c ft. The airscrew will, in general, produce a thrust and therefore there will be a finite speed of flow through the disc. Let this inflow be ignored, however. Then the motion and forces on the element are as shown (Fig. 7.3).

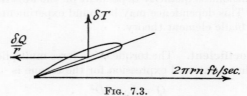

δT

$\dfrac{\delta Q}{r}$

$2\pi rn$ ft/sec.

FIG. 7.3.

$$\frac{\delta Q}{r} = C_D \tfrac{1}{2}\rho(2\pi rn)^2 c \,\delta r$$

and therefore the torque associated with the element is

$$\delta Q = 2\pi^2 \rho C_D n^2(cr^3)\,\delta r$$

It is further assumed that C_D is constant for all blade sections. This will not normally be true, since much of the blade will be stalled. However, within the accuracy required by the concept of Activity Factor, this assumption is acceptable. Then the total torque required to drive an airscrew with B blades is

$$Q = 2\pi^2 \rho C_D B n^2 \int_{root}^{tip} cr^3 \,dr$$

Thus the power absorbed by the airscrew under static conditions is approximately

$$P = 2\pi nQ = 4\pi^3 \rho C_D B n^3 \int_{root}^{tip} cr^3 \,dr$$

In a practical airscrew the blade roots are usually shielded by a spinner, and the lower limit of the integral is, by convention, changed from zero (the root) to $0 \cdot 1D$. Thus

$$P = 4\pi^3 \rho C_D B n^3 \int_{0 \cdot 1D}^{0 \cdot 5D} cr^3 \,dr$$

Defining the Activity Factor (A.F.) as

$$\text{A.F.} = \frac{10^5}{D^5} \int_{0 \cdot 1D}^{0 \cdot 5D} cr^3 \,dr$$

leads to

$$P = 4\pi^3 \rho C_D B n^3 \left(\frac{D}{10}\right)^5 \times (\text{A.F.})$$

Further work on the topic of airscrew coefficients is most conveniently done by means of Examples.

Example 7.3. An airscrew of 11 ft diameter has the following characteristics:

J . . .	1·06	1·19	1·34	1·44
k_Q . .	0·0410	0·0400	0·0378	0·0355
η . . .	0·76	0·80	0·84	0·86

Calculate the forward speed at which it will absorb 1000 B.H.P. at 1250 r.p.m at 12,000 ft ($\sigma = 0 \cdot 693$) and the thrust under these conditions. Compare the efficiency of the airscrew with that of the ideal actuator disc of the same area, giving the same thrust under the same conditions.

$$\text{B.H.P.} = \frac{2\pi nQ}{550}$$

$$\therefore \text{ torque } Q = \frac{550 \times 1000 \times 60}{2\pi \times 1250} = 4200 \text{ lb ft}$$

$$n = \frac{1250}{60} = 20 \cdot 83 \text{ r.p.s}; \quad n^2 = 435 \text{ sec}^{-2}$$

$$\therefore \ k_Q = \frac{Q}{\rho n^2 D^5} = \frac{4200 \times 420 \cdot 5}{0 \cdot 639 \times 435 \times (1 \cdot 1)^5 \times 10^5}$$

$$= 0 \cdot 0365$$

Plotting the given values of k_Q and η against J shows that, for $k_Q = 0 \cdot 0365$, $J = 1 \cdot 40$ and $\eta = 0 \cdot 851$. Now $J = V/nD$, and therefore

$$V = JnD = 1 \cdot 40 \times 20 \cdot 83 \times 11$$

$$= 321 \ \text{ft/sec.}$$

Since the efficiency is $0 \cdot 851$ (or $85 \cdot 1\%$), the thrust horse-power is

$$\text{T.H.P.} = \text{B.H.P. effy.} = 1000 \times 0 \cdot 851 = 851 \ \text{H.P.}$$

Therefore the thrust is

$$T = \frac{550 \ \text{T.H.P.}}{V} = \frac{550 \times 851}{321}$$

$$= 1460 \ \text{lb.}$$

For the ideal actuator disc

$$a(1 + a) = \frac{T}{2\rho SV^2} = \frac{1460 \times 420 \cdot 5}{2 \times 0 \cdot 693 \times \dfrac{\pi}{4}(11)^2 \times (284)^2}$$

$$= 0 \cdot 058$$

whence $\qquad\qquad a = 0 \cdot 055$

Thus the ideal efficiency is

$$\eta_i = \frac{1}{1 \cdot 055} = 0 \cdot 945, \ \text{or} \ 94 \cdot 5\%.$$

Thus the efficiency of the practical airscrew is $(0 \cdot 851/0 \cdot 945)$ of that of the ideal actuator disc. Therefore the relative efficiency of the practical airscrew is $0 \cdot 901$, or $90 \cdot 1\%$.

Example 7.4. An aeroplane is powered by a single engine whose speed-power characteristic is

Speed (r.p.m) . . .	1800	1900	2000	2100
Power (B.H.P.) . . .	1430	1493	1550	1594

The fixed-pitch airscrew of 10 ft diameter has the following characteristics:

J	0·40	0·42	0·44	0·46	0·48	0·50
k_T	0·118	0·115	0·112	0·109	0·106	0·103
k_Q	0·0157	0·0154	0·0150	0·0145	0·0139	0·0132

and is directly coupled to the engine crankshaft.

What will be the airscrew thrust and efficiency during the initial climb at sea-level, when the aircraft speed is 150 ft/sec?

Preliminary calculations required are:

$$Q = k_Q \rho n^2 D^5 = 237 \cdot 8 \ k_Q n^2$$

after using the appropriate values for ρ and D.

$$J = \frac{V}{nD} = \frac{15}{n}$$

The power required to drive the airscrew, B.H.P$_r$, is

$$\mathrm{B.H.P}_r = \frac{2\pi n Q}{550} = \frac{nQ}{86 \cdot 5}$$

With these expressions, the following table may be calculated:

r.p.m	1800	1900	2000	2100
B.H.P$_a$ . . .	1430	1493	1550	1594
n (r.p.s) . . .	30·00	31·67	33·33	35·00
n^2	900	1003	1115	1225
J	0·500	0·474	0·450	0·429
k_Q	0·01320	0·01410	0·01475	0·01523
Q	2820	3360	3900	4440
B.H.P$_r$ . . .	979	1230	1501	1794

In this table B.H.P$_a$ is the brake horse-power available from the engine, as given in the data, while the values of k_Q for the calculated values of J are read from a graph.

A graph is now plotted of B.H.P$_a$ and B.H.P$_r$ against r.p.m, the intersection of the two curves giving the equilibrium condition. This is found to be at a rotational speed of 2019 r.p.m, i.e., $n = 33 \cdot 65$ r.p.s.

For this value of n, $J = 0 \cdot 445$ giving $k_T = 0 \cdot 11125$ and $k_Q = 0 \cdot 01486$. Then

$$T = 0 \cdot 11125 \times 0 \cdot 002378 \times (33 \cdot 65)^2 \times 10^4$$
$$= 2990 \text{ lb}$$

and

$$\eta = \frac{1}{2\pi} \frac{k_T}{k_Q} J = \frac{1}{2\pi} \frac{0 \cdot 11125}{0 \cdot 01486} (0 \cdot 445)$$

$$= 0 \cdot 53, \text{ or } 53\%.$$

As a check on the correctness and accuracy of this result, note that

$$\text{T.H.P.} = \frac{TV}{550} = \frac{3080 \times 150}{550} = \underline{815}.$$

At 2019 r.p.m the engine produces 1557 B.H.P (from engine data), and therefore the efficiency is $815 \times 100/1557 = 52 \cdot 5\%$, which is in satisfactory agreement with the earlier result.

7.3. Airscrew pitch.

By analogy with screw threads, the pitch of an airscrew is 'the advance per revolution'. This definition, as it stands, is of little use vis-à-vis airscrews. Consider two extreme cases. If the airscrew is turning at, say, 2000 r.p.m while the aircraft is stationary, the advance per revolution is zero. If, on the other hand, the aircraft is gliding with the engine stopped the advance per revolution is infinite. Thus the 'pitch' of an airscrew can take any value and is therefore useless as a term describing the airscrew. To overcome this difficulty two more definite measures of airscrew pitch are accepted.

7.3.1. Geometric pitch.

Consider the blade section shown in Fig. 7.4, at radius r from the airscrew axis. The broken line is the zero-lift line of the section, i.e., the direction relative to the section of the undisturbed stream when the section gives no lift. Then the geometric pitch of the element is $2\pi r \tan \theta$. This is the pitch of a screw of radius r and helix angle

(90 — θ) degrees. This geometric pitch is frequently constant for all sections of a given airscrew. In some cases, however, the geometric pitch varies from section to section of the blade. In such cases the geometric pitch of that section at 70% of the airscrew radius is taken, and called the geometric mean pitch.

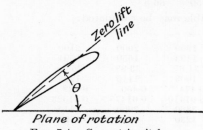

FIG. 7.4.—Geometric pitch.

The geometric pitch is seen to depend solely on the geometry of the blades. It is thus a definite length for a given airscrew, and does not depend on the precise conditions of operation at any instant, though many airscrews are variable in pitch (see § 7.3.3).

7.3.2. Experimental mean pitch. This is defined as 'the advance per revolution when the airscrew is producing zero nett thrust'. It is thus a suitable parameter for experimental measurement on an existing airscrew. Like the geometric pitch, it has a definite value for any given airscrew, provided the conditions of test approximate reasonably well to practical flight conditions.

7.3.3. Effect of geometric pitch on airscrew performance. Consider two airscrews differing only in the helix angles of the blades and let the blade sections at, say, 70% radius be as drawn in Fig. 7.5. That of Fig. 7.5 (a) has a 'fine' pitch, while that of Fig. 7.5 (b) has a 'coarse' pitch. When the aircraft is at rest, e.g., at the start of the take-off run, the air velocity relative to the blade section is the resultant V_R of the velocity due to rotation, $2\pi nr$, and the inflow velocity, V_{in}. The blade section of the fine pitch airscrew is seen to be working at a reasonable incidence, and the lift δL will be large, and the drag δD will be small. Thus the thrust δT will be large and the torque δQ small, and the airscrew is working efficiently. The section of the coarse pitch airscrew, on the other hand, is stalled and therefore gives little lift and much drag. Thus the thrust is small and the torque large, and the airscrew is inefficient.

At high flight speeds the situation is much changed, as shown in Fig. 7.5 (c) and (d). Here the section of the coarse pitch airscrew is working efficiently, whereas the fine pitch airscrew is now giving a negative thrust, a situation which might arise in a steep dive.

Thus an airscrew which has a pitch suitable for low-speed flight and take-off is liable to have a poor performance at high forward speeds, and vice versa. This was one factor which limited aircraft performance in the early days of flight.

A great advance was achieved consequent on the development of the two-pitch airscrew. This is an airscrew in which each blade may be rotated bodily, and set in either of two positions at will. One position gives a fine pitch for take-off and climb, while the other gives a coarse pitch for

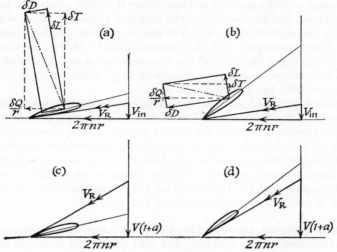

FIG. 7.5.—Effect of geometric pitch on airscrew performance.

cruising and high-speed flight. Consider Fig. 7.6 which shows typical variations of efficiency η with J for (a) a fine pitch and (b) a coarse pitch
airscrew.

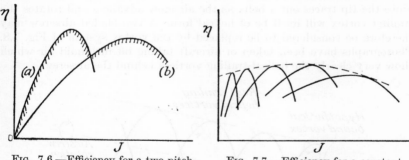

| FIG. 7.6.—Efficiency for a two-pitch airscrew. | FIG. 7.7.—Efficiency for a constant-speed airscrew. |

For low advance ratios, corresponding to take-off and low-speed flight,
the fine pitch is obviously better while for higher speeds the coarse pitch
is preferable. If the pitch may be varied at will between these two values
the overall performance attainable is as given by the hatched line, which
is clearly better than that attainable from either pitch separately.

Subsequent research led to the development of the constant-speed airscrew in which the blade pitch is infinitely variable between pre-determined
limits. A mechanism in the airscrew hub varies the pitch to keep the engine
speed constant, permitting the engine to work at its most efficient speed.
The pitch variations also result in the airscrew working close to its maximum efficiency at all times. Fig. 7.7 shows the variation of efficiency with

J for a number of the possible settings. Since the blade pitch may take any value between the curves drawn, the airscrew efficiency varies with J as shown by the dashed curve, which is the envelope of all the separate η,J curves. The requirement that the airscrew shall be always working at its optimum efficiency while absorbing the power produced by the engine at the pre-determined constant speed calls for very skilful design in matching the airscrew with the engine.

The constant-speed airscrew, in turn, led to the provision of 'feathering' and reverse-thrust facilities. In feathering, the geometric pitch is made so large that the blade sections are almost parallel to the direction of flight. This is used to reduce drag and to prevent the airscrew turning the engine (windmilling) in the event of engine failure. For reverse thrust, the geo-metric pitch is made negative, enabling the airscrew to give a negative thrust to supplement the brakes during the landing ground run, and also to assist in manœuvring the aircraft on the ground.

7.4. Blade element theory.

This theory permits direct calculation of the performance of an airscrew, and also the design of an airscrew to achieve a given performance.

7.4.1. The vortex system of an airscrew.

An airscrew blade is a form of lifting aerofoil, and as such may be replaced by a hypothetical bound vortex. In addition a trailing vortex is shed from the tip of each blade. Since the tip traces out a helix as the airscrew advances and rotates the trailing vortex will itself be of helical form. A two-bladed airscrew may therefore be considered to be replaced by the vortex system of Fig. 7.8. Photographs have been taken of aircraft taking off in humid air which show very clearly the helical trailing vortices behind the airscrew.

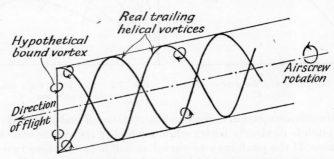

FIG. 7.8.—Simplified vortex system for a two-bladed airscrew.

Rotational Interference. The slipstream behind an airscrew is found to be rotating, in the same sense as the blades, about the airscrew axis. This rotation is due in part to the circulation round the blades (the hypothetical bound vortex) and the remainder is induced by the helical trailing vortices. Consider three planes; plane (i) immediately ahead of the airscrew blades; plane (ii), the plane of the airscrew blades; and plane (iii) immediately behind the blades. Ahead of the airscrew, in plane (i) the angular velocity of the flow is zero. Thus in this plane the effects of the bound and trailing vortices exactly cancel each other. In plane (ii) the angular velocity of the flow is due entirely to the trailing vortices, since the bound vortices cannot produce an angular velocity in their own plane. In plane (iii) the angular velocity due to the bound vortices is equal in magnitude and opposite in sense to that in plane (i), and the effects of the trailing and bound vortices are now additive.

Let the angular velocity of the airscrew blades be Ω rads/sec, the angular velocity of the flow in the plane of the blades be $b\Omega$, and the angular velocity induced by the bound vortices in planes ahead of and behind the disc be $\pm\beta\Omega$ (this assumes that these planes are equidistant from the airscrew disc). It is assumed that the distance between these planes is small so that the effect of the trailing vortices at the three planes is practically constant. Then, ahead of the airscrew (plane i)

$$(b - \beta)\Omega = 0$$

i.e.,
$$b = \beta$$

Behind the airscrew (plane iii), if ω is the angular velocity of the flow

$$\omega = (b + \beta)\Omega = 2b\Omega$$

Thus the angular velocity of the flow behind the airscrew is twice the angular velocity in the plane of the airscrew. The similarity between this result and that for the axial velocity in the simple momentum theory should be noted.

7.4.2. The performance of a blade element.

Consider an element, of length δr and chord c, at radius r of an airscrew blade. This element has a speed in the plane of rotation of Ωr ft/sec. The flow is itself rotating in the same plane and sense at $b\Omega$ rads/sec, and thus the speed of the element relative to the air in this plane is $\Omega r(1 - b)$ ft/sec. If the airscrew is advancing at a speed of V ft/sec the velocity through the disc is $V(1 + a)$ ft/sec, a being the inflow factor at the radius r. (Note that in this theory it is not necessary for a and b to be constant over the disc.) Then the total velocity of the flow relative to the blade is V_R as shown in Fig. 7.9.

If the line CC' represents the zero-lift line of the blade section then θ is, by definition, the geometric helix angle of the element, related to the geometric pitch, and α is the absolute angle of incidence of the section. The element will therefore experience lift and drag forces, respectively perpendicular and parallel to the relative velocity V_R, appropriate to the absolute incidence α. The values of C_L and C_D will be those for a two-dimensional aerofoil of the appropriate section at absolute incidence α, since three-dimensional effects have been allowed for in the rotational interference term, $b\Omega$. This lift and drag may be resolved into components of thrust and 'torque-force' as in Fig. 7.9. Here δL is the lift and δD is the drag on the element. δR is the resultant aerodynamic force, making the angle γ with the lift vector. δR is resolved into components of thrust δT

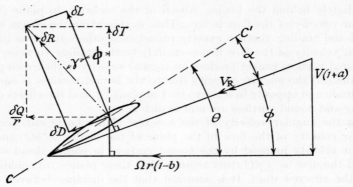

FIG. 7.9.—The general blade element.

and 'torque force' $\delta Q/r$, where δQ is the torque required to rotate the element about the airscrew axis.

Then
$$\tan \gamma = \frac{\delta D}{\delta L} = \frac{C_D}{C_L} \quad . \qquad . \qquad . \qquad . \qquad . \qquad (7.24)$$

$$V_R = V(1 + a) \operatorname{cosec} \phi = \Omega r(1 - b) \sec \phi \quad . \qquad (7.25)$$

$$\delta T = \delta R \cos (\phi + \gamma) \quad . \qquad . \qquad . \qquad . \qquad (7.26)$$

$$\frac{\delta Q}{r} = \delta R \sin (\phi + \gamma) \quad . \qquad . \qquad . \qquad . \qquad (7.27)$$

$$\tan \phi = \frac{V(1 + a)}{\Omega r(1 - b)} \quad . \qquad . \qquad . \qquad . \qquad (7.28)$$

The efficiency of the element, η_l, is the ratio useful power out/power input, i.e.,

$$\eta_l = \frac{V}{\Omega} \frac{\delta T}{\delta Q} = \frac{V \cos (\phi + \gamma)}{\Omega r \sin (\phi + \gamma)} \quad . \qquad . \qquad . \qquad (7.29)$$

Now from the triangle of velocities, and eqn. (7.28),

$$\frac{V}{\Omega r} = \frac{1 - b}{1 + a} \tan \phi$$

whence, by eqn. (7.29),

$$\eta_l = \frac{1 - b}{1 + a} \cdot \frac{\tan \phi}{\tan (\phi + \gamma)} \quad . \qquad . \qquad . \qquad (7.30)$$

Let the solidity of the annulus, σ, be defined as the ratio total area of blade in annulus/total area of annulus. Then

$$\sigma = \frac{Bc}{2\pi r} \frac{\delta r}{\delta r}$$

$$= \frac{Bc}{2\pi r} \quad . \qquad . \qquad . \qquad . \qquad . \qquad (7.31)$$

where B is the number of blades.

Now

$$\delta L = Bc \; \delta r . \tfrac{1}{2}\rho V_R^2 C_L \qquad . \qquad . \qquad . \qquad (7.32.1)$$

$$\delta D = Bc \; \delta r . \tfrac{1}{2}\rho V_R^2 C_D \qquad . \qquad . \qquad . \qquad (7.32.2)$$

From Fig. 7.9

$$\delta T = \delta L \cos \phi - \delta D \sin \phi$$

$$= Bc \; \delta r . \tfrac{1}{2}\rho V_R^2 (C_L \cos \phi - C_D \sin \phi)$$

Therefore
$$\frac{dT}{dr} = Bc . \tfrac{1}{2}\rho V_R^2 (C_L \cos \phi - C_D \sin \phi)$$

$$= 2\pi r \sigma . \tfrac{1}{2}\rho V_R^2 (C_L \cos \phi - C_D \sin \phi) \; . \qquad . \qquad (7.33)$$

Bearing in mind eqn. (7.24), eqn. (7.33) may be written as

$$\frac{dT}{dr} = \pi r \sigma \rho V_R^2 C_L (\cos \phi - \tan \gamma \sin \phi)$$

$$= \pi r \sigma \rho V_R^2 C_L \sec \gamma (\cos \phi \cos \gamma - \sin \phi \sin \gamma)$$

Now for moderate incidences of the blade section, $\tan \gamma$ is small, about 0·02 or so, i.e., $L/D \simeq 50$, and therefore $\sec \gamma \simeq 1$, when the above equation may be written as

$$\frac{dT}{dr} = \pi r \sigma \rho V_R^2 C_L \cos (\phi + \gamma)$$

Writing

$$t = C_L \cos (\phi + \gamma) \qquad . \qquad . \qquad . \qquad . \qquad (7.34)$$

Then

$$\frac{dT}{dr} = \pi r \sigma t \rho V_R^2 \text{ for the airscrew} \qquad . \qquad . \qquad . \qquad (7.35.1)$$

$$= Bc . \tfrac{1}{2}\rho V_R^2 t \text{ for the airscrew} \qquad . \qquad . \qquad (7.35.2)$$

$$= c . \tfrac{1}{2}\rho V_R^2 t \text{ per blade} \qquad . \qquad . \qquad . \qquad (7.35.3$$

Similarly

$$\frac{\delta Q}{r} = \delta L \sin \phi + \delta D \cos \phi$$

whence
$$\frac{dQ}{dr} = 2\pi r^2 \sigma . \tfrac{1}{2}\rho V_R^2 (C_L \sin \phi + C_D \cos \phi)$$

Writing now
$$q = C_L \sin (\phi + \gamma) \qquad . \qquad . \qquad . \qquad . \qquad (7.36)$$

leads to
$$\frac{dQ}{dr} = \pi r^2 \sigma q \rho V_R^2 \text{ total} \qquad . \qquad . \qquad . \qquad . \qquad (7.37.1)$$

$$= Bcr . \tfrac{1}{2}\rho V_R^2 q \text{ total} \; . \qquad . \qquad . \qquad . \qquad (7.37.2)$$

$$= cr . \tfrac{1}{2}\rho V_R^2 q \text{ per blade} \qquad . \qquad . \qquad . \qquad (7.37.3)$$

The quantities dT/dr and dQ/dr are known as the thrust grading and the torque grading respectively.

Consider now the axial momentum of the flow through the annulus.

I

The thrust δT is equal to the product of the rate of mass flow through the element with the change in the axial velocity, i.e., $\delta T = \dot{m}\delta V$.

Now $\dot{m} = $ area of annulus $\times$ velocity through annulus $\times$ density

$$= (2\pi r\ \delta r)\{V(1 + a)\}\rho$$
$$= 2\pi r\rho\ \delta r\ V(1 + a)$$
$$\Delta V = V_s - V = V(1 + 2a) - V = 2aV$$

whence $\delta T = 2\pi r\rho\ \delta r\ V^2.2a(1 + a)$
giving

$$\frac{dT}{dr} = 4\pi\rho r V^2.a\,(1 + a) \quad . \qquad . \qquad . \qquad (7.38)$$

Equating eqns. (7.38) and (7.35.1) leads to, using also eqn. (7.25),

$$4\pi\rho r V^2 a(1 + a) = \pi r\sigma t\rho V^2(1 + a)^2 \cosec^2 \phi$$

whence $\dfrac{a}{1 + a} = \tfrac{1}{4}\sigma t \cosec^2 \phi \quad . \qquad . \qquad . \qquad (7.39)$

In the same way, by considering the angular momentum

$$\delta Q = \dot{m}\Delta\omega r^2$$

where $\Delta\omega$ is the change in angular velocity of the air on passing through the airscrew. Then

$$\delta Q = (2\pi r\ \delta r)[\rho V(1 + a)](2b\Omega)r^2$$
$$= 4\pi r^3\rho Vb(1 + a)\Omega\ \delta r \quad . \qquad . \qquad . \qquad (7.40)$$

whence $\dfrac{\delta Q}{dr} = 4\pi r^3\rho Vb(1 + a)\Omega \quad . \qquad . \qquad . \qquad . \qquad (7.41)$

Now, as derived previously (eqn. (7.37.1)),

$$\frac{dQ}{dr} = \pi r^2\sigma q\rho V_R^2\ . \qquad . \qquad . \qquad . \qquad (7.37.1)$$

Substituting for V_R both expressions of eqn. (7.25), this becomes

$$\frac{dQ}{dr} = \pi r^2\sigma\rho[V(1 + a) \cosec \phi][\Omega r(1 - b) \sec \phi]q$$

Equating this expression for dQ/dr to that of eqn. (7.41) gives after some simple manipulation

$$\frac{b}{1 - b} = \tfrac{1}{4}\sigma q \cosec \phi \sec \phi$$

$$= \tfrac{1}{2}\sigma q \cosec 2\phi\ . \qquad . \qquad . \qquad . \qquad (7.42)$$

The local efficiency of the blade at the element, η_l is found as follows.

$$\text{Useful power output} = V\ \delta T = V\frac{dT}{dr}\ \delta r$$

$$\text{Power input} = 2\pi n\ \delta Q = 2\pi n\frac{dQ}{dr}\delta r$$

$$\therefore \; \eta_l = \frac{V}{2\pi n} \frac{dT/dr}{dQ/dr}$$

$$= \frac{V}{2\pi n} \frac{2\pi r \sigma . \frac{1}{2}\rho V_R^2 t}{2\pi r^2 \sigma . \frac{1}{2}\rho V_R^2 q}$$

$$= \frac{V}{2\pi n r} \frac{t}{q} \qquad . \qquad . \qquad . \qquad . \qquad (7.43)$$

which is an alternative expression to eqn. (7.30).

With the expressions given above, dT/dr and dQ/dr may be evaluated at several radii of an airscrew blade given the blade geometry and section characteristics, the forward and rotational speeds, and the air density. Then, by plotting dT/dr and dQ/dr against the radius r and measuring the areas under the curves, the total thrust and torque per blade and for the whole airscrew may be estimated. In the design of a blade this is the usual first step. With the thrust and torque gradings known, the deflection and twist of the blade under load can be calculated. This furnishes new values of θ along the blade, and the process is repeated with these new values of θ. The iteration may be repeated until the desired accuracy is attained.

A further point to be noted is that portions of the blade towards the tip may attain appreciable Mach numbers, large enough for the effects of compressibility to become important. The principal effect of compressibility in this connection is its effect on the lift curve slope of the aerofoil section. Provided the Mach number of the relative flow does not exceed about 0·75, the effect on the lift curve slope may be approximated by the Prandtl–Glauert correction. This correction states that, if the lift curve slope at zero Mach number, i.e., in incompressible flow, is a_0 the lift curve slope at a subsonic Mach number M is a_M where

$$a_M = \frac{a_0}{\sqrt{1 - M^2}}$$

Provided the Mach number does not exceed about 0·75 as stated above, the effect of compressibility on the section drag is very small. If the Mach number of any part of the blade exceeds the value given above (though the exact value depends on the profile and thickness/chord ratio of the blade section) that part of the blade loses lift while its drag rises sharply, leading to a very marked loss in overall efficiency and increase in noise.

Research has been conducted on airscrews, the blades of which are supersonic at all radii, but such supersonic airscrews have not, as yet, been used in practice.

Example 7.5. At 4 ft radius on an airscrew of $11\frac{1}{4}$ ft diameter the local chord of each of the four blades is 10 in. and the geometric pitch is $14\frac{1}{2}$ ft. The lift curve slope of the blade section in incompressible flow is 0·1 per degree, and the lift/drag ratio may, as an approximation, be taken to be constant at 50. Estimate the thrust and torque gradings and the local efficiency in flight at 15,000 ft ($\sigma = 0.629$, temperature $= -14.7°C$), at a flight speed of 220 ft/sec. T.A.S. and a rotational speed of 1500 r.p.m.

The solution of this problem is essentially a process of successive approximation to the values of a and b.

$$\text{solidity } \sigma = \frac{Bc}{2\pi r} = \frac{4 \times 10}{2\pi \times 4 \times 12} = 0\cdot1326$$

$$1500 \text{ r.p.m} = 25 \text{ r.p.s} = n$$
$$\tan \gamma = \tfrac{1}{50} \quad \text{whence} \quad \gamma = 1\cdot15°$$
$$\text{geometric pitch} = 2\pi r \tan \theta = 14\cdot5$$
whence
$$\tan \theta = 0\cdot577, \quad \theta = 30\cdot0°$$

$$\tan \phi = \frac{V(1 + a)}{\Omega r(1 - b)} = \frac{220(1 + a)}{200\pi(1 - b)}$$
$$= \frac{1\cdot1}{\pi} \cdot \frac{1 + a}{1 - b}$$

$$\text{speed of sound in atmosphere} = 65\cdot9(273 - 14\cdot7)^{\frac{1}{2}}$$
$$= 1058 \text{ ft/sec}$$

Suitable values for initial guesses for a and b are $a = 0\cdot1$, $b = 0\cdot02$. Then

$$\tan \phi = \frac{1\cdot1}{\pi} \cdot \frac{1\cdot1}{0\cdot98} = 0\cdot3935$$
whence
$$\phi = 21\cdot48°, \quad \alpha = 30 - 21\cdot48 = 8\cdot52°$$
$$V_R = V(1 + a) \operatorname{cosec} \phi$$
$$= \frac{V(1 + a)}{\sin \phi} = \frac{220 \times 1\cdot1}{0\cdot3662} = 660\cdot0 \text{ ft/sec}$$
$$M = \tfrac{660}{1058} = 0\cdot625, \quad \sqrt{1 - M^2} = 0\cdot781$$
$$\therefore \frac{dC_L}{d\alpha} = \frac{0\cdot1}{0\cdot781} = 0\cdot128 \text{ per degree}$$

Since α is the absolute incidence, that is, the incidence from zero lift,

$$C_L = \alpha \frac{dC_L}{d\alpha} = 0\cdot128 \times 8\cdot52 = 1\cdot090$$

Then
$$q = C_L \sin(\phi + \gamma) \quad = 1\cdot09 \sin (21\cdot48 + 1\cdot15)°$$
$$= 0\cdot420$$

and
$$t = C_L \cos (\phi + \gamma) = 1\cdot090 \cos 22\cdot63°$$
$$= 1\cdot006$$

$$\frac{b}{1 - b} = \tfrac{1}{2}\sigma q \operatorname{cosec} 2\phi \quad = \frac{\sigma q}{2 \sin 2\phi}$$
$$= \frac{0\cdot1326 \times 0\cdot420}{2 \times 0\cdot68148} = 0\cdot0408$$

giving
$$b = \frac{0\cdot0408}{1\cdot0408} = 0\cdot0392$$

$$\frac{a}{1 + a} = \tfrac{1}{4}\sigma t \operatorname{cosec}^2 \phi = \frac{0\cdot1326 \times 1\cdot006}{4 \times 0\cdot3662 \times 0\cdot3662}$$
$$= 0\cdot2485$$

giving
$$a = \frac{0\cdot2485}{0\cdot7515} = 0\cdot330$$

Thus the assumed values $a = 0\cdot1$ and $b = 0\cdot02$ lead to the better approximations $a = 0\cdot330$ and $b = 0\cdot0392$, and a further iteration may be made using these values of a and b. Rather quicker approach to the final values of a and b may be made by using, as the initial values for an iteration, the arithmetic mean of the input and output values of the previous iteration. Thus, in the present Example, the values for the next iteration would be $a = 0·215$ and $b = 0·0296$. The use of the arithmetic mean is particularly convenient when giving instructions to computers (whether human or electronic).

The iteration process is continued until agreement to the desired accuracy is obtained between the assumed and derived values of a and b. When using a slide rule, the limit of accuracy is usually obtained after two iterations; if greater accuracy is desired, more advanced computers must be used. For the present problem this iteration was performed on the 'Pegasus' computer, the time taken being about two minutes for the iteration and the following calculations of the final results. The results of the iterations were:

$$a = 0·1953 \qquad b = 0·03118$$

to 4 significant figures (the computer actually gave agreement to about 6 sig. figs.). With these values for a and b substituted in the appropriate equations, the following results are obtained.

$$\phi = 0·4078 \text{ rads } = 23° \; 22'$$
$$\alpha = 0·1158 \text{ rads } = 6° \; 38'$$
$$\theta = \phi + \alpha = 30° \quad \text{as a check.}$$
$$V_R = 663·1 \text{ ft/sec} \quad M = 0·6267$$

giving
$$\frac{dT}{dr} = \tfrac{1}{2}\rho V_R^2 ct = \underline{212 \text{ lb/ft per blade.}}$$

and
$$\frac{dQ}{dr} = \tfrac{1}{2}\rho V_R^2 crq = \underline{387 \text{ lb ft/ft per blade}}$$

Thus the thrust grading for the whole airscrew is 848 lb/ft and the torque grading is 1548 lb ft/ft.

The local efficiency is
$$\eta_l = \frac{V}{2\pi nr}\frac{t}{q} = \underline{0·768, \text{ or } 76·8\%.}$$

7.5. The momentum theory applied to the helicopter rotor.
In most, but not all, states of helicopter flight the effect of the rotor may be approximated by replacing it by an ideal actuator disc to which the simple momentum theory applies. More specifically, momentum theory may be used for translational (i.e., forward, sideways or rearwards) flight, climb, slow descent under power, and hovering.

7.5.1. The actuator disc in hovering flight.
In steady hovering flight the speed of the oncoming stream well ahead of the disc is zero, while the thrust equals the helicopter weight (ignoring any downward force arising from the downflow from the rotor acting on the fuselage, etc.). If the weight is W lb, the rotor area A ft², and using the normal notation of the momentum theory, with ρ slug/ft³ as the air density

$$W = \rho A V_0 (V_s - V) = \rho A V_0 V_s \qquad . \qquad . \quad (7.44)$$

since $V = 0$.

The general momentum theory shows that

$$V_0 = \tfrac{1}{2}(V_s + V) \qquad . \qquad . \qquad . \quad (7.8)$$
$$= \tfrac{1}{2}V_s \quad \text{in this case} \qquad . \qquad . \quad (7.45)$$

or
$$V_s = 2V_0$$

which, substituted in eqn. (7.44), gives

$$W = 2\rho A V_0^2 \qquad \qquad \text{(7.46)}$$

i.e.,
$$V_0 = \sqrt{\frac{W}{2\rho A}} \qquad \qquad \text{(7.47)}$$

Defining the 'effective disc loading', l_{de}, as

$$l_{de} = \frac{W}{A\sigma} \qquad \qquad \text{(7.48)}$$

where σ is the relative density of the atmosphere, then

$$\frac{W}{2\rho A} = \frac{W}{A\sigma} \frac{1}{2} \frac{\sigma}{\rho} = \frac{1}{2\rho_0} l_{de}$$

ρ_0 being sea-level standard density.

Then
$$V_0 = \sqrt{\frac{l_{de}}{2\rho_0}} \qquad \qquad \text{(7.49)}$$

The power supplied is equal to the rate of increase of kinetic energy of the air, i.e.,

$$P = \tfrac{1}{2}\rho A V_0(V_s^2 - V^2)$$
$$= \tfrac{1}{2}\rho V_0 V_s^2 A = 2\rho A V_0^3 \qquad \text{(7.50)}$$

Substituting for V_0 from eqn. (7.47) leads to

$$P = 2\rho A \left(\frac{W}{2\rho A}\right)^{\frac{3}{2}} = \sqrt{\frac{W^3}{2\rho A}} \text{ ft lb/sec} \qquad \text{(7.51.1)}$$

$$= W\sqrt{\frac{l_{de}}{2\rho_0}} \text{ ft lb/sec} \qquad \qquad \text{(7.51.2)}$$

$$= \frac{W}{550}\sqrt{\frac{l_{de}}{2\rho_0}} \text{ H.P.} \qquad \qquad \text{(7.51.3)}$$

This is the power which must be supplied to the ideal actuator disc; a real rotor would require a considerably greater power input.

7.5.2. Vertical climbing flight. The problem of vertical climbing flight is identical to that studied in § 7.1, with the thrust equal to the helicopter weight plus the air resistance of the fuselage, etc., to the vertical motion, and with the oncoming stream speed V equal to the rate of climb of the helicopter.

7.5.3. Slow, powered, descending flight. In this case the air approaches the rotor from below and has its momentum decreased on passing through the disc. The associated loss of kinetic energy of the air appears as a power input to the ideal actuator, which therefore acts as a windmill. A real rotor will, however, still require to be driven by the engine, unless the rate of descent is large. This case, for the ideal actuator disc, may be treated by the methods of § 7.1 with the appropriate changes in sign, i.e., V positive, $V_s < V_0 < V$, $p_1 > p_2$, and the thrust $T = -W$.

7.5.4. Translational helicopter flight.

It is assumed that the effect of the actuator disc used to approximate the rotor is to add incremental velocities v_v and v_h, vertically and horizontally respectively, at the disc. It is further assumed, in accordance with the simple axial momentum theory of § 7.1, that in the slipstream well behind the disc these incremental velocities increase to $2v_v$ and $2v_h$ respectively. The resultant speed through the disc is denoted by U and the resultant speed in the fully developed slipstream by U_1. Then, by considering vertical momentum,

$$W = \rho A U(2v_v) = 2\rho A U v_v \quad . \quad . \quad . \quad (7.52)$$

Also, from the vector addition of velocities,

$$U^2 = (V + v_h)^2 + (v_v)^2 \quad . \quad . \quad . \quad (7.53)$$

where V is the speed of horizontal flight.
By consideration of horizontal momentum

$$\tfrac{1}{2}\rho V^2 A C_D = 2\rho A U v_h \quad . \quad . \quad . \quad (7.54)$$

where C_D is the drag coefficient of the fuselage, etc., based on the rotor area A.

Power input = rate of increase of K.E., i.e.,

$$P = \tfrac{1}{2}\rho A U(U_1^2 - V^2) \quad . \quad . \quad . \quad (7.55)$$

while, from vector addition of velocities,

$$U_1^2 = (V + 2v_h)^2 + (2v_v)^2 \quad . \quad . \quad . \quad (7.56)$$

The most useful solution of the five equations eqn. (7.52) to eqn. (7.56) inclusive is obtained by eliminating U_1, v_h and v_v.

$$v_v = \frac{W}{2\rho A U} \quad . \quad . \quad . \quad . \quad (7.52.1)$$

$$v_h = \frac{\tfrac{1}{2}\rho V^2 A C_D}{2\rho A U} = \frac{C_D}{4U} V^2 \quad . \quad . \quad . \quad (7.54.1)$$

Then, from eqn. (7.53),

$$U^2 = V^2 + 2Vv_h + v_h^2 + v_v^2$$

Substituting for v_v and v_h, and multiplying by U^2 gives

$$U^4 - U^2 V^2 = \tfrac{1}{2}C_D U V^3 + \tfrac{1}{16}C_D^2 V^4 + \left(\frac{W}{2\rho A U}\right)^2$$

Introducing the effective disc loading, l_{de}, from eqn. (7.48) leads to

$$U^4 - U^2 V^2 - \tfrac{1}{2}C_D V^3 U = \tfrac{1}{16}C_D^2 V^4 + \left(\frac{l_{de}}{2\rho_0}\right) \quad . \quad (7.57)$$

a quartic equation for U in terms of given quantities.
Since, from eqn. (7.56),

$$U_1^2 = V^2 + 4Vv_h + 4v_h^2 + 4v_v^2$$

then $\qquad P = \frac{1}{2}\rho A U(U_1^2 - V^2) = \frac{1}{2}\rho A U[4Vv_h + 4v_h^2 + 4v_v^2]$

$$= 2\rho A\left[\frac{1}{4}C_D V^3 + \frac{1}{16}C_D^2\frac{V^4}{U} + \frac{1}{U}\left(\frac{l_{de}}{2\rho_0}\right)^2\right] \qquad . \qquad . \qquad (7.58)$$

which, with the value of U calculated from eqn. (7.57) and the given quantities, may be used to calculate the power required.

Example 7.6. A helicopter weighs 5400 lb and has a single rotor of 50 ft diameter. Using the momentum theory, estimate the power required for level flight at a speed of 50 ft/sec at sea-level. The drag coefficient, based on the rotor area, is 0·006.

$$A = \frac{\pi}{4}(50)^2 = 1962 \text{ ft}^2$$

$$l = \frac{W}{A\sigma} = \frac{5400}{1962 \times 1} = 2\cdot 75 \text{ lb/ft}^2$$

$$\therefore \frac{l_{de}}{2\rho_0} = \frac{2\cdot 75 \times 420\cdot 5}{2} = 583\cdot 2 \text{ ft}^2/\text{sec}^2$$

With the above values, and with $V = 50$ ft/sec, eqn. (7.57) is

$$U^4 - 2500U^2 - \frac{1}{2}U(0\cdot 006)(125,000) = (583\cdot 23)^2 + \frac{(0\cdot 006)^2}{16}(2500)^2$$

i.e., $\qquad\qquad U^4 - 2500U^2 - 3750 = 340,156 + 14 = 340,170$

This quartic equation in U may be solved by any of the standard methods (e.g., Newton-Raphson), the solution being $U = 51\cdot 35$ ft/sec, to 4 sig. figs. Then

$$P = \frac{2 \times 1962}{420\cdot 5}\left[\frac{0\cdot 006 \times 125,000}{4} + \frac{14}{51\cdot 35} + \frac{340,156}{51\cdot 35}\right]$$

$$= 63,800 \text{ ft lb/sec}$$

$$= \frac{63,800}{550} = \underline{116 \text{ H.P.}}$$

This is the power required if the rotor behaves as an ideal actuator disc. A practical rotor would require considerably more power than this.

7.6. The rocket motor.

As noted in § 7.0 the rocket motor is the only current example of aeronautical interest in Class II of propulsive systems. Since it does not work by accelerating atmospheric air, it cannot be treated by Froude's momentum theory. It is unique amongst current aircraft power plants in that it can operate independently of air from the atmosphere. The consequences of this are:

(i) it can operate in a rarefied atmosphere, or an atmosphere of inert gas, and

(ii) its maximum speed is not limited by the 'thermal barrier' set up by the high ram-compression of the air in all air-breathing engines.

In a rocket, some form of chemical is converted in the combustion chamber into gas at high temperature and pressure, which is then exhausted at supersonic speed through a nozzle. Suppose a rocket to be travelling at a speed of V ft/sec, and let the gas leave the nozzle with a speed of v ft/sec relative to the rocket. Let the rate of mass flow of gas be $\dot{m}$ slug/sec.* This gas is produced by the consumption, at the same rate, of the chemicals in the rocket fuel tanks (or solid charge). Whilst in the tanks the fuel has a forward momentum of mV. After discharge from the nozzle the gas has a rearward momentum of $m(v - V)$. Thus the rate of increase of rearward momentum of the fuel/gas is

$$\dot{m}(v - V) - (-\dot{m}V) = \dot{m}v \ . \qquad . \qquad . \qquad (7.59)$$

and this rate of change of momentum is equal to the thrust on the rocket. Thus the thrust depends only on the rate of fuel consumption and the velocity of discharge relative to the rocket. The thrust does not depend on the speed of the rocket itself. In particular, the possibility exists that the speed of the rocket V can exceed the speed of the gas relative to both the rocket, v, and relative to the axes of reference, $v - V$.

When in the form of fuel in the rocket, the mass m of the fuel has a kinetic energy of $\frac{1}{2}mV^2$. After discharge it has a kinetic energy of $\frac{1}{2}m(v - V)^2$. Thus the rate of change of kinetic energy is

$$\frac{dE}{dt} = \frac{1}{2}\dot{m}[(v - V)^2 - V^2] = \frac{1}{2}\dot{m}(v^2 - 2vV) \qquad . \qquad (7.60)$$

the units being ft lb/sec.

Useful work is done at the rate TV ft lb/sec, where $T = \dot{m}v$ is the thrust in pounds.

Thus the propulsive efficiency of the rocket is

$$\eta_p = \frac{\text{rate of useful work}}{\text{rate of increase of K.E. of fuel}}$$

$$= \frac{2vV}{v^2 - 2vV}$$

$$= \frac{2}{(v/V) - 1} \qquad . \qquad . \qquad . \qquad . \qquad . \qquad (7.61)$$

Now suppose $v/V = 3$. Then

$$\eta_p = \frac{2}{3 - 1} = 1, \text{ or } 100\%$$

If, further, $v/V < 3$, i.e., $V > v/3$, the propulsive efficiency exceeds 100%.

This derivation of the efficiency, while academically sound, is not normally accepted, since the engineer is unaccustomed to efficiencies in excess of 100%. Accordingly an alternative measure of the efficiency is used. In this the energy input is taken to be the energy liberated in the jet, plus the initial kinetic energy of the fuel while in the tanks. The total energy input is then

$$\frac{dE}{dt} = \frac{1}{2}\dot{m}v^2 + \frac{1}{2}\dot{m}V^2$$

---

* Some authors denote mass flow by m in rocketry, using the mass discharged (per sec. understood) as the parameter.

giving for the efficiency

$$\eta_p = \frac{2(v/V)}{(v/V)^2 + 1} \quad . \qquad . \qquad . \qquad . \quad (7.62)$$

By differentiating with respect to v/V, this is seen to be a maximum when $v/V = 1$, the propulsive efficiency then being 100%. Thus the definition of efficiency leads to a maximum efficiency of 100% when the speed of the rocket equals the speed of the exhaust gas relative to the rocket, i.e., when the exhaust is at rest relative to an observer past whom the rocket has the speed V.

If the speed of the rocket, V, is small compared with the exhaust speed v, as is the case for most aircraft applications, V^2 may be ignored compared with v^2 when

$$\eta_p \simeq \frac{2vV}{v^2} = 2\frac{V}{v} \quad . \qquad . \qquad . \qquad . \quad (7.63)$$

7.6.1. The free motion of a rocket missile.   Imagine a rocket-propelled missile moving in a region where aerodynamic drag and lift and gravitational force may be neglected, i.e., in space remote from any planets, etc. At time t let the mass of the missile plus unburnt fuel be M slugs, and the speed of the missile relative to some axes be V ft/sec. Let the fuel be consumed at a rate of $\dot{m}$ slug/sec, the resultant gas being ejected at a speed of v ft/sec relative to the missile. Further, let the total rearwards momentum of the rocket exhaust, produced from the instant of firing to time t, be I relative to the axes. Then, at time t, the total forward momentum is

$$H_1 = MV - I \quad . \qquad . \qquad . \qquad . \quad (7.64)$$

At time $(t + \delta t)$ the mass of the missile plus unburnt fuel is $(M - \dot{m}\,\delta t)$ and its speed is $(V + \delta V)$, while a mass of fuel $\dot{m}\,\delta t$ has been ejected rearwards with a mean speed, relative to the axes, of $(v - V - \frac{1}{2}\delta V)$. The total forward momentum is then

$$H_2 = (M - \dot{m}\,\delta t)(V + \delta V) - \dot{m}\,\delta t(v - V - \tfrac{1}{2}\delta V) - I$$

Now, by the conservation of momentum of a closed system,

$$H_1 = H_2$$

i.e., $MV - I = MV + M\,\delta V - \dot{m}V\,\delta t - \dot{m}\,\delta t\,\delta V - \dot{m}v\,\delta t + \dot{m}V\,\delta t$
$$+ \tfrac{1}{2}\dot{m}\,\delta t\,\delta V - I$$

which reduces to

$$M\delta V - \tfrac{1}{2}\dot{m}\,\delta t\,\delta V - \dot{m}v\,\delta t = 0$$

Dividing by δt and taking the limit as $\delta t \to 0$, this becomes

$$M\frac{dV}{dt} - \dot{m}v = 0 \quad . \qquad . \qquad . \qquad . \quad (7.65)$$

Note that this equation can be derived directly from Newton's Second Law; force = mass × acceleration, but it is not always immediately clear how to apply this Law to bodies of variable mass. The fundamental appeal to momentum made above removes any doubts as to the legitimacy of such an application.

Eqn. (7.65) may now be rearranged as

$$\frac{dV}{dt} = \frac{\dot{m}}{M}v$$

i.e.,
$$\frac{1}{v}dV = \frac{\dot{m}}{M}dt$$

Now $\dot{m} = -dM/dt$, since $\dot{m}$ is the rate at which fuel is burnt, and therefore

$$\frac{1}{v}dV = -\frac{1}{M}\frac{dM}{dt}dt = -\frac{dM}{M}$$

Therefore
$$\frac{V}{v} = -\log_e M + \text{const.}$$

assuming v, but not necessarily $\dot{m}$, to be constant. If the rate of fuel injection into the combustion chamber is constant, and if the pressure into which the nozzle exhausts is also constant (e.g., the near-vacuum implicit in the initial assumptions), both $\dot{m}$ and v will be closely constant. If the initial conditions are $M = M_0$, $V = 0$ when $t = 0$ then

$$0 = -\log_e M_0 + \text{const.}$$

i.e., the constant of integration is $\log_e M_0$. With this

$$\frac{V}{v} = \log_e M_0 - \log_e M = \log_e (M_0/M)$$

or, finally,
$$V = v \log_e (M_0/M) \qquad . \qquad . \qquad . \qquad . \qquad . \qquad (7.66)$$

The maximum speed of a rocket missile in free space will be reached when all the fuel is burnt, i.e., at the instant the motor ceases to produce thrust. Let the mass of the projectile with all fuel burnt be M_1. Then, from eqn. (7.66)

$$V_{\max} = v \log_e (M_0/M_1) = v \log_e R \qquad . \qquad . \qquad (7.66.1)$$

where R is the 'mass ratio' M_0/M_1. Note that if the mass ratio exceeds $e = 2 \cdot 718 \ldots$, the base of natural logarithms, the speed of the rocket will exceed the speed of ejection of the exhaust relative to the rocket.

Distance travelled during firing. From eqn. (7.66),

$$V = v \log_e (M_0/M) = v \log_e M_0 - v \log_e (M_0 - \dot{m}t)$$

Now if the distance travelled from the instant of firing is x in time t,

$$x = \int_0^t V \, dt$$

$$= v \int_0^t [\log_e M_0 - \log_e (M_0 - \dot{m}t)] \, dt$$

$$= vt \log_e M_0 - v \int_0^t \log_e (M_0 - \dot{m}t) \, dt \, . \qquad . \qquad (7.67)$$

To solve the integral in eqn. (7.67), let

$$y = \log_e (M_0 - \dot{m}t)$$

Then

$$\exp (y) = M_0 - \dot{m}t \quad \text{and} \quad t = \frac{1}{\dot{m}}(M_0 - e^y)$$

whence

$$dt = - \frac{1}{\dot{m}} e^y \, dy$$

Then

$$G = \int_0^t \log_e (M_0 - \dot{m}t) \, dt$$

$$= \int_{y_0}^{y_1} y\left(- \frac{1}{\dot{m}} e^y \, dy\right) \quad \text{where } y_0 = \log_e M_0 \text{ and } y_1 = \log_e (M_0 - \dot{m}t)$$

$$\therefore \; G = - \frac{1}{\dot{m}} \int_{y_0}^{y_1} y e^y \, dy = - \frac{1}{\dot{m}} \int_{y_0}^{y_1} y \, d(e^y)$$

which, on integrating by parts, gives

$$G = - \frac{1}{\dot{m}}\left[e^y(y - 1)\right]_{y_0}^{y_1} = \frac{1}{\dot{m}}\left[e^y(1 - y)\right]_{y_0}^{y_1}$$

Substituting back for y in terms of M_0, $\dot{m}$, and t gives

$$G = \frac{1}{\dot{m}}\left[(M_0 - \dot{m}t)(1 - \log_e \{M_0 - \dot{m}t\})\right]_0^t$$

$$= \frac{1}{\dot{m}}[M(1 - \log_e M) - M_0(1 - \log_e M_0)]$$

where $M = M_0 - \dot{m}t$.
Thus finally

$$G = \frac{1}{\dot{m}}[(M - M_0) - M \log_e M + M_0 \log M_0]$$

Substituting this value of the integral back into eqn. (7.67) gives, for the distance travelled

$$x = vt \log_e M_0 - \frac{v}{\dot{m}}\{(M - M_0) - M \log_e M + M_0 \log_e M_0\} . \quad (7.68)$$

Now, if $\dot{m}$ is constant,

$$t = \frac{1}{\dot{m}}(M_0 - M) . \qquad . \qquad . \qquad . \qquad (7.69)$$

which, substituted into eqn. (7.68) gives

$$x = \frac{v}{\dot{m}}\{(M_0 - M) \log_e M_0 - (M - M_0) + M \log_e M - M_0 \log_e M_0\}$$

$$= v\frac{M_0}{\dot{m}}\left\{\left(1 - \frac{M}{M_0}\right) - \frac{M}{M_0} \log_e \left(\frac{M_0}{M}\right)\right\} \qquad . \qquad . \qquad . \qquad (7.70)$$

For the distance at all-burnt, when $x = X$ and $M = M_1 = M_0/R$

$$X = v\frac{M_0}{\dot{m}}\left\{1 - \frac{1}{R}(1 + \log_e R)\right\} \qquad \qquad (7.71)$$

Alternatively, this may be written as

$$X = \frac{v}{\dot{m}}\frac{M_0}{R}\{(R - 1) - \log_e R\}$$

i.e.,
$$X = v\frac{M_1}{\dot{m}}\{(R - 1) - \log_e R\} . \qquad . \qquad . \qquad (7.72)$$

Example 7.7. A rocket-propelled missile has an initial total mass of 11 tons. Of this mass, 10 tons is fuel which is completely consumed in 5 minutes burning time. The exhaust speed is 5000 ft/sec relative to the rocket. Plot curves showing the variation of acceleration, speed and distance with time during the burning period, calculating these quantities at each half-minute.

For the acceleration, $\dfrac{dV}{dt} = \dfrac{\dot{m}}{M}v$ . . . . (7.65.1)

Now
$$\dot{m} = \tfrac{10}{5} = 2 \text{ tons/minute} = \tfrac{1}{30} \text{ tons/sec}$$

Since masses always appear in ratios it is permissible to work with the ton as the unit of mass.

$$M = M_0 - \dot{m}t = 11 - \frac{t}{30} \text{ tons}$$

where t is the time from firing in seconds, or
$$M = 11 - N \text{ tons}$$

where N is the number of half-minute periods elapsed since firing.

$$\frac{M_0}{\dot{m}} = \frac{11}{1/30}\frac{\text{tons}}{\text{tons/sec}} = 330 \text{ sec}$$

Substituting the above values into the appropriate equations leads to the final results given in the following table.

t (min)	0	$\frac{1}{2}$	1	$1\frac{1}{2}$	2	$2\frac{1}{2}$
M(tons)	11	10	9	8	7	6
acceln. (ft/sec^2) . .	15·2	16·7	18·5	20·8	23·8	27·8
V (ft/sec) . . .	0	475	995	1600	2260	3030
x (st. miles) . . .	0	1·1	5·7	12·7	23·7	38·8

t (min)	3	$3\frac{1}{2}$	4	$4\frac{1}{2}$	5	$5\frac{1}{2}$
M (tons)	5	4	3	2	1	1
acceln. (ft/sec^2) . .	33·3	41·7	55·5	83·4	151·5	0
V (ft/sec) . . .	3940	5055	6500	8520	12,000	12,000
x (st. miles) . . .	58·4	83·9	116·6	158·9	216·0	284·3

The reader should plot the curves defined by the values in the above Table.

It should be noted that, in the five minutes of burning time, the missile travels only 216 statute miles but, at the end of this time, it is travelling at 12,000 ft/sec or 8190 m.p.h. Another point to be noted is the rapid increase in acceleration towards the end of the burning time, consequent on the rapid percentage decrease of total mass.

In the above Table the results are given also for the first half-minute after all-burnt.

EXERCISES

1. If an aircraft of wing area S and drag coefficient C_D is flying at a speed of V in air of density ρ and if its single airscrew, of disc area A, produces a thrust equal to the aircraft drag, show that the speed in the slipstream V_s, is, on the basis of Froude's momentum theory

$$V_s = V\sqrt{1 + \frac{S}{A}C_D}$$

2. A cooling fan is required to produce a stream of air, 1 ft in diameter, with a speed of 10 ft/sec when operating in a region of otherwise stationary air of standard density. Assuming the stream of air to be the fully developed slipstream behind an ideal actuator disc, and ignoring mixing between the jet and the surrounding air, estimate the fan diameter and the power input required. (*Ans.* 17 in. dia.: 0·0017 H.P.)

3. Repeat Example 7.2 in the text for the case where the two airscrews absorb equal powers, and finding (i) the thrust of the second airscrew as a percentage of the thrust of the first, (ii) the efficiency of the second and (iii) the efficiency of the combination. (*Ans.* 84%; 75·5%; 82·75%)

4. Calculate the flight speed at which the airscrew of Example 7.3 of the text will produce a thrust 1700 lb., and the power absorbed, at the same rotational speed. (*Ans.* 286 ft/sec; 1077 B.H.P.)

5. At 5 ft radius, the thrust and torque gradings on each blade of a 3-bladed airscrew revolving at 1200 r.p.m at a flight speed of 200 m.p.h T.A.S. at an altitude where $\sigma = 0·725$ are 200 lb/ft and 400 lb ft/ft respectively. If the blade angle is 28°, find the blade section absolute incidence. (*Ans.* 1° 24′) (N.C.A.T.)

6. At 4 ft radius on a 3-bladed airscrew, the aerofoil section has the following characteristics:

solidity $= 0·1: \theta = 29°\ 7': \alpha = 4°\ 7': C_L = 0·49: L/D = 50$

Allowing for both axial and rotational interference find the local efficiency of the element. (*Ans.* 0·877) (N.C.A.T.)

7. The thrust and torque gradings at 4 ft radius on each blade of a 2-bladed airscrew are 145 lb/ft and 175 lb ft/ft respectively. Find the speed of rotation (in radians/second) of the airstream immediately behind the disc at 4 ft radius. (*Ans.* 735 rads/sec)

8. A 4-bladed airscrew is required to propel an aircraft at 275 m.p.h at sea-level, the rotational speed being 1200 r.p.m. The blade element at 4 ft radius has an absolute incidence of 6° and the thrust grading is 190 lb/ft per blade. Assuming a reasonable value for the sectional lift curve slope, calculate the blade chord at 4 ft radius. Neglect rotational interference and compressibility. (*Ans.* 10 in.)

9. A 3-bladed airscrew is driven at 1560 r.p.m at a flight speed of 250 m.p.h at sea-level. At 4 ft radius the local efficiency is estimated to be 87%, while the lift/drag ratio of the blade section is 57·3. Calculate the local thrust grading, ignoring rotational interference. (*Ans.* 609 lb/ft)

10. Using simple momentum theory develop an expression for the thrust of a propeller in terms of its disc area, the air density and the axial velocities of the air a long way ahead, and in the plane, of the propeller disc.

A helicopter has an engine developing 800 B.H.P. and a rotor of 53 ft diameter with a disc loading of 3·5 lb/ft². When ascending vertically with constant speed at low altitude, the product of the lift and the axial velocity of the air through the rotor disc is 53% of the power available. Estimate the velocity of ascent. (*Ans.* 351 ft/min) (U. of L.)

CHAPTER 8

AIRCRAFT PERFORMANCE IN STEADY FLIGHT

8.1. Straight and level flight. The simplest case of flight is in a straight, horizontal path at constant speed. The forces acting on the aircraft are then the lift and weight acting vertically, and the thrust and drag horizontally. These forces (Fig. 8.1) must be in equilibrium.

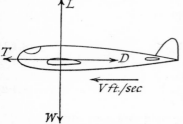

For equilibrium, assuming the thrust to act horizontally:

$$T = D \qquad . \qquad . \qquad (8.1.1)$$

$$L = W \qquad . \qquad . \qquad (8.1.2)$$

FIG. 8.1.—The forces acting in steady, straight and level flight.

Taking the second of these, since by definition

$$L = C_L \tfrac{1}{2}\rho V^2 S \text{ (eqn. (6.6.1))}$$

it follows that

$$W = L = C_L \tfrac{1}{2}\rho V^2 S \qquad (8.2)$$

This equation may be used to find any of the quantities W, C_L, ρ, V or S given values of the other four.

8.1.1. Stalling speed. Eqn. 8.2 may be arranged as

$$V = \left(\frac{W}{\tfrac{1}{2}\rho S C_L}\right)^{\frac{1}{2}} \qquad . \qquad . \qquad . \qquad . \qquad (8.3)$$

As a special use of this equation consider an aeroplane of given weight and wing area, flying at a given altitude (fixing the value of the density ρ). If now the lift coefficient is assumed to take its maximum value for the aeroplane in question, namely $C_{L\,max}$, the corresponding flight speed is given by

$$V_s = \left(\frac{W}{\tfrac{1}{2}\rho S C_{L max}}\right)^{\frac{1}{2}} \qquad . \qquad . \qquad . \qquad (8.3.1)$$

Since C_{Lmax} is the largest possible value of C_L, it follows that this value of the speed, V_s, is the minimum speed at which steady, sustained flight is possible, and it is known as the 'stalling speed'. Note that since C_{Lmax} for a given aircraft depends on whether or not the flaps and undercarriage are extended, the stalling speed depends on the same factors.

Measurement of stalling speed in flight testing. It is not practicable to fly steadily at the stalling speed and therefore the stalling speed is measured in a state of unsteady flight, with the aircraft decelerating until control is lost. To ensure repeatability of measurements it is accepted that the aircraft shall approach the stall with a deceleration of 1 knot/sec and the speed at which control is first lost (usually the nose drops sharply) is taken as the stalling speed.

The stalling speed depends on the aircraft configuration (e.g., flap deflection, undercarriage retracted or extended, etc.) and on whether engine power is being used. Thus an aeroplane has many 'stalling speeds', a power-on and power-off value for each of the possible configurations.

8.2. Significance of equivalent air speed in level flight.

Repeating eqn. (8.2), namely

$$W = C_L \tfrac{1}{2} \rho V^2 S$$

and remembering the definition of equivalent air speed as

$$\tfrac{1}{2}\rho V^2 = \tfrac{1}{2}\rho_0 V_E^2 \text{ (eqn. (4.33))}$$

it is seen that

$$W = C_L \tfrac{1}{2}\rho_0 V_E^2 S \ . \qquad . \qquad . \qquad . \qquad (8.4.1)$$

which may be written as

$$V_E = \left(\frac{W}{\tfrac{1}{2}\rho_0 S C_L}\right)^{\tfrac{1}{2}} \qquad . \qquad . \qquad . \qquad (8.4.2)$$

This shows that, for an aircraft of given weight and wing area

$$V_E \propto \sqrt{\frac{1}{C_L}} \qquad . \qquad . \qquad . \qquad (8.4.3)$$

i.e., with weight and wing area given, the E.A.S. for straight and level flight depends only on the lift coefficient, and is independent of density and therefore altitude. Thus if an aircraft is flown at a constant attitude (or incidence), and therefore constant C_L, the indicated air speed, which approximates to the E.A.S., will tend to be constant. Therefore the reading of the air-speed indicator bears a nearly constant relationship to the flight lift coefficient, independent of the altitude. Thus, to the pilot, the I.A.S. is a useful indication of the state of flight, whereas the true air speed is a less simple and direct indication of the flight attitude. In particular, at constant weight, an aeroplane will always stall at the same I.A.S. and the pilot need therefore only remember one value of the stalling speed. It is thus seen that, although an air-speed indicator does not indicate the true speed of flight, the speed it does indicate is of direct use to the pilot in flying the aeroplane.

8.2.1. The wing loading.

The eqns. (8.3) and (8.4) may be simplified slightly by writing

$$\frac{W}{S} = w \qquad . \qquad . \qquad . \qquad . \qquad (8.5)$$

Then w is known as the 'wing loading', measured in lb/ft². With this relationship, eqn. (8.3) becomes

$$V = \left(\frac{w}{\tfrac{1}{2}\rho C_L}\right)^{\tfrac{1}{2}} \qquad . \qquad . \qquad . \qquad . \qquad (8.6)$$

Example 8.1. An aircraft has a wing area of 900 ft², and weighs 54,000 lb. It has a maximum speed of 400 ft/sec at sea-level, and the maximum lift coefficient is 2·2, flaps down. Plot a curve showing the variation of lift coefficient for straight and level flight over the usable speed range at sea-level. If the maximum lift coefficient of the aircraft without flaps is 1·5, below what true air speed must flaps be used at sea-level and at 20,000 ft, where the relative density is 0·533?

$$W = C_L \tfrac{1}{2} \rho V^2 S$$

which may be rearranged as

$$C_L = \left(\frac{W}{\tfrac{1}{2}\rho V^2 S}\right)$$

Putting in this equation the given values, including $\rho_0 = 0.002378$ slug/ft³ $= 1/420\cdot5$ slug/ft³, this becomes

$$C_L = \frac{54,000 \times 841}{900 V^2} = \frac{50,460}{V^2}$$

With $C_{L\,max} = 2.2$, the stalling speed is given by

$$V_s = \left(\frac{50,460}{2\cdot2}\right)^{\frac{1}{2}} = 152 \text{ ft/sec}$$

Thus C_L can be calculated over the speed range from 150 ft/sec to 400 ft/sec, giving the following table

V (ft/sec) . . .	152	200	250	300	350	400
C_L	2·20	1·26	0·808	0·560	0·413	0·315

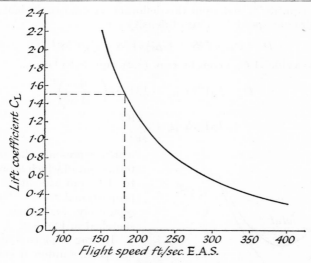

FIG. 8.2.—Lift coefficient versus flight speed.

These results are plotted as Fig. 8.2 and from this graph it is seen that, when $C_L = 1.5$, $V = 183$ ft/sec. Alternatively, since flight speed is inversely proportional to the lift coefficient, the speed for a lift coefficient of 1·5 is

$$V_{1\cdot5} = 152 \sqrt{\frac{2\cdot2}{1\cdot5}} = 183 \text{ ft/sec, T.A.S.}$$

K

at sea-level. Since, at sea-level in the I.S.A., E.A.S. and T.A.S. are identical, the stalling speed with flaps up will be 183 ft/sec E.A.S. at all altitudes and therefore, at 20,000 ft, the corresponding true air speed will be

$$\frac{183}{(0\cdot533)^{\frac{1}{2}}} = 250 \text{ ft/sec, T.A.S.}$$

Flaps must therefore be used below 183 ft/sec, T.A.S. at sea-level and below 250 ft/sec, T.A.S. at an altitude of 20,000 ft.

8.3. Drag. It was seen in Chapter 6 that an aeroplane flying in air and generating a lift experiences (at low Mach numbers) two forms of drag, boundary layer drag and trailing vortex drag, the sum of these being the total drag. Now as an aircraft changes flight speed, the required lift coefficient and therefore the aircraft attitude, changes and, in general, this change in attitude will cause a change in the boundary layer drag coefficient. It is found that, for most aircraft, the boundary layer drag coefficient is, to a good approximation, of the form $(a + bC_L^2)$. As noted before, the trailing vortex drag coefficient is proportional to (lift co-efficient)². Thus a good approximation to the total drag coefficient of an aeroplane is

$$C_D = C_{D0} + C_{D\,L} = C_{D0} + kC_L^2 \qquad . \qquad . \qquad (8.7)$$

where C_{D0} is the zero-lift drag coefficient, $C_{D\,L}$ is the lift-dependent drag coefficient, and k is the lift-dependent drag coefficient factor.

With eqn. (8.7), and from the definition of drag coefficient, the total aircraft drag at speed V in air of density ρ is

$$D = C_D \tfrac{1}{2}\rho V^2 S = C_{D0}\tfrac{1}{2}\rho V^2 S + \tfrac{1}{2}\rho V^2 S(kC_L^2) \qquad . \qquad (8.8)$$

Using the value of C_L given by eqn. (8.2), eqn. (8.8) becomes

$$D = \tfrac{1}{2}\rho V^2 S C_{D0} + \tfrac{1}{2}\rho V^2 S k\left(\frac{W}{\tfrac{1}{2}\rho V^2 S}\right)^2$$

$$= \tfrac{1}{2}\rho V^2 S C_{D0} + \frac{kW^2}{\tfrac{1}{2}\rho V^2 S} \qquad . \qquad . \qquad . \qquad (8.9)$$

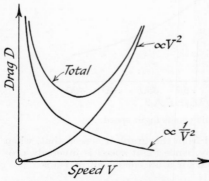

which represents the sum of two terms, one of which is proportional to V^2, and the other inversely proportional to V^2. These terms separately and their sum, are sketched in Fig. 8.3.

If drag is plotted against true air speed, a different curve results for each value of ρ (i.e., altitude), as shown by consideration of eqn. (8.9). This may be avoided by using the equivalent air speed. Again recalling that

$$\tfrac{1}{2}\rho V^2 = \tfrac{1}{2}\rho_0 V_E^2$$

FIG. 8.3.—The variation of total drag with flight speed.

eqn. (8.9) becomes

$$D = \tfrac{1}{2}\rho_0 V_E^2 S C_{D0} + \frac{kW^2}{\tfrac{1}{2}\rho_0 V_E^2 S} \qquad . \qquad . \qquad . \qquad (8.10.1)$$

$$= A V_E^2 + \frac{B}{V_E^2} \qquad . \qquad . \qquad . \qquad . \qquad (8.10.2)$$

where A and B are constants, depending on the geometry and weight of the aeroplane.

Thus for a given aeroplane at given weight, the drag is a function of E.A.S. only, and a plot of total drag against equivalent air speed yields a single curve, of similar shape to Fig. 8.3, which applies to all altitudes.

8.3.1. Minimum drag. The curve of total drag against speed shows a clearly defined minimum, which is of considerable interest. This may be located precisely as follows.

$$D = L\left(\frac{D}{L}\right)$$

and since $L = W$ in straight and level flight,

$$D = W\left(\frac{D}{L}\right) \qquad . \qquad . \qquad . \qquad . \qquad (8.11)$$

Thus, for a given weight, the minimum drag occurs at the minimum value of (D/L), or the maximum value of (L/D). Now

$$\frac{D}{L} = \frac{C_D \tfrac{1}{2}\rho V^2 S}{C_L \tfrac{1}{2}\rho V^2 S} = \frac{C_D}{C_L}$$

$$= \frac{C_{D0} + kC_L^2}{C_L} \qquad . \qquad . \qquad . \qquad (8.12)$$

For the minimum,

$$\frac{d}{dC_L}\left(\frac{C_{D0} + kC_L^2}{C_L}\right) = \frac{(C_{D0} + kC_L^2) - C_L(2kC_L)}{C_L^2} = 0$$

This simplifies to

$$C_{D0} + kC_L^2 - 2kC_L^2 = 0$$

or
$$\qquad\qquad C_{D0} = kC_L^2 = C_{D\,L} \qquad . \qquad . \qquad . \qquad (8.13)$$

Thus for minimum drag the zero-lift drag coefficient is equal to the lift-dependent drag coefficient, and the actual drag forces associated with these coefficients are also equal.

Denoting the lift coefficient for minimum drag by $C_{L\,\mathrm{md}}$, then from eqn. (8.13),

$$C_{L\,\mathrm{md}} = \sqrt{\frac{C_{D0}}{k}} \qquad . \qquad . \qquad . \qquad (8.14)$$

Hence, by eqn. (8.3),

$$V_{\mathrm{md}} = \sqrt{\frac{W}{\tfrac{1}{2}\rho S C_{L\,\mathrm{md}}}} = \left(\frac{W}{\tfrac{1}{2}\rho S}\right)^{\tfrac{1}{2}}\left(\frac{k}{C_{D0}}\right)^{\tfrac{1}{4}} \qquad . \qquad . \qquad (8.15)$$

Also, from eqn. (8.13),

$$C_D = C_{D0} + kC_L^2 = 2C_{D0} \qquad . \qquad . \qquad . \qquad (8.16)$$

The corresponding value of the lift/drag ratio, L/D, is

$$\frac{L}{D} = \frac{C_L}{C_D} = \sqrt{\frac{C_{D0}}{k}} \left(\frac{1}{2C_{D0}} \right)$$

$$= \frac{1}{2\sqrt{kC_{D0}}} \qquad . \qquad . \qquad . \qquad . \qquad (8.17)$$

Since D/L is a minimum at this condition it follows that this value of L/D is the maximum for the aeroplane in question, i.e., $(L/D)_{max}$.

Lift/drag ratio at other speeds. Suppose an aeroplane to be flying at some multiple m of the minimum drag speed. Then since

$$W = \tfrac{1}{2}\rho V^2 S C_L = \text{constant}$$

the lift coefficient at this speed (mV_{md}) is given by

$$C_L(mV_{md})^2 = C_{L\,md} V_{md}^2$$

i.e., $$C_L = \frac{C_{L\,md}}{m^2} \qquad . \qquad . \qquad . \qquad (8.18)$$

The corresponding drag coefficient is given by

$$C_D = C_{D0} + kC_L^2$$
$$= C_{D0} + k\left(\frac{C_{L\,md}}{m^2}\right)^2$$
$$= C_{D0} + \frac{1}{m^4}(kC_{L\,md}^2)$$

But since, from eqn. (8.13),

$$kC_{L\,md}^2 = C_{D0}$$

it follows that $$C_D = C_{D0}\left(1 + \frac{1}{m^4}\right) \qquad . \qquad . \qquad . \qquad (8.19)$$

The lift drag ratio is

$$\frac{C_L}{C_D} = \frac{(1/m^2)C_{L\,md}}{C_{D0}(1 + m^{-4})}$$

$$= \frac{2m^2}{m^4 + 1}\frac{C_{L\,md}}{2C_{D0}}$$

Now $C_{L\,md}/2C_{D0}$ is the maximum lift drag ratio, and therefore

$$\frac{(L/D)}{(L/D)_{max}} = \frac{2m^2}{1 + m^4} \qquad . \qquad . \qquad . \qquad (8.20.1)$$

$$= \frac{2}{m^2 + m^{-2}} \qquad . \qquad . \qquad . \qquad (8.20.2)$$

The ratio of the drag at this speed to the minimum drag may be found, since

$$\frac{D}{D_{\min}} = \frac{W/(L/D)}{W/(L/D)_{\max}} = \frac{(L/D)_{\max}}{(L/D)}$$
$$= \tfrac{1}{2}(m^2 + m^{-2}) \qquad . \qquad . \qquad . \qquad . \quad (8.20.3)$$

The expressions of eqns. (8.20.1), (8.20.2) and (8.20.3) depend only on the quantity m, and are independent of the type of aircraft, its size, altitude, etc., provided only that its drag equation is of the form $C_D = C_{D_0} + kC_L^2$.

8.4. Performance curves in terms of thrust.

This Section is concerned with aircraft fitted with turbo-jet, ram-jet, or rocket engines, whose performance is most conveniently measured in pounds thrust. A curve may be drawn of total drag against equivalent air speed, which applies at all altitudes for a given aircraft at a given weight, as shown by the full curve of Fig. 8.4. On the same axes may be plotted curves representing the nett thrust of the engine(s), each curve relating to the engine performance at some particular altitude and throttle setting (or engine r.p.m). Some typical curves are shown in Fig. 8.4. The vertical broken line in this Figure represents the stalling speed, flaps up.

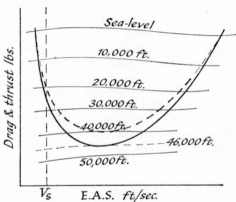

FIG. 8.4.—Performance chart in terms of thrust and drag.

It will be at once realized that a point which is the intersection between the drag curve and an engine-thrust curve represents a solution of eqn. (8.1.1), and thus represents a possible condition of straight and level flight at the appropriate altitude and throttle setting. By noting the speeds corresponding to a number of such intersections relating to a number of different altitudes, and plotting these speeds against the appropriate altitudes, a curve of the form of Fig. 8.5 is obtained, showing the variation of flight E.A.S. with altitude for the given weight and throttle setting.

Note that, in general, a thrust curve has two intersections with the drag curve, giving two possible speeds of straight and level flight, with the following exceptions:

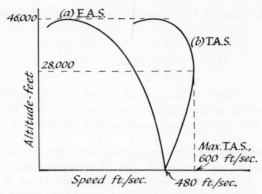

FIG. 8.5.—Variation of flight speed with altitude.

(i) Below about 26,000 ft the low speed solution is below the stalling speed, and therefore unattainable in sustained flight.

(ii) At 46,000 ft (the thrust curve with broken line) the thrust curve is tangential to the drag curve, and the two solutions become coincident. This altitude represents the greatest height at which sustained straight and level flight is possible, and can only be exceeded by reducing the aircraft weight or by increasing the engine thrust (e.g., opening the throttle further).

(iii) Above 46,000 ft, the thrust is always less than the drag, and sustained straight and level flight is not possible, except as noted in (ii) above.

In general, only the higher speed is of interest except for special purposes.

The broken curve in Fig. 8.4 represents the same aircraft at a greater weight. It is seen that the effect of weight increase is to reduce the flight speed at each altitude, and to decrease the maximum altitude attainable.

It should also be noted that the plot obtained for Figs. 8.4 and 8.5 depends largely on the atmospheric conditions used in the calculations, and it is for this reason that the I.S.A. has been formulated and accepted as a standard, see § 3.3.1.

Having, as in Fig. 8.5 (a), a plot of the equivalent air speed against altitude, this may be converted to a plot of T.A.S. against altitude by dividing the E.A.S. by the corresponding value of $(\sigma)^{\frac{1}{2}}$. The result in the present example is given in Fig. 8.5 (b). It is this curve which reveals the economy of flight at high altitude. It is seen that the maximum true air speed is 600 ft/sec, and occurs at an altitude of approximately 28,000 ft, compared with 480 ft/sec, T.A.S. at sea-level. Reference back to Fig. 8.4 shows that this maximum true air speed is achieved with only some 55% of the thrust required for the lower speed at sea-level. Since, with a turbo-jet engine, the rate of fuel consumption in lb/hour is approximately proportional to the thrust, it follows that by flying at 28,000 ft, a 25% increase in true speed is achieved with a 45% decrease in fuel consumption per hour compared with flight at sea-level, and the aeroplane flies further, faster, on a given amount of fuel.

8.5. Horse-power. When an aircraft with drag D lb is flying at a true air speed of V ft/sec work is being done against the drag at a rate of DV ft lb/sec, or

$$P = \frac{DV}{550} \text{ horse-power} \qquad . \qquad . \qquad . \qquad (8.21)$$

Now eqn. (8.9) is

$$D = \tfrac{1}{2}\rho V^2 S C_{D0} + \frac{kW^2}{\tfrac{1}{2}\rho V^2 S} \text{ (eqn. (8.9))}$$

and, therefore, combining eqns. (8.9) and (8.21)

$$P = \frac{1}{1100}\rho V^3 S C_{D0} + \frac{kW^2}{275\rho VS} \qquad . \qquad . \qquad (8.22)$$

$$= AV^3 + \frac{B}{V} \qquad . \qquad . \qquad . \qquad . \qquad (8.23)$$

Writing, from the definition of equivalent air speed, V_E,

$$V = \frac{V_E}{\sqrt{\sigma}}$$

then eqn. (8.22) becomes

$$P = \frac{1}{1100}\left(\frac{V_E}{\sqrt{\sigma}}\right)^3 \rho S C_{D0} + \frac{kW^2\sqrt{\sigma}}{275\rho V_E S}$$

Multiplying both sides of this equation by $\sqrt{\sigma}$ gives

$$(\sqrt{\sigma})P = \frac{1}{1100}\frac{\rho}{\sigma}V_E^3 S C_{D0} + \frac{kW^2}{275(\rho/\sigma)V_E S}$$

Now the relative density is defined by

$$\sigma = \frac{\rho}{\rho_0}$$

and therefore

$$P\sqrt{\sigma} = \frac{1}{1100}\rho_0 V_E^3 S C_{D0} + \frac{kW^2}{275\rho_0 V_E S} \qquad . \qquad . \qquad (8.24)$$

Thus, for a given aircraft at a given weight, the quantity $P\sqrt{\sigma}$ is a function only of the equivalent air speed, and a graph of $(P\sqrt{\sigma})$ against E.A.S. is a unique curve, independent of altitude (Fig. 8.6). It is seen to represent the sum of two terms, one proportional to V_E^3 and the other inversely proportional to V_E. This is sketched in Fig. 8.6.

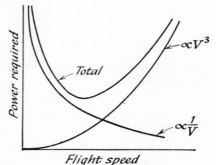

FIG. 8.6.—Variation of power required with flight speed.

8.5.1. Minimum power. At a certain speed, the power required for straight and level flight has a minimum value. This may be investigated as follows.

$$D = W\frac{D}{L} = W\frac{C_D}{C_L} \qquad . \qquad . \qquad . \qquad (8.11)$$

$$V = \sqrt{\left(\frac{W}{\frac{1}{2}\rho S C_L}\right)}$$

Substituting these two expressions into eqn. (8.21), gives

$$P = \frac{1}{550}W\frac{C_D}{C_L}\left(\frac{W}{\frac{1}{2}\rho S C_L}\right)^{\frac{1}{2}}$$

$$= \frac{1}{550}\left(\frac{W^3}{\frac{1}{2}\rho S}\right)^{\frac{1}{2}}\left(\frac{C_D}{C_L^{3/2}}\right) \qquad . \qquad . \qquad (8.25)$$

The power required to overcome the drag in straight and level flight is therefore a minimum when $C_D/C_L^{3/2}$ is itself a minimum. In the case where $C_D = C_{D0} + kC_L^2$, this minimum occurs when

$$\frac{d}{dC_L}\left(\frac{C_{D0} + kC_L^2}{C_L^{3/2}}\right) = 0$$

i.e., when

$$\frac{C_L^{3/2}(2kC_L) - (C_{D0} + kC_L^2)\frac{3}{2}C_L^{1/2}}{C_L^3} = 0$$

i.e., when

$$2kC_L^{5/2} - \frac{3}{2}C_{D0}C_L^{1/2} + \frac{3}{2}kC_L^{5/2} = 0$$

This reduces to the condition that

$$kC_L^2 = 3C_{D0} \qquad . \qquad . \qquad . \qquad (8.26)$$

Now $kC_L^2 = C_{D\,L}$, the lift-dependent drag coefficient. Thus for minimum power the lift-dependent drag coefficient is equal to three times the zero-lift drag coefficient, and the same relationship holds between the actual drag forces associated with these drag coefficients. Using the subscript mp to denote the value of a quantity at the minimum power condition

$$C_{L\,mp} = \sqrt{\frac{3C_{D0}}{k}} = C_{Lmd}\sqrt{3} \qquad . \qquad . \qquad (8.27)$$

$$V_{mp} = \frac{V_{md}}{3^{\frac{1}{4}}} = \frac{V_{md}}{1\cdot316} = 0\cdot76V_{md} \qquad . \qquad . \qquad (8.28)$$

Since, for minimum power, the value of m (page 140) is $(1/3)^{\frac{1}{4}}$, eqn. (8.20.1) gives

$$\frac{(L/D)_{mp}}{(L/D)_{max}} = \frac{2m^2}{1 + m^4}$$

$$= \frac{2/\sqrt{3}}{1 + (1/3)} = \frac{2\sqrt{3}}{4}$$

$$= \frac{\sqrt{3}}{2} = 0\cdot866 \qquad . \qquad . \qquad (8.29)$$

Thus, provided the drag equation of an aeroplane may be expressed in the form $C_D = C_{D0} + kC_L^2$, the minimum power condition occurs at a speed which is 76% of the minimum drag speed, and the corresponding lift/drag ratio is 86·6% of the maximum lift/drag ratio.

The total drag coefficient at the minimum power condition is

$$C_D = C_{D0} + kC_{L\,\mathrm{mp}}^2 = C_{D0} + 3C_{D0} = 4C_{D0} \quad . \quad . \quad (8.30)$$

Thus the lift/drag ratio at minimum power is

$$\left(\frac{L}{D}\right)_{\mathrm{mp}} = \sqrt{\frac{3C_{D0}}{k}\left(\frac{1}{4C_{D0}}\right)}$$

$$= \sqrt{\frac{3}{16kC_{D0}}} \quad . \qquad . \quad . \quad (8.31)$$

Power required at other speeds. Suppose an aeroplane to be flying at n times its minimum power speed. Then

$$C_L(nV_{\mathrm{mp}})^2 = C_{L\,\mathrm{mp}}V_{\mathrm{mp}}^2$$

i.e.,
$$C_L = \frac{C_{L\,\mathrm{mp}}}{n^2} \quad . \qquad . \qquad . \quad (8.32)$$

The corresponding speed is given by

$$V = nV_{\mathrm{mp}}$$

and the corresponding drag coefficient by

$$C_D = C_{D0} + kC_L^2 = C_{D0} + k\left(\frac{C_{L\,\mathrm{mp}}}{n^2}\right)^2$$

$$= C_{D0}\left(1 + \frac{3}{n^4}\right) \quad \text{since} \quad kC_{L\,\mathrm{mp}}^2 = 3C_{D0}$$

Thus the ratio of the power required to the minimum power is

$$\frac{P}{P_{\min}} = \frac{DV}{D_{\mathrm{mp}}V_{\mathrm{mp}}} = \frac{W(C_D/C_L)V}{W(C_{D\,\mathrm{mp}}/C_{L\,\mathrm{mp}})V_{\mathrm{mp}}}$$

Therefore

$$\frac{P}{P_{\min}} = \left(\frac{C_D}{C_{D\,\mathrm{mp}}}\right)\left(\frac{C_{L\,\mathrm{mp}}}{C_L}\right)\left(\frac{V}{V_{\mathrm{mp}}}\right)$$

$$= \frac{1}{4}\left(1 + \frac{3}{n^4}\right)(n^2)(n)$$

$$= \frac{3 + n^4}{4n} \qquad . \qquad . \qquad . \qquad . \quad (8.33)$$

8.6. Performance curves in terms of horse-power.

Eqn. (8.24) showed that the quantity $P\sqrt{\sigma}$, where P is the horse-power required to overcome the drag in straight and level flight, is, for a given aeroplane at a given weight, independent of altitude, being a function of the equivalent air speed V_E only. Thus a graph of $P\sqrt{\sigma}$ against V_E will apply for all altitudes (Fig. 8.7). On the same axes may be plotted curves representing the power available from the engines (after allowing for airscrew efficiency) at various altitudes for some particular throttle setting. These curves are obtained by finding the engine brake horse-power at the appropriate throttle setting, r.p.m and altitude, multiplying by the airscrew efficiency, and finally multiplying by the value of $\sqrt{\sigma}$ appropriate to the altitude considered.

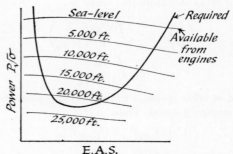

FIG. 8.7.—Performance chart in terms of horse-power.

The comments made in § 8.4 apply also to the present chart (Fig. 8.7), namely that the intersections between the power available and power-required curves represent conditions of straight and level flight at the appropriate altitude, and that the maximum altitude attainable under the prescribed conditions is about 23,000 ft. Other curves analogous to Fig. 8.5 may also be derived.

Example 8.2. An aeroplane has a wing loading of 50 lb/ft², and its drag equation is

$$C_D = 0.016 + 0.055C_L^2$$

Calculate its maximum lift/drag ratio, the minimum drag speed, and the lift/drag ratio at a speed of 350 ft/sec, E.A.S.

For minimum drag, $C_{D_0} = kC_{L\,md}^2$

Therefore, in this case $0.016 = 0.055C_{L\,md}^2$

whence $C_{L\,md} = 0.54$

$$V_{md} = \sqrt{\frac{w}{\tfrac{1}{2}\rho C_{L\,md}}} = \sqrt{\frac{50 \times 841}{0.54}}$$

$$= 279 \text{ ft/sec. E.A.S.}$$

$$\left(\frac{L}{D}\right)_{max} = \frac{C_{L\,md}}{2C_{D_0}} = \frac{0.54}{0.032} = 16.88.$$

At 350 ft/sec, E.A.S.

$$m = \tfrac{350}{279} = 1.255$$

Therefore $\dfrac{(L/D)}{(L/D)_{max}} = \dfrac{2}{(1.255)^2 + (1/1.255)^2} = 0.905$

$$\therefore \frac{L}{D} = 16.88 \times 0.905 = \underline{15.25}.$$

Example 8.3. An aircraft weighing 56,000 lb has a wing area of 900 ft², and its drag equation is

$$C_D = 0.016 + 0.04C_L^2$$

Calculate the minimum thrust required for straight and level flight, and the corresponding true air speeds at sea-level and at 30,000 ft ($\sqrt{\sigma} = 0.6116$). Calculate also the minimum power required, and the corresponding true air speeds, at the above altitudes.

(*a*) *For minimum thrust* (*i.e., minimum drag*),

$$C_{L\,md} = \sqrt{\frac{0.016}{0.040}} = 0.631$$

and

$$\left(\frac{L}{D}\right)_{max} = \frac{0.631}{0.032} = 19.75$$

Therefore

$$\text{minimum thrust} = \frac{W}{(L/D)_{max}} = \frac{56,000}{19.75}$$

$$= 2833 \text{ lb.}$$

(This result holds at all altitudes.)

$$V_{E\,md} = \sqrt{\frac{56,000 \times 841}{900 \times 0.631}} = \sqrt{82,900}$$

$$= 288 \text{ ft/sec}$$

Therefore the minimum drag speed at sea-level is 288 ft/sec T.A.S. while, at 30,000 ft the minimum drag speed is $288/0.6116 = \underline{470 \text{ ft/sec, T.A.S.,}}$

(*b*) *For minimum power,*

$$C_{L\,mp} = \sqrt{\frac{3C_{D_0}}{k}} = \sqrt{\frac{3 \times 0.016}{0.04}} = 1.093$$

$$C_{D\,mp} = 4C_{D_0} = 4 \times 0.016 = 0.064$$

$$\therefore \left(\frac{L}{D}\right)_{mp} = \frac{1.093}{0.064} = 17.1$$

(Note that this is in fact equal to $0.866 (L/D)_{max}$ as required by eqn. (8.29).) Therefore the drag at minimum power condition is

$$D_{mp} = \frac{W}{(L/D)_{mp}} = \frac{56,000}{17.1}$$

$$= \underline{3280 \text{ lb.}}$$

Alternatively, since the ratio of the lift/drag ratios is 0.866 : 1,

$$D_{mp} = \frac{D_{min}}{0.866} = \frac{2840}{0.866} = 3280 \text{ lb,}$$

$$V_{E\,mp} = \sqrt{\frac{56,000 \times 841}{900 \times 1.093}} = 219 \text{ ft/sec}$$

(Note that this is also equal to $0.76V_{E\,md}$, as required by eqn. (8.28).)

Thus, at sea-level, the minimum power speed is 219 ft/sec, T.A.S., and the horse-power required is

$$\frac{3280 \times 219}{550} = \underline{1250 \text{ thrust horse-power}}$$

At 30,000 ft the minimum power speed is $\dfrac{219}{0\cdot6116} = 358$ ft/sec, T.A.S., and the horse-power required is

$$\frac{3280 \times 358}{550} = \underline{2140 \text{ T.H.P.}}$$

Since $P\sqrt{\sigma}$ is constant at constant V_E, this last result may be obtained alternatively as

$$\frac{1250}{0\cdot6116} = \underline{2140 \text{ T.H.P.}} \text{ as before}$$

Example 8.4. The aeroplane of the previous Example is fitted with a turbo-jet engine giving a thrust which is independent of speed, and which, at cruising r.p.m, varies with altitude as in the following table.

Altitude (ft) . .	0	5000	10,000	15,000	20,000	25,000	30,000
Thrust (lb) . .	6420	5810	5200	4590	4000	3360	2700

Derive a curve showing the variation of true air speed in cruising flight with altitude.

$$C_L = \frac{W}{\frac{1}{2}\rho_0 V_E^2 S} = \frac{56,000 \times 841}{900 V_E^2} = \frac{52,400}{V_E^2}$$

$$C_D = 0\cdot016 + 0\cdot04 C_L^2$$

$$D = W\frac{C_D}{C_L}$$

The three equations above are used to produce Table 8.1, from which a curve of drag against E.A.S. is drawn. Note that there is no point in considering speeds below that for minimum drag in this problem.

TABLE 8.1

V_E (ft/sec) .	300	350	400	450	500	550	600
V_E^2 . . .	90,000	122,500	160,000	202,500	250,000	302,500	360,000
C_L . . .	0·580	0·427	0·327	0·259	0·2095	0·173	0·1453
$0\cdot04 C_L^2$ . .	0·0135	0·0073	0·0043	0·0027	0·0018	0·0012	0·0009
C_D . . .	0·0295	0·0233	0·0203	0·0187	0·0178	0·0172	0·0169
C_L/C_D . .	19·70	18·34	16·10	13·85	11·76	10·06	8·60
D (lb) . .	2843	3054	3472	4046	4750	5560	6510

The previously calculated result, that the minimum drag is 2833 lb at 288 ft/sec, E.A.S., may also be used. The points from the table and the engine curves (actually straight lines parallel to the E.A.S. axis) are plotted on the same axes.

The values given below for the cruising E.A.S. are then found from the points of intersection, and then divided by $\sqrt{\sigma}$, to give the true air speeds of cruise, whence the required curve is plotted,

Altitude (ft) . .	0	5000	10,000	15,000	20,000	25,000	30,000
E.A.S. (ft/sec) .	595	564	528	490	446	389	—
$\sqrt{\sigma}$	1	0·928	0·859	0·793	0·730	0·669	0·612
T.A.S. (ft/sec) .	595	607	615	619	613	581	—

From the graph of T.A.S. against altitude it is seen that

   (i) the maximum true air speed is about 620 ft/sec, and is attained at about 15,500 ft, and

  (ii) the maximum altitude attainable at this weight and throttle setting is a little less than 30,000 ft.

8.7. Gliding flight. Suppose an aeroplane to be flying straight and level at some altitude, and the engines then shut down. The drag force will still exist and therefore, as the aircraft follows its flight path, power will be expended in overcoming the drag. The only source from which this power can come, in still air, is the potential energy of the aeroplane. Unless the pilot moves the control column, the aircraft incidence, and therefore the lift coefficient, will be virtually unchanged. The flight speed will therefore change very little, and so there will be negligible change in the kinetic energy. In any case, kinetic energy could be used for only a limited period in a transition form of flight and ultimately a steady state of flight at constant speed must be attained. To give up this potential energy the aircraft must lose height, follow-ing a flight path inclined down-wards from the horizontal.

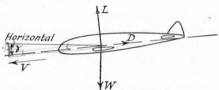

Consider the aircraft in Fig. 8.8, moving steadily under the influence of the lift, drag and weight at speed V ft/sec, T.A.S., along the path inclined at the angle γ to the horizon.

Fig. 8.8.—The forces on an aeroplane in steady gliding flight.

Resolving forces perpendicular to the flight path

$$L - W \cos \gamma = 0 \qquad . \qquad . \qquad . \qquad (8.34)$$

Resolving forces along the flight path

$$D - W \sin \gamma = 0 \qquad . \qquad . \qquad . \qquad (8.35)$$

Rearranging these two equations, and dividing, gives

$$\tan \gamma = \frac{D}{L} = \frac{C_D}{C_L} . \qquad . \qquad . \qquad (8.36)$$

This equation shows a very important point; that the angle of glide, and therefore the distance covered in gliding from a given height, depends only on the lift/drag ratio during the glide, and is independent of the weight of the aeroplane. It also follows from eqn. (8.36), that the flattest glide, and greatest distance covered, are achieved when the lift/drag ratio is a maxi-mum. This condition has already been discussed in § 8.3.1, and the con-clusion may also be explained by a qualitative argument. The work done against the drag per unit length of flight path is numerically equal to the drag, and this work is provided by loss of potential energy. Thus for minimum loss of potential energy per unit length of the flight path, i.e., flattest glide, the drag must be a minimum.

Consider small angles of glide, i.e., γ less than about $10°$. The approximations $\sin \gamma = \tan \gamma = \gamma$ and $\cos \gamma = 1$ are then permissible, and eqn. (8.36) may be written as

$$\sin \gamma = \frac{C_D}{C_L} \qquad . \qquad . \qquad . \qquad . \qquad (8.36.1)$$

while eqn. (8.34) becomes

$$L = W \quad . \qquad . \qquad . \qquad . \qquad . \qquad (8.34.1)$$

when
$$V = \sqrt{\frac{W}{\frac{1}{2}\rho S C_L}} \text{ (eqn. (8.3))}$$

The rate of descent, or sinking speed, v, is given by

$$v = V \sin \gamma \quad . \qquad . \qquad . \qquad . \qquad (8.37)$$

(No approximation is involved in this equation.)

Substituting eqns. (8.36.1) and (8.3) in eqn. (8.37) gives

$$v = \sqrt{\left(\frac{W}{\frac{1}{2}\rho S C_L}\right)}\left(\frac{C_D}{C_L}\right) = \left(\frac{W}{\frac{1}{2}\rho S}\right)^{\frac{1}{2}}\left(\frac{C_D}{C_L^{3/2}}\right) \quad . \qquad . \qquad (8.38)$$

This shows that, unlike the gliding angle, the sinking speed depends on the weight W, and on the altitude by virtue of the density ρ.

For the sinking speed to be a minimum, i.e., for the greatest duration of glide in still air from a given height, $C_D/C_L^{3/2}$ must be a minimum for a given aircraft at a given weight. This is exactly the same condition as that for the minimum power requirement in straight and level flight as discussed in § 8.5.1. This, too, may be explained qualitatively. As the aircraft glides, power is expended in overcoming the drag. This power is obtained by loss of potential energy, the power being equal to the rate of loss of potential energy. This rate of loss of potential energy, and hence the rate of loss of height, is a minimum when the power needed to overcome the drag is itself a minimum.

8.7.1. Steep angles of glide. On relaxing the restriction to shallow angles of glide the approximations made above are no longer permissible. Eqn. (8.34) gives

$$L = W \cos \gamma \quad . \qquad . \qquad . \qquad . \qquad (8.34.2)$$

whence
$$V = \sqrt{\frac{L}{\frac{1}{2}\rho S C_L}} = \sqrt{\frac{W \cos \gamma}{\frac{1}{2}\rho S C_L}}$$

$$= \sqrt{\frac{W}{\frac{1}{2}\rho S C_L}} (\cos \gamma)^{\frac{1}{2}} \quad . \qquad . \qquad . \qquad (8.39)$$

and the actual gliding speed is seen to be less than that for straight and level flight at the same weight, incidence, and altitude by the factor $(\cos \gamma)^{\frac{1}{2}}$.

Eqn. (8.36) still applies as it stands, since it involves no approximation, i.e.,

$$\tan \gamma = \frac{D}{L} = \frac{C_D}{C_L}$$

Reference to Fig. 8.9 shows that

$$\sin \gamma = \frac{C_D}{(C_L^2 + C_D^2)^{\frac{1}{2}}} \qquad . \qquad . \qquad . \qquad (8.40.1)$$

and

$$\cos \gamma = \frac{C_L}{(C_L^2 + C_D^2)^{\frac{1}{2}}} \qquad . \qquad . \qquad . \qquad (8.40.2)$$

The sinking speed, v, is then given by

$$v = V \sin \gamma = \left(\frac{W}{\frac{1}{2}\rho S C_L}\right)^{\frac{1}{2}} \left(\frac{C_L}{(C_L^2 + C_D^2)^{\frac{1}{4}}}\right)^{\frac{1}{2}} \left(\frac{C_D}{(C_L^2 + C_D^2)^{\frac{1}{4}}}\right)$$

$$= \left(\frac{W}{\frac{1}{2}\rho S}\right)^{\frac{1}{2}} \frac{C_D}{(C_L^2 + C_D^2)^{\frac{3}{4}}} \qquad . \qquad . \qquad . \qquad (8.41)$$

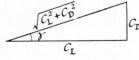

FIG. 8.9.—Showing the relationship between γ, C_D, and C_L.

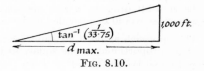

FIG. 8.10.

Example 8.5. A sailplane weighs 1000 lb and has a wing loading of 12·5 lb/ft². Its drag equation is

$$C_D = 0{\cdot}010 + 0{\cdot}022C_L^2$$

After completing a launch at 1000 ft in still air, what is the greatest distance the sailplane can cover, and what is the greatest duration of flight possible, assuming in both cases flight over level ground? Find also the corresponding speeds of flight. Ignore changes of density of the atmosphere.

(i) For greatest distance,

$$C_{L\,md} = \sqrt{\frac{C_{D_0}}{k}} = \sqrt{\frac{0{\cdot}010}{0{\cdot}022}} = 0{\cdot}675$$

$$C_{D\,md} = 2C_{D_0} = 0{\cdot}020$$

$$\therefore \left(\frac{L}{D}\right)_{max} = \frac{0{\cdot}675}{0{\cdot}020} = 33{\cdot}75$$

$$\therefore d_{max} = 1000 \times 33{\cdot}75 = 33{,}750 \text{ ft} \quad \text{(from Fig. 8.10)}$$
$$= \underline{6{\cdot}4 \text{ statute miles.}}$$

$$V_{md} = \sqrt{\frac{w}{\frac{1}{2}\rho C_{L\,md}}} = \sqrt{\frac{12{\cdot}5 \times 841}{0{\cdot}675}}$$

$$= \underline{125 \text{ ft/sec}}$$

(ii) For greatest duration (or time).

$$C_{L\,mp} = C_{L\,md}\sqrt{3} = 0{\cdot}675\sqrt{3} = 1{\cdot}17$$

$$C_{D\,mp} = 4C_{D_0} = 0{\cdot}040$$

$$\therefore \left(\frac{L}{D}\right)_{mp} = \frac{1{\cdot}17}{0{\cdot}04} = 29{\cdot}2$$

$$V_{mp} = \sqrt{\frac{12{\cdot}5 \times 841}{1{\cdot}17}} = 94{\cdot}9 \text{ ft/sec}$$

Since the angle of glide is small, the approximations

$$\sin \gamma = \tan \gamma = \frac{1}{29 \cdot 2}$$

may be made. Therefore

$$v = V \sin \gamma = 94 \cdot 9 \times \frac{1}{29 \cdot 2} = 3 \cdot 25 \text{ ft/sec}$$

$$\therefore \text{ time of descent } = \frac{1000}{3 \cdot 25} = 308 \text{ sec}$$

$$= \underline{5 \text{ min } 8 \text{ sec}}$$

Example 8.6. The sailplane of the previous Example is fitted with a flapped wing with a maximum lift coefficient of 2·50. When approaching to land the aircraft is flown at a speed 15% greater than the stalling speed in the glide, and is required to have an approach gliding angle of 20°. Estimate the increase in the zero-lift drag coefficient necessary to attain this gliding angle. (This drag increase would be provided in part by the flaps and in part by air brakes.)

The approach angle is 20°, and cos 20° = 0·94. Since the lift coefficient is inversely proportional to the square of the flight speed, the lift coefficient on the approach is $2 \cdot 50/(1 \cdot 15)^2 = 1 \cdot 89$.

$$\therefore \text{ approach gliding speed } = \sqrt{\frac{w \cos \gamma}{\frac{1}{2}\rho C_L}}$$

$$= \sqrt{\frac{12 \cdot 5 \times 841 \times 0 \cdot 94}{1 \cdot 89}} = 72 \cdot 5 \text{ ft/sec}$$

Now

$$\tan \gamma = \tan 20° = 0 \cdot 364 = \frac{C_D}{C_L}$$

$$\therefore C_D = 0 \cdot 364 C_L = 0 \cdot 364 \times 1 \cdot 89 = 0 \cdot 689$$

The total drag coefficient according to the original drag equation is

$$C_D = 0 \cdot 010 + 0 \cdot 022(1 \cdot 89)^2 = 0 \cdot 0885$$

$\therefore$ extra zero-lift drag coefficient required

$$= 0 \cdot 689 - 0 \cdot 0885 = \underline{0 \cdot 6005}.$$

It should be noted that, in practice, the flaps and air-brakes would also increase the lift-dependent drag coefficient factor, but this has been ignored here.

Example 8.7. With air-brakes extended, the sailplane of the two prior Examples has the drag equation

$$C_D = 0 \cdot 700 + 0 \cdot 022 C_L^2$$

Estimate the gliding angle and rate of descent when diving with air-brake extended at 100 ft/sec at sea-level.

$$V = \left(\frac{w \cos \gamma}{\frac{1}{2}\rho C_L}\right)^{\frac{1}{2}}$$

i.e., in this particular case,

$$100 = \left(\frac{12 \cdot 5 \times 841 \cos \gamma}{C_L}\right)^{\frac{1}{2}}$$

i.e.,

$$\frac{\cos \gamma}{C_L} = \frac{(100)^2}{12 \cdot 5 \times 841} = 0 \cdot 950$$

Now
$$\cos \gamma = \frac{C_L}{(C_L^2 + C_D^2)^{\frac{1}{2}}}$$

$$\therefore \frac{1}{(C_L^2 + C_D^2)^{\frac{1}{2}}} = \frac{\cos \gamma}{C_L} = 0\cdot950$$

whence $C_L^2 + C_D^2 = 1\cdot11$

Now $C_D = 0\cdot700 + 0\cdot022C_L^2$

and therefore

$$C_D^2 = 0\cdot4900 + 0\cdot0308C_L^2 + 0\cdot000484C_L^4$$

$$\therefore \ C_L^2 + C_D^2 = 0\cdot49 + 1\cdot0308C_L^2 + 0\cdot000484C_L^4 = 1\cdot11$$

Now the factor multiplying C_L^4 is much smaller than that multiplying C_L^2. Since C_L may be expected to be less than unity, $C_L^4 < C_L^2$, and thus the term in C_L^4 may safely be ignored in this present Example.

Thus the last equation above reduces approximately to
$$1\cdot0308C_L^2 = 1\cdot11 - 0\cdot49 = 0\cdot62$$
whence a good approximation to C_L is

$$C_L = 0\cdot7756$$

Then $C_D = 0\cdot7 + 0\cdot022(0\cdot7756)^2 = 0\cdot7132$

$$\therefore \tan \gamma = \frac{C_D}{C_L} = \frac{0\cdot7132}{0\cdot7756} = 0\cdot9196$$

From tables $\gamma = \underline{42° \ 36'}$.

The correctness of this result may be checked as follows:

$$L = C_L \tfrac{1}{2}\rho V^2 S = 0\cdot7756 \times \frac{1}{841} \times (100)^2 \times \frac{1000}{12\cdot5}$$
$$= 738 \text{ lb}$$

Also $L = W \cos \gamma = 1000 \cos (42° \ 36')$
$$= 736\cdot1 \text{ lb}$$

The discrepancy between these two values for the lift is only $1\cdot9$ lb, i.e., well within the accuracy of the arithmetic, and it is therefore safe to conclude that the result of $42° \ 36'$ for the gliding angle is correct. Then

rate of descent $v = V \sin \gamma = 100 \sin 42° \ 36'$
$$= \underline{67\cdot7 \text{ ft/sec}}$$

8.7.2. Time of descent. If an aircraft is gliding at a constant incidence (e.g., that for flattest glide or minimum sinking speed) its equivalent air speed and gliding angle are, from the foregoing work, independent of the altitude.

Then

$$v = V \sin \gamma = (V_E \sin \gamma)\sigma^{-\frac{1}{2}} = v_0\sigma^{-\frac{1}{2}}$$

where $v_0 = V_E \sin \gamma$, the rate of descent at sea-level I.S.A.

Now since $v = -\dfrac{dh}{dt}$, where $t =$ time in seconds

$$dt = -\frac{1}{v}dh$$

L

If an aircraft is at height h_1 at time t_1, and glides to a lower altitude h_2, arriving there at a later time t_2, then

$$\int_{t_1}^{t_2} dt = -\frac{1}{v_0} \int_{h_1}^{h_2} \sigma^{\frac{1}{2}} dh \qquad . \qquad . \qquad . \qquad (8.42)$$

Now, from the work on the troposphere in § 3.3,

$$\sigma = \left(\frac{T_0 - Lh}{T_0}\right)^{\frac{g-LR}{LR}} = \left(1 - \frac{L}{T_0}h\right)^{\frac{g-LR}{LR}}$$

where L is the temperature lapse rate, °C/ft
and T_0 is the temperature at sea-level.

With this expression for σ, the integral on right-hand side of eqn. (8.42) becomes

$$\int_{h_1}^{h_2} \sigma^{\frac{1}{2}} dh = \int_{h_1}^{h_2} \left[1 - \frac{L}{T_0}h\right]^{\frac{g-LR}{2LR}} dh$$

$$= \left[\frac{1}{m}\left(1 - \frac{L}{T_0}h\right)^m\left(-\frac{T_0}{L}\right)\right]_{h_1}^{h_2}$$

where $m = \dfrac{g - LR}{2LR} + 1 = \dfrac{g + LR}{2LR}$

Thus

$$\int_{h_1}^{h_2} \sigma^{\frac{1}{2}} dh = -\frac{T_0}{mL}\left[\left(1 - \frac{L}{T_0}h_2\right)^m - \left(1 - \frac{L}{T_0}h_1\right)^m\right]$$

$$= -\frac{T_0}{mL}\left[\left(\frac{T_0 - Lh_2}{T_0}\right)^m - \left(\frac{T_0 - Lh_1}{T_0}\right)^m\right]$$

But $T = T_0 - Lh$, and therefore the above expression becomes

$$-\frac{T_0}{mL}\left[\left(\frac{T_2}{T_0}\right)^m - \left(\frac{T_1}{T_0}\right)^m\right]$$

where T_1 is the atmospheric temperature at h_1
and T_2 is the atmospheric temperature at h_2.

Therefore eqn. (8.42) may now be written as

$$t_2 - t_1 = \int_{t_1}^{t_2} dt = \frac{T_0}{v_0 mL}\left[\left(\frac{T_2}{T_0}\right)^m - \left(\frac{T_1}{T_0}\right)^m\right]$$

and $t_2 - t_1 = t_d$, the time of descent.

In the International Standard Atmosphere, $T_0 = 288°\text{K}$ and $L = 0\cdot00198°\text{C/ft}$. Using these values, and also the standard values for R for air, and of g,

$$m = 3\cdot128 \quad \text{and} \quad \frac{T_0}{mL} = 46{,}500$$

Therefore, in the I.S.A. troposphere,

$$t_d = \frac{46{,}500}{v_0}\left[\left(\frac{T_2}{288}\right)^{3\cdot128} - \left(\frac{T_1}{288}\right)^{3\cdot128}\right] \qquad . \qquad . \qquad (8.43)$$

t_d being in seconds.

If the lower altitude h_2 is sea-level, eqn. (8.43) reduces to

$$t_d = \frac{46{,}500}{v_0}\left[1 - \left(\frac{T_1}{288}\right)^{3\cdot128}\right] \text{ sec} \qquad . \qquad . \quad (8.43.1)$$

Example 8.8. Estimate the maximum duration in still air for the sailplane of the previous Examples after reaching 20,000 ft above a plain which is 1000 ft above mean-sea-level.

From the results of Example 8.5, the minimum sinking speed at sea-level is 3·25 ft/sec, i.e., for this problem $v_0 = 3\cdot25$ ft/sec.

At 20,000 ft,

$$\text{temperature} = 288 - 20 \times 1\cdot98 = 288 - 39\cdot6$$
$$= 248\cdot4°\text{K}$$

$$\therefore \left(\frac{288}{T_1}\right)^{3\cdot128} = \left(1 + \frac{39\cdot6}{248\cdot6}\right)^{3\cdot128} = 1\cdot589$$

At 1000 ft,

$$\text{temperature} = 286\cdot02°\text{K}$$

and

$$\left(\frac{288}{T_2}\right)^{3\cdot128} = 1\cdot0216$$

Therefore time of descent t_d is given by

$$t_d = \frac{46{,}500}{3\cdot25}\left(\frac{1}{1\cdot0216} - \frac{1}{1\cdot589}\right)$$
$$= \frac{46{,}500}{3\cdot25}\left(\frac{1\cdot589 - 1\cdot022}{1\cdot589 \times 1\cdot022}\right) = 5000 \text{ sec}$$
$$= \underline{83 \text{ min } 20 \text{ sec}}$$

8.8. Climbing flight. Suppose an aeroplane to be flying straight and level at some speed and altitude, and the engine thrust and power is increased above that required for straight and level flight. Then more work is being done on the aircraft than is needed to overcome the drag, and the energy of the aircraft must increase. Either the kinetic energy or the potential energy, or both, may increase.

If the pilot moves the control column, allowing the aircraft incidence to change suitably, the aircraft will accelerate, absorbing the extra work in increasing its own kinetic energy, until a speed is reached at which the new drag and thrust are in equilibrium.

If, on the other hand, the pilot keeps the control column fixed, the aircraft incidence cannot change, and therefore the speed cannot increase. Thus the extra work done must be absorbed in increasing the potential energy of the aeroplane, and the aircraft must climb to a greater altitude.

Consider the aircraft of Fig. 8.11, climbing steadily with speed V ft/sec along a flight path inclined at the angle θ to the horizontal under the influence of the lift, the drag, the weight and the engine thrust.

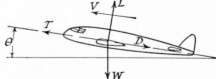

Fig. 8.11.—The forces on an aeroplane in steady climbing flight.

Resolving forces perpendicular to the flight path

$$L - W \cos \theta = 0 \qquad . \qquad . \qquad . \qquad (8.44)$$

It will be noted that this equation is identical with eqn. (8.34). Resolving forces parallel to the flight path

$$T - D - W \sin \theta = 0 \qquad . \qquad . \qquad . \qquad (8.45)$$

Eqn. (8.44) gives

$$L = W \cos \theta \qquad . \qquad . \qquad . \qquad . \qquad (8.44.1)$$

and it follows, as in § 8.7 (gliding flight), that the flight speed is less than that for straight and level flight under the same conditions by the factor $(\cos \theta)^{\frac{1}{2}}$.

Rearranging eqn. (8.45) gives

$$\sin \theta = \frac{T - D}{W} \qquad . \qquad . \qquad . \qquad . \qquad (8.46)$$

The rate of climb, v, is given by

$$v = V \sin \theta \qquad . \qquad . \qquad . \qquad . \qquad (8.47)$$

8.8.1. Climb at shallow angles; engine performance expressed in terms of thrust.

The restriction to a small angle of climb, i.e., less than about 13°, permits the approximation

$$\cos \theta = 1$$

It then follows that

$$L = W \qquad . \qquad . \qquad . \qquad . \qquad . \qquad (8.48)$$

and

$$V = \sqrt{\frac{W}{\frac{1}{2}\rho S C_L}} \qquad . \qquad . \qquad . \qquad . \qquad (8.49)$$

Example 8.9. An aeroplane weighs 36,000 lb and has a wing area of 450 ft². At a flight speed of 300 ft/sec the engines give a thrust of 6000 lb. If the aircraft drag equation is

$$C_D = 0.014 + 0.05C_L^2$$

find the angle and rate of climb at sea-level at 300 ft/sec flight speed.

Assuming the angle of climb to be small,

$$L = W = 36,000 \text{ lb}$$

$$\therefore \ C_L = \frac{36,000 \times 841}{450 \times 300 \times 300} = 0.749$$

$$\therefore \ C_D = 0.014 + 0.05(0.749)^2 = 0.0420$$

$$\therefore \ \frac{L}{D} = \frac{0.749}{0.042} = 17.81$$

$$\therefore \ \text{drag } D = \frac{W}{L/D} = \frac{36,000}{17.81} = 2020 \text{ lb}$$

$$\therefore \ \sin \theta = \frac{T - D}{W} = \frac{6000 - 2020}{36,000} = 0.1106$$

whence

$$\theta = 6° 21',$$

which is small within the present approximation.

rate of climb $v = V \sin \theta = 300 \times 0.1106 = 33.18$ ft/sec
$$= \underline{1990 \text{ ft/min.}}$$

Note that it is conventional to express rates of climb in feet/minute.

Maximum rate of climb at shallow angles of climb; engine performance expressed in terms of thrust. The rate of climb, v, may, for small angles of climb, be written as

$$v = V \sin \theta = \left(\frac{W}{\tfrac{1}{2}\rho S C_L}\right)^{\tfrac{1}{2}}\left(\frac{T-D}{W}\right)$$

i.e.,

$$v = \left(\frac{W}{\tfrac{1}{2}\rho S}\right)^{\tfrac{1}{2}}(C_L)^{-\tfrac{1}{2}}\left(\frac{T}{W} - \frac{D}{W}\right) \qquad . \qquad . \qquad (8.50)$$

Now since, to the present approximation, $L = W$, eqn. (8.50) becomes

$$v = \left(\frac{W}{\tfrac{1}{2}\rho S}\right)^{\tfrac{1}{2}}\left[\frac{T}{W}C_L^{-1/2} - \frac{C_{D0} + kC_L^2}{(C_L)^{3/2}}\right] \qquad . \qquad . \qquad (8.51)$$

For a given aeroplane to have the maximum rate of climb, the quantity in the square brackets must be a maximum. An assumption, which is frequently made in examples and examination questions, is that the thrust is independent of flight speed, and therefore independent of C_L. This assumption, in practice, gives a fair approximation for turbo-jet engines, and applies with good accuracy to rockets. With this assumption, the condition for maximum rate of climb may be found from

$$\frac{d}{dC_L}\left[\frac{T}{W}C_L^{-1/2} - \frac{C_{D0} + kC_L^2}{(C_L)^{3/2}}\right] = 0$$

i.e.,

$$-\frac{1}{2}\frac{T}{W}C_L^{-3/2} - \frac{C_L^{3/2} . 2kC_L - (C_{D0} + kC_L^2)\tfrac{3}{2}C_L^{\tfrac{1}{2}}}{C_L^3} = 0$$

Multiplying by $2C_L^{5/2}$ this becomes, after very slight rearrangement

$$kC_L^2 + \frac{T}{W}C_L - 3C_{D0} = 0 \qquad . \qquad . \qquad . \qquad (8.52)$$

which is a simple quadratic equation in C_L.

Example 8.10. Estimate the maximum rate of climb at sea-level for the aircraft of the previous Example 8.9 and the corresponding flight speed and angle of climb, if the engine thrust is 6000 lb at all speeds at sea-level.

Putting the appropriate numbers in eqn. (8.52) gives

$$0.05C_L^2 + \frac{6000}{36,000}C_L - 3(0.014) = 0$$

i.e., $0.3C_L^2 + C_L - 0.252 = 0$ (after multiplying by 6). The two solutions to this equation are

$$C_L = 0.2352 \quad \text{and} \quad C_L = -3.5 \text{ approx.}$$

The negative root is obviously unsuitable, and therefore the positive root is taken.

Since the angle of climb is assumed to be small,

$$V = \sqrt{\frac{36,000 \times 841}{450 \times 0.2352}} = \underline{535 \text{ ft/sec}}$$

$$C_D = 0.014 + (0.2352)^2 \times 0.05 = 0.01676$$

$$\therefore \text{ drag } D = W\frac{C_D}{C_L} = \frac{36,000 \times 0.01676}{0.2352} = 2570 \text{ lb}$$

$$\therefore \sin \theta = \frac{6000 - 2570}{36,000} = 0.0953$$

whence the angle of climb θ is $\underline{5° \ 28'}$.

Now $\quad\quad\quad \cos \theta = 0.9955,$ and so $(\cos \theta)^{\frac{1}{2}} = 0.9978$

The speed calculated above (535 ft/sec) should strictly be multiplied by $(\cos \theta)^{\frac{1}{2}}$, i.e., by 0.9978. It will be realized that the effect of this factor is negligible, and thus the assumption made, that $\cos \theta = 1$, is justified. The rate of climb,

$$v = V \sin \theta = 535 \times 0.0953 = 51.0 \text{ ft/sec}$$
$$= \underline{3060 \text{ ft/min}}$$

Note that although this is a smaller angle of climb than found in the previous Example, the speed along the flight path is so much higher, that a higher rate of climb is obtained.

In practical cases, where the engine thrust varies with speed, this direct method of finding the maximum rate of climb is not applicable. It is then necessary to calculate the rate of climb for a number of flight speeds, and find the maximum by plotting, or by trial and error. The value given by this direct method is then useful as a guide to suitable speeds to be used.

8.8.2. Climb at shallow angles; engine performance expressed in terms of thrust horse-power.
When the angle of climb is small, i.e., less than about 13°, the changes in lift, drag and speed caused by flight path inclination can be ignored. It follows that the power required to overcome the drag on the climb is negligibly different from that required for straight and level flight under the same conditions. The curve of $P\sqrt{\sigma}$ against equivalent air speed, calculated for straight and level flight, may therefore be taken to represent the power required to overcome the drag on the climb.

It has been seen that a speed V_1, say, represents the condition for straight and level flight at sea-level. Suppose now that the aircraft is flying, with the same throttle setting, at sea-level at a lower speed V_2. The power available is $P_a\sqrt{\sigma}$ while the power required to overcome the drag, $P_r\sqrt{\sigma}$, is considerably less. There is therefore an excess of power, ΔP, given by

$$P_a - P_r = \Delta P = \frac{\Delta(P\sqrt{\sigma})}{\sqrt{\sigma}} \quad . \quad\quad . \quad\quad . \quad (8.53)$$

This excess power will be absorbed directly in increasing the potential energy of the aircraft, which may therefore be regarded as a dead load being raised by application of power ΔP.

Then
$$\Delta P = \frac{Wv}{33,000} \qquad \qquad (8.54)$$

where W = weight of the aircraft (lb)
and v = rate of climb (ft/min)

which may be rearranged as

$$v = \frac{33,000\Delta P}{W} \qquad \qquad (8.55)$$

Example 8.11. If the aeroplane of the two previous examples be fitted with engines and airscrews which, at 300 ft/sec at sea-level, give 3500 thrust H.P., calculate the rate and angle of climb at that speed.

The drag at 300 ft/sec has already (Example 8.9) been found to be 2020 lb, and therefore the thrust horse-power required to overcome the drag is

$$P_r = \frac{2020 \times 300}{550} = 1100 \text{ T.H.P.}$$

The excess H.P. is therefore

$$3500 - 1100 = 2400 \text{ H.P.}$$

Therefore the rate of climb is

$$v = \frac{33,000 \times 2400}{36,000} = 2200 \text{ ft/min.}$$

The angle of climb, θ, is obtained from

$$v = V \sin \theta$$

i.e., $$\sin \theta = \frac{v}{V} = \frac{2200}{300 \times 60} = 0\cdot122$$

whence $$\theta = 7°\ 0'.$$

Maximum rate of climb at shallow angles; engine performance expressed in terms of thrust horse-power. In most practical cases the thrust horse-power available varies with flight speed, partly due to variations in engine power at the crankshaft, and partly due to variations in airscrew efficiency. Small effects are also produced by variation in the power absorbed by engine cooling. (It is interesting to note that a well-designed cooling system for a reciprocating engine may actually produce slight positive power, the radiator or cowl acting as a small ram-jet engine.)

Inspection of eqn. (8.55) shows that the maximum rate of climb occurs when the value of ΔP is a maximum. This maximum may be found by plotting the values of ΔP, measured from the $P\sqrt{\sigma}$, E.A.S. graph, against speed and inspecting for the maximum.

A simplification which may often be made, and which will usually give a good approximation to the maximum rate of climb, is to assume that the thrust horse-power available is independent of speed. It is then seen (Fig. 8.7) that the maximum excess horse-power, and therefore the maximum rate of climb, occurs at the minimum power condition, as discussed in § 8.5.1.

Example 8.12. The aircraft in the previous Examples is re-engined with turbo-prop engines giving the same maximum speed at sea-level as was obtained with the original turbo-jets. Calculate the maximum rate of climb and the speed at which it occurs if the available thrust horse-power is independent of the flight speed.

The maximum speed with the turbo-jets can be found by means of eqn. (8.20.3), namely

$$\frac{D}{D_{\min}} = \tfrac{1}{2}(m^2 + m^{-2})$$

For the minimum drag, $\quad C_{L\,\mathrm{md}} = \sqrt{\dfrac{C_{D0}}{k}} = 0.53$

Since the drag coefficient $\quad C_{D\,\mathrm{md}} = 2C_{D0} = 0.028,$
the minimum drag is

$$D_{\min} = 36,000 \times \frac{0.028}{0.530} = 1905 \text{ lb}$$

The thrust available is 6000 lb and therefore, at top speed,

$$\frac{6000}{1905} = \tfrac{1}{2}(m^2 + m^{-2})$$

whence $\qquad\qquad m^2 + m^{-2} = 6.3,\quad$ or $\quad m^4 - 6.3m^2 + 1 = 0$

a quadratic equation in m^2 the solutions to which are $m^2 = 0.163$ or 6.137. The first of these represents the low-speed solution and is therefore ignored. Thus the required value of m is $\sqrt{(6.137)} = 2.48$, i.e., the maximum speed is 2.48 times the minimum drag speed.
Since $C_{L\,\mathrm{md}} = 0.53$, the minimum drag speed is

$$V_{\mathrm{md}} = 29\sqrt{\frac{36,000}{450 \times 0.53}} = 356 \text{ ft/sec}$$

i.e., the maximum speed is

$$356 \times 2.48 = 884 \text{ ft/sec}$$

At such a high speed the effects of Mach number on the drag would be appreciable, but are ignored here for simplicity.
The thrust horse-power required at this maximum speed is

$$P_{\max} = \frac{TV}{550} = \frac{6000 \times 884}{550} = 9640 \text{ T.H.P.}$$

and this power is available at all speeds.
The maximum rate of climb will occur at the minimum power speed, at which $V_{\mathrm{mp}} = 0.76V_{\mathrm{md}} = \underline{271 \text{ ft/sec}}$ by eqn. (8.28) and since

$$(L/D)_{\mathrm{mp}} = 0.866(L/D)_{\max}$$

$$D_{\mathrm{mp}} = D_{\min}/0.866 = \frac{1905}{0.866} = 2200 \text{ lb}$$

Thus the minimum power required is

$$P_{\min} = \frac{2200 \times 271}{550} = 1084 \text{ T.H.P.}$$

The excess horse-power is therefore $9640 - 1084 = 8556$ H.P. and the maximum rate of climb is then

$$v_{\max} = \frac{8556 \times 33,000}{36,000} = \underline{7950 \text{ ft/min}}$$

It can be seen that this gives an angle of climb which is well in excess of the limit for the 'shallow climb' approximation to hold, but it does represent a first approximation to the true rate of climb, which could be found from the methods of the following section.

It should be noted that a single, fairly small, turbo-jet engine will give a thrust of 6000 lb, whereas a number of large turbo-prop engines would be required to give the 10,000 T.H.P. required in this Example. This Example is unrealistic to this extent, but serves a useful illustrative purpose.

Comparison of the answers to Examples 8.10 and 8.12 shows that, for the latter, the maximum rate of climb occurs at a considerably lower flight speed than for the former. This may be explained by reference to Fig. 8.12, which shows a typical curve of power required against speed. Line (a) represents the thrust horse-power available from an idealized turbo-jet engine giving a thrust independent of speed (thrust horse-power proportional to flight speed), while line (b) represents an engine giving a thrust horse-power which is independent of the speed (e.g., an idealized turbo-prop or piston engine and airscrew combination). It is at once seen that the maxi-

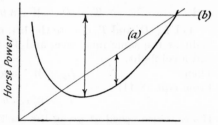

Fig. 8.12.—Comparison of speeds for maximum rate of climb for (a) idealized turbo-jet engine and (b) idealized piston or turbo-prop engine.

mum excess horse-power occurs at a much higher speed for line (a) than for line (b).

Maximum angle of climb at shallow angles; engine performance expressed in terms of horse-power. Since, for small angles of climb,

$$\sin \theta = \frac{T - D}{W} = \frac{T}{W} - \frac{D}{L}$$

and

$$T = \frac{550P}{V}$$

it is, in principle, possible to find the condition for the angle of climb to be a maximum. Analysis for this case leads, however, to an equation of the form

$$aC_L^{3/2} - bC_L^2 + c = 0$$

where a, b and c are constants related to the power available, the lift-dependent drag coefficient factor k, and the zero-lift drag coefficient. Such an equation is difficult to solve, and the easiest method of finding the maximum angle of climb is by trial and error, calculating the angle of climb for a number of assumed speeds, and plotting for the maximum.

Calculation of the maximum angle of climb is of importance in connection with take-off and balked landing performance. A *balked landing* is an attempted landing, which for some reason cannot be completed, the aeroplane being required to climb away before touching-down and to make another circuit before a second attempt to land. Since, in a balked landing, the wing-flaps are usually in the fully down position, giving high drag, the balked landing requirement is among the most difficult of the Airworthiness Requirements to meet.

8.8.3. Correction for steep angles of climb. When the angle of climb exceeds about 13° it is no longer acceptable to ignore the effect of this angle without undue loss of accuracy. Instead the equations must be solved incorporating the correct values of the trigonometric functions of θ. The equations are:

$$L - W \cos \theta = 0 \text{ (eqn. (8.44))}$$

and $$T - D - W \sin \theta = 0 \text{ (eqn. (8.45))}$$

Let L_0, D_0 and T_0 denote the lift, drag and thrust in straight and level flight at the same incidence, and V_0 the corresponding speed of straight and level flight.

Then $$L_0 = W \quad \text{and} \quad D_0 = T_0$$

From eqn. (8.44)

$$L = W \cos \theta = L_0 \cos \theta \qquad . \qquad . \qquad . \qquad (8.56)$$

Hence, since speed at given lift coefficient is proportional to the square root of the lift,

$$V = V_0 (\cos \theta)^{\frac{1}{2}} \qquad . \qquad . \qquad . \qquad . \qquad (8.57)$$

Since the climb, and the related straight and level flight are supposed to occur at the same incidence, the lift/drag ratio of the aeroplane is the same in both cases, and therefore

$$\frac{L}{D} = \frac{L_0}{D_0} \qquad . \qquad . \qquad . \qquad . \qquad (8.58)$$

Thus eqns. (8.56), (8.57) and (8.58) may be combined as

$$\frac{L}{L_0} = \frac{D}{D_0} = \left(\frac{V}{V_0}\right)^2 = \cos \theta \qquad . \qquad . \qquad . \qquad (8.59)$$

$$\therefore T = D + W \sin \theta \text{ (from eqn. (8.45))}$$

$$= D\left(1 + \frac{W}{D} \sin \theta\right)$$

$$= D_0 \cos \theta\left(1 + \frac{W}{D_0 \cos \theta} \sin \theta\right)$$

$$= D_0 \cos \theta\left(1 + \frac{L_0}{D_0} \tan \theta\right) \qquad . \qquad . \qquad . \qquad (8.60)$$

Now L_0/D_0 is the lift/drag ratio for the incidence concerned. Since also $T_0 = D_0$, eqn. (8.60) becomes

$$\frac{T}{T_0} = \left(1 + \frac{L}{D} \tan \theta\right) \cos \theta \qquad . \qquad . \qquad . \qquad (8.61.1)$$

$$= \cos \theta + \frac{L}{D} \sin \theta \qquad . \qquad . \qquad . \qquad (8.61.2)$$

T/T_0 is plotted against θ for various values of the lift/drag ratio in Fig. 8.13. Two points may be noted from this plot:

(i) When $\theta = 90°$, $\dfrac{T}{T_0} = \dfrac{L}{D}$. This is merely a reflection of the fact that for vertical flight at constant speed the lift must equal the weight.

(ii) For any given lift/drag ratio, there is a maximum value of T/T_0, which may be located as follows:

for the maximum

$$\frac{d}{d\theta}\left(\cos\theta + \frac{L}{D}\sin\theta\right) = -\sin\theta + \frac{L}{D}\cos\theta = 0$$

whence

$$\tan\theta = \frac{L}{D} \qquad . \qquad . \qquad . \qquad . \qquad (8.62)$$

Then the maximum value of T/T_0 is, from eqn. (8.61.1),

$$\left(\frac{T}{T_0}\right)_{max} = \sqrt{1 + \left(\frac{L}{D}\right)^2} \qquad . \qquad . \qquad . \qquad (8.63)$$

since $\qquad \sec^2\theta = 1 + \tan^2\theta$, and $\tan\theta = \dfrac{L}{D}$

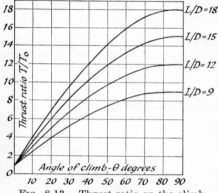

FIG. 8.13.—Thrust ratio on the climb.

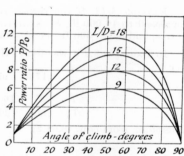

FIG. 8.14.—Power ratio on the climb.

If P is the thrust horse-power used on the climb and P_0 is the power required for straight and level flight at the same weight, incidence and altitude,

$$\frac{P}{P_0} = \frac{TV}{T_0 V_0} = \left(1 + \frac{L}{D}\tan\theta\right)(\cos\theta)(\cos\theta)^{\frac{1}{2}}$$

$$= \left(1 + \frac{L}{D}\tan\theta\right)(\cos\theta)^{\frac{3}{2}} \qquad . \qquad . \qquad . \qquad . \qquad (8.64)$$

P/P_0 is plotted against θ for various values of the lift/drag ratio in Fig. 8.14.

Again, two points are noted:

(i) When $\theta = 90°$, $P/P_0 = 0$. From eqn. (8.57), when $\theta = 90°$ cos $\theta = 0$ and $V = 0$. This means that the weight is completely balanced by the engine thrust, and no lift is needed from the wings, and thus no forward speed is necessary. Since $V = 0$, the power required is zero. This is, however, the thrust horse-power; considerable engine power would be required to drive the airscrews which are producing a thrust equal to the weight of the aircraft. This state of flight is of interest in connection with vertical take-off aircraft.

(ii) It is seen that, in general, any given value of P/P_0 produces two values of θ for a given lift/drag ratio. For example, if the power ratio is 2 : 1 and the lift/drag ratio is 15, the two possible angles of climb are 4° and 89°. The lower value is a practical possibility for a conventional aeroplane, while the higher value is relevant to the transition phase of a vertical take-off, though in such a case the aeroplane would probably be accelerating, in addition to climbing. With a lift/drag ratio of 6 and a power ratio of 4, the two solutions become coincident and an aircraft with this lift/drag ratio cannot use a greater power ratio than 4 : 1. Attempts to use a greater power ratio than 4 : 1 at this lift/drag ratio lead to no solution for θ. The physical meaning of this is that rectilinear climb becomes impossible, and either the power available or the lift/drag ratio must be changed. It will be noted from Fig. 8.14 that these limiting values of the power ratio occur for angles of climb in the neighbourhood of 50° to 55°.

Example 8.13. If the thrust available on the aircraft of Example 8.9 is increased to 16,000 lb, estimate the angle and rate of climb at the incidence corresponding to 300 ft/sec in straight and level flight.

In Example 8.9 it was found that

$$\frac{L}{D} = 17\cdot81 \quad \text{and the drag is 2020 lb}$$

$$\therefore \frac{T}{T_0} = \frac{T}{D_0} = \frac{16{,}000}{2020} = 7\cdot92$$

Therefore, from eqn. (8.61.2),

$$7\cdot92 = \cos\theta + 17\cdot81\sin\theta$$

or
$$17\cdot81\sin\theta = 7\cdot92 - \cos\theta$$

i.e.,
$$(17\cdot81)^2(1 - \cos^2\theta) = (7\cdot92 - \cos\theta)^2$$

which reduces to

$$318\cdot20\cos^2\theta - 15\cdot84\cos\theta - 254\cdot47 = 0$$

a simple quadratic equation in cos θ, the solutions to which are cos $\theta = 0\cdot9195$ or a negative number, which is ignored.

From tables, $\theta = 23° 9'$

and $\sin\theta = 0\cdot3931$

while $(\cos\theta)^{\frac{1}{2}} = 0\cdot9589$

Then $V = V_0(\cos\theta)^{\frac{1}{2}} = 300 \times 0\cdot9589$

$$= 288 \text{ ft/sec}$$

$$\therefore \text{ rate of climb } v = V\sin\theta = 288 \times 0\cdot3931 = 113 \text{ ft/sec}$$

$$= \underline{6780 \text{ ft/min.}}$$

As an alternative to forming and solving the quadratic equation in $(\cos \theta)$, it is possible to solve the equation

$$7 \cdot 92 = \cos \theta + 17 \cdot 81 \sin \theta$$

by trial and error. If an accurate graph of T/T_0 against θ is available for the given lift/drag ratio, the value of θ may, of course, be read off directly.

Eqn. (8.64) is more difficult to solve directly for θ, given P/P_0 and L/D, and is most easily solved by trial and error, or graphically.

8.8.4. Time to height. A problem of great practical importance is the time required by an aircraft to climb to a given altitude.

If an aeroplane is climbing at a rate of v ft/min, then

$$v = \frac{dh}{dt} \qquad . \qquad . \qquad . \qquad . \qquad (8.65)$$

where h is the altitude, in feet
and t is the time, in minutes.

Rearranging, and integrating between limits 1 and 2

$$\int_{t_1}^{t_2} dt = \int_{h_1}^{h_2} \frac{1}{v} \, dh \qquad . \qquad . \qquad . \qquad (8.66)$$

or

$$t_2 - t_1 = \int_{h_1}^{h_2} \frac{dh}{v} \qquad . \qquad . \qquad . \qquad (8.67)$$

and $t_2 - t_1$ is the time in minutes required to climb from altitude h_1 to altitude h_2. Thus if a curve is plotted of $1/v$ against h, the area under that curve between the limits h_1 and h_2 is the time taken to climb between those heights (see Fig. 8.15).

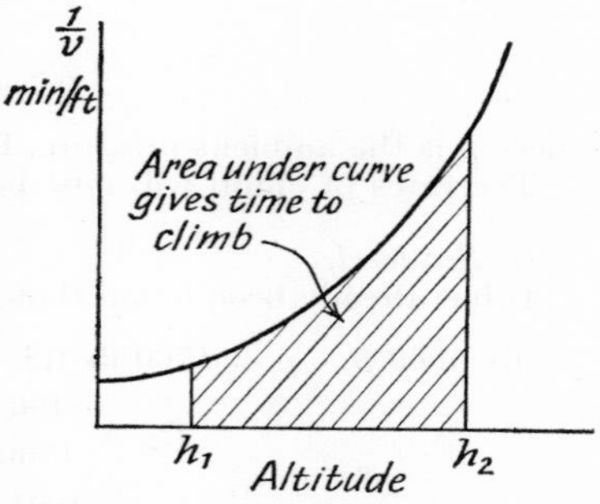

Example 8.14. The aeroplane of Example 8.10 climbs at a constant Mach number equal to that for the maximum rate of climb at sea-level, as calculated in that Example. The engine thrust decreases linearly with height at a rate such that the absolute ceiling of the aircraft at a weight of 36,000 lb is 35,000 ft. Estimate the time required to climb from sea-level to 20,000 ft, assuming the angle of climb to be small at all times, and neglecting the weight of fuel burnt.

FIG. 8.15.—Calculation of time to height.

It was found in Example 8.10 that the speed for maximum rate of climb is 535 ft/sec, and the maximum rate of climb is 3060 ft/min, both quantities being for climb at sea-level. Now 535 ft/sec at sea-level represents a Mach number of 0·48, and this Mach number is maintained constant on the climb. The correction factor for climb in the troposphere is therefore (§ 9.5)

$$\frac{1}{1 - 0 \cdot 1335(0 \cdot 48)^2} = \frac{1}{0 \cdot 97}$$

Thus the true rate of climb at sea-level is

$$\frac{3060}{0 \cdot 97} = 3160 \text{ ft/min}$$

At the absolute ceiling the thrust available will be equal to the minimum drag of the aeroplane (assuming the thrust to be independent of flight speed). Now the aircraft characteristics are

$$W = 36,000 \text{ lb} \qquad S = 450 \text{ ft}^2$$

$$C_D = 0.014 + 0.05C_L^2$$

and therefore, for minimum drag,

$$C_{L\,md} = \sqrt{\frac{0.014}{0.050}} = 0.53$$

$$\therefore \left(\frac{L}{D}\right)_{max} = \frac{0.53}{2 \times 0.014} = 18.9$$

$$\therefore \text{ minimum drag} = \frac{36,000}{18.9} = 1900 \text{ lb}$$

and this is equal to the thrust available at 35,000 ft, as compared with 6000 lb at sea-level. Since the thrust varies linearly with altitude, it may be written as

$$T = 6000 - kh$$

where T is the thrust at an altitude of $1000h$ ft
and k is a constant.

Then $\qquad 1900 = 6000 - 35k$, i.e., $k = \dfrac{4100}{35} = 117$

Therefore the thrust at any altitude, $1000h$ ft is

$$T = 6000 - 117h$$

Also $\qquad C_L = \dfrac{W}{\frac{1}{2}\rho V^2 S} = \dfrac{W}{0.7pM^2 S}$

$$= \frac{36,000}{0.7p(0.48)^2 \times 450} = \frac{496}{p}$$

where p is the ambient pressure, lb/ft^2.
The rates of climb will now be calculated at each 5000 ft.

(i) *Sea-level.*
It has already been found that the rate of climb at sea-level is 3160 ft/min.

(ii) *5000 ft.* $\quad p = 1760 \text{ lb/ft}^2$

$$\therefore \quad C_L = \frac{496}{1760} = 0.282$$

$$C_D = 0.014 + 0.05(0.282)^2 = 0.0180$$

$$\therefore \text{ drag } D = \frac{36,000 \times 0.018}{0.282} = 2300 \text{ lb}$$

$$\text{thrust } T = 6000 - 5 \times 117 = 5415 \text{ lb}$$

$$\therefore \sin\theta = \frac{T - D}{W} = \frac{5415 - 2300}{36,000} = 0.0865$$

speed of sound, $a = 1098$ ft/sec,

$$\therefore \quad V = Ma = 0.48 \times 1098 = 526 \text{ ft/sec,}$$

$$\therefore \text{ uncorrected rate of climb, } v_0 = V\sin\theta$$
$$= 526 \times 0.0865 \times 60 = 2735 \text{ ft/min}$$

$$\therefore \text{ true rate of climb, } v = \frac{2735}{0.97} = \underline{2820 \text{ ft/min.}}$$

(iii) *10,000 ft.* $p = 1450$ lb/ft^2

$$\therefore C_L = \frac{496}{1450} = 0.342 \quad C_D = 0.0199$$

$$D = 2090 \text{ lb}$$
$$T = 6000 - 10 \times 117 = 4830 \text{ lb}$$
$$\sin \theta = \frac{4830 - 2090}{36,000} = 0.0761$$
$$a = 1078 \text{ ft/sec} \quad V = 516 \text{ ft/sec}$$
$$v_0 = 516 \times 0.0761 \times 60 = 2360 \text{ ft/min}$$
$$v = \frac{2360}{0.97} = \underline{2435 \text{ ft/min.}}$$

(iv) *15,000 ft.* $p = 1190$ lb/ft^2

$$C_L = 0.417 \qquad C_D = 0.0227$$
$$D = 1960 \text{ lb} \qquad T = 4245 \text{ lb}$$
$$\sin \theta = 0.0635$$
$$a = 1058 \text{ ft/sec} \qquad V = 507 \text{ ft/sec}$$
$$v_0 = 1930 \text{ ft/min} \qquad v = \underline{1990 \text{ ft/min}}$$

(v) *20,000 ft.* $p = 974$ lb/ft^2

$$C_L = 0.510 \qquad C_D = 0.0270$$
$$D = 1910 \text{ lb} \qquad T = 3660 \text{ lb}$$
$$\sin \theta = 0.0486$$
$$a = 1038 \text{ ft/sec} \qquad V = 498 \text{ ft/sec}$$
$$v_0 = 1450 \text{ ft/min} \qquad v = \underline{1500 \text{ ft/min}}$$

The above results give the following table:

Alt. (ft)	R.o.C. [v] (ft/min)	$\dfrac{1}{v}$
0	3160	3.16×10^{-4}
5000	2820	3.55×10^{-4}
10,000	2435	4.11×10^{-4}
15,000	1990	5.02×10^{-4}
20,000	1500	6.67×10^{-4}

The time to climb to 20,000 ft may be found either by plotting the curve of $1/v$ against altitude, and measuring the area between $h = 0$ and $h = 20,000$ ft, or alternatively by applying Simpson's Rule (or a similar method) to the tabulated values of $1/v$. This leads to the result that:

$$\text{time to climb to 20,000 ft} = \underline{8.72 \text{ min.}}$$

Allowance for weight of fuel burnt. If it is required to make allowance for the weight of fuel consumed during the climb it is necessary to proceed as follows.

Select the altitudes at which the rate of climb is to be calculated. Taking the lowest of these altitudes, calculate the rate of climb. Assuming this to be constant over the first interval of altitude, calculate the time to climb through this first interval. Multiplying this time by the thrust and specific fuel consumption, calculate an approximation to the amount of fuel consumed in this interval, and hence find the weight of the aircraft at the upper limit of this interval. Calculate the rate of climb at this upper limit using the new value of the weight, and thence find the amount of fuel burnt during the second interval. Continue this process through all intervals. The values of the reciprocal of the rates of climb may then be integrated as above. The sum of all the times found above will be an approximation to the time to height; the nature of the approximation is illustrated in Fig. 8.16.

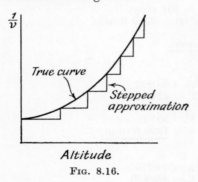

FIG. 8.16.

It will be realized that the actual time taken in each interval is greater than the value calculated by the above procedure, and suggests that the estimate of the fuel used will be lower than the true value, leading to errors in the calculated weights. The following points must, however, be borne in mind:

(i) the thrust was assumed constant at its value at the lower limit of the interval. In fact the thrust will decrease slightly with altitude, reducing the error;

(ii) the change in weight is only a small proportion of the total weight, and thus a small error in estimating the fuel burnt gives a very small error in the estimated value of the aircraft weight.

It is, in fact, found that the above step-by-step procedure gives an accuracy which is well within the limits of other approximations made, and within the limits resulting from variations between nominally identical aircraft-engine combinations as built and operated in practice.

Example 8.15. Repeat the previous Example allowing for the weight of fuel burnt, if the specific fuel consumption is 1 lb fuel/lb thrust/hour.

$$0.7M^2S = (0.7)(0.48)^2(450) = 72.5 \text{ ft}^2$$

(i) *Sea-level.*

$$\text{Rate of climb, } v = \underline{3160 \text{ ft/min}}$$

$$\therefore \text{ time to climb 5000 ft} = \frac{5000}{3160} = 1.58 \text{ min}$$

$$\text{thrust} = 6000 \text{ lb,}$$

$$\therefore \text{ fuel used} = 1.0 \times 6000 \times \frac{1.58}{60} = 158 \text{ lb}$$

$$\therefore \text{ weight of aircraft at 5000 ft} = 36,000 - 160 \text{ lb}$$
$$= 35,840 \text{ lb}$$

(ii) *5000 ft.* $p = 1760 \text{ lb/ft}^2$

$$C_L = \frac{W}{0.7pM^2S} = \frac{35,840}{72.5 \times 1760} = 0.282$$

$$C_D = 0.014 + 0.05(0.282)^2 = 0.0180$$

$$D = 35,840 \times \frac{0.0180}{0.282} = 2285 \text{ lb}$$

$$\sin \theta = \frac{5415 - 2285}{35,840} = 0 \cdot 0874$$

$$v_0 = 2760 \text{ ft/min} \quad v = \underline{2840 \text{ ft/min}}$$

$$\therefore \text{ time to climb 5000 ft} = \frac{5000}{2840} = 1 \cdot 76 \text{ min}$$

$$\therefore \text{ fuel consumed} = 1 \cdot 0 \times 5415 \times \frac{1 \cdot 76}{60} = 159 \text{ lb}$$

$\therefore$ fuel consumed up to 10,000 ft $= 158 + 159 = 317$ lb
$\therefore$ aircraft weight at 10,000 ft $= 36,000 - 320 = 35,680$ lb

(iii) *10,000 ft.*

$$C_L = \frac{35,680}{72 \cdot 5 \times 1450} = 0 \cdot 338 \quad C_D = 0 \cdot 0198$$

$$D = 35,680 \times (0 \cdot 0198/0 \cdot 338) = 2087 \text{ lb}$$

$$\sin \theta = \frac{4830 - 2087}{35,680} = 0 \cdot 0769$$

$$v_0 = 2380 \text{ ft/min} \quad v = \underline{2460 \text{ ft/min}}$$

$$\therefore \text{ time to climb 5000 ft} = 2 \cdot 03 \text{ min}$$
$$\therefore \text{ fuel used ,, ,, ,, ,,} = 163 \text{ lb}$$
$$\therefore \text{ total fuel used} = 480 \text{ lb}$$
$$\therefore \text{ aircraft weight at 15,000 ft} = 35,520 \text{ lb}$$

(iv) *At 15,000 ft.*

$$C_L = 0 \cdot 411 \quad C_D = 0 \cdot 0225 \quad D = 1940 \text{ lb}$$
$$\sin \theta = 0 \cdot 0650$$
$$v_0 = 1980 \text{ ft/min} \quad v = \underline{2040 \text{ ft/min}}$$

$$\therefore \text{ time to climb 5000 ft} = 2 \cdot 45 \text{ min}$$
$$\therefore \text{ fuel used ,, ,, ,, ,,} = 173 \text{ lb}$$
$$\therefore \text{ total fuel used to 20,000 ft} = 653 \text{ lb}$$
$$\therefore \text{ aircraft weight at 20,000 ft} = 36,000 - 650$$
$$= 35,350 \text{ lb}$$

(v) *At 20,000 ft.*

$$C_L = 0 \cdot 500 \quad C_D = 0 \cdot 0265 \quad D = 1870 \text{ lb}$$
$$\sin \theta = 0 \cdot 0506$$
$$v_0 = 1510 \text{ ft/min} \quad v = \underline{1560 \text{ ft/min}}$$

This gives the following table:

Alt. (ft)	v (ft/min)	$\frac{1}{v}$ (min/ft)
0	3160	$3 \cdot 16 \times 10^{-4}$
5000	2840	$3 \cdot 52 \times 10^{-4}$
10,000	2460	$4 \cdot 06 \times 10^{-4}$
15,000	2040	$4 \cdot 90 \times 10^{-4}$
20,000	1560	$6 \cdot 40 \times 10^{-4}$

from which the time required to climb to 20,000 ft is found to be 8·56 min, as compared with 7·82 min found by adding together the separate times calculated for each interval of the climb, and 8·72 min found by ignoring the consumption of fuel.

The total fuel used was estimated to be 653 lb, or 1·8% of the original

M

weight of the aircraft. Thus quite a large percentage error in the estimate of the fuel used could be tolerated without leading to appreciable error in the estimated rate and time of climb although, of course, for many purposes an accurate estimate of the fuel used is of importance in itself.

There are cases, rocket-propelled aircraft for example, where the fuel consumed on the climb can represent a considerable proportion of the all-up-weight (the total weight at take-off) of the aircraft, and errors in estimation of the fuel consumed may be important. In such cases a second approximation to the fuel consumed may be necessary. An approximate result for the variation of altitude with time may be obtained from the graph of $1/v$ against h. Then the fuel used, Δf lb, between times t_1 and t_2 may be found from

$$\Delta f = \frac{1}{60} \int_{t_1}^{t_2} cT \, dt \ . \qquad . \qquad . \qquad . \qquad (8.68)$$

where c is the specific fuel consumption, lb fuel/lb thrust/hour
and T is the thrust, lb.

From the variation of altitude with time certain selected times may be converted to corresponding altitudes, and the corresponding values of c and T read from the engine data. The integration of eqn. (8.68) may then be performed graphically or numerically, and thus a better approximation obtained to the fuel consumed, and therefore to the aircraft weight, at the selected altitudes. The rates of climb at the revised weights may then be calculated, and a new version of Fig. 8.16 plotted. The whole process may be repeated, using as many iterations as necessary to give a result of the required accuracy. When using this process, slide-rule accuracy is seldom adequate, and some more accurate means of computation (e.g., desk machine) is needed.

8.9. Other methods of solution to performance problems.

The preceding sections have been based on the assumption that the drag equation of the aeroplane can be expressed in the form

$$C_D = C_{D0} + kC_L^2$$

and many examples have been worked starting from this expression. There are, however, many problems for which this method of approach is not suitable. These problems may be divided into two distinct classes.

Class A. In this class, the drag coefficient still takes the form

$$C_D = C_{D0} + kC_L^2$$

but the problem is solved without direct reference to this equation.

It was shown (§ 8.3) that, for this type of drag coefficient variation,

$$D = AV^2 + \frac{B}{V^2}$$

Then, for minimum drag

$$\frac{dD}{dV} = 2AV - \frac{2B}{V^3} = 0$$

whence
$$V_{md}^4 = \frac{B}{A} \qquad . \qquad . \qquad . \qquad . \qquad . \qquad . \qquad (8.69)$$

and
$$A V_{md}^2 = \frac{B}{V_{md}^2}$$

whence
$$D_{min} = 2A V_{md}^2 = \frac{2B}{V_{md}^2}$$

$$= 2(AB)^{\frac{1}{2}} \quad \text{since } V_{md}^2 = \left(\frac{B}{A}\right)^{\frac{1}{2}}$$

results which are identical in fact, though different in form, to those of § 8.3.1.

Also, from eqn. (8.9),

$$A = \tfrac{1}{2}\rho S C_{D_0} \quad \text{and} \quad B = \frac{k W^2}{\tfrac{1}{2}\rho S}$$

Further study of this topic will be made by means of Examples.

Example 8.20. An aircraft flying at sea-level has a maximum speed of 600 ft/sec and a maximum angle of climb of 11° 41′ at a flight speed of 300 ft/sec. Estimate the values of these quantities when the weight of the aircraft is increased by 10%. The thrust available may be assumed to be constant throughout.

Since the thrust available is independent of speed, the maximum angle of climb will occur at the minimum drag speed, from eqn. (8.46).

Assuming

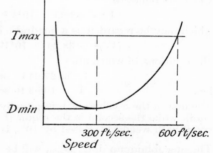

FIG. 8.17.—Performance chart for the aircraft of Example 8.20 at the original weight.

$$D = A V^2 + \frac{B}{V^2}$$

then
$$\frac{B}{A} = V_{md}^4 = (300)^4 = 81 \times 10^8$$

Thus
$$B = 81 \times 10^8 A$$

and
$$D = A\left\{V^2 + \frac{81 \times 10^8}{V^2}\right\}$$

At maximum speed,

$$T_{max} = D = A(600)^2 + \frac{81 \times 10^8 A}{(600)^2}$$
$$= (36 \times 10^4 + 2 \cdot 25 \times 10^4)A$$
$$= 38 \cdot 25 \times 10^4 A$$

At the minimum drag speed, i.e., max. angle of climb,

$$D = D_{min} = 2(AB)^{\frac{1}{2}} = 2(81 \times 10^8 A^2)^{\frac{1}{2}}$$
$$= 18 \times 10^4 A$$

Now $\qquad\qquad\sin \theta = \dfrac{T - D}{W},\quad$ and $\sin (11° \, 41') = 0{\cdot}2025$

$$\therefore \; 0{\cdot}2025 = \frac{1}{W}(38{\cdot}25 - 18{\cdot}00) \times 10^4 A$$

i.e., $\qquad\quad 20{\cdot}25 \times 10^{-2} = 20{\cdot}25 \times 10^4 \dfrac{A}{W}$

whence $\qquad\qquad A = 10^{-6} W$
Then $\qquad\qquad B = 81 \times 10^8 A = 81 \times 10^2 W$
and $\qquad\qquad T_{\max} = 38{\cdot}25 \times 10^4 A = 38{\cdot}25 \times 10^{-2} W$
Now $\qquad\qquad A = \tfrac{1}{2}\rho S C_{D_0}$

and is therefore independent of the aircraft weight. It is therefore unaffected by the 10% increase in weight.

B, on the other hand, is proportional to the square of the aircraft weight, and therefore the new value of B, denoted by B' is given by

$$B' = B(1{\cdot}1)^2 = 1{\cdot}21 B = 98{\cdot}01 \times 10^2 W$$

where W is the *original* weight of the aircraft. Thus, for the new top speed,

$$38{\cdot}25 \times 10^{-2} W = 10^{-6} W V^2 + \frac{98{\cdot}01 \times 10^2 W}{V^2}$$

which simplifies to

$$V^4 - 38{\cdot}25 \times 10^4 V^2 + 98{\cdot}01 \times 10^8 = 0$$

which may be regarded as a quadratic equation in V^2, namely

$$(V^2)^2 - 38{\cdot}25 \times 10^4 V^2 + 98{\cdot}01 \times 10^8 = 0$$

the solutions to which are

$$V^2 = 27{,}645 \quad \text{or} \quad 354{,}850$$

i.e., $\qquad\qquad V = 166{\cdot}3 \text{ ft/sec} \quad \text{or} \quad 595 \text{ ft/sec}$

The first of these values of V is actually the minimum speed (disregarding the stall), while the second is the required maximum speed. Thus the maximum speed with weight increased by 10% is 595 ft/sec.

The new minimum drag, $D'_{\min}$, will be

$$D'_{\min} = 2(AB')^{\frac{1}{2}} = 2[(10^{-6} W)(98{\cdot}01 \times 10^2 W)]^{\frac{1}{2}}$$
$$= 19{\cdot}80 \times 10^{-2} W$$

$\therefore$ the new maximum angle of climb is given by

$$\sin \theta' = \frac{38{\cdot}25 \times 10^{-2} W - 19{\cdot}80 \times 10^{-2} W}{1{\cdot}1 W} = 0{\cdot}1675$$

$$\therefore \; \theta' = 9° \, 39'.$$

Since the minimum drag will occur at the same incidence, the speed will be proportional to the square root of the weight, i.e.,

$$V'_{\mathrm{md}} = 300(1{\cdot}1)^{\frac{1}{2}} = 314 \text{ ft/sec.}$$

Note. The minimum drag at the new weight was found the 'hard' way, to illustrate the method on a simple example. However, since the lift/drag ratio for minimum drag (i.e., the maximum lift/drag ratio) is constant for a given aeroplane, $D'_{\min}$ could have been found more simply by

$$\frac{D'_{\min}}{D_{\min}} = \frac{W'}{W} = 1{\cdot}1$$

whence $\qquad\qquad D'_{\min} = 1{\cdot}1(18 \times 10^{-2} W) = 19{\cdot}80 \times 10^{-2} W$

identical to the result obtained above.

Example 8.21. The aircraft of the previous Example was fitted with wings of aspect ratio 8. Estimate the change in the maximum angle of climb consequent on a reduction of aspect ratio to 6, if this is accompanied by a 4% reduction in total aircraft weight, all other aircraft characteristics remaining unchanged.

It was found that, for the original conditions,

$$A = 10^{-6}W$$
$$B = 81 \times 10^2 W$$
$$T = 38 \cdot 25 \times 10^{-2} W$$

Since
$$B = \frac{kW^2}{\frac{1}{2}\rho S} \quad \text{and} \quad k = \frac{1 + \delta}{\pi(\mathcal{R})}$$

where $(\mathcal{R})$ is the wing aspect ratio, then

$$B = \frac{W^2(1 + \delta)}{\frac{1}{2}\pi \rho S(\mathcal{R})}$$

i.e., B is proportional to the square of the weight and inversely proportional to the aspect ratio. The new value of B, B', is therefore

$$B' = B\frac{8}{6}(0 \cdot 96)^2 = 1 \cdot 23B = 99 \cdot 4 \times 10^2 W$$

Then the new minimum drag is given by

$$D'_{\min} = 2(AB')^{\frac{1}{2}} = 2[(10^{-6}W)(99 \cdot 4 \times 10^2 W)]$$
$$= 19 \cdot 94 \times 10^{-2} W$$

whence, as before, the new maximum angle of climb is given by

$$\sin \theta' = \frac{(38 \cdot 25 - 19 \cdot 94) \times 10^{-2} W}{0 \cdot 96 W} = 0 \cdot 191$$

whence $\theta' = 11°$, and the maximum angle of climb is therefore decreased by 41′.

The corresponding speed is

$$V'_{\text{md}} = \left(\frac{B'}{A}\right)^{\frac{1}{4}} = \left(\frac{99 \cdot 4 \times 10^2 W}{10^{-6} W}\right)^{\frac{1}{4}}$$
$$= \underline{316 \text{ ft/sec.}}$$

The method just described applies to those problems where the engine performance is expressed in terms of thrust, in pounds. For piston and turbo-prop engines, where the engine performance is expressed in terms of horse-power, the following treatment is more convenient.

Eqn. (8.23) gives

$$P = AV^3 + \frac{B}{V}$$

where
$$A = \frac{1}{1100}\rho SC_{D_0} \quad \text{and} \quad B = \frac{kW^2}{275\rho S}$$

For minimum power,

$$\frac{dP}{dV} = 3AV^2 - \frac{B}{V^2} = 0$$

whence
$$V^4_{\text{mp}} = \frac{B}{3A}$$

Then the power required to overcome the drag associated with the zero-lift drag coefficient is

$$P_0 = A V_{mp}^3 = A\left(\frac{B}{3A}\right)^{\frac{3}{4}} = (3)^{-\frac{3}{4}}A^{\frac{1}{4}}B^{\frac{3}{4}}$$

while the power to overcome the lift-dependent drag is

$$P_L = \frac{B}{V_{mp}} = B\left(\frac{3A}{B}\right)^{\frac{1}{4}} = 3^{\frac{1}{4}}A^{\frac{1}{4}}B^{\frac{3}{4}}$$

It is thus seen that $P_L = 3P_0$ (cf. § 8.5.1), and the total minimum power is given by several alternative expressions, namely,

$$P_{min} = 4A V_{mp}^3 = \frac{4}{3}\frac{B}{V_{mp}}$$

$$= 4(3^{-\frac{3}{4}}A^{\frac{1}{4}}B^{\frac{3}{4}}) = 1{\cdot}755A^{\frac{1}{4}}B^{\frac{3}{4}}$$

Again, this technique will be illustrated by examples.

Example 8.22. An aircraft flying at sea-level has a maximum speed of 350 ft/sec and a maximum rate of climb of 1500 ft/min at a flight speed of 170 ft/sec, the thrust horse-power available from each engine being independent of speed. Estimate the maximum rate of climb if one of the four engines fails, the idle airscrew increasing the zero-lift drag coefficient of the aircraft by 7%.

Assuming $P = A V^3 + B/V$ then, for minimum power, the condition at which the maximum rate of climb will be achieved,

$$V_{mp}^4 = (170)^4 = 8{\cdot}3521 \times 10^8 = \frac{B}{3A}$$

$$\therefore B = 25{\cdot}0563 \times 10^8 A$$

Now the minimum power, P_{min} is given by

$$P_{min} = 4A V_{mp}^3 = 4A(170)^3 = 19{\cdot}652 \times 10^6 A$$

At maximum speed,

$$P_{max} = A(350)^3 + \frac{B}{350}$$

$$= A(350)^3 + \frac{25{\cdot}056 \times 10^8 A}{350}$$

$$= 5 \times 10^7 A$$

From the given rate of climb, the excess horse-power may be found to be

$$\Delta P = \frac{Wv}{33,000} = \frac{1500W}{33,000} = \frac{W}{22}$$

where W is the aircraft weight.
Now,

$$P_{max} = P_{min} + \Delta P$$

i.e.,

$$50 \times 10^6 A = 19{\cdot}65 \times 10^9 A + \frac{W}{22}$$

whence

$$A = 1{\cdot}497 \times 10^{-9}W$$

Then, with this value for A,

$$B = 25{\cdot}056 \times 10^8 A = 37{\cdot}45 \times 10^{-1}W$$
$$= 3{\cdot}745W$$

and $\qquad P_{\max} = 5 \times 10^7 A = 7 \cdot 485 \times 10^{-2} W$

After failure of one of the four engines, the power available, $P'_{\max}$ is

$$P'^{ax}_m = \tfrac{3}{4}(7 \cdot 485 \times 10^{-2})W$$
$$= 5 \cdot 614 \times 10^{-2} W$$

The factor A is proportional to C_{D_0}, and therefore it has the new value

$$A' = 1 \cdot 07A = 1 \cdot 6 \times 10^{-9} \ W = 1600 \times 10^{-12} W$$

B is unchanged, and therefore the new minimum power is

$$P'_{\min} = 1 \cdot 753(1600 \times 10^{-12})^{\frac{1}{4}}(3 \cdot 745)^{\frac{3}{4}} W$$
$$= 2 \cdot 98 \times 10^{-2} W$$

Therefore the new excess horse-power is

$$\Delta P' = (5 \cdot 614 - 2 \cdot 98) \times 10^{-2} W$$
$$= 2 \cdot 634 \times 10^{-2} W$$
$$\therefore \text{ maximum rate of climb} = \frac{2 \cdot 634 \times 10^{-2} W \times 33{,}000}{W}$$
$$= \underline{870 \text{ ft/min.}}$$

Example 8.23. An aeroplane flying at sea-level has a maximum speed of 340 ft/sec and a maximum rate of climb of 1650 ft/min, which occurs at a flight speed of 170 ft/sec, the thrust horse-power available being independent of speed. The engine is supercharged so that its power output is constant up to an altitude of 5000 ft ($\sigma = 0 \cdot 862$) while above this altitude the available thrust horse-power is proportional to $(\sigma/\sigma_{5000})^{0 \cdot 85}$, where σ_{5000} is the relative density at 5000 ft.

Estimate the maximum rate of climb at 15,000 ft ($\sigma = 0 \cdot 629$) if the aircraft weight is then 15% less than when the performance figures were taken at sea-level.

This problem could be solved by a method very similar to that used for the previous Example. A slightly different method will, however, be used.

Since the maximum rate of climb occurs at the minimum power speed, this speed is 170 ft/sec, and the ratio n from eqn. (8.33) is

$$n = \tfrac{340}{170} = 2 \cdot 00$$

Then, from eqn. (8.33),

$$\frac{P_{\max}}{P_{\min}} = \frac{3 + n^4}{4n} = \frac{3 + 16}{8} = 2 \cdot 375$$

From the given climb performance at sea-level,

$$\Delta P = P_{\max} - P_{\min} = \frac{W \times 1650}{33{,}000} = 0 \cdot 05W$$
$$\therefore (2 \cdot 375 - 1)P_{\min} = 0 \cdot 05W$$

Hence $\qquad P_{\min} = 0 \cdot 0364W$

and $\qquad P_{\max} = 2 \cdot 375 P_{\min} = 0 \cdot 0864W$

Denoting quantities at 15,000 ft with a prime, e.g., P'

then $\qquad \dfrac{P_{\max}}{P'_{\max}} = \left(\dfrac{0 \cdot 862}{0 \cdot 629}\right)^{0 \cdot 85} = 1 \cdot 308$

$$\therefore P'_{\max} = \frac{0 \cdot 0864W}{1 \cdot 308} = 0 \cdot 0660W$$

Now $\qquad P = \dfrac{1}{550}\left(\dfrac{W^3}{\tfrac{1}{2}\rho S}\right)^{\frac{1}{2}}\left(\dfrac{C_D}{C_L^{3/2}}\right) \quad$ (eqn. (8.25))

Thus, with no change of aircraft geometry, and since at the minimum power condition the factor $(C_D/C_L^{3/2})$ is constant for a given aeroplane, it follows that

$$P_{\min} \propto \left(\frac{W^3}{\sigma}\right)^{\frac{1}{2}}$$

$\therefore$ at 15,000 ft and 15% weight reduction,

$$\frac{P'_{\min}}{P_{\min}} = \sqrt{(0\cdot85)^3\left(\frac{1}{0\cdot629}\right)} = (0\cdot976)^{\frac{1}{2}} = 0\cdot988$$

$$\therefore P'_{\min} = 0\cdot988 \times 0\cdot0364W = 0\cdot0360W$$

$$\therefore \text{ new excess power, } \Delta P' = P'_{\max} - P'_{\min}$$
$$= 0\cdot0660W - 0\cdot0360W$$
$$= 0\cdot0300W$$

$$\therefore \text{ new rate of climb} = \frac{0\cdot0300W \times 33{,}000}{0\cdot85W}$$

$$= \underline{1165 \text{ ft/min.}}$$

Class B. In this class of problems the drag equation is not of the form assumed earlier, namely

$$C_D = C_{D0} + kC_L^2$$

but rather of the form

$$C_D = C_{D0} + \mathrm{f}\,(C_L) + kC_L^2$$

where $\mathrm{f}(C_L)$ is some function of the lift coefficient, not necessarily rational.

Typical of such cases is the problem in which the characteristics of the wing alone are given in the form of a table of L/D against C_L, or of C_D against C_L. Other data in the problem permit calculation of the zero-lift drag coefficient of all parts of the aircraft other than the wing (the extra-to-wing drag coefficient), which is assumed to be constant (independent of the lift coefficient).

Example 8.24. The wings of an aircraft weighing 60,000 lb (wing loading 61 lb/ft²) have the following characteristics:

C_L . . .	0·2	0·4	0·6	0·8	1·2
L/D . . .	20	28	22·5	18	11

With a maximum of 8000 lb thrust available, a maximum speed of 300 knots E.A.S. is possible at 20,000 ft ($\sigma = 0\cdot534$).

With power off at this altitude find the rate of descent at the minimum gliding angle, and the minimum rate of descent. (U. of L.)

$$1 \text{ knot} = 1 \text{ nautical mile per hour}$$

$$= 6080 \text{ ft per hour} = \frac{6080}{3600} \text{ ft/sec}$$

$$= 1\cdot689 \text{ ft/sec}$$

$$\therefore 300 \text{ knots} = 300 \times 1\cdot689 = 506 \text{ ft/sec}$$

$\therefore$ at maximum speed of 300 knots E.A.S. at 20,000 ft

$$C_L = \frac{61 \times 841}{(506)^2} = 0.200$$

By plotting the given values of L/D against C_L (remembering also that when $C_L = 0$, $L/D = 0$) gives, for a lift coefficient of 0.200, a lift/drag ratio of 20 for the wings only. Thus the wing drag coefficient (including both the zero-lift and the lift-dependent drag coefficients) is

$$C_{Dw} = \frac{0.200}{20} = 0.010$$

Now, at maximum speed, the total drag is equal to the maximum thrust available, and is therefore 8000 lb, and therefore the overall lift/drag ratio for the whole aircraft is

$$\frac{L}{D} = \frac{60,000}{8000} = 7.5$$

and therefore the total drag coefficient is

$$C_D = \frac{0.200}{7.5} = 0.0267$$

Therefore the extra-to-wing drag coefficient is

$$C_{D\ ew} = 0.0267 - 0.010 = 0.0167$$

and it is assumed that this is constant.

The minimum gliding angle will occur when the lift/drag ratio is a maximum, while the minimum sinking speed will occur when $C_L^{1.5}/C_D$ is a maximum. Perhaps the quickest and easiest way of finding these maxima is by the 'polar plotting' method. This requires calculation of the following table:

C_L	0.2	0.4	0.6	0.8	1.2
$C_L^{3/2}$	0.089	0.253	0.465	0.715	1.313
$(L/D)_{\text{wing}}$ . . .	20	28	22.5	18	11
C_{Dw}	0.010	0.0143	0.0267	0.0445	0.1090

Two graphs are now plotted. The first has C_L as ordinate and C_{Dw} as abscissa, while the second has $C_L^{3/2}$ as ordinate and C_{Dw} as abscissa.

Consider the first of these (Fig. 8.18). If the origin is shifted 0.0167 (i.e., $C_{D\ ew}$) units of C_D to the left, the horizontal ordinates measured from this new origin represent the total drag coefficient, $C_D = C_{Dw} + C_{D\ ew}$. Now consider the line drawn from this new origin tangential to the C_L, C_{Dw} curve. The slope of this line is equal to (C_L/C_D), i.e., is equal to L/D and, since the line is tangential to the curve, this value of L/D is the maximum possible for the aircraft. Thus it is found that, for the maximum lift/drag ratio

$$C_L = 0.59 \quad \text{and} \quad C_D = 0.026 + 0.0167 = 0.0427$$

whence the lift/drag ratio is 13.8.

The gliding speed $V = 29\sqrt{\dfrac{w}{C_L}} = 29\sqrt{\dfrac{61}{0.59}}$

$$= 295 \text{ ft/sec, E.A.S.}$$

$$= \frac{295}{\sqrt{0.534}} = 404 \text{ ft/sec, T.A.S.}$$

Since the lift/drag ratio is 13.8, the gliding angle is small, and therefore it is permissible to make the approximations:

$$\sin \gamma = \tan \gamma = \frac{1}{13.8}$$

Therefore the rate of descent, v, is given by

$$v = V \sin \gamma = \frac{404}{13 \cdot 8} = 29 \cdot 2 \text{ ft/sec}$$

$$= \underline{1755 \text{ ft/min.}}$$

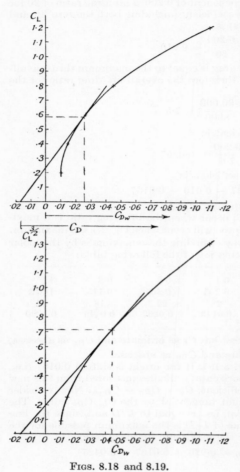

FIGS. 8.18 and 8.19.

To find the minimum sinking speed, a similar operation is performed on the graph of $C_L^{3/2}$, C_{Dw} (Fig. 8.19). This gives

$$C_L^{3/2} = 0 \cdot 715$$

whence $C_L = (0 \cdot 715)^{2/3} = 0 \cdot 80$
while

$$C_D = 0 \cdot 0445 + 0 \cdot 0167$$

$$= 0 \cdot 0612$$

and therefore

$$\frac{L}{D} = 13 \cdot 07$$

gliding speed

$$= 29 \sqrt{\frac{61}{0 \cdot 8}}$$

$$= 253 \text{ ft/sec, E.A.S.}$$

$$= 346 \text{ ft/sec, T.A.S.}$$

and therefore

$$v = \frac{346}{13 \cdot 07} = 26 \cdot 5 \text{ ft/sec}$$

$$= \underline{1590 \text{ ft/min.}}$$

It will be noted that the results of this example do not obey eqns. (8.27), (8.28) and (8.29). This is simply because those equations assume a particular form of drag coefficient variation which does not hold in this problem, and therefore the equations cannot be expected to apply in the present case.

8.10. The 'Hovercraft'.

The earlier sections in this chapter have dealt with the performance of conventional winged aircraft in which lift, associated with circulation round the wings, is used to balance the weight. A radically different principle is used for sustentation of the 'Hovercraft', of which an experimental prototype, the Saunders-Roe SRN-1, flew in June 1959. In machines of this type a more or less static region of air, at slightly more than atmospheric pressure, is formed and maintained below the craft. The difference between the pressure of the air on the lower side and the atmospheric pressure on the upper side produces a force tending to lift the craft. The trapped mass of air under the craft is formed by the effect of an annular jet of air, directed inwards and downwards from near the periphery of the underside. The downwards ejection of the annular jet produces an upwards reaction on the craft, tending to lift it. In steady hovering, the weight is balanced by the jet thrust and the force due to the 'cushion' of air below the craft. The difference between the flight of 'Hovercraft' and normal direct jet lift machines lies in the air cushion effect which amplifies the vertical force available, permitting the direct jet thrust to be only a small fraction of the weight of the craft. The 'cushion effect' requires that the hovering height/diameter ratio of the craft be small (e.g., 1/50), and this imposes a severe limitation on the altitude attainable by the 'Hovercraft'.

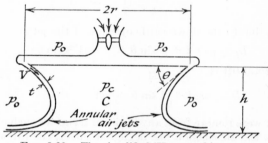

Fig. 8.20.—The simplified 'Hovercraft' system.

Consider the simplified system of Fig. 8.20, showing a 'Hovercraft' whose planform is a circle of radius r, hovering a height h above a flat, rigid horizontal surface. An annular jet of radius r, thickness t, velocity V and density ρ is ejected at an angle θ to the horizontal surface. The jet is directed inwards but, in a steady, equilibrium state, must turn to flow outwards as shown; if it did not, there would be a continuous increase of mass within the region C, which is impossible. (Note that such an increase of mass will occur for a short time immediately after starting, while the air cushion is being built up.) The curvature of the path of the air jet shows that it possesses a centripetal acceleration and this is produced by a difference between the pressure p_c within the air cushion and the atmospheric pressure p_0. Consider a short length δs of the annular jet and assume:

(i) that the pressure p_c is constant over the depth h of the air cushion, and

(ii) that the speed V of the annular jet is unchanged throughout the motion.

Then the rate of mass flow within the element of peripheral length δs is $\rho V t \, \delta s$ slug/sec. This mass has an initial momentum parallel to the rigid surface (or ground) of $\rho V t \, \delta s \, V \cos \theta = \rho V^2 t \cos \theta \, \delta s$ inwards.

After turning to flow radially outwards, the air has a momentum parallel to the ground of $\rho V t\,\delta s\ V = \rho V^2 t\,\delta s$ outwards. Therefore there is a rate of change of momentum parallel to the ground of $\rho V^2 t(1 + \cos\theta)\,\delta s$.

This rate of change of momentum is due to the pressure difference $(p_c - p_0)$ and must, indeed, be equal to the force exerted on the jet by this pressure difference, parallel to the ground, which is $(p_c - p_0)h\,\delta s$. Thus

$$(p_c - p_0)h\,\delta s = \rho V^2 t(1 + \cos\theta)\,\delta s$$

or
$$(p_c - p_0) = \frac{\rho V^2 t}{h}(1 + \cos\theta).\qquad\qquad (8.70)$$

Thus the lift L_c due to the cushion of air on a circular body of radius r is

$$L_c = \pi r^2(p_c - p_0)$$

$$= \frac{\pi\rho r^2 V^2 t}{h}(1 + \cos\theta)\qquad\cdot\qquad\cdot\qquad (8.71)$$

The direct lift due to the downwards ejection of the jet is

$$L_j = \rho V t\,2\pi r\ V\sin\theta = 2\pi r\rho V^2 t\sin\theta\qquad\cdot\qquad (8.72)$$

and thus the total lift is

$$L = \pi r\rho V^2 t\left\{2\sin\theta + \frac{r}{h}(1 + \cos\theta)\right\}\qquad\cdot\qquad (8.73)$$

If the craft were remote from any horizontal surface such as the ground or sea, so that the air cushion has negligible effect, the lift would be due only to the direct jet thrust, with the maximum value $L_{j_0} = 2\pi r\rho V^2 t$ when $\theta = 90°$.

Thus the 'lift amplification factor', L/L_{j_0}, is

$$\frac{L}{L_{j_0}} = \sin\theta + \frac{r}{2h}(1 + \cos\theta)\,.\qquad\cdot\qquad (8.74)$$

Differentiation with respect to θ shows that this has a maximum value when

$$\tan\theta = \frac{2h}{r}\qquad\cdot\qquad\cdot\qquad\cdot\qquad (8.75)$$

Since machines of this type are intended to operate under conditions such that h is very small compared to r, it follows that the maximum amplification is achieved when θ is close to zero, i.e., the jet is directed radially inwards. Then with the approximations $\sin\theta = 0$, $\cos\theta = 1$,

$$\frac{L}{L_{j_0}} = \frac{r}{h}\qquad\cdot\qquad\cdot\qquad\cdot\qquad\cdot\qquad (8.76)$$

and
$$L = \frac{r}{h}L_{j_0} = \frac{r}{h}2\pi r\rho V^2 t$$

$$= \frac{2\pi r^2\rho V^2 t}{h}\qquad\cdot\qquad\cdot\qquad\cdot\qquad (8.77)$$

(It will be noted that the direct jet lift is now, in fact, negligible.)

The power supplied is equal to the kinetic energy contained in the jet per unit time,* which is

$$\tfrac{1}{2}.2\pi r\rho V t V^2 = \pi r\rho V^3 t \text{ ft lb/sec} \qquad . \qquad . \qquad (8.78)$$

Denoting this by P, combining eqns. (8.77) and (8.78), and setting lift L equal to the weight W, leads to

$$\frac{P}{W} = \frac{Vh}{2r} \text{ ft lb/sec/lb A.U.W.}$$

as the minimum power necessary for sustentation, while, if $\theta \neq 0$,

$$\frac{P}{W} \simeq \frac{Vh}{r(1 + \cos\theta)} \text{ ft lb/sec/lb A.U.W.}$$

$$\simeq \frac{1}{550}\frac{Vh}{r(1 + \cos\theta)} \text{ H.P./lb A.U.W.}$$

ignoring a term involving $\sin\theta$.

Thus if V is small, and if h is small compared to r, it becomes possible to lift the craft with a comparatively small power.

The foregoing analysis applies to hovering flight and has, in addition, involved a number of simplifying assumptions. The first is the assumption of a level, rigid surface below the machine. This is reasonably accurate for operation over land but is not justified over water, when a depression will be formed in the water below the craft. (It must be remembered that the weight of the craft will be reacted by a pressure distributed over the surface below the machine, and this will lead to deformation of a non-rigid surface.)

Another assumption is that the pressure p_c is constant throughout the air cushion. In fact, mixing between the annular jet and the air cushion will produce eddies leading to non-uniformity of the pressure within the cushion.† The mixing referred to above, together with friction between the air jet and the ground (or water) will lead to a loss of kinetic energy and speed of the air jet, whereas it was assumed that the speed of the jet remained constant throughout the motion. It is to be expected that these effects will only produce small corrections to the analysis above.

If the power available is greater than is necessary to sustain the craft at the selected height h, the excess may be used either to raise the machine to a greater height, or to propel the craft forwards.

EXERCISES

1. An aeroplane has a wing loading of 45 lb/ft^2 and flies at a constant lift coefficient of 0·4. Draw curves showing the variation of indicated air speed

---

* The power supplied to the jet will also contain a term relating to the increase in potential (pressure) energy, since the jet static pressure will be slightly greater than atmospheric. Since the jet pressure will be approximately equal to p_c, which is, typically, about 15 lb/ft^2 above atmospheric, the increase in pressure energy will be very small and has been neglected in this simplified analysis.

† The authors suggest that the jet entrains an annular vortex within the cushion from which pressure non-uniformity, and hence lift, can be determined.

(assuming the A.S.I. to be calibrated for incompressible flow at sea-level), true air speed and Mach number over the altitude range from sea-level to 55,000 ft.

2. Calculate the maximum speed and maximum rate of climb at sea-level for the aircraft with the following characteristics: weight = 56,000 lb, wing area = 900 ft^2, aspect ratio = 9, giving 10% more trailing vortex drag than the minimum. $C_{D_0} = 0.018$, thrust horse-power = 3500 at all speeds. (*Ans.* 442 ft/sec: 1290 ft/min)

3. The engines of the aircraft of Ex. 2 have a power output which varies with altitude as $\sigma^{0.45}$. Estimate (i) the absolute ceiling and the corresponding true air speed, (ii) the maximum T.A.S. and the altitude at which it occurs and (iii) the minimum time to climb to that altitude from sea-level, ignoring the effects of acceleration and of fuel consumed. (*Ans.* (i) 31,300 ft at 354 ft/sec. (ii) 456 ft/sec at approx. 14,000 ft. (iii) 32.9 min)

4. An aircraft is powered by a turbo-jet engine whose thrust is independent of the flight speed. The aircraft weighs 35,000 lb, its wing area is 500 ft^2, and the drag equation is $C_D = 0.016 + 0.045C_L^2$. At sea-level the maximum rate of climb of 5250 ft/min occurs at a flight speed of 500 ft/sec. Calculate the rate of climb at the same incidence with a rocket motor giving 10,000 lb additional thrust. (*Ans.* 13,300 ft/min)

5. Flight testing shows that at speeds of 150 ft/sec and 300 ft/sec at sea-level an aeroplane weighing 50,000 lb requires 800 T.H.P. and 1200 T.H.P. respectively for straight and level flight. Its top speed is 400 ft/sec. Estimate the maximum rate of climb at sea-level at this weight and at a 10% higher weight. Assume that the thrust horse-power available is independent of speed. (*Ans.* 1000 ft/min; 850 ft/min)

6. A sailplane weighs 700 lb and has a wing area of 220 ft^2. The wings, of aspect ratio 12, give 8% more trailing vortex drag than the minimum. A model of the wings, tested in a wind-tunnel at the correct Reynolds number, gave the following variation of total wing drag coefficient with lift coefficient:

C_L . . .	0.2	0.4	0.6	0.8	1.0	1.2	1.4
C_D . . .	0.0053	0.0086	0.0144	0.0237	0.0372	0.0523	0.0693

At sea-level the flattest gliding angle is 1 : 28.1 and occurs at a speed of 40 knots. Estimate the minimum sinking speed at 10,000 ft ($\sqrt{\sigma} = 0.8594$) with these wings and also if a new set of wings, of aspect ratio 16 and weighing 30 lb more, are fitted. (*Ans.* 2.58 ft/sec with original wings, 2.18 ft/sec with new wings)

7. Show that the low angle of steady climb, θ, of an aeroplane may be given approximately by:

$$\sin \theta = \tau - \frac{1}{\Delta}$$

where τ is the ratio of thrust to all-up-weight and Δ is the ratio of lift to overall drag at the flight incidence concerned.

An aircraft of weight 115,000 lb, wing loading 59 lb/ft^2, has four jet engines each producing a thrust, assumed constant, of 6900 lb.

At normal flight incidences the overall drag coefficient of the aircraft is:

$$C_D = 0.0216 + 0.04C_L^2$$

Estimate the maximum angle of climb and the maximum rate of climb at low altitude. (*Ans.* 10° 26′; 3830 ft/min) (U. of L.)

CHAPTER 9

AIRCRAFT PERFORMANCE IN ACCELERATED FLIGHT

9.1. Take-off performance. The take-off performance of an aircraft is usually quoted as the distance required to attain an altitude of 50 ft after starting from rest, on level ground, in still air, at sea-level, in I.S.A. conditions, at the maximum all-up-weight and with all engines operative. These specified conditions give a nominal figure which serves as a useful measure of the take-off performance.

Airline operators find that conditions in practical operation are seldom those specified above, and an essential part of their assessment of an aircraft is its take-off performance in non-standard conditions. For example, certain airfields in tropical regions combine high altitudes with high atmospheric temperatures. This particular combination of conditions is very difficult for take-off. With low pressure and high temperature the speed at which the aircraft leaves the ground is relatively high, due to the low relative density. In addition the same conditions lead to a considerable reduction in engine power (particularly for turbine engines) and the acceleration is correspondingly less. Thus the aircraft must attain a higher take-off speed, but with a lower acceleration, leading to a very considerable increase in the distance required to attain the specified 50 ft altitude.

To enable the aircraft to take-off in the distance available (governed by the runway length and the position of any high obstacles outside the aerodrome boundary) it may be necessary to take-off at a weight less than the nominal maximum weight of the aircraft. This may mean reducing the pay-load carried, with adverse effects on the operator's costs for a particular flight. Alternatively the fuel load may be reduced, but this will reduce the distance the aircraft can fly before the next landing, and may not always be possible. In such circumstances the standard value for the take-off distance defined in the first paragraph is of little value. Since, also, the operator wishes to carry as much payload as possible it is necessary that he should be able to calculate accurately the take-off distance for any given conditions of weight, airfield altitude, temperature, runway slope and wind.

There are two distances recognized in the measurement of take-off performance:

(i) *the take-off ground run.* This is the distance travelled from the position of rest to the point where the aircraft just leaves the ground and becomes fully air-borne;

(ii) *the take-off distance.* This is the horizontal distance from the position of rest to the point at which no part of the aircraft is less than 50 ft above the ground (i.e., the aircraft could clear an obstacle 50 ft high).

183

9.1.1. Calculation of the take-off ground run. The aircraft may be considered as a body accelerating from rest to some specified take-off speed V_{TO}, under the influence of certain forces (Fig. 9.1). These forces include the lift, weight, drag and thrust. In addition there is a vertical reaction R between the wheels and the ground. Associated with this reaction is the rolling resistance of the tyres on the ground, μR. It is assumed that throughout the ground run the wing lift coefficient is constant at the value C_{Lg} and that the drag coefficient is also constant. This holds with good accuracy for aircraft with nose-wheel undercarriages. Aircraft with tail-wheel or tail-skid undercarriages, however, start with the tail down and travel a short distance before attaining the tail-up attitude corresponding to C_{Lg}, which is held for the remainder of the ground run.

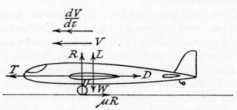

Fig. 9.1.—The forces on an aircraft during the take-off ground run.

At the instant shown the aircraft has a speed of V ft/sec and an acceleration of dV/dt ft/sec². Resolving forces vertically

$$L + R - W = 0 . \qquad . \qquad . \qquad . \qquad (9.1)$$

Resolving forces horizontally

$$T - D - \mu R = \frac{W}{g}\frac{dV}{dt} \qquad . \qquad . \qquad . \qquad (9.2)$$

From eqn. (9.1)

$$R = W - L \qquad . \qquad . \qquad (9.3)$$

whence, by eqn. (9.2),

$$\frac{W}{g}\frac{dV}{dt} = T - D - \mu(W - L)$$

or

$$\frac{1}{g}\frac{dV}{dt} = \left(\frac{T}{W} - \mu\right) - \frac{1}{W}(D - \mu L) \qquad . \qquad . \qquad (9.4)$$

Putting the lift and drag in coefficient form this becomes

$$\frac{1}{g}\frac{dV}{dt} = \left(\frac{T}{W} - \mu\right) - \frac{\frac{1}{2}\rho V^2 S}{W}\left(C_D - \mu C_{Lg}\right) \qquad . \qquad (9.5)$$

Now the thrust during the take-off is not, in general, independent of speed and it is found in practice that a good approximation to the variation of thrust with speed is

$$T = T_0 - aV^2 . \qquad . \qquad . \qquad . \qquad (9.6)$$

although other expressions have been used,

where T_0 is the thrust at zero-forward speed (static thrust)

    a is a constant

and T is the thrust at a speed V.

Substituting this in eqn. (9.5) gives

$$\frac{1}{g}\frac{dV}{dt} = \left(\frac{T_0}{W} - \mu\right) - \frac{V^2}{W}\{\tfrac{1}{2}\rho S(C_D - \mu C_{Lg}) + a\} \quad . \tag{9.7}$$

i.e.,
$$\frac{dV}{dt} = A - BV^2 \quad . \quad . \quad . \quad . \quad . \quad . \tag{9.7.1}$$

where
$$A = g\left(\frac{T_0}{W} - \mu\right) \quad . \quad . \quad . \quad . \quad . \tag{9.8}$$

and
$$B = \frac{g}{W}\{\tfrac{1}{2}\rho S(C_D - \mu C_{Lg}) + a\} \quad . \quad . \quad . \tag{9.9}$$

A and B being constants for a given aircraft.

Solving eqn. (9.7) gives

$$\frac{dV}{A - BV^2} = dt$$

i.e.,
$$t = (AB)^{-\frac{1}{2}}\tanh^{-1}\left(V\sqrt{\frac{B}{A}}\right) + C \quad . \tag{9.10}$$

C being a constant of integration. Taking as initial condition $V = 0$ when $t = 0$, it follows that $C = 0$, and the time taken on the ground run is

$$t = (AB)^{-\frac{1}{2}}\tanh^{-1}\left(V_{TO}\sqrt{\frac{B}{A}}\right) \quad . \quad . \tag{9.11}$$

To find the distance of the take-off ground run, eqn. (9.7) is

$$\frac{dV}{dt} = A - BV^2 \text{ (eqn. (9.7))}$$

Now
$$\frac{dV}{dt} = \frac{dV}{dx}\frac{dx}{dt} = V\frac{dV}{dx} \quad . \quad . \quad . \tag{9.12}$$

where x is distance.

Then
$$V\frac{dV}{dx} = A - BV^2 \quad . \quad . \quad . \quad . \tag{9.13}$$

or
$$dx = \frac{VdV}{A - BV^2} \quad . \quad . \quad . \quad . \tag{9.14}$$

Integrating, this becomes

$$x = -\frac{1}{2B}\log_e(A - BV^2) + C \quad . \quad . \tag{9.15}$$

Taking as the initial conditions $x = 0$ when $V = 0$, this becomes

$$0 = -\frac{1}{2B}(\log_e A) + C$$

N

whence
$$C = \frac{1}{2B} \log_e A$$

and therefore
$$x = -\frac{1}{2B} \log_e \left(\frac{A - BV^2}{A} \right) . \qquad . \qquad . \qquad (9.16)$$

for the distance x travelled in accelerating from rest to a speed V. In particular, if the speed is the take-off speed V_{TO} and the take-off ground run is X, then

$$X = -\frac{1}{2B} \log_e \left(1 - \frac{B}{A} V_{TO}^2 \right) . \qquad . \qquad . \qquad (9.17)$$

As a very rough approximation to X the logarithm may be expanded as a series in $(B/A)V_{TO}^2$, and the first term only taken. To this approximation

$$X = -\frac{1}{2B} \left(-\frac{B}{A} V_{TO}^2 \right) = \frac{1}{2A} (V_{TO}^2) \qquad . \qquad . \qquad (9.18)$$

Minimum ground run. Considerable interest attaches to the condition for minimum ground run; in particular to the ground lift coefficient which gives this condition. This may be found by reference to eqn. (9.7), namely

$$\frac{1}{g} \frac{dV}{dt} = \left(\frac{T_0}{W} - \mu \right) - \frac{V^2}{W} \left\{ \tfrac{1}{2} \rho S (C_D - \mu C_{Lg}) + a \right\}$$

It is assumed that:

   (i) C_{Lg} and C_D are the only variable characteristics of the aircraft,
  (ii) $C_D = C_{D0} + kC_L^2$ and
 (iii) the take-off speed is independent of C_{Lg}. In practice this means that the aircraft moves at a constant incidence during the ground run and, when the take-off speed is reached, increases incidence suddenly to give the lift coefficient required for flight at that speed. This lift coefficient is invariably larger than C_{Lg} and is usually close to $C_{L\,max}$.

Since the take-off ground run is a case of acceleration from rest to some specified speed, it follows that the distance will be a minimum when the acceleration is at all times the maximum possible. To find the condition for maximum acceleration eqn. (9.7) may be differentiated with respect to C_{Lg} and the result equated to zero. In view of the assumed constancy of all aircraft characteristics other than C_{Lg} and C_D this differentiation gives

$$\frac{d}{dC_{Lg}} (C_{D0} + kC_{Lg}^2 - \mu C_{Lg}) = 0$$

i.e.,
$$2kC_{Lg} - \mu = 0$$

or
$$C_{Lg} = \frac{\mu}{2k} \qquad . \qquad . \qquad (9.19)$$

This is not a rigorous proof but does in fact give a minimum and not a maximum. It should be noted that the values of C_{Lg}, C_{D0}, and k are for the aircraft in the take-off configuration, i.e., with flaps and undercarriage lowered, and with allowance made for ground effect on the lift coefficient and lift-dependent drag. (See § 13.5.3.)

The complete take-off consists of the ground run, a transition from the ground run to climbing flight, and finally the climb-out itself. The analysis of the transition segment is beyond the scope of this book, while the climb may be calculated by the methods in Chapter 8.

Example 9.1. An aeroplane weighs 56,000 lb and has a wing area of 1000 sq. ft. With flaps in the take-off position the maximum lift coefficient is 2·2, and the aircraft takes-off at a speed 15% above the stalling speed. In the take-off configuration the drag equation is

$$C_D = 0·024 + 0·04C_L^2$$

The coefficient of ground friction μ is 0·025. The two engines each produce a total of 2400 B.H.P. At the take-off speed the airscrew efficiency is 75%, while the static thrust of each engine and airscrew is 6500 lb. Calculate the minimum ground run in standard conditions.

For the take-off speed,

$$V_s = \sqrt{\frac{56,000 \times 841}{1000 \times 2·2}} = 146 \text{ ft/sec}$$

$$\therefore\ V_{TO} = 1·15V_s = 168 \text{ ft/sec}$$

and $V_{TO}^2 = 28,400$

At take-off speed,

$$\text{T.H.P.} = 0·75 \times 2400 = 1800 \text{ H.P.}$$

$$\therefore\ \text{thrust at take-off} = \frac{1800 \times 550}{168} = 5900 \text{ lb per engine}$$

$$= 11,800 \text{ lb for two engines}$$

$$\text{total static thrust} = 2 \times 6500 = 13,000 \text{ lb}$$

$$\therefore\ 11,800 = 13,000 - 28,400a \text{ (from eqn. (9.6))}$$

whence $a = 0·0422$

and $T = 13,000 - 0·0422V^2$

For the minimum ground run,

$$C_{Lg} = \frac{\mu}{2k} = \frac{0·025}{0·080} = 0·3125$$

and therefore

$$C_D = 0·024 + 0·04(0·3125)^2 = 0·0279$$

Then $A = g\left(\dfrac{T_0}{W} - \mu\right) = 32·18\left(\dfrac{13,000}{56,000} - 0·025\right) = 6·65$

and $B = \dfrac{g}{W}\{\tfrac{1}{2}\rho S(C_D - \mu C_{Lg}) + a\}$

$$= \frac{32·18}{56,000}\left\{\frac{1000}{841}(0·0279 - 0·3125 \times 0·025) + 0·0422\right\}$$

$$= 3·80 \times 10^{-5}$$

$$\therefore \; X = - \frac{1}{7 \cdot 6 \times 10^{-5}} \log_e \left(\frac{6 \cdot 65 - (3 \cdot 8 \times 10^{-5})(2 \cdot 84 \times 10^4)}{6 \cdot 65} \right)$$

$$= - \frac{10^5}{7 \cdot 6} \log_e \left(\frac{6 \cdot 65 \equiv 1 \cdot 08}{6 \cdot 65} \right) - \frac{10^5}{7 \cdot 6} \log_e \left(\frac{6 \cdot 65}{5 \cdot 53} \right)$$

$$= 2420 \text{ ft} = \underline{807 \text{ yds}}$$

and this is the minimum ground run, since the appropriate value of C_L was used.

9.1.2. Assisted take-off. To achieve satisfactory take-off performance under unfavourable conditions it is often necessary to use some form of assistance or thrust augmentation.

The thrust available from a turbo-jet or turbo-prop engine decreases with increase in the ambient temperature. This loss of thrust may be eliminated or reduced by the injection of a water/methanol mixture into the air in the intake. This reduces the temperature of the air and permits, over a limited range of temperature, attainment of the full rated thrust of the engine, and gives a useful improvement in engine thrust at still higher temperatures (Fig. 9.2).

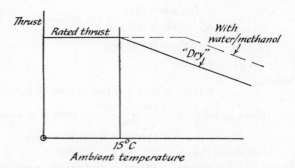

FIG. 9.2.—Effect of ambient temperature and water/methanol injection on gas-turbine engine performance.

Alternatively additional thrust may be provided by extra power units, commonly rockets. These may be built into the aircraft as permanent fittings for use during take-off, or they may be fitted externally and jettisoned after use. Calculation of the take-off performance then follows the lines indicated above, but may need to be performed in two parts, since the extra thrust may not be available for the whole of the take-off.

Naval aircraft, operating from aircraft carriers, are frequently launched by catapult. Aerodynamics has little part to play in such 'brute force' activities except in determining the stalling speed of the aircraft, thereby setting a lower limit for the catapult performance.

Example 9.2. Estimate the minimum ground run for the aeroplane of the previous Example if assistance is given by a rocket motor, whose thrust is constant at 5000 lb and which is operative for the whole ground run.

This extra thrust will affect only the value of A, which becomes

$$A = 32 \cdot 18 \Big(\frac{18,000}{56,000} - 0 \cdot 025 \Big) = 9 \cdot 55$$

Then

$$X = \frac{10^5}{7 \cdot 6} \log_e \Big(\frac{9 \cdot 55}{9 \cdot 55 - 1 \cdot 08} \Big)$$

$$= 1585 \text{ ft} = \underline{528 \text{ yds.}}$$

This represents a 35% reduction in the ground run.

9.2. Landing performance. The landing performance of an aircraft determines the ease and safety with which a given aeroplane can land at a given aerodrome. The economic value of the aircraft depends on its landing performance in the same way as on its take-off performance.

The landing distance is usually specified for similar conditions to those described in § 9.1. As with the take-off, landing performance depends on the prevailing atmospheric conditions, though the effect of these conditions on the engine performance is of less importance for landing. In the event of a balked landing, the engine performance is obviously of vital importance (§ 8.8.2).

Analogous to the take-off, landing performance is measured in two ways:

(i) *Landing distance*, the horizontal distance required by the aircraft to come to rest after passing over an obstacle 50 ft high.

(ii) *Landing ground run*, the distance between the point where the aircraft undercarriage first touches the ground and the point where the aircraft first comes to rest.

9.2.1. Calculation of the landing ground run. The dynamics of this problem are identical to those of the take-off process, the only differences being that dV/dt is numerically negative, the thrust T may be negative, and the coefficient of ground friction μ is normally much larger than during take-off, because of the use of wheel brakes.

It follows that the expression for the landing ground run is identical to eqn. (9.15), namely

$$x = - \frac{1}{2B} \log_e (A - BV^2) + C \text{ (eqn. (9.15))}$$

The initial conditions are now $x = 0$ when $V = V_L$, the landing speed. Then

$$0 = - \frac{1}{2B} \log_e (A - BV_L^2) + C$$

whence

$$C = \frac{1}{2B} \log_e (A - BV_L^2)$$

leading to

$$x = + \frac{1}{2B} \log_e \Big(\frac{A - BV_L^2}{A - BV^2} \Big). \qquad . \qquad . \qquad (9.20)$$

Further if X is the landing ground run, other conditions are $x = X$ when $V = 0$, which gives finally,

$$X = + \frac{1}{2B} \log_e \left(1 - \frac{B}{A} V_L^2\right) \quad . \qquad . \qquad . \qquad (9.21)$$

The full landing manœuvre consists of the glide, possibly using some engine power, from 50 ft above the runway down to the runway, a transition from the glide to a state of unsteady, decelerating, level flight just above the runway (the hold-off, flare-out, round-out or float), and finally the landing ground run. The analysis of the transition segment is beyond the scope of this book, while the glide may be treated by the methods in Chapter 8.

9.2.2. High-lift flaps. The kinetic energy of an aircraft is proportional to the square of its speed. Thus the lower the landing speed, the easier the problem of stopping the aircraft, which involves dissipating its kinetic energy. Since the landing speed is normally slightly greater than the stalling speed it is desirable that the stalling speed should be as low as practicable. To this end high-lift flaps are employed to increase the maximum lift coefficient of the wing.

Such a flap is essentially a section of the rear of the wing which may be rotated downwards, increasing the effective camber of the aerofoil

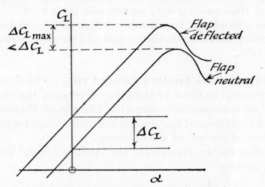

FIG. 9.3.—Effect of flap deflection on lift curve.

section. In many cases the flap also slides rearwards, increasing the effective area of the wing.

A further function of the flap is to increase the drag of the aircraft, steepening the approach gliding angle and thus shortening the total landing distance.

A typical lift curve for a wing with and without flap deflection is shown in Fig. 9.3. The linear parts of the two curves are almost parallel, the flap increasing the lift coefficient at any moderate incidence by the amount ΔC_L. The maximum lift coefficient is increased by the amount $\Delta C_{L \max}$ which is always rather less than ΔC_L. The stall occurs, with flap deflected, at a rather smaller incidence (typically some 4° or 5° less) than with flaps neutral. This is advantageous in that the landing may be made at a smaller aircraft incidence (i.e., a less nose-up attitude), permitting a shorter under-carriage and easing the problem of providing adequate view of the ground for the pilot.

9.2.3. Types of flap.

Many different types of flap have been used on aircraft. Some of the more common are described below. Table 9.1 gives typical values of $C_{L\,max}$.

TABLE 9.1

Maximum lift coefficients of various high-lift combinations; sectional values on 12% thick aerofoil

Flap type	$C_{L\,max}$
Plain aerofoil	1·5
With H-P nose slat	1·9
With split flap	2·4
With double-slotted flap	2·8
Double-slotted flap and nose slot . . .	3·4
Plain flap with blowing from shroud . . .	4·7
Jet flap	>10

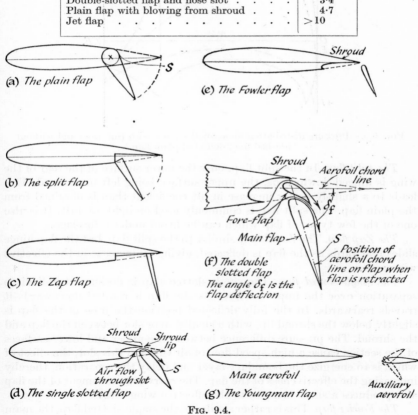

(a) The plain flap

(c) The Fowler flap

(b) The split flap

(c) The Zap flap

(f) The double slotted flap
The angle δ_f is the flap deflection

(d) The single slotted flap

(g) The Youngman flap

Fig. 9.4.

The plain flap. A portion of the trailing edge of the aerofoil section is hinged so that it may be rotated downwards (Fig. 9.4). Fig. 9.5 shows the pressure distribution over a typical aerofoil section with and without deflected plain flap, the section itself being just below stalling incidence. It is seen that the deflection of the flap modifies the pressure distribution over the whole section, and most of the lift increase occurs on the main aerofoil and not on the flap itself. This comment is true for most types of flap.

With a plain flap the flow is unable to follow the surface of the flap, and separates from the surface as indicated by the line marked S. This leads to a considerable reduction in the effectiveness of the flap compared with what is theoretically attainable, and the simple plain flap is seldom used in practice, except as a control surface (§ 14.20).

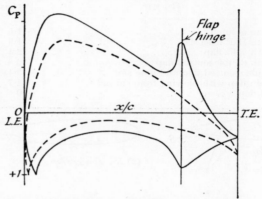

Fig. 9.5.—Pressure distribution on aerofoil section with (full line) and without (dashed line) deflected plain flap.

The split flap. In the split flap, only the lower surface of the rear of the wing is hinged downwards, the upper surface being left unchanged. This leads to a slightly better increase in lift coefficient than is obtained from the plain flap. The split flap is commonly used on light aircraft. It is also one of the few types of flap which can be fitted under a fuselage.

The Zap flap. The Zap flap is similar to the split flap, but the flap hinge slides rearwards as the flap is deflected, giving an increase in the effective wing area.

The single-slotted flap. The single-slotted flap is designed to alleviate separation over the upper surface. As the flap is rotated downwards it travels rearwards. In the fully deflected position the nose of the flap is slightly below the shroud lip, with a small gap or slot between the flap and the shroud. The pressure difference between the upper and lower surfaces of the section cause a high-speed flow of air through this slot, the effect of which is to energize the boundary layer and delay the separation, thereby increasing the effectiveness of the flap. The rearward movement of the flap also produces a small increase in the effective wing area.

The Fowler flap. This is rather similar to the single-slotted flap, the main difference being in the shroud length and the distance moved by the flap. The shroud extends to the trailing edge of the basic aerofoil section, as shown. The Fowler flap produces a comparatively large increase in the effective wing area.

The double-slotted flap. The single-slotted flap, by having attached flow over a greater extent of the flap chord than can be attained on a plain flap, is more effective than the plain flap. Separation is further delayed by the double-slotted flap. The flap itself is in two portions, normally connected rigidly together and moving as a single unit, between which is a second slot. The stream of air through this second slot delays separation to a point nearer the trailing edge than does a single slot, leading to a useful increase in flap effectiveness.

Further slight improvements may be effected by additional slots and/or by causing the relative positions of shroud, fore-flap and main flap to vary

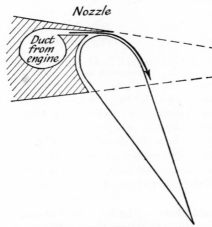

FIG. 9.6.—The blown plain flap.

with the flap deflection. This latter alternative, however, leads to mechanical complication and is seldom employed.

The Youngman flap. The Youngman flap consists of a separate or auxiliary aerofoil permanently exposed to the airstream behind the main aerofoil. The incidence of this auxiliary aerofoil is variable. When deflected downwards it is, essentially, a Fowler flap. The Youngman flap is seldom used.

The blown flap. This is a very successful attempt to enjoy the mechanical simplicity of the plain flap while avoiding the disadvantage of its poor performance. The flap is so arranged that, when it is deflected, a narrow slit in the rear of the main aerofoil is opened (Fig. 9.6). Air from a compressed air source (frequently the compressor of the gas turbine engines, where fitted) is ejected as a high-speed jet from this slit, tangentially over the upper nose of the flap. Such a jet follows the curvature of the surface (this is the *Coanda effect*) and, if the jet is sufficiently powerful, separation

is delayed to the trailing edge of the flap. The flap can then produce the
full theoretical lift increment (see § 12.4.1). In addition the jet itself represents a small increase in the circulation round the aerofoil (super-circula-
tion) thereby producing a further, small, increase in the lift.

The jet flap. Here the entire exhaust from the turbo-jet engines is
ejected as a high-speed jet through a narrow slit along the trailing edge of

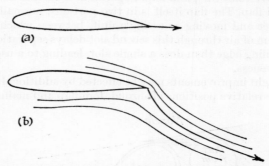

(a)

(b)

FIG. 9.7.—(a) The jet-flap in normal flight, (b) the jet-flap in the high-lift
configuration.

the wing. The direction of the jet may be rotated about a spanwise axis.
With the jet directed chordwise it produces a thrust (Fig. 9.7 (a)). When
the jet is directed downwards it acts rather like a very large flap behind
the wing, producing very large lift coefficients (Fig. 9.7 (b)). During early
experiments (see § 12.5) lift coefficients of 10 or so were achieved under
laboratory conditions, compared with 3, which is about the maximum
attainable by any of the other types of flap discussed above.

9.2.4. Nose flaps and slots. The low-speed stalling of an aerofoil section is due to the flow failing to follow the curvature of the upper surface
of the section, and separating from the surface to flow along the line
marked S in Fig. 9.8. The stall may therefore be delayed by assisting
the air to remain attached.

The Handley-Page slat. This is a small, highly cambered, auxiliary aerofoil positioned just above the upper nose of the main aerofoil (Fig. 9.9).
The pressure difference between the upper and lower surfaces causes a
high-speed jet of air to flow through the slot between the slat and the main
aerofoil. This stream of air, directed tangentially over the main aerofoil,
delays the separation and increases the stalling incidence, and therefore
the maximum lift coefficient (Fig. 9.10). The slat may be fixed permanently
in the operative position, or it may be 'automatic'. The automatic slat is
held against the surface (e.g., by springs) at low incidences but is pulled
into the operative position by the large negative pressure coefficients on
the slat which occur at incidences near the stall. In some aircraft the
effect is obtained by a permanent slot between the upper and lower surfaces of the basic aerofoil section over part of the span (Fig. 9.11).

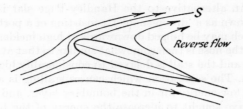

FIG. 9.8.—Flow around a stalled aerofoil section.

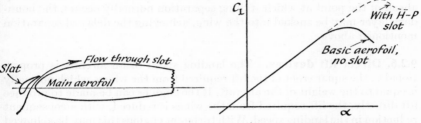

FIG. 9.9.—The Handley-Page slot.

FIG. 9.10.—Lift curve with and without Handley-Page slot.

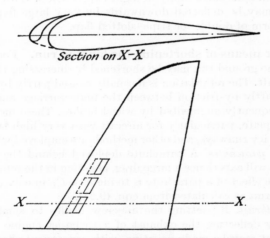

FIG. 9.11.—One form of the Handley-Page slot.

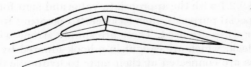

FIG. 9.12.—The nose-flap.

Nose flap. An alternative to the Handley-Page slat is the nose flap (colloquially known as a 'droop-snoot'), consisting of a portion of the nose of the wing which may be hinged downwards at high incidences (Fig. 9.12). The flow round the nose is then somewhat similar to that at incidences well below the stall, and the stall is delayed to considerably higher incidences.

Nose suction. The separation which causes stalling is associated with the build-up of low-energy air in the boundary layer, and methods mentioned above have sought to increase the energy of the boundary layer. Another method of delaying separation is to remove the boundary layer by suction. If a narrow slot or porous surface is fitted in the aerofoil slightly ahead of the point at which stalling separation normally occurs, the boundary layer may be sucked into the wing, achieving the delay of separation mentioned above.

9.2.5. Direct lift devices. The landing speed of an aircraft is proportional to the square root of the lift required from the wings, which normally is equal to the weight of the aircraft. If the engines can be made to produce lift directly, the lift required from the wings is reduced, with a consequent reduction in the landing speed. With turbo-jet engines this may be achieved by deflecting the jet downwards, giving a vertical component of thrust. This has been done successfully in flight experiments. With airscrews, the slipstream may be deflected downwards by very large flaps, usually an advanced form of double- or triple-slotted flap.

9.2.6. Other means of shortening the landing run. For a given landing speed the ground run may be shortened by increasing the retardation of the aircraft. The retardation is normally caused partly by aerodynamic drag and partly by friction between the undercarriage and the ground, which is frequently augmented by wheel brakes. These methods are not always adequate, particularly for aircraft with very high landing speeds, or on wet or icy runways, and other methods are employed when necessary.

Braking parachutes. A parachute deployed behind the aircraft after touch-down will experience a large drag, assisting in the retardation of the aircraft. The effect of a parachute is to increase C_D in eqn. (9.9), affecting the ground run as calculated from eqn. (9.21).

Reverse thrust. By setting the airscrew blades to small or negative pitch, or by deflecting the exhaust of a turbo-jet engine forwards, the engine thrust may be made negative, with consequent shortening of the landing run. The ground run with reverse thrust may be calculated by the method of § 9.2.1 with the appropriate value and sign for the thrust T.

For some special purposes, such as aircraft operating from an aircraft carrier, arrestor wires are used. These are simply strong wires lying close to the carrier deck, which are caught in a hook lowered by a landing aircraft. The wires are connected at their ends to hydraulic dampers which produce a progressive resisting force, bringing the aircraft rapidly to a stop.

Other devices which have been tried are: a barrier of strong netting to catch and stop the aircraft, and a mattress on to which the aircraft may land, wheels up.

9.3. Range and endurance. The range of an aircraft is the horizontal distance the aircraft can cover in flight, while the endurance is the time for which the aircraft can remain in flight. For most types of aircraft, range is the more important, and endurance is incidental. For a few classes of aircraft, such as ocean patrol aircraft, endurance is of prime importance.

9.3.1. Definitions of range. There are three generally accepted definitions of the range of an aircraft.

Safe Range. This is the maximum horizontal distance between two aerodromes between which the aircraft can fly a safe, 'reliably regular' service. 'Reliably regular' does not mean that the aircraft shall be able to make the flight under any conditions, such as in a strong head-wind, but shall be able to do so on most occasions.

In calculating the safe range, the aircraft is assumed to take-off with the fuel tanks full. It then carries out a normal flight, consisting of take-off, climb, cruise, descent and landing at the destination aerodrome. Allowances are however made for extra fuel consumed due to head-winds, navigational errors, and deterioration in airframe and engine performance. The aircraft is also required to have sufficient reserves of fuel to enable it, if necessary, to divert to some specified alternative airfield and in addition to wait in the air over this alternative airfield for a specified period, until it is allowed to land. It is also recognized that the take-off and landing may well be in the opposite direction to the rest of the flight. Therefore, although the fuel used in take-off and landing is debited, the corresponding distances are ignored.

Calculation of the safe range is a very lengthy and complicated procedure. Accordingly two simpler, though artificial, measures of the range have been accepted.

Still air range. In calculating the still air range (S.A.R.) the aircraft is assumed to take-off with full fuel tanks. It then climbs and flies in still air according to any cruise pattern selected by the designer until all the fuel is consumed. The horizontal distance covered, excluding the take-off distance, is the still air range. It is an artificial concept since the aircraft is assumed to run out of fuel in mid-air. It is, however, far simpler to calculate than the safe range.

Gross still air range. This is an even more artificial concept than still air range, but is very useful in the early project stages of the design of a new aircraft, and calculation of the gross still air range of an aircraft takes only a few minutes. For calculating the gross still air range (G.S.A.R.) the aircraft is supposed to be at the selected altitude at which the cruise is started, with full flying speed and full fuel tanks and the take-off and climb segments of the flight are ignored completely. The aircraft is then supposed to cruise in still air according to any desired pattern until all the fuel is consumed. The horizontal distance covered during this cruise is the gross still air range. Its great value during the early stages of project design is as follows.

Suppose, for example, that it is desired to design an aircraft for non-stop flight across the North Atlantic at some specified speed with a stated payload or number of passengers. The general configuration of the aircraft is supposed to have been fixed, or a small number of alternative configurations may be selected for comparison. The actual flight distance (stage length) on the North Atlantic route, London to New York, is about 3030 nautical miles. A few plausible guesses based on past experience will suggest that an aircraft of the type considered with a safe range of 3030 n.m. would have a gross still air range of, say, 4800 n.m.; the actual figure will vary with the class of aircraft, e.g., turbo-prop, high-subsonic turbo-jet, etc. The first problem is to decide the smallest size of aircraft capable of performing the specified task. To pursue this, a number (say 20) of hypothetical aircraft are proposed, covering, say, four values of wing area and

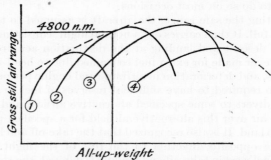

FIG. 9.13.—Illustrating the use of gross still air range in project design. The curves 1, 2, 3 and 4 refer to the different wing areas assumed.

five different all-up-weights for each wing area. For each of these aircraft the G.S.A.R. is calculated, and the results plotted as G.S.A.R. against A.U.W. for the various wing areas, as in Fig. 9.13. A curve is then drawn (the broken curve in Fig. 9.13) representing the envelope of the plotted curves. The intersection of this envelope with the line representing the required G.S.A.R. gives the all-up-weight and, by interpolation, the wing area of the smallest and therefore most economical aircraft of the selected configuration capable of performing the specified task. This aircraft is then the subject of fuller investigations, e.g., calculation of the safe range as a check, investigation of the take-off and landing performance and stability studies. If these checks are satisfactory and unless the Chief Designer decided on any drastic changes in configuration, the aircraft would be the basis of the final project design.

It will be realized that it is far easier and quicker to find the G.S.A.R. for a number of hypothetical aircraft than to find the safe ranges for the same number of aircraft. Since the simpler procedure detailed above is entirely satisfactory, the concept of gross still air range is extremely useful.

9.3.2. Calculation of range during cruising flight, when engine performance is expressed in terms of thrust.

For turbo-jet and rocket engines the specific fuel consumption, c, is defined as the weight of fuel used per pound of thrust per hour (lb/lb/hr) and is approximately independent of flight speed. If the engine thrust is T lb, the rate of fuel consumption is cT lb/hr. Now when fuel is burnt the weight of the aircraft is decreased by the amount of fuel consumed. Therefore

$$\frac{dW}{dt} = -cT \qquad . \qquad . \qquad . \qquad (9.22)$$

Now in straight and level flight,

$$T = D \quad \text{and} \quad L = W$$

Hence

$$\frac{dW}{dt} = -c\frac{D}{L}W . \qquad . \qquad . \qquad (9.23)$$

Rearranging, this becomes

$$dt = -\frac{L}{D}\frac{1}{c}\frac{dW}{W}$$

Integrating this between limits 1 and 2, where 1 represents the start of cruise and 2 represents the end of the cruise, gives

$$t_2 - t_1 = -\frac{1}{c}\frac{L}{D}(\log_e W_2 - \log_e W_1)$$

$$= \frac{1}{c}\frac{L}{D}\log_e (W_1/W_2). \qquad . \qquad . \qquad (9.24)$$

This gives the time spent on the cruise while the weight of the aircraft is being reduced, by burning fuel, from W_1 to W_2. Since c is based on the hour, this time of cruise is given by eqn. (9.24) in hours.

If the aircraft cruises at a constant true air speed of V knots, the distance covered during this time is

$$R = V(t_2 - t_1) = \frac{V}{c}\frac{L}{D}\log_e (W_1/W_2) \qquad . \qquad . \qquad (9.25)$$

R being the cruise range in nautical miles. If V is in statute miles per hour, the range R is given in statute miles. The expression for R in eqn. (9.25) is the Breguet formula for range.

Consideration of the cruise conditions. In deriving the Breguet formula three major assumptions were made, namely that the specific fuel consumption, the lift/drag ratio, and the true air speed were all constant throughout the cruise. For turbo-jet engines in the troposphere these three assumptions are rather self-contradictory but, for flight in the stratosphere, they can all be satisfied in a particularly simple manner. This follows from the fact that, because of the constancy of the temperature in the stratosphere, the thrust of a turbo-jet engine at a fixed throttle setting is proportional to the relative density, ignoring variation with flight speed.

Now for the lift/drag ratio to be constant the lift coefficient must be constant. Comparing flight at two weights W_1 and W_2 at constant true air speed V and constant lift coefficient,

$$\left.\begin{array}{l} W_1 = C_L \tfrac{1}{2}\rho_0\sigma_1 V^2 S \\ W_2 = C_L \tfrac{1}{2}\rho_0\sigma_2 V^2 S \end{array}\right\} \qquad \cdot \qquad \cdot \qquad \cdot \qquad (9.26)$$

giving

$$\frac{W_2}{W_1} = \frac{\sigma_2}{\sigma_1} \qquad \cdot \qquad \cdot \qquad \cdot \qquad \cdot \qquad (9.27)$$

This shows that, under the given conditions of constant T.A.S. and constant C_L, the relative density must decrease as the weight decreases. Thus as fuel is burnt the aircraft must gain altitude ('float-up').
Since the lift/drag ratio is constant

$$\frac{D_2}{D_1} = \frac{L_2}{L_1} = \frac{\sigma_2}{\sigma_1} \qquad \cdot \qquad \cdot \qquad \cdot \qquad (9.28)$$

Now, as noted above, the thrust is proportional to the relative density, and therefore

$$\frac{T_2}{T_1} = \frac{\sigma_2}{\sigma_1} \qquad \cdot \qquad \cdot \qquad \cdot \qquad (9.29)$$

Thus if at conditions 1 the thrust and drag are equal, i.e., $T_1 = D_1$, it follows from eqns. (9.28) and (9.29) that

$$T_2 = D_2$$

Thus the thrust is at all times equal to the drag automatically, without throttle adjustment, and the specific fuel consumption is constant.

To sum up this argument: as fuel is consumed, decreasing the aircraft weight, the aircraft gains altitude. In the stratosphere this gain in altitude automatically reduces the thrust, maintaining equality between the drag and the thrust, without any action on the part of the pilot. Moreover, in the stratosphere, constant true air speed corresponds to constant Mach number and therefore, if the aircraft is equipped with a Machmeter, the pilot need only maintain constant Machmeter reading and the whole 'drift-up' process will occur without any other act of pilotage. If, however, the aircraft is not fitted with a Machmeter, but with an ordinary air-speed indicator, a practical difficulty arises. The E.A.S. V_E, to which the indicated air speed is an approximation, is given by

$$V_E = V\sqrt{\sigma}$$

i.e.,

$$\frac{V_{E2}}{V_{E1}} = \frac{V\sqrt{\sigma_2}}{V\sqrt{\sigma_1}} = \sqrt{\frac{W_2}{W_1}} \qquad \cdot \qquad \cdot \qquad \cdot \qquad (9.30)$$

Thus as height increases the E.A.S. must decrease, and a pilot flying by the A.S.I. is required continually to reduce the I.A.S. as the weight decreases. This difficulty is avoided by adopting a 'stepped' flight pattern. In this the aircraft is flown at a constant I.A.S. and altitude for a specified time. At the end of this time the aircraft is climbed to a predetermined altitude and again flown at a constant, lower, I.A.S. This is repeated throughout the cruise. The steady, gradual, drift-up of the ideal flight pattern is thus approximated by a series of steps. Provided these steps are small the departure from the ideal, and therefore the loss in range, is negligible.

Flight for maximum duration. From eqn. (9.24) it is seen that the maximum endurance with given weight limits W_1 and W_2 is obtained when the lift/drag ratio is a maximum, if c is constant. The condition for maximum lift/drag ratio has been discussed in § 8.3.1.

Flight for maximum range. The Breguet formula, eqn. (9.25), is

$$R = \frac{V}{c}\frac{L}{D}\log_e\left(W_1/W_2\right) \text{ (eqn. (9.25))}$$

Again with c constant, for maximum range with a given weight ratio, $V(L/D)$ must be a maximum, and it is required to find the value of C_L for which this is so.

Now
$$V\frac{L}{D} = \left(\frac{W}{\frac{1}{2}\rho S C_L}\right)^{\frac{1}{2}} \cdot \frac{C_L}{C_D} = \left(\frac{W}{\frac{1}{2}\rho S}\right)^{\frac{1}{2}} \cdot \frac{C_L^{1/2}}{C_D}$$

Therefore for the maximum value of $C_L^{1/2}/C_D$, or the minimum value of $C_D/C_L^{1/2}$

$$\frac{d}{dC_L}\left(\frac{C_{D0} + kC_L^2}{C_L^{1/2}}\right) = 0$$

Hence,
$$C_L^{1/2}(2kC_L) - (C_{D0} + kC_L^2)(\tfrac{1}{2}C_L^{-1/2}) = 0$$

i.e.,
$$3kC_L^2 = C_{D0} \qquad . \qquad . \qquad . \qquad . \qquad (9.31)$$

Thus for maximum range the lift-dependent drag is one-third of the zero-lift drag, while

$$C_{L\,mr} = \sqrt{\frac{C_{D0}}{3k}} = \frac{C_{L\,md}}{\sqrt{3}}$$

$$V_{mr} = V_{md}(3)^{\frac{1}{4}} \simeq 1\cdot3\,V_{md}$$

$$C_{D\,mr} = \tfrac{4}{3}C_{D0}$$

From the value of lift coefficient for maximum range as found above, the equivalent air speed for flight at the 'start of cruise' weight W_1 may be found. Then from the engine performance data, the altitude at which the engine thrust, at cruising r.p.m, equals the aircraft drag at that E.A.S. and weight may be estimated. This altitude is then the altitude at which the cruise will start. Thus in Fig. 9.14, the cruise will start at 40,000 ft. Subsequently the altitude will vary so as to satisfy eqn. (9.27).

For high-subsonic aircraft it may happen that the true air speed for maximum range calculated as above will exceed the critical Mach number for the aircraft, and is therefore unattainable. In such cases the estimation of the optimum speed is complicated, since the cruise speed cannot exceed the limiting Mach number and this varies with the lift coefficient. It then

o

becomes an *ad hoc* procedure, by trial and error for each aircraft considered.

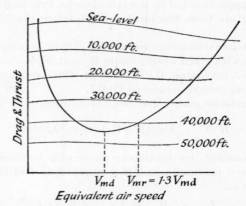

FIG. 9.14.—Determination of altitude at start of cruise.

9.3.3. Calculation of range for engines whose performance is expressed in terms of horse-power.

In this case, the specific fuel consumption, c, is defined as the weight of fuel burnt per B.H.P. per hour (lb/B.H.P./hr), and is approximately constant. Then, if the brake horse-power produced by the engine is P

$$\frac{dW}{dt} = - cP$$

Now in straight and level flight,

$$\eta P = \frac{DV}{375}$$

where V is the flight speed in statute miles per hour and η is the propulsive (airscrew) efficiency.

Therefore

$$\frac{dW}{dt} = - \frac{c}{\eta} \frac{DV}{375}$$

Rearranging,

$$dt = - \frac{375\eta}{Vc} \frac{L}{D} \frac{dW}{W}$$

which, on integrating, gives,

$$t_2 - t_1 = \frac{375\eta}{Vc} \frac{L}{D} \log_e (W_1/W_2) \qquad . \qquad . \qquad (9.32)$$

This is the cruise duration in hours, and the corresponding range is

$$R = \frac{375\eta}{c} \frac{L}{D} \log_e (W_1/W_2) \qquad . \qquad . \qquad (9.33)$$

the range R being in statute miles.

Consideration of the cruise conditions. Derivation of eqn. (9.33) assumed flight at constant lift coefficient, true air speed, and lift/drag ratio, and therefore a steady increase in altitude and decrease in engine thrust as fuel is consumed.

Turbo-prop engines have much the same variation of power with altitude as the thrust-altitude variation for turbo-jets. If the true air speed is constant it follows that, for turbo-prop engines, the thrust in the stratosphere varies approximately according to eqn. (9.29), and thus the comments of § 9.3.2 apply to turbo-prop powered aircraft.

Piston engines, however, do not have this same self-regulating property and in addition piston engined aircraft seldom cruise in the stratosphere. In practice, except on very long-range flights, piston engined aircraft tend to be flown on the cruise at constant altitude and constant throttle setting, the equivalent and true air speeds being allowed to vary as necessary as weight changes, implying a continual variation of T.A.S. and lift coefficient (and therefore lift/drag ratio). Thus two of the important assumptions made in deriving the range are violated. To overcome this complication, mean values for the various quantities are used. These mean quantities are those calculated for the mean cruise weight, which is the geometric mean of the starting and finishing values, i.e.,

$$W_{\text{mean}} = (W_1 W_2)^{\frac{1}{2}}. \qquad . \qquad . \qquad (9.34)$$

This approximation is found to give acceptable accuracy.

Flight for maximum duration. Inspection of eqn. (9.32) shows that, assuming c and η to be independent of the flight speed, the maximum endurance is attained when the radical $\dfrac{1}{V}\dfrac{L}{D}$ is a maximum. This corresponds to the minimum power condition, discussed in § 8.5.1. This result could also be seen intuitively, since the minimum rate of fuel consumption will occur when the power produced is a minimum, assuming c to be constant.

Flight for maximum range. Again assuming the specific fuel consumption and the airscrew efficiency to be independent of flight speed, eqn. (9.33) shows that the maximum range is obtained when flying at the maximum lift/drag ratio, i.e., at the minimum drag speed.

Uses of the Breguet formula. The range calculated from the Breguet formula may be used for:

(i) calculation of the cruise segment of the safe range. In this case the weights W_1 and W_2 are respectively the weight at the end of the climb, and the weight when sufficient fuel remains to allow for the descent and the rest of the flight;

(ii) calculation of the still air range. The weights used are the weight at the end of the climb, and the weight with all fuel burnt;

(iii) calculation of the whole of the gross still air range. The weights used are the maximum all-up-weight permitted, and the weight with all fuel consumed.

Example 9.3. An aircraft of 1000 sq. ft wing area has for its drag equation
$$C_D = 0 \cdot 014 + 0 \cdot 038 C_L^2$$

At the start of cruise it weighs 55,000 lb, of which 20% is fuel. It is estimated that at the end of the cruise 3000 lb of fuel should remain in the tanks.

Estimate the maximum cruise distance in nautical miles, and the altitudes at the start and end of the cruise, if the engine thrust at 36,090 ft is 3200 lb and is proportional, in the stratosphere, to the relative density. Further, if 5000 lb of fuel is used before starting the cruise, estimate the gross still air range. The specific fuel consumption is 0·85 lb fuel/lb thrust/hr.

For maximum range

$$C_L = \sqrt{\frac{C_{D_0}}{3k}} = 0.35$$

$$C_D = 0.014 + 0.038(0.35)^2 \quad \text{or} \quad = \tfrac{4}{3}(0.014)$$
$$= 0.01866$$

Therefore, at the start of cruise, the drag D is

$$D = 55,000 \times \frac{0.01866}{0.35} = 2930 \text{ lb}$$

The equivalent air speed at start of cruise, V_{E1}, is

$$V_{E1} = \sqrt{\frac{55,000 \times 841}{1000 \times 0.35}} = 363 \text{ ft/sec, E.A.S.}$$

Now the thrust at an altitude where the relative density is σ_1 is given by

$$T = 3200\left(\frac{\sigma_1}{\sigma}\right)$$

where σ is the relative density at 36,090 ft $= 0.2981$. Then for the thrust to be 2930 lb,

$$\frac{\sigma_1}{\sigma} = \frac{2930}{3200} = 0.918$$

$$\therefore \ \sigma_1 = 0.918 \times 0.2981 = 0.2734$$

whence the altitude at start of cruise is, from tables of the atmosphere, 37,800 ft approx. and the constant T.A.S. on the cruise is

$$V = \frac{363}{\sqrt{0.2734}} = 695 \text{ ft/sec, T.A.S.}$$

Of the 55,000 lb at the start of cruise, 20%, or 11,000 lb is fuel. Thus 8000 lb of fuel may be used on the cruise, and the weight at the end of cruise is therefore 47,000 lb.

Then, if the relative density at the end of cruise altitude is σ_2

$$\frac{\sigma_2}{\sigma_1} = \frac{47,000}{55,000}$$

whence
$$\sigma_2 = 0.2734 \times \frac{47}{55} = 0.234$$

which gives 41,000 ft for the altitude at the end of cruise.

From the Breguet formula,

$$R = \frac{V}{c}\frac{L}{D}\log_e\left(W_1/W_2\right)$$

$$= \frac{0.35}{0.1866}\frac{V}{0.85}\log_e\left(\frac{55}{47}\right) \text{ nautical miles,}$$

where V is the flight T.A.S. in knots.

Now 1 nautical mile $= 6080$ ft, and therefore

$$1 \text{ ft/sec} = \tfrac{1}{6080} \times 3600 \text{ knots} = 0.5921 \text{ kts.}$$
$$\therefore \ 695 \text{ ft/sec} = 411 \text{ kts.}$$
$$\therefore \ \text{range } R = \underline{1420 \text{ n.m.}}$$

For the G.S.A.R., the initial all-up-weight is $55,000 + 5000 = 60,000$ lb, while the weight after consuming all the fuel is $55,000 - 11,000 = 44,000$ lb.

$$\therefore \ \text{G.S.A.R.} = \frac{0.35}{0.1866} \frac{411}{0.85} \log_e \left(\frac{60}{44}\right)$$
$$= \underline{2820 \text{ n.m.}}$$

9.4. Aircraft efficiency.

From the viewpoint of an operator, an aircraft is a device for carrying a certain payload a certain distance, the aircraft itself is actually a necessary complication, and his assessment of its efficiency is based largely on the amount of fuel used in transporting this payload.

The aeronautical engineer, however, regards the aeroplane as an object of intrinsic interest, and bases his measurement of its efficiency on the fuel used in moving the whole machine and its payload.

An efficiency is the ratio of two amounts of mechanical work. In measuring the efficiency of an aeroplane, use is made of two quantities, both of which are related to mechanical work, but neither of which is itself mechanical work. When an aircraft of weight W tons flies a distance δR miles (nautical or statute), it may be said that 'useful work' of amount $W \, \delta R$ ton miles is done. Note that this is an artificial term, since the true work done is equal to the product of drag and distance, and not the product of weight and distance. In doing this useful work a certain mass, δf, of fuel is burnt. Since this mass of fuel, when unburnt, contains a certain amount of unreleased (chemical) energy, the mass of fuel burnt is a measure of the energy used, or the work supplied. Thus a measure of the efficiency of a complete aircraft may be obtained from

$$\text{efficiency } \eta = \frac{W \, \delta R}{\delta f} \text{ ton miles/lb of fuel}$$

Now $\qquad \delta f = cT \, \delta t, \quad \delta t$ being the time of flight, in hours

Also $\qquad \delta R = V \, \delta t$

Combining the above three equations,

$$\eta = W \frac{V \, \delta t}{cT \, \delta t} = \frac{V}{c} \frac{W}{T}$$

In straight and level flight, since $L = W$ and $T = D$,

$$\eta = \frac{V}{c} \frac{L}{D} \text{ ton miles/lb fuel} \quad . \qquad . \qquad . \qquad (9.35)$$

Similar analysis for piston and turbo-prop engines leads to

$$\eta = \frac{375}{c} \frac{L}{D} \eta_p \quad . \qquad . \qquad . \qquad . \qquad (9.36)$$

where η_p is the efficiency of the airscrew.

It must be emphasized that this is not a true efficiency in the sense in which this term is normally applied to a mechanical system, and the word 'economy' would be more apt than 'efficiency'. It is, in fact, possible to derive a true efficiency for an aeroplane as a mechanical system, though this is seldom done in practice. Assuming the calorific value of the fuel to be about 560 A.H.U./lb (18,000 C.H.U./lb), the expression for the mechanical efficiency of an aircraft is approximately

$$\eta_A = \frac{1}{70} \frac{V}{c} \%$$

Taking typical values, such as $V = 650$ ft/sec and $c = 0.85$ lb/lb/hr gives an efficiency of about 11%. Thus the mechanical efficiency of an aircraft is quite low, comparable to that of a steam engine. The economic advantage of an aeroplane lies in its ability to carry useful loads at high speeds over considerable distances, whatever the terrain to be covered.

9.5. Climb with allowance for acceleration.

In the earlier discussion of climbing flight it has been assumed that the aircraft is flying at constant true air speed. This is seldom the case in practice. For example, if an aircraft climbs at constant incidence and therefore (ignoring change in weight) at constant equivalent air speed, the true air speed will increase as height is gained. Thus the kinetic energy of the aircraft will increase. This increase in kinetic energy must come from the excess work done by the thrust. Therefore less of this excess work will be used in increasing the potential energy of the aircraft, and the rate of climb will be less than that estimated by ignoring the acceleration.

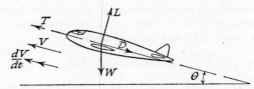

FIG. 9.15.—Forces acting on an aircraft in an accelerated climb.

Consider the forces shown in Fig. 9.15. Then, resolving forces,

$$L - W \cos \theta = 0 \text{ (eqn. (8.44))}$$

and

$$T - D - W \sin \theta = \frac{W}{g} \frac{dV}{dt} \qquad \cdot \qquad \cdot \qquad \cdot \qquad (9.37)$$

Now

$$\frac{dV}{dt} = \frac{dV}{dh} \frac{dh}{dt} \quad \text{where } h \text{ is the altitude}$$

and

$$\frac{dh}{dt} = v, \quad \text{the rate of climb}$$

$$\therefore \frac{W}{g} \frac{dV}{dh} v = T - D - W \sin \theta$$

or
$$\sin \theta = \frac{T - D}{W} - \frac{v}{g}\frac{dV}{dh}$$

But the rate of climb $v = V \sin \theta$, and therefore
$$v = V\left(\frac{T - D}{W}\right) - \frac{vV}{g}\frac{dV}{dh}$$

i.e.,
$$v\left(1 + \frac{V}{g}\frac{dV}{dh}\right) = V\left(\frac{T - D}{W}\right)$$

Now $V\left(\dfrac{T - D}{W}\right)$ is the rate of climb for the same aircraft under the influence of the same forces but ignoring the effects of acceleration, and may be denoted by v_0. Then

$$v = \frac{v_0}{1 + \dfrac{V}{g}\dfrac{dV}{dh}} \qquad \qquad (9.38)$$

Thus the effect of acceleration is to decrease the non-accelerated rate of climb, v_0, by the factor*

$$\frac{1}{1 + \dfrac{V}{g}\dfrac{dV}{dh}}$$

Interest therefore attaches to the problem of finding dV/dh. This will be done for two cases of practical interest; climb at constant E.A.S., and climb at constant Mach number.

Climb at constant E.A.S. in the troposphere. If V_E is the constant E.A.S., the true air speed at any altitude is V where
$$V = V_E(\sigma)^{-\frac{1}{2}}$$
$$\therefore \frac{dV}{dh} = \frac{d}{dh}(V_E\sigma^{-\frac{1}{2}}) = -\tfrac{1}{2}\sigma^{-\frac{3}{2}}\frac{d\sigma}{dh}V_E$$

Now from the work on the atmosphere (§ 3.3), in the troposphere
$$\sigma = \left(\frac{T_0 - Lh}{T_0}\right)^{\frac{g-LR}{LR}} = \left(1 - \frac{L}{T_0}h\right)^{\frac{g-LR}{LR}}$$
where T_0 is the temperature at sea-level, °K
and L is the lapse rate, °C/ft.

* The denominator of the factor may be written as
$$\frac{1}{g}\frac{d}{dh}(gh + \tfrac{1}{2}V^2).$$
Now the sum of the kinetic and potential energies of the aircraft,
$$E = mgh + \tfrac{1}{2}mV^2,$$
and thus the denominator is in fact $\dfrac{1}{g}\dfrac{d}{dh}\left(\dfrac{E}{m}\right)$. This quantity is $1/g$ times the rate of change with height of the total mechanical energy per unit mass of the aircraft.

$$\therefore \frac{d\sigma}{dh} = \left(\frac{g-LR}{LR}\right)\left(1 - \frac{L}{T_0}h\right)^{\left(\frac{g-LR}{LR}-1\right)}\left(-\frac{L}{T_0}\right)$$

$$= -\frac{L}{T_0}\frac{g-LR}{LR}\left(1 - \frac{L}{T_0}h\right)^{\frac{g-2LR}{LR}} \qquad . \qquad . \qquad (9.39)$$

Using the expression for σ given above, eqn. (8.67) becomes

$$\frac{d\sigma}{dh} = -\frac{L}{T_0}\left(\frac{g-LR}{LR}\right)(\sigma)^{\frac{g-2LR}{g-LR}} \qquad . \qquad . \qquad . \qquad . \qquad (9.40)$$

Then

$$\frac{dV}{dh} = \{-\tfrac{1}{2}V_E(\sigma)^{-\frac{3}{2}}\}\left\{-\frac{L}{T_0}\left(\frac{g-LR}{LR}\right)(\sigma)^{\frac{g-2LR}{g-LR}}\right\}$$

$$= \tfrac{1}{2}V_E\frac{L}{T_0}\left(\frac{g-LR}{LR}\right)(\sigma)^{-\frac{g+LR}{2(g-LR)}}$$

With this expression for dV/dh,

$$1 + \frac{V}{g}\frac{dV}{dh} = 1 + \left[\frac{V_E}{g}(\sigma)^{-\frac{1}{2}}V_E\frac{L}{2T_0}\left(\frac{g-LR}{LR}\right)(\sigma)^{-\frac{g+LR}{2(g-LR)}}\right]$$

$$= 1 + \frac{V_E^2}{g}\frac{L}{2T_0}\left(\frac{g-LR}{LR}\right)(\sigma)^{-\frac{g}{g-LR}} \qquad . \qquad . \qquad (9.41)$$

Note that $(g-LR)/LR$ is the index in the expression for σ, eqn. (3.16), and has the value $4\cdot256$ in the I.S.A. while $g/(g-LR)$ is the index n in the equation $p = k\rho^n$, eqn. (3.18), and has the value $1\cdot235$ for the I.S.A. Thus, in the troposphere of the International Standard Atmosphere,

$$1 + \frac{V}{g}\frac{dV}{dh} = 1 + 4\cdot55 \times 10^{-7}V_E^2(\sigma)^{-1\cdot235} \qquad . \qquad (9.41.1)$$

Note that this 'correction factor' involves V_E^2, and therefore varies quite rapidly with the speed. Also, since σ appears with the index $-1\cdot235$, it follows that the correction factor increases with altitude. At sea-level ($\sigma = 1$), the factor varies with E.A.S. as in the table below.

E.A.S. (ft/sec) . .	100	300	600
Factor	1·00455	1·0410	1·1638

Hence, it can be seen that the factor produces only 4% reduction in the rate of climb at 300 ft/sec E.A.S., but 16% at 600 ft/sec E.A.S.

Climb at constant E.A.S. in the stratosphere. In the stratosphere,

$$\frac{p_2}{p_1} = \frac{\rho_2}{\rho_1} = \exp\left\{\frac{g(h_1 - h_2)}{RT_s}\right\} \text{ (eqn. (3.12))}$$

where T_s is the constant temperature in the stratosphere. Then

$$\sigma = \frac{\rho_2}{\rho_0} = \frac{\rho_2}{\rho_1}\frac{\rho_1}{\rho_0}$$

and conditions '1' may conveniently be taken to be the tropopause.

$$\therefore \ \sigma = \frac{\rho_1}{\rho_0}\exp\left\{\frac{g}{RT_s}(h_1 - h_2)\right\}$$

whence $$\frac{d\sigma}{dh} = \frac{\rho_1}{\rho_0}\left(-\frac{g}{RT_s}\right)\exp\left\{\frac{g}{RT_s}(h_1 - h_2)\right\}$$

(h_2 being the variable and h_1 constant),

$$= \frac{\rho_1}{\rho_0}\left(-\frac{g}{RT_s}\right)\frac{\rho_2}{\rho_1} = -\frac{g}{RT_s}\sigma \quad . \quad . \quad . \quad (9.42)$$

Therefore

$$\frac{dV}{dh} = -\tfrac{1}{2}V_E(\sigma)^{-\frac{3}{2}}\left\{-\frac{g}{RT_s}\sigma\right\}$$

$$= V_E\frac{g}{2RT_s}(\sigma)^{-\frac{1}{2}}$$

and the correction factor becomes

$$1 + \frac{V}{g}\frac{dV}{dh} = 1 + \frac{1}{g}V_E(\sigma)^{-\frac{1}{2}}\left\{V_E\frac{g}{2RT_s}(\sigma)^{-\frac{1}{2}}\right\}$$

$$= 1 + \frac{1}{2RT_s}\left(\frac{V_E^2}{\sigma}\right)$$

But $$\frac{V_E^2}{\sigma} = V^2$$

and therefore

$$1 + \frac{V}{g}\frac{dV}{dh} = 1 + \frac{V^2}{2RT_s} \quad . \quad . \quad . \quad . \quad (9.43)$$

In the I.S.A., with $T_s = 216 \cdot 5°K$, the correction factor becomes

$$1 + 7 \cdot 46 \times 10^{-7}V^2 \quad . \quad . \quad . \quad (9.43.1)$$

Climb at constant Mach number in the troposphere. If the aircraft is climbing at constant Mach number, M, then

$$V = Ma = M(65 \cdot 9T^{\frac{1}{2}}) = 65 \cdot 9M(T_0 - Lh)^{\frac{1}{2}}$$

$$\therefore \ \frac{dV}{dh} = 65 \cdot 9M \cdot \tfrac{1}{2}(T_0 - Lh)^{-\frac{1}{2}}(-L)$$

Since $T_0 - Lh = T$, the ambient temperature of the atmosphere,

$$\frac{dV}{dh} = -32 \cdot 95LMT^{-\frac{1}{2}}$$

and therefore

$$1 + \frac{V}{g}\frac{dV}{dh} = 1 + \frac{Ma}{g}\frac{dV}{dh}$$

$$= 1 + \frac{M}{g}(65 \cdot 9T^{\frac{1}{2}})(- 32 \cdot 95LMT^{-\frac{1}{2}})$$

$$= 1 - 0 \cdot 1335M^2 \qquad . \qquad . \qquad . \qquad (9.44)$$

This gives

$$v = \frac{v_0}{1 - 0 \cdot 1335M^2} > v_0$$

showing that the rate of climb at constant Mach number is greater than the rate of climb at the same, but constant, true air speed. This is because the speed of sound, and therefore of flight for constant Mach number, decreases with altitude in the troposphere.

When $M \doteqdot 2 \cdot 74$ the denominator of eqn. (9.44) becomes zero. Thus if there is an exact balance between thrust and drag ($T = D$), v_0 is zero and the true rate of climb v becomes indeterminate. At this Mach number any change in altitude (in the troposphere) leads to a change in true air speed such that the aircraft total mechanical energy E remains constant. Thus the increase in potential energy associated with a gain in height is derived entirely from the loss in kinetic energy, and it is not necessary for any work to be done by the 'thrust minus drag' term. Climb at this Mach number is, in fact, a special case of a 'zoom' in which the aircraft may climb or dive indefinitely within the troposphere, always at the same Mach number, provided that an exact balance between thrust and drag is maintained.

For flight at any constant Mach number greater than $2 \cdot 74$ the denominator (eqn. (9.44)) becomes negative, and the true rate of climb may be positive even though v_0 is negative (thrust less than drag). In terms of the aircraft energy this means that, as the aircraft climbs, its total mechanical energy E decreases. This rate of loss of aircraft energy may be used to supply part of the work necessary to overcome the drag, and thus the engine thrust required is less than the aircraft drag. On the other hand, suppose that, for this condition of constant $M > 2 \cdot 74$, it is required to *descend*. Then v is negative, which requires v_0 to be positive, with $T > D$. Thus flight at these high Mach numbers in the troposphere gives the paradoxical condition that to climb at constant Mach number the engine thrust must be made less than the drag, while to descend the thrust must be made greater than the drag. This may complicate piloting techniques under these conditions. (If the Mach number is not held constant this condition may not arise.)

It should be noted that the value of $2 \cdot 74$ derived above for the Mach number of this critical flight condition is for the standard lapse rate. Any other lapse rate will give a different value.

Climb at constant Mach number in the stratosphere. In the stratosphere the temperature is constant with altitude and thus the speed of sound, and therefore of flight at constant Mach number, does not vary with altitude. It follows that there is no acceleration under these conditions, and therefore no correction is necessary.

9.6. The effect of air brakes. Many current aircraft are fitted with some form of air brake. These are fitted with three principal objects in mind:

(i) limitation of speed in a dive;

(ii) increase of drag, and therefore of angle of descent, on the approach to land;

(iii) assistance in the reduction of flight speed, for combat or other purposes.

The first two of these have been considered briefly in § 8.7.1. The third purpose will be considered now.

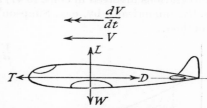

FIG. 9.16.—Forces on an aircraft during accelerated flight.

Consider the aircraft shown in Fig. 9.16. Resolving forces horizontally,

$$\frac{W}{g}\frac{dV}{dt} = T - D \ . \qquad . \qquad . \qquad . \qquad (9.45)$$

The thrust T will not in general be zero; with turbo-jet engines there is usually some small idling thrust with the throttle fully closed, while airscrews may provide a negative thrust (i.e., an extra drag) when idling.

The methods of Chapter 8 may be used to find the drag D at a number of speeds, and the aircraft retardation $- dV/dt$ may be calculated. If the problem is to find the time and distance required to decelerate from a speed V_1 to a lower speed V_2,

$$\frac{dV}{dt} = - a \qquad . \qquad . \qquad . \qquad . \qquad (9.46)$$

calculated from eqn. (9.45).

Then
$$dt = - \frac{dV}{a}$$

Integrating this between limits 1 and 2

$$t_2 - t_1 = t = - \int_1^2 \frac{dV}{a} = \int_2^1 \frac{dV}{a} \qquad . \qquad . \qquad (9.47)$$

If a curve of $1/a$ is plotted against V, the area under the curve between the limits V_1 and V_2 represents the time taken to decelerate (Fig. 9.17).

To find the distance travelled during deceleration,

$$\frac{dV}{dt} = \frac{dV}{dx}\frac{dx}{dt} = V\frac{dV}{dx}$$

Therefore
$$V\frac{dV}{dx} = - a$$

Rearranging, and integrating between limits 1 and 2,

$$x_2 - x_1 = X = - \int_1^2 \frac{V dV}{a} = \int_2^1 \frac{V}{a} dV \quad . \quad . \quad (9.48)$$

Thus the area under a curve of V/a against V, between limits V_1 and V_2, represents the distance travelled during deceleration (see Fig. 9.18). The integrations involved in eqns. (9.47) and (9.48) may be performed graphically, numerically by, e.g., Simpson's Rule, or by any other convenient method.

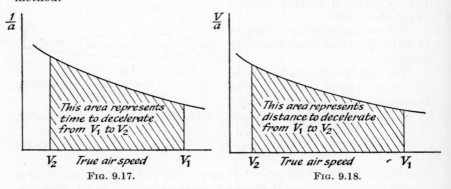

FIG. 9.17.   FIG. 9.18.

Although the foregoing applies to decelerated flight, similar analysis may be used to find the time and distance required for acceleration from one speed to another.

Example 9.4. An aircraft of wing area 300 ft² weighs 18,000 lb and has for its drag equation, with dive brakes retracted

$$C_D = 0{\cdot}014 + 0{\cdot}06 C_L^2$$

The single turbo-jet engine gives an idling thrust at sea-level of 250 lb at all speeds. The dive brakes have a total area of 20 ft², and their drag coefficient is 1·0 based on their area.

Estimate the time and distance required to decelerate from 600 ft/sec to 300 ft/sec at sea-level, with dive brakes extended.

Consider speeds of 600(50)300 ft/sec.

$$C_L = \frac{18{,}000 \times 841}{300 V^2} = \frac{50{,}460}{V^2}$$

$$\text{mass of aircraft} = \frac{18{,}000}{32{\cdot}18} = 560 \text{ slugs}$$

At a speed V the drag of the dive brakes will be

$$D_b = \tfrac{1}{2}\rho V^2 S_b C_{Db}$$

where S_b = area of dive brakes, = 20 ft²

                 C_{Db} = drag coefficient based on dive brake area

                      = 1·0

Expressing this as a drag coefficient C_{DB}, based on the wing area

$$D_b = \tfrac{1}{2}\rho V^2 S C_{DB}$$

Thus $C_{DB} = C_{Db}\frac{S_B}{S} = (1{\cdot}0)\frac{20}{300} = 0{\cdot}0667$

Thus at any given speed the values of drag coefficient calculated for the 'clean' aircraft must be increased by $0{\cdot}0667$.

The complete calculation for a speed of 600 ft/sec is as follows.

$$V = 600, \quad V^2 = 360{,}000, \quad C_L = \frac{50{,}460}{360{,}000} = 0{\cdot}140$$

$$C_D = 0{\cdot}014 + 0{\cdot}0667 + 0{\cdot}060(0{\cdot}140)^2$$
$$= 0{\cdot}08184$$

$$\text{total drag } D = 18{,}000 \times \frac{0{\cdot}08184}{0{\cdot}140} = 10{,}510 \text{ lb}$$

$$\text{drag–thrust} = 10{,}510 - 250 = 10{,}260 \text{ lb}$$

$$\text{deceleration} = \frac{10{,}260}{560} = 18{\cdot}30 \text{ ft/sec}^2$$

$$\frac{1}{a} = 0{\cdot}0546 \text{ sec}^2/\text{ft}$$

$$\frac{V}{a} = \frac{600}{18{\cdot}30} = 32{\cdot}8 \text{ sec}$$

Performing a similar calculation for each of the stated speeds leads to the following table.

V (ft/sec) .	300	350	400	450	500	550	600
$\dfrac{1}{a}$ . . .	0·190	0·151	0·118	0·096	0·078	0·065	0·055
$\dfrac{V}{a}$ . . .	57·0	52·9	46·5	43·0	39·1	35·6	32·8

Performing the integrations required (by Simpson's Rule in this case) leads to the results that the time taken to decelerate is $31{\cdot}4$ sec, and the distance travelled is 13,100 ft, or $2{\cdot}48$ statute miles.

Performing the same calculation for the aircraft with dive brakes retracted gives a time of 2 min 42 sec, and a distance of $13{\cdot}2$ statute miles, which shows clearly the effectiveness of the air brakes.

9.7. Flight in a horizontal circle.

Flight in a horizontal circle may be executed in two distinct ways; with the aircraft correctly banked to the horizon, or with the aircraft not banked or only partially banked. The first case only will be considered here.

Consider the aircraft in Fig. 9.19 flying steadily at the correct angle of bank round a circle of radius R ft with a true speed of V ft/sec. The words 'at the correct angle of bank' mean that, at any instant, the aircraft centre-line is aligned exactly along the direction of flight, i.e., the aircraft is not flying 'crab-wise' in any degree, there is no sideslip, and therefore there is no component of aerodynamic force on the aircraft in the

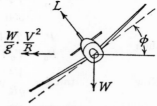

FIG. 9.19.—Forces acting on an aircraft in horizontal, correctly banked, circling flight.

spanwise direction. Then the only forces on the aircraft are the lift and weight as shown, together with the thrust and drag, which are not shown in Fig. 9.19.

Let the suffix $_0$ denote quantities (such as the lift, drag, speed, etc.) for straight and level flight at the same incidence, weight and altitude, as obtain in the circle. Then, resolving forces vertically,

$$L \cos \phi - W = 0 . \qquad . \qquad . \qquad . \qquad (9.49)$$

Resolving forces horizontally,

$$L \sin \phi = \frac{W}{g} \frac{V^2}{R} . \qquad . \qquad . \qquad . \qquad (9.50)$$

since the aircraft has a centripetal acceleration of V^2/R.

Rearranging these two equations, and then dividing,

$$\tan \phi = \frac{V^2}{gR} \qquad . \qquad . \qquad . \qquad . \qquad (9.51)$$

Now, for straight and level flight,

$$L_0 = W \quad \text{and} \quad T_0 = D_0$$
$$\therefore \ L = L_0 \sec \phi > L_0 . \qquad . \qquad . \qquad . \qquad (9.52)$$

showing that the lift of the wings is greater in the circle than in the related straight and level flight. Since the incidence is the same in the circle and in the related straight and level flight, the lift coefficient and the lift/drag ratio are also the same, and therefore,

$$V = V_0 (\sec \phi)^{\frac{1}{2}} . \qquad . \qquad . \qquad . \qquad (9.53)$$

and

$$\frac{L}{D} = \frac{L_0}{D_0} \qquad . \qquad . \qquad . \qquad . \qquad (9.54)$$

Also, for the aircraft in the circle, since the motion is steady,

$$T = D \qquad . \qquad . \qquad . \qquad . \qquad (9.55)$$

Combining eqns. (9.52), (9.53), (9.54) and (9.55),

$$\frac{T}{T_0} = \frac{D}{D_0} = \left(\frac{V}{V_0} \right)^2 = \frac{L}{L_0} = \sec \phi \qquad . \qquad (9.56)$$

Since the thrust horse-power P is given by

$$P = \frac{TV}{550}$$

then

$$\frac{P}{P_0} = \frac{T}{T_0} \frac{V}{V_0} = (\sec \phi)(\sec \phi)^{\frac{1}{2}} = (\sec \phi)^{\frac{3}{2}} \qquad . \qquad (9.57)$$

Now

$$\tan \phi = \frac{V^2}{gR} \quad (\text{eqn. } (9.51))$$

and

$$V^2 = V_0^2 \sec \phi \quad \text{from eqn. } (9.53) . \qquad . \qquad . \qquad (9.58)$$

and therefore

$$\tan \phi = \frac{V_0^2 \sec \phi}{gR}$$

$$\therefore \ \sin \phi = \frac{V_0^2}{gR} \qquad . \qquad . \qquad . \qquad . \qquad (9.59)$$

Time to turn through a given angle.

$$\text{circumference of flight path circle} = 2\pi R \text{ ft}$$

$$\therefore \text{ time for one complete circle } = \frac{2\pi R}{V} \text{ sec}$$

$$\therefore \text{ time to turn through } \psi \text{ radians} = \frac{2\pi R}{V}\frac{\psi}{2\pi}$$

$$= \frac{\psi R}{V} \text{ sec} \qquad . \qquad (9.60)$$

Now, from eqn. (9.51)

$$R = \frac{V^2}{g \tan \phi}$$

and therefore the time to turn through ψ radians is t sec, where

$$t = \frac{\psi}{V}\frac{V^2}{g \tan \phi} = \frac{V\psi}{g \tan \phi} \qquad . \qquad . \qquad . \qquad (9.61)$$

Load factor in a turn. As shown earlier, the lift of the wings, L, is

$$L = W \cos \phi \qquad . \qquad . \qquad . \qquad . \qquad (9.49.1)$$

which may be written as

$$L = nW \qquad . \qquad . \qquad . \qquad . \qquad (9.49.2)$$

where n is the load factor in the turn. A turn involving a particular value of n is known as an 'n'g turn (e.g., a $5g$ turn if $n = 5$), since the apparent weight of any part of the aircraft and of the pilot is n times the weight in straight and level, or 'one g', flight. For some categories of aircraft, the load factor in a turn is one of the criteria in designing and stressing the wing structure.

Minimum time to turn through a given angle. The minimum time required for a given aircraft to turn through a given angle is, in general, determined by one or the other of two criteria; the strength of the structure or the maximum power available.

Taking the first of these criteria, eqn. (9.61) may be written in terms of the load factor n as follows.

$$t = \frac{V\psi}{g \tan \phi} = V_0 \left(\frac{\psi}{g}\right)\frac{(\sec \phi)^{\frac{1}{2}}}{\tan \phi} \qquad . \qquad . \qquad . \qquad (9.61.1)$$

since $V = V_0(\sec \phi)^{\frac{1}{2}}$.

Now V_0 is the speed of straight and level flight at the incidence and lift coefficient used in the turn, and therefore

$$V_0 = \sqrt{\frac{W}{\frac{1}{2}\rho S C_L}}$$

Also $\qquad \sec \phi = n$

and $\qquad \tan \phi = (\sec^2 \phi - 1)^{\frac{1}{2}} = (n^2 - 1)^{\frac{1}{2}}$

This gives that the time to turn through the angle ψ is

$$t = \frac{\psi}{g}\sqrt{\frac{W}{\frac{1}{2}\rho S C_L}}\sqrt{\frac{n}{n^2 - 1}} \qquad . \qquad . \qquad . \qquad (9.62)$$

If, then, the strength of the aircraft is the limiting factor, there being a specified value of n which cannot be exceeded without overstressing the structure, the only variable on the right-hand side of eqn. (9.62) is the lift coefficient. It follows that the quickest turn will be made when the lift coefficient is a maximum, i.e., the turn must be made with the aircraft on the point of stalling.

The second limitation on the time of turn, caused by the power available being limited, is not amenable to analysis and will be illustrated by an example.

Example 9.5. A light aircraft, weighing 2000 lb and with a wing area of 125 ft^2 has a maximum lift coefficient of 1·5 and its drag equation is

$$C_D = 0·020 + 0·050 C_L^2$$

It is powered by a single turbo-jet engine giving a thrust of 300 lb at all speeds at sea-level. Estimate the minimum time required to turn through 180° at sea-level, and the corresponding load factor and wing lift.

This problem is solved by selecting a number of values of V_0 and finding, for each, the time of turn achieved when using the full available thrust. The calculation for $V_0 = 100$ ft/sec is given below.

$$C_L = \frac{841 W}{125}\left(\frac{1}{V_0^2}\right) = \frac{13,456}{V_0^2}$$

Hence for $\quad V_0 = 100$ ft/sec $\qquad C_L = 1·3456$

Then $\qquad C_D = 0·020 + 0·050(1·3456)^2 = 0·1105$

$$\therefore D_0 = 2000\left(\frac{0·1105}{1·3456}\right) = 164·2 \text{ lb},$$

$$\frac{T}{D_0} = \sec \phi = \frac{300}{164·2} = 1·825$$

and $\qquad \tan \phi = (\sec^2 \phi - 1)^{\frac{1}{2}} = 1·525$

Now the time to turn through a given angle is proportional to $V_0(\sec \phi)^{\frac{1}{2}}/\tan \phi$ by eqn. (9.61.1), and thus the minimum time will occur when this quantity is a minimum. For $V_0 = 100$ ft/sec this quantity has the value

$$\frac{100 \times (1·825)^{\frac{1}{2}}}{1·525} = 88·6$$

Repeating this calculation for a few other speeds gives the following table.

V_0 (ft/sec)	100	105	110	120
gt/ψ	88·6	87·9	88·1	91·0

Plotting these results shows that the minimum value of gt/ψ occurs for a value of V_0 of 105 ft/sec, and the minimum value is 87·9, for which condition $\sec \phi = n = 1·944$, and the wing lift is $2000 \times 1·944 = 3888$ lb.

$$\frac{gt}{\psi} = 87·9$$

$$\therefore t = \frac{87·9}{32·2}\pi = 8·56 \text{ sec}$$

The actual flight speed $V = V_0(\sec \phi)^{\frac{1}{2}} = 105(1·944)^{\frac{1}{2}}$
$$= 146 \text{ ft/sec}$$

Thus the minimum time required to turn through 180° is 8½ sec, the aircraft flying at a speed of 146 ft/sec, the wing lift being 3890 lb. The incidence is that corresponding to a straight and level flight speed of 105 ft/sec, the angle of bank being 57·4 degrees.

It should be noted that the lift coefficient used in the circle is 1·22, which is appreciably less than the maximum lift coefficient of the wing.

Example 9.6. The aircraft of the above Example is stressed to permit a maximum load factor of 3. Calculate the minimum time to turn through 180° at sea-level, and the engine thrust required for this turn.

The minimum time may be calculated from eqn. (9.62) using the maximum value, 1·5, for the lift coefficient, and with $n = 3$. This gives:

$$t = \frac{\pi}{g} \sqrt{\frac{841 \times 2000}{125 \times 1\cdot5}} \sqrt{\frac{3}{8}} = 5\cdot65 \text{ sec}$$

With $C_L = 1\cdot5$, $C_D = 0\cdot020 + 0\cdot050(1\cdot5)^2 = 0\cdot1323$

$$\therefore \ D_0 = 2000\left(\frac{0\cdot1323}{1\cdot5}\right) = 176\cdot8 \text{ lb}$$

$$\therefore \ D = D_0 \sec \phi = nD_0 = 3 \times 176\cdot8 = 530 \text{ lb}$$

Thus if the structure were designed for a load factor of 3, the aircraft could turn through 180° in 5·6 sec, but would require an engine thrust of 530 lb to do so. To achieve this turn, with the aircraft on the point of stalling, would need very skilful piloting.

Example 9.7. When flying straight and level at a speed of 250 ft/sec at sea-level, an aeroplane weighing 56,000 lb requires a thrust of 4000 lb. At full throttle at 15,000 ft ($\sigma = 0\cdot629$) the engines produce a total of 6900 thrust horse-power.

Calculate the radius of the tightest banked horizontal turn which can be made at 15,000 ft while flying at the same incidence as for a flight speed of 250 ft/sec at sea-level. Calculate also the flight speed and the load on the wings in the circle, and the time taken to turn through 180°.

Eqn. (9.59) is
$$\sin \phi = \frac{V_0^2}{gR}$$

i.e.,
$$R = \frac{V_0^2}{g \sin \phi}$$

Thus for the tightest turn (minimum radius), $\sin \phi$ must have the largest possible value, V_0 being specified. This is attained when $\sec \phi$ has the largest possible value. Since

$$\frac{P}{P_0} = (\sec \phi)^{\frac{3}{2}}$$

it follows that the maximum value of $\sec \phi$ will occur when P is the maximum available, which is given as 6900 H.P. Now, for straight and level flight at sea-level, the thrust horse-power required is

$$P_r = \frac{4000 \times 250}{550} = 1820 \text{ T.H.P.}$$

For straight and level flight at the same incidence at 15,000 ft the lift coefficient, lift/drag ratio and equivalent air speed will be the same as for flight at sea-level, and therefore $P_r \sqrt{\sigma}$ will be the same.

P

If, then, the power required at 15,000 ft is P_0,

$$P_0 = \frac{1820}{\sqrt{0 \cdot 629}} = 2300 \text{ T.H.P.}$$

and

$$V_0 = \frac{250}{\sqrt{0 \cdot 629}} = 316 \text{ ft/sec}$$

Now the maximum power available is 6900 T.H.P. and therefore

$$\frac{6900}{2300} = 3 = (\sec \phi)^{\frac{3}{2}}$$

$$\therefore \sec \phi = (3)^{\frac{2}{3}} = 2 \cdot 08$$

whence

$$\phi = \underline{61° \ 16'}.$$

$$V = V_0 (\sec \phi)^{\frac{1}{2}} = 316(2 \cdot 08)^{\frac{1}{2}}$$
$$= \underline{455 \text{ ft/sec, T.A.S.}}$$

The load on the wings is

$$L = W \sec \phi = 56{,}000 \times 2 \cdot 08$$
$$= \underline{116{,}600 \text{ lb.}}$$

Since

$$\sec \phi = 2 \cdot 08, \quad \tan^2 \phi = \sec^2 \phi - 1$$
$$= 3 \cdot 326$$

$$\therefore \tan \phi = 1 \cdot 824$$

$$\therefore R = \frac{V^2}{g \tan \phi} = \frac{(455)^2}{32 \cdot 2 \times 1 \cdot 824}$$
$$= 3520 \text{ ft} = \underline{1173 \text{ yds.}}$$

The time to turn through 180° (π radians) is

$$t = \frac{455 \times 3 \cdot 142}{32 \cdot 2 \times 1 \cdot 824} = \underline{24 \cdot 4 \text{ sec.}}$$

Example 9.8. While flying straight and level at sea-level at a speed of 300 ft/sec a pilot causes his aircraft to enter a horizontal, correctly banked, circle of 2850 ft radius while maintaining the same incidence, the engine thrust being altered as necessary. Without altering either the incidence or the engine thrust, the pilot then brings the aircraft out of the turn and allows it to climb. Estimate the rate of climb if, at that incidence, the lift/drag ratio is 9.

$$\sin \phi = \frac{V_0^2}{gR} = \frac{90{,}000}{32 \cdot 2 \times 2850} = 0 \cdot 98072$$

then

$$\cos \phi = (1 - \sin^2 \phi)^{\frac{1}{2}} = 0 \cdot 19547$$

and

$$\sec \phi = 1/\cos \phi = 5 \cdot 1157$$

$$\therefore \frac{T}{T_0} = \sec \phi = 5 \cdot 1157$$

Turning now to consideration of the climb, the ratio T/T_0 found above, the ratio of the maximum thrust used to the thrust for straight and level flight, is identical to the ratio T/T_0 of eqn. (8.61.2). Therefore, if θ is the angle of climb

$$5 \cdot 1157 = \cos \theta + 9 \sin \theta$$

i.e.,

$$(5 \cdot 1157 - \cos \theta)^2 = 81(1 - \cos^2 \theta)$$

the solutions to which are:

$$\cos \theta = 0 \cdot 881 \quad \text{and} \quad -0 \cdot 76$$

the second of which is ignored. Then

$$\sin \theta = 0.474$$
$$\text{the speed on the climb} = V(\cos \theta)^{\frac{1}{2}} = 300(0.881)^{\frac{1}{2}}$$
$$= 282 \text{ ft/sec}$$
$$\text{the rate of climb} = 282 \times 0.474$$
$$= 133 \text{ ft/sec} = \underline{8000 \text{ ft/min.}}$$

EXERCISES

1. Describe the general features of take-off and landing with reference to the appropriate equations for the ground runs, and discuss the application of flaps. (U. of L.)

2. Calculate the minimum take-off ground run for the aircraft of Example 9.1 of the text in Tropical Maximum conditions at sea-level.

(i) if the engine thrust is decreased by 15% at all speeds from its value at 15°C, and

(ii) if the thrust is maintained at its value at 15°C by the use of water/methanol injection. (*Ans.* 1047 yds; 867 yds)

3. An aeroplane has a wing area of 3000 ft² and its drag equation is $C_D = 0.015 + 0.05C_L^2$. It starts to cruise at 36,000 ft at the speed for maximum range at a weight of 120,000 lb, adopting the 'drift-up' technique of cruise. After flying for a certain distance it drops a payload of 8000 lb and then returns to the point at which the cruise was started, but at a different altitude. The weight at that point is 50,000 lb.

Calculate the distance between the point at which the payload was released and the start-of-cruise point, if the specific fuel consumption is 0.7 lb/lb thrust/hr, assuming instantaneous change of altitude on releasing the payload. (*Ans.* 3090 n.m.)

4. The single turbo-jet engine fitted to the aircraft of Example 9.4 of the text produces, at sea-level, a maximum thrust of 10,000 lb at all flight speeds. Estimate the minimum time and distance required for this aircraft to accelerate, in level flight at sea-level, from 300 ft/sec to 600 ft/sec and to decelerate back to 300 ft/sec. (*Ans.* 67½ sec, 4.15 st. miles)

5. While flying at 80 m.p.h, E.A.S. at 10,000 ft ($\sqrt{\sigma} = 0.8594$), an aeroplane weighing 2000 lb makes a 90° turn in 15 sec, maintaining the same incidence and altitude. The wing loading is 20 lb/ft² and, at the given speed, the lift/drag ratio is 10. Calculate the radius of the turn, the load factor in the turn, and the thrust horse-power required. (*Ans.* 1370 ft, 1.103, 57.5 H.P.)

6. An aeroplane weighing 11,000 lb is powered by a single jet engine producing 5000 lb thrust along a line parallel to the mean chord line of the wings, from which the incidence is measured. The wings have a planform area of 245 ft², no-lift incidence $= -2.2°$, and the lift curve slope $dC_L/d\alpha = 4.6$.

Find the radius of a correctly banked '4g' turn at an altitude where the relative density is 0.8, the wing incidence then being $+ 8°$. Work from first principles and derive any formulae used. (*Ans.* 1819 ft) (U. of L.)

CHAPTER 10

THE ELEMENTS OF TWO-DIMENSIONAL FLUID FLOW

Although Aeronautics is largely concerned with the overall effects of air pressure on bodies, pressure distributions, aerodynamic forces, and the like, it is the behaviour of elementary particles or molecules of air that must be studied in order to convert physical behaviour into mathematical equations. This is not to say that the symbolic equation of every practical characteristic of real fluid should be taken and introduced into the general solution for a particular problem. The resulting mathematics would be far too complicated for easy solution and, whenever possible, characteristics of little influence in the problem are omitted. However, it is first necessary to develop equations for the fundamentals of fluid dynamics and, for this, the motion and behaviour of fluid elements will be studied.

10.1. The Equations of Motion, and Equation of Continuity. It is convenient in what follows to consider flow in two dimensions only. Various names have been given to this type of flow, 'sheet' flow being useful. The flow is the same as that between two planes set parallel and a little distance apart. The fluid can then flow in any direction between and parallel to the planes but *not* at right angles to them. This means that in the subsequent mathematics there are only two variables, x and y in Cartesian (or rectangular) coordinates or r and θ in polar coordinates. It is further assumed that the thickness of the fluid between the planes is unity; this simplifies the understanding of two-dimensional flow problems but care must be taken in the matter of units.

In practice if two-dimensional flow is to be simulated, the method of constraining the flow between two close parallel plates is often used; small smoke tunnels and some high-speed tunnels are examples of this.

To summarize: Two-dimensional flow is fluid motion where the velocity at all points is parallel to a given plane.

10.1.1. Component velocities. In general the local velocity in a flow is inclined to the reference axes Ox, Oy and it is usual to resolve the velocity q into two components mutually at right-angles.

In a Cartesian coordinate system let a particle move from point $P(x, y)$ to point $Q(x + \delta x, y + \delta y)$, a distance of δs in time δt (Fig. 10.1). Then the velocity of the particle is

$$\underset{\delta s \to 0}{\text{Lim}} \frac{\delta s}{\delta t} = \frac{ds}{dt} = q$$

Going from P to Q the particle moves horizontally through δx giving the horizontal velocity $u = dx/dt$ positive to the right. Similarly going from

P to Q the particle moves vertically through δy and the vertical velocity $v = dy/dt$ (upwards positive).

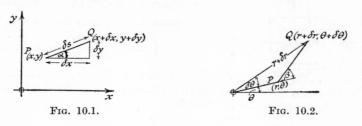

FIG. 10.1.   FIG. 10.2.

By geometry $$(\delta s)^2 = (\delta x)^2 + (\delta y)^2$$
thus $$q^2 = u^2 + v^2$$

and the direction of q relative to the x-axis is $\alpha = \tan^{-1} \dfrac{v}{u}$.

In a polar coordinate system (Fig. 10.2) the particle moves from $P(r, \theta)$ to $Q(r + \delta r, \theta + \delta\theta)$ in time δt.

The component velocities are:

$$\text{radially (outwards positive) } q_n = \frac{dr}{dt} \quad \text{and}$$

$$\text{tangentially (anti-clockwise positive) } q_t = r\frac{d\theta}{dt}$$

Again $$(\delta s)^2 = (\delta r)^2 + (r\delta\theta)^2$$
thus $$q^2 = q_n{}^2 + q_t{}^2$$

and the direction of q relative to the radius vector is given by

$$\beta = \tan^{-1}\frac{q_t}{q_n}$$

10.1.2. Continuity. A fundamental of every homogeneous flow is that of continuity, § 4.3. In the simple case of virtually incompressible fluid such as water flowing through a pipe, if 10 gallons per second is put in at one end 10 gal/sec will emerge at the other. If this were not the case, if for example only 5 gallons emerged per second at the end, then 5 gal/sec must be lost somewhere between the two ends of the pipe, and if the pipe were whole this could not be.

For a general equation expressing this fundamental, the density and velocity change at any point in a fluid must be investigated.

10.1.3. The derivation of the Equation of Continuity in Cartesian Coordinates. Consider a small rectangular region of space of side δx, δy and unity, centred at the point $P(x, y)$ in a fluid motion which is referred to the axes Ox, Oy. At $P(x, y)$ the local velocity components are u and v and the density ρ, where each of these three quantities are functions of x, y and t (Fig. 10.3).

Dealing with the flow into the 'box' in the Ox direction, the amount of mass flowing into the region of space per second through the left-hand vertical face is:

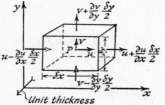

mass flow per unit area $\times$ area

i.e.,
$$\left(\rho u - \frac{\partial(\rho u)}{\partial x}\frac{\delta x}{2}\right)\delta y \cdot 1 \ . \qquad (10.1)$$

The amount of mass leaving the box per second through the right-hand vertical face is:

$$\left(\rho u + \frac{\partial(\rho u)}{\partial x}\frac{\delta x}{2}\right)\delta y \cdot 1 \ . \qquad (10.2)$$

The accumulation of mass per second in the box due to the horizontal flow is the difference of (10.1) and (10.2),

i.e.,
$$-\frac{\partial(\rho u)}{\partial x}\delta x\,\delta y \ . \qquad . \qquad . \qquad . \qquad (10.3)$$

Similarly, the accumulation per second in the Oy direction is

$$-\frac{\partial(\rho v)}{\partial y}\delta x\,\delta y \ . \qquad . \qquad . \qquad . \qquad (10.4)$$

so that the total accumulation per second is

$$-\left\{\frac{\partial(\rho u)}{\partial x} + \frac{\partial(\rho v)}{\partial y}\right\}\delta x\,\delta y \ . \qquad . \qquad . \qquad (10.5)$$

As mass cannot be destroyed or created, eqn. (10.5) must represent the rate of change of mass of the fluid in the box and can be written as

$$\frac{\partial(\rho \cdot \text{volume})}{\partial t}$$

but with the elementary 'box' having constant volume ($\delta x\,\delta y.1$) this becomes

$$\frac{\partial \rho}{\partial t} \cdot \delta x\,\delta y.1 \ . \qquad . \qquad . \qquad . \qquad (10.6)$$

Equating (10.5) and (10.6) gives the general Equation of Continuity, thus:

$$\frac{\partial \rho}{\partial t} + \frac{\partial(\rho u)}{\partial x} + \frac{\partial(\rho v)}{\partial y} = 0 \qquad . \qquad . \qquad (10.7)$$

This can be expanded to:

$$\frac{\partial \rho}{\partial t} + u\frac{\partial \rho}{\partial x} + v\frac{\partial \rho}{\partial y} + \rho\left\{\frac{\partial u}{\partial x} + \frac{\partial v}{\partial y}\right\} = 0 \quad . \qquad . \qquad (10.8)$$

and if the fluid is incompressible and the flow steady the first three terms are all zero since the density cannot change and the equation reduces for *incompressible fluid* to

$$\frac{\partial u}{\partial x} + \frac{\partial v}{\partial y} = 0 \quad . \quad . \quad . \quad . \quad (10.9)$$

This equation is fundamental and important but remember, it expresses a physical reality.
e.g., in the case given by eqn. (10.9)

$$\frac{\partial u}{\partial x} = -\frac{\partial v}{\partial y}$$

If the fluid velocity increases in the x direction it must decrease in the y direction.

10.1.4. The Equation of Continuity in polar coordinates.

A corresponding equation can be found in the polar coordinates r and θ where the velocity components are q_n and q_t radially and tangentially.

By carrying out a similar development for the accumulation of fluid in a segmental elemental 'box' of space, the equation of continuity corresponding to (10.7) above can be found as follows. Taking the element to be at $P(r, \theta)$ where the mass flow is ρq per unit length (Fig. 10.4), the accumulation per second radially is:

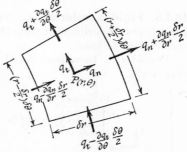

FIG. 10.4.—'Rectangular' element at $P(r, \theta)$ in a system of polar ordinates.

$$\left\{\rho q_n - \frac{\partial(\rho q_n)}{\partial r}\frac{\delta r}{2}\right\}\left(r - \frac{\delta r}{2}\right)\delta\theta - \left\{\rho q_n + \frac{\partial(\rho q_n)}{\partial r}\frac{\delta r}{2}\right\}\left(r + \frac{\delta r}{2}\right)\delta\theta$$

$$= -\rho q_n \,\delta r\,\delta\theta - \frac{\partial(\rho q_n)}{\partial r}\,\delta r\,\delta\theta \quad . \quad (10.10)$$

and accumulation per second tangentially is:

$$\left\{\rho q_t - \frac{\partial(\rho q_t)}{\partial \theta}\frac{\delta\theta}{2}\right\}\delta r - \left\{\rho q_t + \frac{\partial(\rho q_t)}{\partial \theta}\frac{\delta\theta}{2}\right\}\delta r = -\frac{\partial(\rho q_t)^r}{\partial \theta}\,\delta r\,\delta\theta. \quad (10.11)$$

$$\text{Total accumulation/sec} = -\left\{\frac{\rho q_n}{r} + \frac{\partial(\rho q_n)}{\partial r} + \frac{1}{r}\frac{\partial(\rho q_t)}{\partial \theta}\right\}r\,\delta r\,\delta\theta \quad . \quad (10.12)$$

and this by the previous argument equals the rate of change of mass within the region of space,

$$= \frac{\partial(\rho . r\,\delta r\,\delta\theta)}{\partial t} \quad . \quad . \quad . \quad . \quad (10.13)$$

Equating (10.12) and (10.13) gives:

$$\frac{\rho q_n}{r} + \frac{\partial \rho}{\partial t} + \frac{\partial(\rho q_n)}{\partial r} + \frac{1}{r}\frac{\partial(\rho q_t)}{\partial \theta} = 0 \quad . \quad . \quad (10.14)$$

hence for steady flow $\qquad \dfrac{\partial(\rho r q_n)}{\partial r} + \dfrac{\partial(\rho q_t)}{\partial \theta} = 0$ . . . (10.15)

and the incompressible equation in this form becomes:

$$\frac{q_n}{r} + \frac{\partial q_n}{\partial r} + \frac{1}{r}\frac{\partial q_t}{\partial \theta} = 0 \qquad . \qquad . \qquad . \quad (10.16)$$

10.1.5. The Equations of Motion.

All bodies possessing mass require force systems to be applied to them to cause a change in motion. Fluid in general and fluid particles in particular are all subject to this same basic requirement which is expressed in Newton's Laws of Motion.

The forces acting on a fluid particle are somewhat different from the tractions and drags applied to solid bodies but the process of equating the rate of change of momentum (i.e., mass × acceleration) to the applied force system is still applicable.

10.1.6. Fluid acceleration.

The equation of acceleration of a fluid particle is rather different from that of a vehicle (say), and a note on fluid acceleration follows.

Consider a two-dimensional flow system about the Ox, Oy axes (Fig. 10.5).

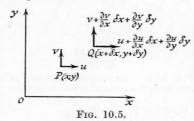

FIG. 10.5.

At some point $P(x, y)$ the velocity components are u and v horizontally and vertically respectively. At an adjacent point $Q(x + \delta x, y + \delta y)$ the velocity components are $u + \delta u$ and $v + \delta v$. That is, in general the velocity component has changed in each direction by an increment δu or δv. This incremental change is the result of a spatial displacement, and as u and v are functions of x and y the total velocity components at Q are

$$u + \delta u = u + \frac{\partial u}{\partial x}\delta x + \frac{\partial u}{\partial y}\delta y \quad \text{and} \quad v + \delta v = v + \frac{\partial v}{\partial x}\delta x + \frac{\partial v}{\partial y}\delta y \quad (10.17)$$

The component of acceleration in the Ox direction is thus

$$\frac{d(u + \delta u)}{dt} = \frac{\partial u}{\partial t} + \frac{\partial u}{\partial x}\frac{dx}{dt} + \frac{\partial u}{\partial y}\frac{dy}{dt}$$

$$= \frac{\partial u}{\partial t} + u\frac{\partial u}{\partial x} + v\frac{\partial u}{\partial y} \qquad . \qquad . \qquad . \quad (10.18)$$

and in the Oy direction

$$\frac{d(v + \delta v)}{dt} = \frac{\partial v}{\partial t} + u\frac{\partial v}{\partial x} + v\frac{\partial v}{\partial y}. \qquad . \qquad . \quad (10.19)$$

10.1.7. Euler's Equations of Motion.

Consider the behaviour of a fluid particle moving under a system of forces. Assuming the particle is discrete and possessing mass, it will, according to Newton's Law, accelerate in the direction of the resultant force. Its Equation of Motion then can be taken as

$$\text{applied force} = \text{mass} \times \text{acceleration}$$

For the fluid particle then, the application of this equation in the two directions chosen as the two ordinates must be considered, and in addition account is taken of the ways in which a force can be applied to the fluid particle.

Consider, for convenience, a rectangular element of side δx, δy.1, which at the instant considered is at $P(x, y)$, where the static pressure is p lb/ft² (Fig. 10·6). By Bernoulli's Equation, p is related to the square of the total velocity and must therefore be a function of two independent variables x and y, as is the velocity. The pressure force acting on the left-hand vertical face of the particle, trying to push the particle to the right, is:

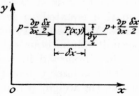

FIG. 10.6.—Two-dimensional fluid particle at $P(x, y)$ where static pressure is $p = f(x, y)$.

$$\left(p - \frac{\partial p}{\partial x}\frac{\delta x}{2}\right)\delta y.1 \qquad . \qquad . \qquad . \quad (10.20)$$

whilst the opposing pressure force on the right-hand vertical face is:

$$\left(p + \frac{\partial p}{\partial x}\frac{\delta x}{2}\right)\delta y.1 \qquad . \qquad . \qquad . \quad (10.21)$$

The nett pressure thrust on the particle in the Ox direction is thus (10.20) — (10.21), which is

$$-\frac{\partial p}{\partial x}\,\delta x\,\delta y.1 \qquad . \qquad . \qquad . \quad (10.22)$$

Other forces to which the particle may be subjected, such as attractions due to a system of gravity, may be introduced as X lb/ft³ in direction Ox and Y lb/ft³ in direction Oy, so that the resultant thrust on the particle in the Ox direction is

$$\left(X - \frac{\partial p}{\partial x}\right)\delta x\,\delta y.1 \qquad . \qquad . \qquad . \quad (10.23)$$

and this must equal the product of the mass of the particle and the acceleration in the Ox direction, which is:

$$\rho\,\delta x\,\delta y.1\left(\frac{\partial u}{\partial t} + u\frac{\partial u}{\partial x} + v\frac{\partial u}{\partial y}\right) \qquad . \qquad . \quad (10.24)$$

The Equation of Motion in the Ox direction is thus:

$$\left.\begin{array}{l}\dfrac{\partial u}{\partial t} + u\dfrac{\partial u}{\partial x} + v\dfrac{\partial u}{\partial y} = \dfrac{1}{\rho}\left(X - \dfrac{\partial p}{\partial x}\right) \\[2mm] \text{and similarly in the } Oy \text{ direction} \\[2mm] \dfrac{\partial v}{\partial t} + u\dfrac{\partial v}{\partial x} + v\dfrac{\partial v}{\partial y} = \dfrac{1}{\rho}\left(Y - \dfrac{\partial p}{\partial y}\right)\end{array}\right\} \qquad . \qquad . \quad (10.25)$$

Before leaving the Equations of Motion, the physical realities behind the symbols given in eqns. (10.25) above can be reaffirmed. The general statement they represent is that the fluid will accelerate under the action of a pressure gradient $(\partial p/\partial x)$ and/or an external force system.

The left-hand side of the equation shows that fluid will accelerate in steady flow from place to place. Thus, even with the terms $\partial u/\partial t$ and $\partial v/\partial t$ zero, fluid can change its velocity by virtue of its change of position. All steady flow states have this property. The right-hand side of the equation equated to zero gives $Y - \partial p/\partial y = 0$; or $Y = \partial p/\partial y$ which states Archimedes' Principle in mathematical terms. Here the Y force per unit volume equals the pressure gradient in the y direction. For a body floating immersed in stationary fluid the buoyancy (Y force upwards) per unit volume equals the vertical pressure gradient which arises from, and is, the weight per unit volume of fluid (see § 3.2).

Hence   buoyancy = weight of fluid displaced

In aerodynamics this effect is met wherever there is a pressure gradient.

10.1.8. Vorticity. While it is convenient to distinguish between smooth and turbulent states in the behaviour of a fluid, it is more necessary to describe the type of motion of its elementary parts. This yields definite and fundamental descriptions of the types of flow in Aerodynamics.

10.1.9. Rotational and irrotational flow. If the possible distortion of the particle by severe viscous tractions is ignored (this assumption is valid in much of Aerodynamic theory) there remain only three possible ways in which a particle can move.

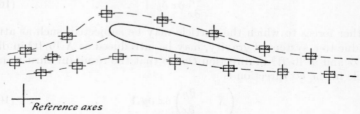

Reference axes

FIG. 10.7.

(a) *In pure translation.* The particle is free to move anywhere in space but contrives to keep its axes parallel to reference axes fixed in space (Fig. 10.7). This type of flow is substantially that in the airstream past an aerofoil *outside* the boundary layer.

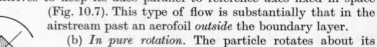

FIG. 10.8.

(b) *In pure rotation.* The particle rotates about its own axis which remains fixed in space (Fig. 10.8).

(c) *In the general motion* into which (a) and (b) above are compounded. Such a particle motion is found, for example, in the wake of bluff body.

A flow in which all the particles behave as in (a) above is called a *potential flow* or an irrotational flow. All others exhibit, to a greater or lesser extent, the spinning property of some of the constituent particles and are said to possess *vorticity,* which is the Aerodynamicist's word for elemental spin. The flow is then termed a *rotational flow.*

Here, then, are properties which can define a type of flow. A fluid either possesses *vorticity* and is *rotational,* or it does not, when it is, by definition, *irrotational.* Furthermore, these are properties which can be examined analytically and for which characteristic equations can be obtained to determine an unknown flow.

10.1.10. The Equation for vorticity in rectangular coordinates.
A fluid possesses vorticity if any element is rotating or spinning. It is a convenient 'dodge' to investigate the motion of a circular element as if it were 'solid' at the instant of time considered. Let the circular element be centred at $P(x, y)$ where the velocity components are u and v (Fig. 10.9).

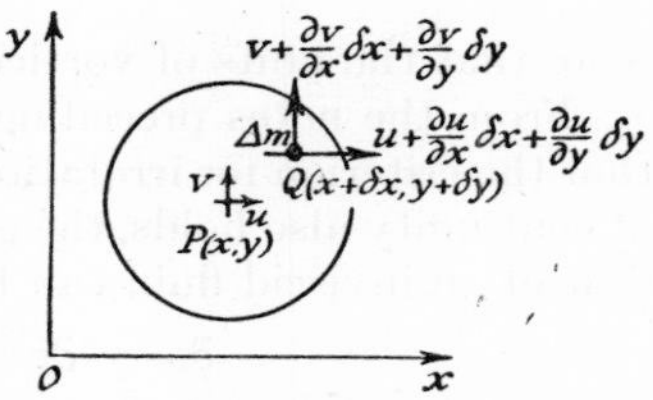

FIG. 10.9.

Assume that the element is composed of numerous particles of fluid of mass Δm such as one at the point $Q(x + \delta x, y + \delta y)$ where the velocity components are

$$u + \frac{\partial u}{\partial x}\delta x + \frac{\partial u}{\partial y}\delta y \quad \text{and} \quad v + \frac{\partial v}{\partial x}\delta x + \frac{\partial v}{\partial y}\delta y$$

The moment of momentum (or angular momentum) of the fluid element about P is the sum of the moments of momentum of all the particles Q about P. Taking anti-clockwise as positive

$$= \sum \left\{ \left(\frac{\partial v}{\partial x}\delta x + \frac{\partial v}{\partial y}\delta y\right)\delta x - \left(\frac{\partial u}{\partial x}\delta x + \frac{\partial u}{\partial y}\delta y\right)\delta y \right\}\Delta m$$

$$= \sum \Delta m\frac{\partial v}{\partial x}(\delta x)^2 - \sum \Delta m\frac{\partial u}{\partial y}(\delta y)^2 + \sum \Delta m\, \delta x\, \delta y\left(\frac{\partial v}{\partial y} - \frac{\partial u}{\partial x}\right)$$

Now for a circular disc about its centre

$$\sum \Delta m\, \delta x\, \delta y = 0$$

Therefore the angular momentum of the disc

$$= \sum \Delta m\, \frac{\partial v}{\partial x}(\delta x)^2 - \sum \Delta m\, \frac{\partial u}{\partial y}(\delta y)^2$$

If the disc were solidified instantaneously, its angular momentum would be $I\omega$, where I is its polar moment of inertia about P and ω its angular velocity about P.

Making this assumption and recognizing that for a disc

$$I = \sum \Delta m\{(\delta x)^2 + (\delta y)^2\} \quad \text{and} \quad \sum \Delta m\, (\delta x)^2 = \sum \Delta m\, (\delta y)^2,$$

then $\quad \omega \sum \Delta m\{(\delta x)^2 + (\delta y)^2\} = \sum \Delta m\frac{\partial v}{\partial x}(\delta x)^2 - \sum \Delta m\frac{\partial u}{\partial y}(\delta y)^2$

giving
$$2\omega = \frac{\partial v}{\partial x} - \frac{\partial u}{\partial y}$$

The quantity 2ω is the elemental spin and is referred to as the *vorticity* and is given the symbol ζ.

Thus
$$\text{vorticity} = \zeta = \frac{\partial v}{\partial x} - \frac{\partial u}{\partial y} \quad . \quad . \quad . \quad (10.26)$$

10.1.11. The Equation for vorticity in polar coordinates.

The corresponding equation in polars is

$$\zeta = \frac{q_t}{r} + \frac{\partial q_t}{\partial r} - \frac{1}{r}\frac{\partial q_n}{\partial \theta} \quad . \quad . \quad . \quad (10.27)$$

Note that the units of vorticity, as of spin, are radians per second.

From the notes preceding the development of eqn. (10.26), it is clear that the criterion for irrotational flow is that $\zeta = 0$, and since the equation of continuity also holds, the general criteria for the continuous irrotational flow of an inviscid fluid can be written as:

$$\frac{\partial u}{\partial x} + \frac{\partial v}{\partial y} = 0 \quad \text{and} \quad \frac{\partial v}{\partial x} - \frac{\partial u}{\partial y} = 0 \quad . \quad . \quad (10.28)$$

10.2. The stream function ψ.

Assume you are on the banks of a shallow river of a constant depth of 1 foot at a position O (Fig. 10.10) with a friend

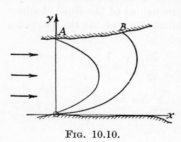

directly opposite at A, 40 feet away. Mathematically your bank can be represented by the Ox axis, and the line joining you to your friend at A the Oy axis in the two-coordinate system. Now if the stream speed is 2 ft/sec the *amount* of water passing between you and your friend is $40 \times 1 \times 2 = 80$ ft³/sec and this is the *amount* of water flowing past any point anywhere along the river which could be measured at a weir downstream. Suppose you now throw a grass line to your friend who catches the end but allows the slack to fall in the river and float into a curve as shown.

Fig. 10.10.

The *amount* of water flowing under the line every second is still 80 ft³/sec no matter what shape the rope takes, and is unaffected by the configuration of the rope.

Suppose he moves along to a point B somewhere downstream, still holding his end of the line but with sufficient rope payed out as he goes. The volume of water passing under the rope is still only 80 ft³/sec providing he has not stepped over a tributary stream, or an irrigation drain in the bank. It follows, that if no water can enter or leave the stream the *quantity* flowing past the line will be the same as before and furthermore will be unaffected by the shape of the line between O and B.

The *amount* or *quantity* of fluid passing such a line per second is called the *stream function* or current function and when given as a mathematical expression is denoted by ψ.

Consider now a pair of coordinate axes set in a two-dimensional stream of fluid which is moving generally from left to right (Fig. 10.11). The axes are arbitrary space references and in no way interrupt the fluid streaming past.

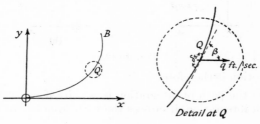

FIG. 10.11.

Similarly the line joining O to a point B in the flow in no way interrupts the flow since it is as artificial as the reference axes Ox and Oy. An algebraic expression can be found for the line in x and y.

Let the flow past the line at any point Q on it be at q ft/sec over a small length δs of line where direction of q makes angle β to the tangent of the curve at Q.

The component of the velocity q perpendicular to the element δs is $q \sin \beta$ and therefore, assuming the depth of stream flow to be unity, the amount of fluid crossing the element of line δs is $q \sin \beta \times \delta s \times 1$ per second. Adding up all such quantities crossing similar elements along the line from O to P, the total amount of flow past the line (sometimes called flux) is $\int_{OP} q \sin \beta \, ds$ or in words; the line integral of the normal velocity component from O to P.

If this quantity of fluid flowing between O and P remains the same irrespective of the path of integration (independent of the curve of the grass line) then $\int_{OP} q \sin \beta \, ds$ is called the stream function of P with respect to O and

$$\psi_P = \int_{OP} q \sin \beta \, ds$$

Note: It is implicit that $\psi_o = 0$.

10.2.1. Sign convention for stream functions.

It is necessary here to consider a sign convention since *quantities* of fluid are being considered.

When integrating the 'cross-wise' component of flow along a curve, the component can go either from left to right, or vice versa across the path of integration (Fig. 10.12).

Integrating the normal flow components from O to P, the flow components are, *looking in the direction of integration,* either (I) from left to right or (II) from right to left.

The former is considered *positive* flow whilst the latter is negative flow.

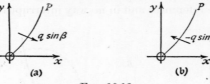

FIG. 10.12.

The convention is therefore

Flow *across* the path of integration is *positive* if, when looking in the direction of integration, it crosses the path from left to right.

10.2.2. The streamline.
From the statement above, ψ_P = the flow *across* the line OP.

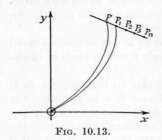

FIG. 10.13.

Suppose there is a point P_1 close to P which has the same value of stream function as point P (Fig. 10.13). Then the flow across any line OP_1 equals that across OP, and the amount of fluid flowing into area OPP_1O across OP equals the amount flowing out across OP_1. Therefore, no fluid crosses line PP_1 and the velocity of flow must be along, or tangential to, PP_1.

All other points P_2, P_3, etc. which have a stream function equal in value to that of P have, by definition, the same flow across any lines joining them to O, so by the same argument the velocity of the flow in the region of P_1, P_2, P_3, etc. must be along P_1, P_2, P_3, etc., and no fluid crosses the line PP_1, P_2, P_n.

Since $\psi_{P_1} = \psi_{P_2} = \psi_{P_3} = \psi_P$ = constant, the line PP_1, P_2, P_n, etc. is a *line of constant ψ* and is called a streamline.

It follows further that since no flow can cross the line $P - P_n$ the velocity along the line must always be in the direction tangential to it.

This leads to the two common definitions of a streamline, both of which indirectly have the other's meaning. They are:

A *streamline* is a line of constant ψ

and/or

A *streamline* is a line of fluid particles, the velocity of each particle being tangential to the line.

Note: The velocity can change in magnitude along a streamline but by definition the direction is always that of the tangent to the line.

10.2.3. Solid boundary substitution and image systems.
The fact that the flow is always *along* a streamline and not *through* it has an im-

portant fundamental consequence. This is that a streamline of an inviscid flow can be replaced by a solid boundary of the same shape *without affecting the remainder of the flow pattern.*

If, as often is the case, a streamline is continuous, i.e., it forms a closed curve which separates the flow pattern into two separate streams, one inside and one outside, then a solid body can replace the closed curve and the flow inside or outside, without altering the shape of the flow (Fig. 10.14 (a)). To represent the flow in the region of a contour or body it is only necessary to replace the contour by a similarly shaped streamline. The following sections contain examples of simple flows which provide continuous streamlines in the shapes of circles and aerofoils, and these emerge as consequences of the flow combinations chosen.

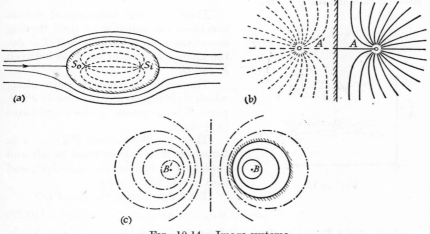

FIG. 10.14.—Image systems.

When arbitrary contours and their adjacent flows have to be replaced by identical flows containing similarly shaped streamlines, image systems have to be placed within the contour, which are the 'reflections' of the external flow system in the 'solid' streamline.

Fig. 10.14 (b) shows the simple case of a source A placed a short distance from an infinite plane wall. The effect of the solid boundary on the flow from the source is adequately represented by considering the effect of the image source A' 'reflected' in the wall. The source pair has a long straight streamline (the vertical axis of symmetry) which separates the flows from the two sources and which may be replaced by a solid boundary without affecting the flow.

Fig. 10.14 (c) shows the flow in the cross-section of a vortex lying parallel to the axis of a circular duct. The circular duct wall can be replaced by the corresponding streamline in the vortex pair system given by the original vortex B and its image B'. It can easily be shown that B' is a distance R^2/s from the centre of the duct on the diameter produced passing through B, where R is the radius of the duct and s is the distance of the vortex axis from the centre of the duct.

More complicated contours require more complicated image systems and these are left until discussion of the cases in which they arise. It will be seen that Fig. 10.14 (a) which is the flow of § 10.2.9, has an internal image system, the source being the image of a source at $-\infty$ and the sink being the image of a sink at $+\infty$. This external source and sink combination produces the undisturbed uniform stream.

10.2.4. Velocity components in terms of ψ.

(a) *In Cartesian coordinates.* Let point $P(x, y)$ be on the streamline AB in Fig. 10.15 of constant ψ and point $Q(x + \delta x, y + \delta y)$ be on the streamline CD of constant $\psi + \delta\psi$.

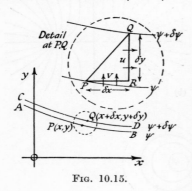

Then from the definition of stream function, the amount of fluid flowing *across* any path between P and $Q = \delta\psi$, the change of stream function between P and Q.

The most convenient path along which to integrate in this case is PRQ, point R being given by the coordinates $(x + \delta x, y)$.

Then the flow across $PR = -v\,\delta x$ (since the flow is from right to left and thus by our convention negative), and that across $RQ = u\,\delta y$.

FIG. 10.15.

Total flow across the line PRQ

$$\delta\psi = u\,\delta y - v\,\delta x \qquad . \qquad . \qquad . \quad (10.29)$$

Now ψ is a function of two independent variables x and y in steady motion, and thus

$$\delta\psi = \frac{\partial\psi}{\partial x}.\delta x + \frac{\partial\psi}{\partial y}.\delta y \qquad . \qquad . \qquad . \quad (10.30)$$

$\partial\psi/\partial x$ and $\partial\psi/\partial y$ being the partial differentials with respect to x and y respectively.

Then, equating terms:

$$u = \frac{\partial\psi}{\partial y}$$

and

$$v = -\frac{\partial\psi}{\partial x}$$

these being the velocity components at a point x, y in a flow given by stream function ψ.

(b) *In polar coordinates.* Let the point $P(r, \theta)$ be on the streamline AB (Fig. 10.16) of constant ψ, and point $Q(r + \delta r)(\theta + \delta\theta)$ be on the streamline CD of constant $\psi + \delta\psi$. The velocity components are q_n and q_t radially and tangentially respectively.

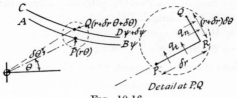

FIG. 10.16.

Here the most convenient path of integration is PRQ where OP is produced to R so that $PR = \delta r$, i.e., R is given by ordinates $(r + \delta r, \theta)$. Then

$$\delta\psi = - q_t \, \delta r + q_n (r + \delta r) \, \delta\theta$$
$$= - q_t \, \delta r + q_n r \, \delta\theta + q_n \, \delta r \, \delta\theta$$

to the 1st order of small quantities,

$$\delta\psi = - q_t \, \delta r + q_n r \, \delta\theta \quad . \quad . \quad . \quad . \quad . \quad (10.31)$$

But here ψ is a function of (r, θ) and again

$$\delta\psi = \frac{\partial \psi}{\partial r} \delta r + \frac{\partial \psi}{\partial \theta} \delta\theta \quad . \quad . \quad . \quad . \quad . \quad (10.32)$$

and equating terms in eqns. (10.31) and (10.32)

$$q_t = - \frac{\partial \psi}{\partial r}$$

$$q_n = \frac{1}{r} \frac{\partial \psi}{\partial \theta}$$

these being velocity components at a point r, θ in a flow given by stream function ψ.

10.2.5. ψ for constant velocity flow.

Flow of constant velocity parallel to Ox axis from L to R. Consider flow streaming past the coordinate axes Ox, Oy at velocity U ft/sec parallel to Ox (Fig. 10.17). By definition the stream function ψ at a point $P(x, y)$ in the flow is given by the *amount* of fluid crossing any line between O and P. For convenience the line OTP is taken where T is on the Ox axis x along from O, i.e., point T is given by (x, O).

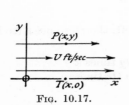

FIG. 10.17.

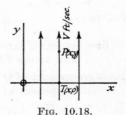

FIG. 10.18.

Q

Then

$$\psi = \text{flow across line } OTP$$
$$= \text{flow across line } OT \text{ plus flow across line } TP$$
$$= 0 + U.\text{length } TP$$
$$= 0 + Uy$$

Therefore $\psi = Uy$ ft²/sec   .   .   .   .   .   .   (10.33)

The streamlines (lines of constant ψ) are given by drawing the curves

$$\psi = \text{constant} = Uy$$

Now the velocity is constant, therefore

$$y = \frac{\psi}{U} = \text{constant}$$

The lines $\psi = $ constant are all straight lines parallel to Ox.

Flow of constant velocity parallel to Oy axis. Consider flow streaming past the Ox, Oy axes at velocity V ft/sec parallel to Oy (Fig. 10.18).

Again by definition the stream function ψ at a point $P(xy)$ in the flow is given by the amount of fluid crossing any line between O and P. For convenience take OTP where T is given by (x, O).

Then $\psi = \text{flow across } OT + \text{flow across } TP$
$$= -Vx + O$$

(Note here that when going from O towards T the flow appears from the right and disappears to the left and therefore is of negative sign.)

i.e., $\psi = -Vx$ ft²/sec   .   .   .   (10.34)

The streamlines being lines of constant ψ are given by $x = -\psi/V$ and are parallel to Oy axis.

Flow of constant velocity in any direction. Consider the flow streaming past the xy axes at some velocity Q ft/sec making angle θ with the Ox axis (Fig. 10.19).

The velocity Q can be resolved into two components U and V parallel to the Ox and Oy axes respectively where $Q^2 = U^2 + V^2$ and $\tan \theta = V/U$.

Again the stream function ψ at a point P in the flow is a measure of the *amount* of fluid flowing past any line joining OP. Let the most convenient line be OTP, T being given by (x, O).

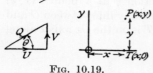

Fig. 10.19.

Therefore

$$\psi = \text{flow across } OT \text{ (going right to left, therefore negative in sign)}$$
$$+ \text{flow across } TP$$

$$= -\text{ component of } Q \text{ parallel to } Oy \text{ times } x$$
$$+ \text{ component of } Q \text{ parallel to } Ox \text{ times } y$$

$$\psi = -Vx + Uy$$.   .   .   .   (10.35)

Lines of constant ψ or streamlines are the curves

$$- Vx + Uy = \text{constant}$$

assigning a different value to ψ for every streamline.

Then in the equation V and U are constant velocities and the equation is that to a series of straight lines depending on the value of constant ψ.

Example 10.1. Interpret the flow given by the stream function

$$\psi = 6x + 12y$$

The velocity in the horizontal direction $= \dfrac{\partial \psi}{\partial y} = + 12$ ft/sec constant

The velocity in the vertical direction $= \dfrac{\partial \psi}{\partial x} = - 6$ ft/sec constant

Therefore the flow equation represents uniform flow inclined to the Ox axis by angle θ where $\tan \theta = - \frac{6}{12}$, i.e., inclined downward.

The velocity of flow is given by

$$Q = \sqrt{6^2 + 12^2} = \underline{\sqrt{180} \text{ ft/sec.}}$$

10.2.6. Two-dimensional flow from a source (or towards a sink).

A source (sink) of strength $m(- m)$ is a point at which fluid is appearing (or disappearing) at a uniform rate of $m(- m)$ ft²/sec.

Consider the analogy of a small hole in a large flat plate through which fluid is welling (the source).

If there is no obstruction and the plate is perfectly flat and level, the fluid 'puddle' will get larger and larger all the while remaining circular in shape. The path that any particle of fluid will trace out as it emerges from the hole and travels outwards is a purely radial one, since it cannot go sideways, because its fellow particles are also moving outwards.

Also its velocity must get less as it goes outwards. Fluid issues from the hole at a rate of m ft²/sec. The velocity of flow over a ring boundary of 1 ft radius is $m/2\pi$ ft/sec. Over a ring boundary of 2 ft radius it is $m/2\pi2$, i.e., half as much, and over a ring of diameter $2r$ the velocity is $m/2\pi r$ ft/sec.

Therefore the velocity of flow is inversely proportional to the distance of the particle from the source.

All the above applies to a sink except that fluid is being drained away through the hole and is moving *towards* the sink radially, increasing in speed as the sink is approached.

Hence the particles all move radially, and the streamlines must be radial lines with their origin at the source (or sink).

To find the stream function ψ of a source. Place the source for convenience at the origin of a system of axes, to which the point P has ordinates (x, y) and (r, θ) (Fig. 10.20).

Putting the line along the x-axis as $\psi = 0$ (a

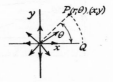

FIG. 10.20.

datum) and taking the most convenient line for integration as OQP where QP is an arc of a circle of radius r,

$$\psi = \text{flow across } OQ + \text{flow across } QP$$
$$= \text{velocity across } OQ \times OQ + \text{velocity across } QP \times QP$$
$$= \qquad 0 \qquad + \frac{m}{2\pi r} \times r\theta$$

$$\therefore \ \psi = \frac{m\theta}{2\pi} \quad . \qquad . \qquad . \qquad . \quad (10.36)$$

or putting

$$\theta = \tan^{-1}\frac{y}{x}$$

$$\psi = \frac{m}{2\pi} \tan^{-1}\frac{y}{x} \quad . \qquad . \qquad . \qquad . \quad (10.37)$$

There is a limitation to the size of θ here. θ can have values only between 0 and 2π. For $\psi = m\theta/2\pi$ where θ is $2\frac{1}{2}\pi$ (say) would mean that ψ (i.e., the amount of fluid flowing) was greater than m ft²/sec, which is impossible since m is the capacity of the source and integrating a circuit round and round a source will not increase its strength.

Therefore $0 < \theta < 2\pi$.

For a sink

$$\psi = -\frac{m}{2\pi}\theta$$

10.2.7. A source in a uniform horizontal stream. Let a source of strength m be situated at the origin with a uniform stream of $-U$ ft/sec moving from right to left (Fig. 10.21).

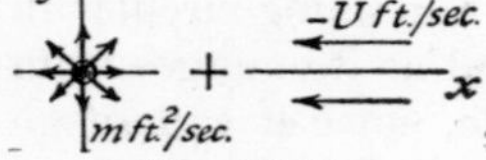

Then

$$\psi = \frac{m\theta}{2\pi} - Uy$$

FIG. 10.21.

which is a combination of two previous cases.

Eqn. (10.37) can be re-written

$$\psi = \frac{m}{2\pi} \tan^{-1}\frac{y}{x} - Uy \quad . \qquad . \qquad . \quad (10.38)$$

to make the variables the same in each term.

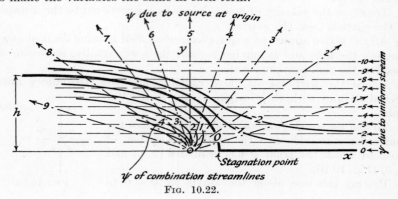

ψ due to source at origin

ψ of combination streamlines

Stagnation point

FIG. 10.22.

. Streamline patterns can be found by substituting constant values for ψ and plotting eqn. (10.37) or (10.38), or *alternatively* by adding algebraically the ψ's due to the two cases involved. The *second* method is easier here.

Method (see Fig. 10.22)

1. Plot the streamlines due to a source at the origin taking the strength of the source equal to 20 ft²/sec (say). (The streamlines are $\pi/10$ apart.) It is necessary to take positive values of y only since the pattern is symmetrical about the Ox axis.

2. Superimpose on the plot horizontal lines to a scale so that $\psi = -Uy = -1, -2, -3$, etc., are lines about 1 unit apart on the paper. Where the lines intersect, add the ψ's of the lines of intersection. Connect up all points of constant ψ (streamlines) by smooth lines.

The resulting flow pattern shows that the streamlines can be separated into two distinct groups, (a) the fluid from the source moves from the source to infinity without mingling with the uniform stream, being constrained within the streamline $\psi = 0$, (b) the uniform stream is split along the Ox axis, the two resulting streams being deflected in their path towards infinity by $\psi = 0$.

It is possible to replace any streamlines by a solid boundary without interfering with the flow in any way. If $\psi = 0$ is replaced by a solid boundary the effects of the source are truly cut off from the horizontal flow and it can be seen that here is a mathematical expression which represents the flow round a curved fairing (say) in a uniform stream.

The same expression can be used for an approximation to the behaviour of a wind sweeping in off a plain or the sea and up over a cliff. The upward components of velocity of such an airflow are used in gliding.

The vertical velocity component at any point in the flow is given by $-\partial\psi/\partial x$.

Now
$$\psi = \frac{m}{2\pi}\tan^{-1}\left(\frac{y}{x}\right) - Uy \qquad . \qquad . \qquad (10.38)$$

$$-\frac{\partial\psi}{\partial x} = -\frac{m}{2\pi}\frac{\partial\tan^{-1}(y/x)}{\partial(y/x)}\cdot\frac{\partial(y/x)}{\partial x}$$

$$= -\frac{m}{2\pi}\frac{1}{1+(y/x)^2}\cdot\frac{-y}{x^2}$$

or
$$v = \frac{m}{2\pi}\frac{y}{x^2+y^2}$$

and this is upwards.

This expression also shows, by comparing it, in the rearranged form $x^2 + y^2 - (m/2\pi v)y = 0$, with the general equation to a circle

$$(x^2 + y^2 + 2gx + 2hy + f = 0),$$

that lines of constant vertical velocity are circles with centres $(0, m/4\pi v)$ and radii $m/4\pi v$.

The ultimate thickness, $2h$ (or height of cliff h) of the shape given by $\psi = 0$ for this combination is found by putting $y = h$ and $\theta = \pi$ in the general expression.

That is, substituting the appropriate data in eqn. (10.37),

$$\psi = \frac{m\pi}{2\pi} - Uh = 0$$

Therefore

$$h = \frac{m}{2U} \qquad . \qquad . \qquad . \qquad . \qquad (10.39)$$

Note: when $\theta = \dfrac{\pi}{2}$, $y = \dfrac{h}{2}$.

The position of the stagnation point. By finding the stagnation point, the distance of the foot of the cliff, or the front of the fairing from the source can be found.

A stagnation point is given by $u = 0$, $v = 0$.

i.e.,

$$\frac{\partial \psi}{\partial y} = 0 = \frac{m}{2\pi}\frac{x}{x^2 + y^2} - U \qquad . \qquad . \qquad . \qquad (10.40)$$

$$-\frac{\partial \psi}{\partial x} = 0 = \frac{m}{2\pi}\frac{y}{x^2 + y^2} \qquad . \qquad . \qquad . \qquad (10.41)$$

From eqn. (10.41) $v = 0$ when $y = 0$.
Substituting in eqn. (10.40) when $y = 0$ and $x = x_0$

$$u = 0 = \frac{m}{2\pi}\frac{1}{x_0} - U$$

when

$$x_0 = \frac{m}{2\pi U} \qquad . \qquad . \qquad . \qquad . \qquad (10.42)$$

The local velocity. The local velocity $q = \sqrt{u^2 + v^2}$.

$$u = \frac{\partial \psi}{\partial y} \quad \text{and} \quad \psi = \frac{m}{2\pi}\tan^{-1}\frac{y}{x} - Uy$$

Therefore

$$u = \frac{m}{2\pi}\frac{1/x}{1 + (y/x)^2} - U$$

giving

$$u = \frac{m}{2\pi}\frac{x}{x^2 + y^2} - U$$

and from $v = -\dfrac{\partial \psi}{\partial x}$

$$v = \frac{m}{2\pi}\frac{y}{x^2 + y^2}$$

From which the local velocity can be obtained from $q = \sqrt{u^2 + v^2}$ and the direction being given by $\tan^{-1} v/u$ in any particular case.

10.2.8. Source–sink pair.

This is a combination of a source and sink of equal (but opposite) strengths situated a distance $2c$ apart.

Let $\pm m$ ft²/sec be the strengths of a source and sink situated at points $A(c, O)$ and $B(-c, O)$, that is at a distance of c ft on either side of the origin (Fig. 10.23).

The stream function at a point $P(x, y)(r, \theta)$ due to the combination is,

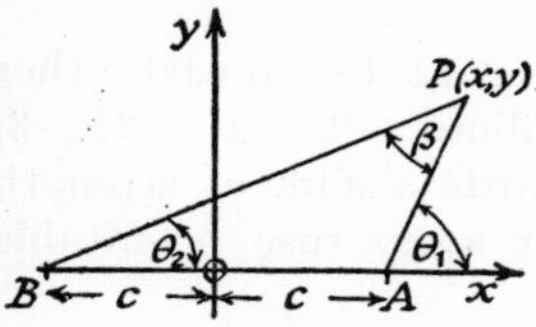

Fig. 10.23.

$$\psi = \frac{m\theta_1}{2\pi} - \frac{m\theta_2}{2\pi}$$

$$= \frac{m}{2\pi}(\theta_1 - \theta_2) \qquad . \qquad . \qquad (10.43)$$

or $\quad \psi = \frac{m}{2\pi}\beta$

Transposing the equation to Cartesian coordinates,

$$\tan\theta_1 = \frac{y}{x - c} \qquad \tan\theta_2 = \frac{y}{x + c}$$

$$\tan(\theta_1 - \theta_2) = \frac{\tan\theta_1 - \tan\theta_2}{1 + \tan\theta_1\tan\theta_2} = \frac{\dfrac{y}{x - c} - \dfrac{y}{x + c}}{1 + \dfrac{y^2}{x^2 - c^2}}$$

Therefore $\qquad \beta = \theta_1 - \theta_2 = \tan^{-1}\dfrac{2cy}{x^2 + y^2 - c^2} \qquad . \qquad . \quad (10.44)$

and substituting in eqn. (10.43),

$$\psi = \frac{m}{2\pi}\tan^{-1}\frac{2cy}{x^2 + y^2 - c^2} \qquad . \qquad . \qquad (10.45)$$

To find the shape of the streamlines associated with this combination · it is necessary to investigate eqn. (10.45).

Rearranging

$$\tan\left(\frac{2\pi}{m}\psi\right) = \frac{2cy}{x^2 + y^2 - c^2}$$

or $\qquad x^2 + y^2 - c^2 = \dfrac{2cy}{\tan\left(\dfrac{2\pi\psi}{m}\right)}$

or $\qquad x^2 + y^2 - 2c\cot\dfrac{2\pi\psi}{m}.y - c^2 = 0$

Now this is the equation to a circle of radius $c\sqrt{\cot^2\dfrac{2\pi\psi}{m} + 1}$, and centre,

$c\cot\dfrac{2\pi\psi}{m}.$ $\qquad\qquad = c\sqrt{\text{cosec}^2\,\dfrac{2\pi\psi}{m}} = c.\,\text{cosec}\,\dfrac{2\pi\psi}{m}.$

Therefore streamlines for this combination consist of a series of circles with centres on the Oy axis and intersecting in the source and sink, the flow being from the source to the sink (Fig. 10.24).

Alternatively this can be obtained by the superpositioning method.

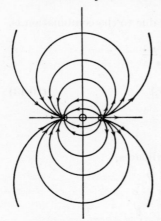

1. Draw radial lines at 18° to each other to represent streamlines 0, 1, 2, 3, etc., emanating from a source of strength 20 ft²/sec.

2. Draw radial lines at 18° to each other to represent streamlines −0, −1, −2, −3, etc., converging towards a sink of strength −20 ft²/sec set 2 ft away (use a suitable scale).

3. Add, algebraically, values at points of intersection of 1 and 2.

4. Join up points of constant value with smooth curves. These are the streamlines.

FIG. 10.24.—Streamlines due to a source and sink pair.

10.2.9. A source set upstream of an equal sink in a uniform stream. The stream function due to this combination is:

$$\psi = \frac{m}{2\pi} \tan^{-1} \frac{2cy}{x^2 + y^2 - c^2} - Uy \quad . \quad . \quad (10.46)$$

Here the first term represents a source and sink combination set with the source to the *right* of the sink. For the source to be upstream of the sink the uniform stream must be from right to left (i.e., negative).

If the source is placed downstream of the sink an entirely different stream pattern is obtained.

The streamline $\psi = 0$ gives a closed oval curve (not an ellipse), which is symmetrical about the Ox and Oy axes. Flow of stream function ψ greater than $\psi = 0$ shows the flow round such an oval set at zero incidence in a uniform stream.

Streamlines can be obtained by plotting or by superpositioning of the separate standard flows (Fig. 10.25).

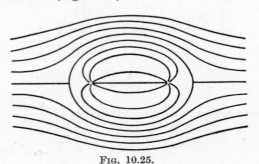

FIG. 10.25.

The streamline $\psi = 0$ again separates the flow into two distinct regions.

The first is wholly contained within the closed oval and consists of the flow out of the source and into the sink.

The second is that of the uniform stream which flows around the oval curve and returns to its uniformity again.

Again replacing $\psi = 0$ by a solid boundary, or indeed a solid body whose shape is given by $\psi = 0$, does not influence the flow pattern in any way.

Thus the stream function ψ of eqn. (10.46) can be used to represent the flow around a long cylinder of oval section set with its major axis parallel to a steady stream. To find the stream function representing a flow round such an oval cylinder it must be possible to obtain m and c (the strengths of the source and sink and distance apart) in terms of the size of the body and the speed of the incident stream.

Suppose there is an oval of breadth $2b_0$ and thickness $2t_0$ set in a flow of U ft/sec^2. The problem is to find m and c in the stream function, eqn. (10.46), which will then represent the flow round the oval.

(a) The oval must conform to eqn. (10.46).

$$\psi = 0 = \frac{m}{2\pi} \tan^{-1} \frac{2cy}{x^2 + y^2 - c^2} - Uy$$

(b) On streamline $\psi = 0$ maximum thickness t_0 occurs at $x = 0$, $y = t_0$.

Therefore, substituting in the above equation,

$$0 = \frac{m}{2\pi} \tan^{-1} \frac{2ct_0}{t_0^2 - c^2} - Ut_0$$

and rearranging

$$\tan \frac{Ut_0 2\pi}{m} = \frac{2 t_0 c}{t_0^2 - c^2} \qquad . \qquad . \qquad . \quad (10.47)$$

(c) A stagnation point (point where the local velocity is zero) is situated at the 'nose' of the oval, i.e., at the point $y = 0$, $x = b_0$,

i.e., $\quad u = 0 = \dfrac{\partial \psi}{\partial y} = \dfrac{\partial}{\partial y}\left(\dfrac{m}{2\pi} \tan^{-1} \dfrac{2cy}{x^2 + y^2 - c^2} - Uy\right)$.

$$\frac{\partial \psi}{\partial y} = \frac{m}{2\pi} \frac{1}{1 + \left(\dfrac{2cy}{x^2 + y^2 - c^2}\right)^2} \cdot \frac{(x^2 + y^2 - c^2).2c - 2y.2cy}{(x^2 + y^2 - c^2)^2} - U$$

and putting $y = 0$ and $x = b_0$ with $\partial \psi / \partial y = 0$,

$$0 = \frac{m}{2\pi} \frac{(b_0^2 - c^2)2c}{(b_0^2 - c^2)^2} - U = \frac{m}{2\pi} \cdot \frac{2c}{b_0^2 - c^2} - U$$

$$\therefore \quad m = \pi U . \frac{b_0^2 - c^2}{c} \qquad . \qquad . \qquad . \qquad . \qquad . \quad (10.48)$$

The simultaneous solution of eqns. (10.47) and (10.48) will furnish values of m and c to satisfy any given set of conditions.

Alternatively (a), (b) and (c) above can be used to find the thickness and length of the oval formed by the streamline $\psi = 0$. This form of the problem is more often set in examinations than the preceding one.

10.2.10. Line (point) vortex. This flow is that associated with a straight line vortex. A line vortex can best be described as a string of rotating particles. A chain of fluid particles are spinning on their common axis and carrying round with them a swirl of fluid particles which flow around in circles.

A cross-section of such a string of particles and its associated flow shows a spinning *point* 'outside' of which is streamline flow in concentric circles (Fig. 10.26).

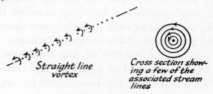

Straight line vortex

Cross section showing a few of the associated stream lines

FIG. 10.26.

Vortices are common in nature, the difference between a real vortex as opposed to a theoretical line vortex, is that the former has a core of fluid which is rotating as a 'solid' although the associated 'swirl' outside is the same as the flow 'outside' the point vortex (see § 6.8).

The streamlines associated with a line vortex are circular and therefore the particle velocity at any point must be tangential only.

Putting a vortex of strength K at the origin of a polar system of coordinates and taking any point $P(r, \theta)$, the velocity at P is tangential only, that is the radial velocity at any point P is zero.

Or
$$\frac{1}{r}\frac{\partial \psi}{\partial \theta} = 0$$

and for this to be true the function ψ is a function of r only.

It was shown that the tangential velocity at any point $P = q_t = K/2\pi r$ (see § 6.8.1, eqn. (6.33))

Then
$$q_t = \frac{K}{2\pi r} = -\frac{\partial \psi}{\partial r}$$

Therefore
$$\psi = \int -\frac{K}{2\pi r}dr$$

Integrating along the most convenient boundary from radius (r_0) to $P(r, \theta)$ which in this case is any radial line (Fig. 10.27).

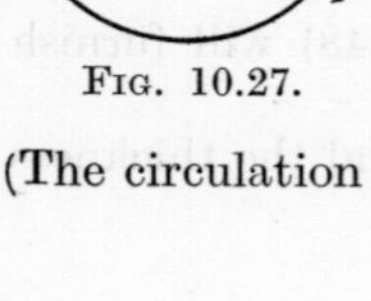

$$\psi = -\int_{r_0}^{r}\frac{K}{2\pi r}dr \ (r_0 = \text{radius of streamline, } \psi = 0)$$

$$\psi = -\left[\frac{K}{2\pi}\log_e r\right]_{r_0}^{r}$$

FIG. 10.27.

giving $\psi = -\frac{K}{2\pi}\log_e \frac{r}{r_0}$ . . . . . (10.49)

(The circulation K of a flow is positive when it is anti-clockwise.)

10.2.11. Doublet. A doublet is a source and sink combination as described in § 10.2.8 but with the separation extremely small. A doublet is considered to be at a *point* and the definition of the *strength* of a doublet contains the measure of separation. The strength (μ) of a doublet is the product of the small distance of separation, and the strength of source and sink. The doublet *axis* is the line from the sink to the source in that sense.

Now the streamlines due to a source and sink combination are circles each intersecting in the source and sink. As the source and sink approach, the points of intersection also approach until in the limit, when separated by an infinitesimal distance, the circles are all touching (intersecting) at one point—the doublet. This can be shown as follows:

For the source and sink,

$$\psi = \frac{m}{2\pi}\beta \quad \text{from eqn. (10.43)}$$

By constructing the perpendicular of length p from the source to the line joining the sink and P it can be seen that as the source and sink approach (Fig. 10.28)

$$p \rightarrow 2c \sin \theta \quad \text{and also} \quad p \rightarrow r\beta$$

Therefore in the limit

$$2c \sin \theta = r\beta \quad \text{or} \quad \beta = \frac{2c \sin \theta}{r}$$

$$\psi = \frac{m}{2\pi}\frac{2c}{r}\sin \theta$$

Fɪɢ. 10.28.

and putting $\mu = 2cm$ = strength of the doublet in ft³/sec,

$$\psi = \frac{\mu}{2\pi r}\sin \theta \quad . \quad (10.50)$$

On converting to Cartesian coordinates where

$$r = \sqrt{x^2 - y^2}, \quad \sin \theta = \frac{y}{\sqrt{x^2 + y^2}}$$

$$\psi = \frac{\mu}{2\pi}\frac{y}{x^2 + y^2} \quad . \quad . \quad (10.51)$$

and rearranging gives

$$(x^2 + y^2) - \frac{\mu}{2\pi\psi}y = 0$$

which, when ψ is a constant, is the equation to a circle.

Therefore lines of constant ψ are circles of radius $\mu/4\pi\psi$ and centres $(0, \mu/4\pi\psi)$ (Fig. 10.29), i.e., circles, with centres lying on the Oy axis, passing through the origin as deduced above.

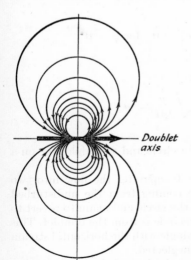

Doublet axis

Fɪɢ. 10.29.—Streamlines due to a doublet.

10.2.12. Flow around a circular cylinder given by a doublet in a uniform horizontal stream.

The stream function due to this combination is:

$$\psi = \frac{\mu}{2\pi r} \sin \theta - Uy \qquad . \qquad . \qquad . \qquad (10.52)$$

(*Note:* The terms in the stream functions must be opposite in sign to obtain the useful results below. Here again the source must be upstream of the sink in the flow system.)

The equation converted to rectangular coordinates gives:

$$\psi = \frac{\mu}{2\pi} \frac{y}{x^2 + y^2} - Uy \qquad . \qquad . \qquad . \qquad (10.53)$$

and for the streamline $\psi = 0$

$$y\left[\frac{\mu}{2\pi(x^2 + y^2)} - U\right] = 0$$

i.e.,
$$y = 0$$

or
$$x^2 + y^2 = \frac{\mu}{2\pi U}$$

This shows the streamline $\psi = 0$ to consist of the Ox axis together with a circle, centre O, of radius $\sqrt{\dfrac{\mu}{2\pi U}} = a$ (say)

Alternatively by converting eqn. (10.52) to polar coordinates

$$\psi = \frac{\mu}{2\pi r} \sin \theta - Ur \sin \theta$$

rearranging

$$\psi = \sin \theta\left[\frac{\mu}{2\pi r} - Ur\right] = 0 \quad \text{for } \psi = 0$$

giving

$$\sin \theta = 0 \quad \therefore \ \theta = 0 \text{ or } \pm \pi$$

or
$$\frac{\mu}{2\pi r} - Ur = 0 \quad \text{giving } r = \sqrt{\frac{\mu}{2\pi U}} = a$$

the two solutions as before.

The streamline $\psi = 0$ thus consists of a circle and a straight line on a diameter produced (Fig. 10.30).

Again in this case the streamline $\psi = 0$ separates the flow into two distinct patterns: that outside the circle coming from the undisturbed flow a long way upstream, to flow around the circle and again to revert to uniform flow downstream. That inside the circle is from the doublet. This is confined within the circle and does not mingle with the horizontal stream at all. This inside flow pattern is usually neglected.

This combination is consequently a mathematical device for giving expression to the ideal two-dimensional flow around a circular cylinder.

The streamlines can be obtained directly by plotting using the super-positioning method outlined in previous cases.

Rewriting eqn. (10.52) in polars

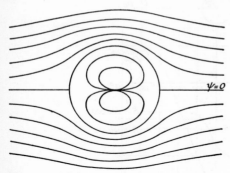

$$\psi = \frac{\mu}{2\pi r} \sin\theta - Ur\sin\theta$$

and rearranging, this becomes

$$\psi = U\sin\theta\left[\frac{\mu}{2\pi rU} - r\right]$$

and with $\mu/2\pi U = a^2$ a constant (a = radius of the circle $\psi = 0$)

FIG. 10.30.—Streamlines due to a doublet in a uniform stream.

$$\psi = U\sin\theta\left[\frac{a^2}{r} - r\right] . \quad (10.54)$$

Differentiating this partially with respect to r and θ in turn will give expressions for the velocity everywhere, viz.:

$$\left.\begin{array}{l} q_n = \dfrac{1}{r}\dfrac{\partial\psi}{\partial\theta} = U\cos\theta\left[\dfrac{a^2}{r^2} - 1\right] \\[4mm] q_t = -\dfrac{\partial\psi}{\partial r} = U\sin\theta\left[\dfrac{a^2}{r^2} + 1\right] \end{array}\right\} \quad . \quad . \quad (10.55)$$

Putting $r = a$ (the cylinder radius) in eqns. (10.55) gives:

(i) $q_n = U\cos\theta[1 - 1] = 0$ which is expected since the velocity must be parallel to the surface everywhere, and

(ii) $q_t = U\sin\theta[1 + 1] = 2U\sin\theta$.

Therefore the velocity on the surface is $2U\sin\theta$ and it is important to note that the velocity at the surface is *independent* of the radius of the cylinder.

The pressure distribution around a cylinder. If a long circular cylinder is set in a moving stream of fluid the motion around it will, ideally, be given by the expression (10.54) above, and the velocity anywhere on the surface by the formula

$$q = 2U\sin\theta \quad . \quad . \quad . \quad . \quad (10.56)$$

By the use of Bernoulli's Equation, the pressure p acting on the surface of the cylinder where the velocity is q can be found.

If p_0 is the static pressure of the free stream where the velocity is U then by Bernoulli's Equation,

$$p_0 + \tfrac{1}{2}\rho U^2 = p + \tfrac{1}{2}\rho q^2$$
$$= p + \tfrac{1}{2}\rho(2U\sin\theta)^2$$

Therefore $\qquad\qquad p - p_0 = \tfrac{1}{2}\rho U^2[1 - 4\sin^2\theta] \quad . \quad . \quad (10.57)$

Plotting this expression gives a curve as shown on Fig. 10.31.

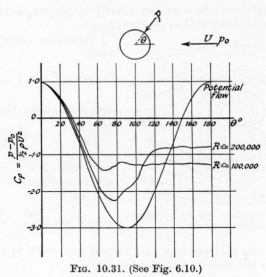

FIG. 10.31. (See Fig. 6.10.)

Important points to note are:

1. At the stagnation points (0° and 180°) the pressure difference $(p - p_0)$ is positive and equal to $\frac{1}{2}\rho U^2$.

2. At 30° and 150° where $\sin \theta = \frac{1}{2}$, $(p - p_0)$ is zero; and at these points the local velocity is the same as that of the free stream.

3. Between 30° and 150° C_p is negative, showing that p is less than p_0.

4. The pressure distribution is symmetrical about the vertical axis and therefore there is no drag force. Comparison of this ideal pressure distribution with that obtained by experiment shows that the actual pressure distribution is similar to the theoretical value up to about 70° but departs radically from it thereafter. Furthermore it can be seen that the pressure over the rear portion of the cylinder remains negative. This destroys the symmetry about the vertical axis and produces a force in the direction of motion (see § 6.6.9).

10.2.13. A spinning cylinder in a uniform stream. This is given by the stream function due to a doublet, in a uniform horizontal stream, with a line vortex superimposed at the origin.

By adding these cases

$$\psi = \frac{\mu}{2\pi r} \sin \theta - Uy - \frac{K}{2\pi} \log_e \frac{r}{r_0}$$

Converting to homogeneous coordinates

$$\psi = Ur \sin \theta \left[\frac{\mu}{2\pi r^2 U} - 1 \right] - \frac{K}{2\pi} \log_e \frac{r}{r_0}$$

but from the previous case $\sqrt{\mu/2\pi U} = a$, the radius of the cylinder.

Also since the cylinder periphery marks the inner limit of the vortex flow, $r_0 = a$, therefore the stream function becomes:

$$\psi = Ur \sin \theta \left[\frac{a^2}{r^2} - 1\right] - \frac{K}{2\pi} \log_e \frac{r}{a} \qquad . \qquad (10.58)$$

and differentiating partially with respect to r and θ the velocity components of the flow anywhere outside the cylinder become, respectively,

$$\left. \begin{array}{l} q_t = -\dfrac{\partial \psi}{\partial r} = U \sin \theta \left[\dfrac{a^2}{r} + 1\right] + \dfrac{K}{2\pi r} \\[3mm] q_n = \dfrac{1}{r}\dfrac{\partial \psi}{\partial \theta} = U \cos \theta \left[\dfrac{a^2}{r^2} - 1\right] \end{array} \right\} \qquad . \qquad (10.59)$$

and $\qquad\qquad q = \sqrt{q_n^2 + q_t^2}$

On the surface of the spinning cylinder $r = a$.

Therefore $\qquad\qquad q_n = 0$

and $\qquad\qquad q_t = 2U \sin \theta + \dfrac{K}{2\pi a} \qquad . \qquad . \qquad (10.60)$

Therefore $\qquad q = q_t = 2U \sin \theta + \dfrac{K}{2\pi a}$

and applying Bernoulli's Equation between a point a long way upstream and a point on the cylinder where the static pressure is p,

$$p_0 + \tfrac{1}{2}\rho U^2 = p + \tfrac{1}{2}\rho q^2$$
$$= p + \tfrac{1}{2}\rho \left[2U \sin \theta + \frac{K}{2\pi a}\right]^2$$

Therefore $\qquad p - p_0 = \tfrac{1}{2}\rho U^2 \left[1 - \left(2 \sin \theta + \dfrac{K}{2\pi U a}\right)^2\right] \qquad . \quad (10.61)$

This equation differs from that of the non-spinning cylinder in a uniform stream of the previous section by the addition of the term $(K/2\pi U a)$ $= B$ (a constant), in the squared bracket. This has the effect of altering the symmetry of the pressure distribution about a *horizontal* axis. This is indicated by considering the extreme top and bottom of the cylinder and denoting the pressures there by p_T and p_B respectively.

At the top $p = p_T$ when $\theta = \pi/2$ and $\sin \theta = 1$.

Then eqn. (10.61) becomes

$$p_T - p_0 = \tfrac{1}{2}\rho U^2 [1 - (2 + B)^2]$$
$$= -\tfrac{1}{2}\rho U^2 [3 + 4B + B^2] \qquad . \qquad (10.62)$$

At the bottom $p = p_B$ when $\theta = -\pi/2$ and $\sin \theta = -1$.

$$p_B - p_0 = -\tfrac{1}{2}\rho U^2 [3 - 4B + B^2] \qquad . \qquad (10.63)$$

Clearly (10.62) does not equal (10.63) which shows that a pressure difference exists between the top and bottom of the cylinder equal in magnitude to

$$p_T - p_B = 8B = -\frac{4K}{\pi U a}$$

This suggests that if the pressure distribution is integrated round the cylinder then a resultant force would be found *normal* to the direction of motion.

The normal force on a spinning circular cylinder in a uniform stream.

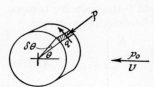

FIG. 10.32. — The pressure and velocity on the surface of unit length of cylinder of radius δ.

Consider a surface element of cylinder of unit span (Fig. 10.32). The area of the element $= a\,\delta\theta.1$, the static pressure acting on element $= p$, resultant force $= (p - p_0)a\,\delta\theta$, vertical component $= (p - p_0)a\,\delta\theta\sin\theta$.

Substituting for $(p - p_0)$ from eqn. (10.63) and retaining the notation $B = K/2\pi Ua$, the vertical component of force acting on the element

$$= \tfrac{1}{2}\rho U^2[1 - (2\sin\theta + B)^2]a\,\delta\theta\sin\theta$$

The total vertical force per unit span by integration is

$$l = \int_0^{2\pi} \tfrac{1}{2}\rho U^2 a[1 - (2\sin\theta + B)^2]\sin\theta\,d\theta$$

which becomes

$$l = \tfrac{1}{2}\rho U^2 a \int_0^{2\pi} \{\sin\theta(1 - B^2) - 4B\sin^2\theta - 4\sin^3\theta\}\,d\theta$$

On integrating from 0 to 2π the 1st and 3rd terms vanish leaving

$$\int_0^{2\pi} 4B\sin^2\theta\,d\theta = 4B\pi$$

Therefore
$$l = \tfrac{1}{2}\rho U^2 a 4B\pi$$

replacing B by $K/2\pi Ua$ and cancelling gives the well-known equation for the lift force per unit span

$$l = \rho UK \qquad . \qquad . \qquad . \qquad (10.64)$$

The lift per unit span in lb is equal to the product of density ρ (slug/ft³), the linear velocity U (ft/sec), and the circulation K (ft²/sec).

This expression is the algebraic form of the Kutta–Zhukovsky Theorem, and is valid for any system which produces a circulation superimposed on a linear velocity (see § 10.6). The spinning cylinder is used here as it lends itself to stream function theory as well as being of interest later.

It is important to note that the diameter of the cylinder has no influence on the final expression, so if a line vortex of strength K moved with velocity U in a uniform stream of density ρ, the same 'sideways' force $l = \rho UK$ per unit length of vortex would be found.

This 'sideways' force commonly associated with a spinning object moving through the air has been recognized, and used in ball games, etc., since ancient times. It is usually referred to as the *Magnus effect* after the scholar and philosopher Magnus.

The flow pattern around a spinning cylinder. The flow pattern around the spinning cylinder is also altered as the strength of the circulation increases.

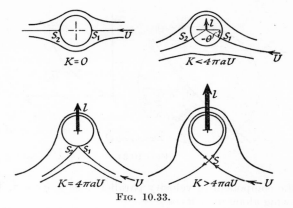

FIG. 10.33.

In Fig. 10.33 when $K = 0$ the flow pattern is that associated with the previous non-spinning case with front and rear stagnation points S_1 and S_2 respectively, occurring on the horizontal axis. As K is increased positively a small amount the stagnation points move *down* below the horizontal axis.

Since from the equation for the velocity anywhere on the surface

$$q_t = 2U \sin \theta + \frac{K}{2\pi a} = 0 \quad \text{at the stagnation points}$$

$$\theta = \text{arc sin} \left(-\frac{K}{4\pi a U} \right)$$

which is negative.

As K is further increased a limiting condition occurs when $\theta = -\pi/2$, i.e., $K = 4\pi a U$, the stagnation points merge at the bottom of the cylinder.

When K is greater than $4\pi a U$ the stagnation point (S_1, S_2) leaves the cylinder. The cylinder continues to rotate within the closed loop of the stagnation streamline, carrying round with it a region of fluid confined within the loop.

10.3. The velocity potential. The stream function at a point has been defined as the quantity of fluid moving *across* some convenient imaginary line in the flow pattern, and lines of constant stream function (amount of flow or flux) were plotted to give one picture of the flow pattern.

Another mathematical definition, giving a different plot of constants, can be obtained for the same flow system.

In this case an expression giving the amount of flow *along* the convenient imaginary line is found.

In a general two-dimensional stream of fluid, consider any (imaginary) line OP joining the origin of a pair of axes to the point $P(x, y)$. [Again the axes and this line do not impede the flow, and are used only to form a

R

reference datum.] At a point Q on the line let the local velocity q meet the line OP in β (Fig. 10.34).

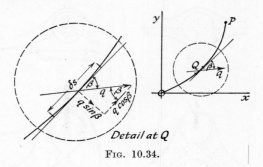

Detail at Q

FIG. 10.34.

Then the component of velocity parallel to $\delta s = q \cos \beta$. The amount of fluid flowing along $\delta s = q \cos \beta \, \delta s$.

The total amount of fluid flowing along the line towards P is the sum of all such amounts and is given mathematically as the integral $\int q \cos \beta \, ds$. This function is called the *velocity potential of P* with respect to O and denoted by ϕ.

Now OQP can be any line between O and P and a necessary condition for $\int q \cos \beta \, ds$ to be the velocity potential ϕ, is that the value of ϕ is unique for the point P *irrespective* of the path of integration. Then:

$$\text{Velocity potential } \phi = \int_{OP} q \cos \beta \, ds \quad . \qquad . \quad (10.65)$$

If this were *not* the case, if integrating the tangential flow component from O to P via A (Fig. 10.35) did *not* produce the same magnitude of ϕ as integrating from O to P via some other path such as B, there would be some flow components 'circulating' in the circuit $OAPBO$. This in turn would imply that the fluid within the circuit possessed vorticity.

FIG. 10.35.

The existence of a velocity potential must therefore imply zero vorticity in the flow, or in other words, a potential (irrotational) flow.

This fundamental flow condition is used in § 10.5 to re-define circulation.

10.3.1. Sign convention for velocity potential.

The tangential flow along a curve is the product of the local velocity component and the elementary length of the curve. Now, if the velocity component is *in the direction of* integration, it is considered a *positive* increment to the velocity potential.

10.3.2. The equipotentials.   Consider a point P having a velocity potential ϕ (recapitulating, ϕ is the integral of the flow component *along OP*) and let another point P_1 close to P have the same velocity potential ϕ. This then means that the integral of flow along OP_1 equals the integral of flow along OP (Fig. 10.36).

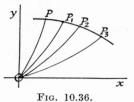

But by definition OPP_1 is another path of integration from O to P_1. Therefore

FIG. 10.36.

$$\phi = \int_{OP} q \cos \beta \, ds = \int_{OP_1} q \cos \beta \, ds = \int_{OPP_1} q \cos \beta \, ds$$

but since the integral along OP equals that along OP_1 there can be no flow *along* the remaining portions of the path of the third integral, that is along PP_1.

Similarly for other points such as P_2, P_3, having the same velocity potential, there can be no flow along the line joining P_1 to P_2.

The line joining P, P_1, P_2, P_3 is a line joining points having the same velocity potential and is called an *equipotential* or a line of constant velocity potential—a line of constant ϕ. The significant characteristic of an equipotential is that there is no flow *along* such a line. (Notice the correspondence between an equipotential and a streamline which is a line *across* which there is no flow.)

Investigate the flow in the region of points P and P_1 more closely. From the above there can be no flow along the line PP_1. But there is fluid flowing in this region so it must be flowing in such a manner that there is no component of velocity in the direction PP_1. This manner can only be at right-angles to PP_1, that is the flow in the region PP_1 must be normal to PP_1. Now the streamline in this region, the line to which the flow is tangential, must also be at right-angles to PP_1 which is itself the local equipotential.

This relation applies at all points in a homogeneous continuous fluid and is most concisely stated thus. Streamlines and equipotentials meet orthogonally, i.e., always at right-angles.

It follows from this statement that for a given streamline pattern there is one equipotential pattern which is such that the equipotentials are everywhere normal to the streamlines.

10.3.3. Local velocity components in terms of ϕ.

(a) *In Cartesian coordinates.* Let a point $P(x, y)$ be on an equipotential of value ϕ and a neighbouring point $Q(x + \delta x, y + \delta y)$ be on the equipotential $\phi + \delta\phi$ (Fig. 10.37).

Then by definition the increase in velocity potential from P to Q is the line integral of the *tangential* velocity component along *any* path between P and Q. Taking PRQ as the most convenient path where the local velocity components are u and v,

$$\delta\phi = u\delta x + v\delta y$$

but

$$\delta\phi = \frac{\partial\phi}{\partial x}\delta x + \frac{\partial\phi}{\partial y}\delta y$$

Thus, equating terms

$$u = \frac{\partial\phi}{\partial x}$$

and

$$v = \frac{\partial\phi}{\partial y} \qquad \left.\vphantom{\begin{array}{c}a\\b\\c\end{array}}\right\} \qquad (10.66)$$

(b) *In polar coordinates.* Let a point $P(r, \theta)$ be on an equipotential ϕ and a neighbouring point $Q(r + \delta r, \theta + \delta\theta)$ be on an equipotential $\phi + \delta\phi$ (Fig. 10.38).

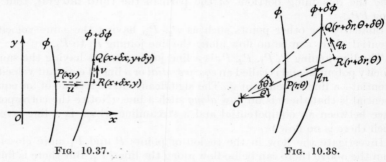

FIG. 10.37.   FIG. 10.38.

By definition the increase $\delta\phi$ is the line integral of the *tangential* component of velocity along any path.

For convenience choose PRQ where point R is $(r + \delta r, \theta)$.

Then integrating along PR and RQ where the velocities are q_n and q_t respectively, and are *both* in the direction of integration,

$$\delta\phi = q_n \, \delta r + q_t(r + \delta r) \, \delta\theta$$
$$= q_n \, \delta r + q_t r \, \delta\theta \quad \text{to the first order of small quantities,}$$

but since ϕ is a function of two independent variables,

$$\delta\phi = \frac{\partial\phi}{\partial r}\delta r + \frac{\partial\phi}{\partial\theta}\delta\theta$$

$$q_n = \frac{\partial\phi}{\partial r}$$

and

$$q_t = \frac{1}{r}\frac{\partial\phi}{\partial\theta} \qquad \left.\vphantom{\begin{array}{c}a\\b\\c\end{array}}\right\} \qquad (10.67)$$

10.3.4. Flow of constant velocity.

Flow parallel to Ox axis from left to right. Consider flow streaming past the axes of coordinates Ox and Oy with velocity U ft/sec parallel to Ox (Fig. 10.39).

By definition the velocity potential at a point $P(x, y)$ in the flow is given by the line integral of the *tangential* velocity component along any line from O to P. For convenience take line OTP where T has ordinates (x, O).

Then $\phi =$ flow along line OTP

$= $ flow along $OT +$ flow along TP

$= Ux + 0$

Therefore $\phi = Ux$ ft²/sec   .   .   .   .   .   (10.68)

The lines of constant ϕ, the equipotentials, are given by $Ux =$ constant, and since the velocity is constant the equipotentials must be lines of constant x, or lines parallel to Oy which are everywhere normal to the streamlines corresponding to this case (§ 10.2.5).

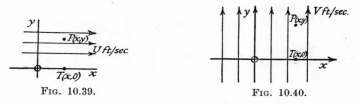

FIG. 10.39.   FIG. 10.40.

Flow of constant velocity parallel to Oy axis. Consider flow streaming past the Ox, Oy axes with velocity V ft/sec parallel to the Oy axis (Fig. 10.40). Again, taking the most convenient boundary as OTP where T is given by (x, O)

$\phi =$ flow along $OT +$ flow along TP

$= 0 + Vy$

Therefore $\phi = Vy$ ft²/sec   .   .   .   .   .   (10.69)

The lines of constant velocity potential, ϕ (equipotentials), are given by $Vy =$ constant, which means, since V is constant, lines of constant y, are lines parallel to Ox axis.

Flow of constant velocity in any direction. Let the flow of constant velocity Q ft/sec stream past the axes Ox, Oy, in a direction making angle θ

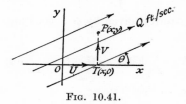

FIG. 10.41.

with the Ox axis (Fig. 10.41). The velocity Q can be resolved into components U and V parallel and perpendicular to the Ox axis giving

$$Q = \sqrt{U^2 + V^2} \quad \text{and} \quad \theta = \arctan \frac{V}{U}$$

Here the velocity potential at P is a measure of the flow along any line joining P to O.

Taking OTP as the line of integration $[T(x, O)]$ we have

$$\phi = \text{flow along } OT + \text{flow along } TP$$
$$= U.x + V.y$$

or $\qquad\qquad \phi = Ux + Vy .$ . . . . . . (10.70)

10.3.5. Source (sink). Place the source at the origin of the two-coordinate system (Fig. 10.42).

The velocity everywhere in the field is radial, i.e., the velocity at any point $P(r, \theta)$ is given by $q = \sqrt{q_n^2 + q_t^2}$ and $q = q_n$ here since $q_t = 0$.

Integrating round OQP where Q is point (r, θ)

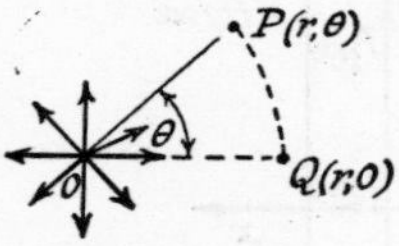

FIG. 10.42.

$$\phi = \int_{OQ} q \cos \beta \, ds + \int_{QP} q \cos \beta \, ds$$

$$= \int_{OQ} q_n \, dr + \int_{QP} q_t r \, \delta\theta = \int_{OQ} q_n \, ds + 0$$

But $\qquad\qquad q_n = \dfrac{m}{2\pi r}$

Therefore $\qquad \phi = \int_{r_0}^{r} \dfrac{m}{2\pi r} dr = \dfrac{m}{2\pi} \log_e \dfrac{r}{r_0}$ . . . (10.71)

where r_0 is the radius of the equipotential $\phi = 0$.

Alternatively, since the velocity q is *always* radial ($q = q_n$) it must be some function of r only and the tangential component is zero.

Now $\qquad\qquad q_n = \dfrac{m}{2\pi r} = \dfrac{\partial \phi}{\partial r}$

Therefore $\qquad \phi = \int_{r_0}^{r} \dfrac{m}{2\pi r} dr = \dfrac{m}{2\pi} \log_e \dfrac{r}{r_0}$ . . (10.71)

In Cartesian coordinates with $\phi = 0$ on the curve $r_0 = 1$

$$\phi = \dfrac{m}{4\pi} \log_e (x^2 + y^2) \qquad . \qquad . \qquad (10.72)$$

The equipotential pattern is given by $\phi = $ constant.

From eqn. (10.71)

$$\phi = \dfrac{m}{2\pi} \log_e r - C, \quad C = \dfrac{m}{2\pi} \log_e r_0$$

or $\qquad\qquad r = e^{2\pi(\phi + C)/m}$ . . . . . . (10.73)

squaring, $\qquad r^2 = e^{4\pi(\phi + C)/m}$

which is the equation of a circle of centre at the origin and radius $e^{2\pi(\phi + C)/m}$ when ϕ is constant.

Thus equipotentials for a source (or sink) are concentric circles and satisfy the requirement of meeting the streamlines orthogonally.

10.3.6. Source in a uniform horizontal stream. Combining the velocity potentials,

$$\phi = \frac{m}{2\pi} \log_e \frac{r}{r_0} - Ux$$

or $$\phi = \frac{m}{4\pi} \log_e \left(\frac{x^2}{r_0^2} + \frac{y^2}{r_0^2}\right) - Ux. \qquad . \qquad . \qquad (10.74)$$

or in polar coordinates

$$\phi = \frac{m}{2\pi} \log_e \frac{r}{r_0} - Ur \cos\theta \qquad . \qquad . \qquad . \qquad (10.75)$$

These equations give, for constant values of ϕ, the equipotential lines everywhere normal to the streamlines.

10.3.7. Source and sink pair. Let $\pm m$ ft²/sec be the strengths of the source and sink situated at points $A(c, 0)$ and $B(-c, 0)$, that is a distance apart $2c$ on the Ox axis (Fig. 10.43).

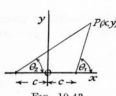

FIG. 10.43.

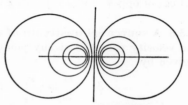

FIG. 10.44.—Equipotential lines due to a source and sink pair.

Consider the velocity potential at any point $P(r, \theta)(x, y)$.*

$$\phi = \frac{m}{2\pi} \log_e \frac{r_1}{r_0} - \frac{m}{2\pi} \log_e \frac{r_2}{r_0} = \frac{m}{2\pi} \log_e \frac{r_1}{r_2} \qquad . \qquad (10.76)$$

$$r_1^2 = (x - c)^2 + y^2 = x^2 + y^2 + c^2 - 2xc$$

$$r_2^2 = (x + c)^2 + y^2 = x^2 + y^2 + c^2 + 2xc$$

Therefore $$\phi = \frac{m}{4\pi} \log_e \frac{x^2 + y^2 + c^2 - 2xc}{x^2 + y^2 + c^2 + 2xc}$$

Rearranging

$$e^{4\pi\phi/m} = \frac{x^2 + y^2 + c^2 - 2xc}{x^2 + y^2 + c^2 + 2xc} = \lambda \text{ (say)}$$

then $$(x^2 + y^2 + c^2 + 2xc)\lambda = x^2 + y^2 + c^2 - 2xc$$

$$(x^2 + y^2 + c^2)[\lambda - 1] + 2xc(\lambda + 1) = 0$$

or $$x^2 + y^2 + 2xc\left(\frac{\lambda + 1}{\lambda - 1}\right) + c^2 = 0. \qquad . \qquad . \qquad (10.77)$$

* *Note.* Here r_0 is the radius of the equipotential $\phi = 0$ for the isolated source and the isolated sink but not for the combination.

which is the equation to a circle of centre

$$x = -c\left(\frac{\lambda + 1}{\lambda - 1}\right), \quad y = 0, \quad x = -c\frac{e^{(4\pi\phi/m)} + 1}{e^{(4\pi\phi/m)} - 1}$$

or

$$x = -c \coth\frac{2\pi\phi}{m}$$

and radius

$$c\sqrt{\left(\frac{\lambda + 1}{\lambda - 1}\right)^2 - 1} = 2c\frac{\sqrt{\lambda}}{\lambda - 1} = 2c\frac{e^{2\pi\phi/m}}{e^{(4\pi\phi/m)} - 1}$$

$$= 2c \operatorname{cosech}\frac{2\pi\phi}{m}$$

That is, the equipotentials due to a source and sink combination are sets of eccentric non-intersecting circles with their centres on the Ox axis (Fig. 10.44).

This pattern is exactly the same as the streamline pattern due to point vortices of opposite sign separated by a distance $2c$.

10.3.8. A source set upstream of an equal sink in a uniform stream.
The velocity potential at any point in the flow due to this combination is given by

$$\phi = \frac{m}{2\pi}\log_e\frac{r_1}{r_2} - Ur\sin\theta \quad . \qquad . \qquad . \qquad . \quad (10.78)$$

or

$$\phi = \frac{m}{4\pi}\log_e\frac{x^2 + y^2 + c^2 - 2xc}{x^2 + y^2 + c^2 + 2xc} - Ux \quad . \qquad . \quad (10.79)$$

10.3.9. Line (or point) vortex.
Since the flow due to a line vortex gives streamlines which are concentric circles, the equipotentials, shown to be always normal to the streamlines, must be radial lines emanating from the vortex.

Since $\qquad\qquad q_n = 0 \qquad \phi$ is a function of θ

$$q_t = \frac{1}{r}\frac{d\phi}{d\theta} = \frac{K}{2\pi r}$$

Therefore $\qquad\qquad d\phi = \frac{K}{2\pi}d\theta$

and on integrating

$$\phi = \frac{K}{2\pi}\theta + \text{constant}$$

By defining $\phi = 0$ when $\theta = 0$,

$$\phi = \frac{K}{2\pi}\theta \qquad . \qquad . \qquad . \qquad . \quad (10.80)$$

10.3.10. Doublet. Consider again a source and sink set a very small distance, $2c$, apart (Fig. 10.45).

Then
$$\phi = \frac{m}{2\pi} \log_e \frac{r_1}{r_0} - \frac{m}{2\pi} \log_e \frac{r_2}{r_0} \quad *$$

where $\pm\, m$ is the strength of the source and sink respectively.

Then
$$\phi = \frac{m}{2\pi} \log_e \frac{r_1}{r_2} = \frac{m}{4\pi} \log_e \frac{r_1^2}{r_2^2}$$

now
$$r_1^2 = x^2 + y^2 - 2xc + c^2$$

and
$$r_2^2 = x^2 + y^2 + 2xc + c^2$$

Therefore
$$\phi = \frac{m}{4\pi} \log_e \frac{x^2 + y^2 - 2xc + c^2}{x^2 + y^2 + 2xc + c^2}$$

Fɪɢ. 10.45.

and dividing out

$$= \frac{m}{4\pi} \log_e \left(1 - \frac{4xc}{x^2 + y^2 + c^2 + 2xc}\right)$$

$$\left[\text{Remember that on expanding, } \log_e (1 - t) = -\,t - \frac{t^2}{2} - \frac{t^3}{3} - \frac{t^4}{4} \cdots \right]$$

Therefore:

$$\phi = \frac{m}{4\pi}\left[- \frac{4xc}{x^2 + y^2 + c^2 + 2xc} - \frac{16x^2c^2}{2(x^2 + y^2 + c^2 + 2xc)^2} - \cdots \right]$$

Since c is very small c^2 can be neglected. Therefore ignoring c^2 and higher powers of c

$$\phi = \frac{m}{4\pi} \frac{4xc}{x^2 + y^2 + 2xc}$$

and as $c \to 0$, and $2mc = \mu$ (which is the strength of the doublet) a limiting value of ϕ is given by

$$\phi = - \frac{\mu}{2\pi} \frac{x}{x^2 + y^2} \quad \text{but} \quad \frac{x}{\sqrt{x^2 + y^2}} = \cos \theta$$

Therefore
$$\phi = - \frac{\mu}{2\pi r} \cos \theta \ . \qquad . \qquad . \qquad . \quad (10.81)$$

10.3.11. Doublet in a uniform horizontal stream. The velocity potential due to this combination is that caused by a uniform stream flowing parallel to the Ox axis, and that by a doublet at the origin.

Putting $x = r \cos \theta$,

$$\phi = -\, Ur \cos \theta + \frac{\mu}{2\pi r} \cos \theta$$

$$\phi = -\, U \cos \theta\left(r + \frac{a^2}{r}\right) \qquad . \qquad . \qquad (10.82)$$

where $a = \sqrt{\mu/2\pi U}$ is the radius of the streamline $\psi = 0$.

* See footnote on p. 255.

10.4. Laplace's Equation. As a focus of all the new ideas met in this chapter, the main fundamentals are summarized, using Cartesian coordinates for convenience.

I. *The Equation of Motion in two dimensions.*

$$\left.\begin{array}{l} \dfrac{\partial u}{\partial t} + u\dfrac{\partial u}{\partial x} + v\dfrac{\partial u}{\partial y} = \dfrac{1}{\rho}\left(X - \dfrac{\partial p}{\partial x}\right) \\[2mm] \dfrac{\partial v}{\partial t} + u\dfrac{\partial v}{\partial x} + v\dfrac{\partial v}{\partial y} = \dfrac{1}{\rho}\left(Y - \dfrac{\partial p}{\partial y}\right) \end{array}\right\} \qquad . \qquad . \qquad \text{(i)}$$

II. *The Equation of Continuity in two dimensions* (Incompressible Flow).

$$\frac{\partial u}{\partial x} + \frac{\partial v}{\partial y} = 0 \qquad . \qquad . \qquad . \qquad . \qquad \text{(ii)}$$

III. *The Equation of Vorticity.*

$$\frac{\partial v}{\partial x} - \frac{\partial u}{\partial y} = \zeta \qquad . \qquad . \qquad . \qquad . \qquad \text{(iii)}$$

IV. *The Stream Function* (Incompressible flow). ψ describes a continuous flow in two dimensions where the velocity is at any point given by

$$u = \frac{\partial \psi}{\partial y}, \quad v = -\frac{\partial \psi}{\partial x} \qquad . \qquad . \qquad . \qquad \text{(iv)}$$

V. *The Velocity Potential.* ϕ describes an irrotational flow in two dimensions where the velocity at any point is given by

$$u = \frac{\partial \phi}{\partial x}, \quad v = \frac{\partial \phi}{\partial y} . \qquad . \qquad . \qquad . \qquad \text{(v)}$$

Substituting (iv) in (ii) gives the identity

$$\frac{\partial^2 \psi}{\partial x \partial y} - \frac{\partial^2 \psi}{\partial x \partial y} = 0$$

which demonstrates the validity of (IV), while substituting (v) in (iii) gives the identity

$$\frac{\partial^2 \phi}{\partial x \partial y} - \frac{\partial^2 \phi}{\partial x \partial y} = 0$$

demonstrating the validity of (V), i.e., that a flow described by a unique velocity potential must be irrotational.

Alternatively substituting (iv) in (iii) and (v) in (ii) the criteria for irrotational continuous flow are that

$$\frac{\partial^2 \phi}{\partial x^2} + \frac{\partial^2 \phi}{\partial y^2} = 0 = \frac{\partial^2 \psi}{\partial x^2} + \frac{\partial^2 \psi}{\partial y^2} . \qquad . \qquad . \qquad (10.83)$$

also written as $\nabla^2 \phi = \nabla^2 \psi = 0$, where the operator *nabla squared*

$$\nabla^2 = \frac{\partial^2}{\partial x^2} + \frac{\partial^2}{\partial y^2}$$

Eqn. (10.83) is Laplace's equation.

10.5. Circulation. The velocity potential ϕ is defined as the line integral of the tangential velocity component of flow along a line of integration between any two points, i.e., if the velocity of flow across AB at P is q, inclined at β to the tangent to the curve at P, then

$$\phi = \int_{AB} q \cos \beta \, ds$$

which can be recast in the form

$$\phi = \int_{AB} (u \, dx + v \, dy) \qquad . \qquad . \qquad . \quad (10.84)$$

If the line AB forms a closed loop or circuit in the flow (Fig. 10.46) (remember the circuit is imaginary and does not influence the flow, i.e., is *not* a boundary), then the line integral of eqn. (10.84) taken round the circuit is defined as the *circulation* and symbolized by K.

i.e., $$K = \oint (u \, dx + v \, dy)$$

<table>
<tr><td>Fɪɢ. 10.46.</td><td>Fɪɢ. 10.47. (See also Fig. 6.16.)</td></tr>
</table>

Circulation implies a component of *rotation* of flow in the system. This is not to say that there are circular streamlines or that elements of fluid are actually moving around some closed loop although this is a possible flow system.

Circulation in a flow means that the flow system could be resolved into a uniform irrotational portion and a circulating portion. Fig. 10.47 shows an idealized concept. The implication is that if circulation is present in a fluid motion, then vorticity must be present, even though it may be confined to a restricted space, e.g. as in the 'core' of a point vortex. Alternatively, as in the case of the circular cylinder with circulation, the vorticity at the centre of the cylinder may actually be excluded from the region of flow considered, namely that outside the cylinder.

Consider this by the reverse argument. Look again at Fig. 10.46. By definition the velocity potential of C relative to A (ϕ_{CA}) must be equal to the velocity potential of C relative to B (ϕ_{CB}) in a potential flow.

The integration continued round ACB gives

$$K = \phi_{CA} + - \phi_{CB} = 0$$

This is for a potential flow only. Thus, if K is finite the definition of the velocity potential breaks down and the curve ACB must contain a region of rotational flow. If the flow is not potential then eqn. (iii) must have a finite value for ζ.

An alternative equation for K is found by considering the circuit of integration to consist of a large number of rectangular elements of side $\delta x\ \delta y$. Applying the integral $K = \int (u\ dx + v\ dy)$ round *abcd*, say, which is the element at $P(x, y)$ where the velocity is u and v, gives (Fig. 10.48),

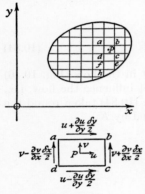

$$\Delta K = \left(v + \frac{\partial v}{\partial x}\frac{\delta x}{2}\right)\delta y - \left(u + \frac{\partial u}{\partial y}\frac{\delta y}{2}\right)\delta x$$

$$- \left(v - \frac{\partial v}{\partial x}\frac{\delta x}{2}\right)\delta y + \left(u - \frac{\partial u}{\partial y}\frac{\delta y}{2}\right)\delta x$$

$$\Delta K = \left(\frac{\partial v}{\partial x} - \frac{\partial u}{\partial y}\right)\delta x\ \delta y$$

The sum of the circulations of all the areas is clearly the circulation of the circuit as a whole because, as the ΔK of each element is added to the ΔK of the neighbouring element the contributions of the common sides disappear.

Fig. 10.48.

Applying this argument from element to neighbouring element throughout the area, the only sides contributing to the circulation when the ΔK's of all areas are summed together are those sides which actually form the circuit itself. This means that for the circuit as a whole

$$K = \underbrace{\iint \left(\frac{\partial v}{\partial x} - \frac{\partial u}{\partial y}\right) dx\ dy}_{\text{over the area}} = \underbrace{\oint (u\ dx + v\ dy)}_{\text{round the circuit}}$$

and
$$\frac{\partial v}{\partial x} - \frac{\partial u}{\partial y} = \zeta$$

This is a result which is not of immediate interest but which will simplify the understanding of many advanced topics outside the immediate scope of this text.

If the strength of the circulation K remains constant whilst the circuit shrinks to encompass an ever smaller area—until it shrinks to an area the size of a rectangular element, then:

$$K = \zeta \times \delta x\ \delta y = \zeta \times \text{area of element}$$

$$\therefore \text{vorticity} = \underset{\text{area} \to 0}{\text{Lim}} \frac{K}{\text{area of circuit}} . \qquad . \quad (10.85)$$

This is a result which permits the easy derivation of the formula for vorticity in polar coordinates.

A suitably shaped element here is the segment subtending $\delta\theta$ at the origin and of width δr (Fig. 10.49). If this is located at the point $P(r, \theta)$ where the velocity components are q_n and

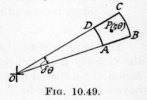

Fig. 10.49.

q_t the velocities *along* the sides AB, BC, CD, DA in those directions are respectively:

$$q_n - \frac{\partial q_n}{\partial \theta}\frac{\delta\theta}{2}, \quad q_t + \frac{\partial q_t}{\partial r}\frac{\delta r}{2}, \quad -\left(q_n + \frac{\partial q_n}{\partial \theta}\frac{\delta\theta}{2}\right), \quad -\left(q_t - \frac{\partial q_t}{\partial r}\frac{\delta r}{2}\right)$$

The corresponding lengths of side are:

$$\delta r, \quad \left(r + \frac{\delta r}{2}\right)\delta\theta, \quad \delta r, \quad \text{and} \quad \left(r - \frac{\delta r}{2}\right)\delta\theta$$

The circulation about the element is the line integral of the tangential velocity component of flow which is

$$K = \left(q_n - \frac{\partial q_n}{\partial \theta}\frac{\delta\theta}{2}\right)\delta r + \left(q_t + \frac{\partial q_t}{\partial r}\frac{\delta r}{2}\right)\left(r + \frac{\delta r}{2}\right)\delta\theta,$$

$$- \left(q_n + \frac{\partial q_n}{\partial \theta}\frac{\delta\theta}{2}\right)\delta r - \left(q_t - \frac{\partial q_t}{\partial r}\frac{\delta r}{2}\right)\left(r - \frac{\delta r}{2}\right)\delta\theta$$

$$K = \left(\frac{q_t}{r} + \frac{\partial q_t}{\partial r} - \frac{1}{r}\frac{\partial q_n}{\partial \theta}\right)r\,\delta r\,\delta\theta$$

$$K = \text{vorticity . area of element}$$

Since the area of the element is $r\,\delta r\,\delta\theta$ it follows that vorticity

$$\zeta = \frac{q_t}{r} + \frac{\partial q_t}{\partial r} - \frac{1}{r}\frac{\partial q_n}{\partial \theta} \qquad . \qquad . \qquad . \qquad (10.86)$$

10.5.1. Bernoulli's Equation for rotational flow.

Consider fluid moving in a circular path. Higher pressure must be exerted from the outside, towards the centre of rotation, in order to provide the centripetal force. That is, some outside pressure force must be available to prevent the particle flowing in a straight line. This suggests that the pressure is growing in magnitude as the radius increases— and a corollary is that the velocity of flow must fall as the distance from the centre increases.

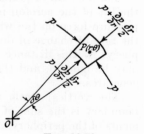

With a segmental particle at $P(r, \theta)$ where the velocity is q_t only and the pressure p the pressures on the sides will be as shown in Fig. 10.50 and the resultant pressure thrust inwards is

FIG. 10.50.

$$\left(p + \frac{\partial p}{\partial r}\frac{\delta r}{2}\right)\left(r + \frac{\delta r}{2}\right)\delta\theta - \left(p - \frac{\partial p}{\partial r}\frac{\delta r}{2}\right)\left(r - \frac{\delta r}{2}\right)\delta\theta - p\,\delta r\,\delta\theta$$

which reduces to

$$\frac{\partial p}{\partial r}r\,\delta r\,\delta\theta \qquad . \qquad . \qquad . \qquad (10.87)$$

This must provide the centripetal force = mass × centripetal acceleration

$$= \rho r\,\delta r\,\delta\theta.\frac{q_t^2}{r} \qquad . \qquad . \qquad . \qquad (10.88)$$

Equating (10.87) and (10.88),

$$\frac{\partial p}{\partial r} = \frac{\rho q_t^2}{r} \qquad . \qquad . \qquad . \qquad . \qquad . \qquad (10.89)$$

The rate of change of total pressure H is

$$\frac{\partial H}{\partial r} = \frac{\partial(p + \frac{1}{2}\rho q_t^2)}{\partial r} = \frac{\partial p}{\partial r} + \rho q_t \frac{\partial q_t}{\partial r}$$

and substituting for eqn. (10.89),

$$\frac{\partial H}{\partial r} = \rho \frac{q_t^2}{r} + \rho q_t \frac{\partial q_t}{\partial r} = \rho q_t \left(\frac{q_t}{r} + \frac{\partial q_t}{\partial r} \right)$$

Now for this system $\dfrac{1}{r} \dfrac{\partial q_n}{\partial \theta}$ is zero since the streamlines are circular and the vorticity is $\dfrac{q_t}{r} + \dfrac{\partial q_t}{\partial r}$

giving

$$\frac{\partial H}{\partial r} = \rho q_t \zeta \qquad . \qquad . \qquad . \qquad . \qquad (10.90)$$

10.6. The lift on an aerofoil (Kutta–Zhukovsky Theorem). The lift on any aerofoil moving relative to a bulk of fluid can be derived by direct analysis.

Consider the aerofoil in Fig. 10.51 generating a circulation of K ft²/sec when in a stream of velocity V ft/sec, density ρ slug/ft³, and static pressure p_0 lb/ft².

The lift produced by the aerofoil must be sustained by any boundary (imaginary or real) surrounding the aerofoil.

For a circuit of radius R, which is very large compared to the aerofoil, the lift of the aerofoil upwards must be equal to the sum of the static pressure force on the whole periphery of the circuit and the reaction to the rate of change of downward momentum of the air through the periphery. At this distance the effects of the aerofoil thickness distribution may be ignored, and the aerofoil represented only by the circulation it generates.

The vertical static pressure force or buoyancy l_b on the circular boundary is the sum of the vertical pressure components acting on elements of the periphery. At the element subtending $\delta\theta$ at the centre of the aerofoil the static pressure is p and the local velocity is the resultant of V and the velocity v induced by the circulation.

By Bernoulli's Equation

$$p_0 + \tfrac{1}{2}\rho V^2 = p + \tfrac{1}{2}\rho[V^2 + v^2 + 2Vv \sin\theta]$$

giving

$$p = p_0 - \rho Vv \sin\theta$$

if v^2 may be neglected compared with V^2, which is permissible since R is large.

The vertical component of pressure force on this element is

$$- pR \sin\theta \; \delta\theta$$

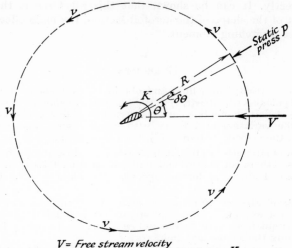

V = Free stream velocity
v = Velocity induced by circulation = $\frac{K}{2\pi R}$

FIG. 10.51.

and, on substituting for p and integrating, the contribution to lift due to the buoyancy on the boundary is

$$l_b = - \int_0^{2\pi} (p_0 - \rho V v \sin \theta) R \sin \theta \, d\theta$$

$$= + \rho V v R \pi \quad . \qquad . \qquad . \qquad . \qquad . \qquad (10.91)$$

with p_0 and R constant.

The mass flow through the elemental area of the boundary is given by $\rho V R \cos \theta \, \delta\theta$. This mass flow has a vertical velocity increase of $v \cos \theta$, and therefore the rate of change of downward momentum through the element is $- \rho V v R \cos^2 \theta \, \delta\theta$ whence, by integrating round the boundary, the inertial contribution to the lift, l_I, is

$$l_I = + \int_0^{2\pi} \rho V v R \cos^2 \theta \, d\theta$$

$$= \rho V v R \pi \quad . \qquad . \qquad . \qquad . \qquad (10.92)$$

Thus the total lift is:

$$l = 2\rho V v R \pi \quad . \qquad . \qquad . \qquad (10.93)$$

From eqn. (6.33),

$$v = \frac{K}{2\pi R}$$

giving finally, for the lift per unit span, l,

$$l = \rho V K \quad . \qquad . \qquad . \qquad (10.94)$$

This expression can be obtained without consideration of the behaviour of air in a boundary circuit, by integrating pressures on the surface of the aerofoil directly. It can be shown that this lift force is theoretically independent of the shape of the aerofoil section, the main effect of which is to produce a pitching moment.

EXERCISES

1. Define 'vorticity' in a fluid and obtain an expression for vorticity at a point with polar coordinates (r, θ) the motion being assumed two-dimensional.

From the definition of a line vortex as irrotational flow in concentric circles determine the variation of velocity with radius, hence obtain the stream function (ψ), the velocity potential (ϕ), for a line vortex. (U. of L.)

2. A sink of strength 120 ft²/sec is situated 2 ft downstream from a source of equal strength in an irrotational uniform stream of 30 ft/sec. Find the fineness ratio of the oval formed by the streamline $\psi = 0$. (*Ans.* 1·34) (N.C.A.T.)

3. A sink of strength 20 ft²/sec is situated 3 ft upstream of a source of 40 ft²/sec, in a uniform irrotational stream. It is found that at the point 2·5 ft equidistant from both source and sink, the local velocity is normal to the line joining the source and sink.

Find the velocity at this point and the velocity of the undisturbed stream. (*Ans.* 1·02 ft/sec, 2·29 ft/sec) (N.C.A.T.)

4. A line source of strength m and a sink of strength $2m$ are separated a distance c. Show that the field of flow consists in part of closed curves. Locate any stagnation points and sketch the field of flow. (U. of L.)

5. Derive the expression giving the stream function for irrotational flow of an incompressible fluid past a circular cylinder of infinite span. Hence determine the position of generators on the cylinder at which the pressure is equal to that of the undisturbed stream. (*Ans.* ± 30°, ± 150°) (U. of L.)

6. Determine the stream function for a two-dimensional source of strength m.

Sketch the resultant field of flow due to three such sources, each of strength m, located at the vertices of an equilateral triangle. (U. of L.)

7. Derive the irrotational flow formula

$$p - p_0 = \tfrac{1}{2}\rho U_0{}^2(1 - 4 \sin^2 \theta)$$

giving the intensity of normal pressure p on the surface of a long, circular cylinder set at right-angles to a stream of velocity U_0, the undisturbed static pressure in the fluid is p_0 and θ is the angular distance round from the stagnation point.

Describe briefly an experiment to test the accuracy of the above formula and comment on the results obtained. (U. of L.)

8. A long right circular cylinder of diameter a ft is set horizontally in a steady stream of velocity u ft/sec and caused to rotate at ω radians/sec. Obtain an expression in terms of ω and u for the ratio of the pressure difference between the top and the bottom of the cylinder to the dynamic pressure of the stream.

Describe briefly the behaviour of the stagnation lines of such a system as ω is increased from zero, keeping u constant. $\left(Ans. \dfrac{8a\omega}{u}\right)$ (N.C.A.T.)

9. A line source is immersed in a uniform stream. Show that the resultant flow, if irrotational, may represent the flow past a two-dimensional fairing. If the maximum thickness of the fairing is 18 in. and the undisturbed velocity of the stream 60 ft/sec, determine the strength and location of the source. Obtain also an expression for the pressure at any point on the surface of the fairing, taking the pressure at infinity as datum. (*Ans.* 90 ft²/sec, 2·86 in.) (U. of L.)

10. A long right circular cylinder of radius a ft is held with its axis normal to an irrotational inviscid stream of V ft/sec. Obtain an expression for the drag force acting on unit length of the cylinder due to the pressures exerted on the front half only. (*Ans.* $-\frac{1}{3}\rho V^2 a$) (N.C.A.T.)

11. Show that a velocity potential exists in a two-dimensional steady irrotational incompressible fluid motion.

The stream function of a two-dimensional motion of an incompressible fluid is given by

$$\psi = \frac{a}{2}x^2 + bxy - \frac{c}{2}y^2$$

where a, b and c are arbitrary constants. Show that, if the flow is irrotational, the lines of constant pressure never coincide with either the streamlines or the equipotential lines. Is this possible for rotational motion? (U. of L.)

12. State the stream function and velocity potential for each of the motions induced by a source, vortex and doublet in a two-dimensional incompressible fluid.

Show that a doublet may be regarded, either as
 (i) the limiting case of a source and sink, or
 (ii) the limiting case of equal and opposite vortices, indicating clearly the direction of the resultant doublet. (U. of L.)

13. Define (a) the stream function, (b) irrotational flow and (c) the velocity potential for two-dimensional motion of an incompressible fluid, indicating the conditions under which they exist.

Determine the stream function for a point source of strength σ at the origin. Hence, or otherwise, show that for the flow due to any number of sources at points on a circle, the circle is a streamline provided that the algebraic sum of the strengths of the sources is zero. (U. of L.)

14. A line vortex of strength K is mechanically fixed at the point $(l, 0)$ referred to a system of rectangular axes in an inviscid incompressible fluid at rest at infinity bounded by a plane wall coincident with the y-axis. Find the velocity in the fluid at the point $(0, y)$ and determine the force that acts on the wall (per unit depth) if the pressure on the other side of the wall is the same as at infinity.

Bearing in mind that this must be equal and opposite to the force acting on unit length of the vortex show that your result is consistent with the Kutta–Zhukovsky Theorem. (U. of L.)

15. Write down the velocity potential for the two-dimensional flow about a circular cylinder with a circulation K in an otherwise uniform stream of velocity V. Hence show that the lift on unit span of the cylinder is ρVK. Produce a brief but plausible argument that the same result should hold for the lift on a cylinder of arbitrary shape, basing your argument on consideration of the flow at large distances from the cylinder. (U. of L.)

16. Define the terms Velocity Potential, Circulation, and Vorticity as used in two-dimensional fluid mechanics, and show how they are related.

The velocity distribution in the laminar boundary layer of a wide flat plate is given by

$$u = u_0 \left[\frac{3}{2}\frac{y}{\delta} - \frac{1}{2}\left(\frac{y}{\delta}\right)^3 \right]$$

where u_0 is the velocity at the edge of the boundary layer where y equals δ.

Find the vorticity on the surface of the plate. $\left(Ans. \ -\frac{3}{2}\frac{u_0}{\delta} \right)$ (U. of L.)

s

17. A two-dimensional fluid motion is represented by a point vortex of strength K set at unit distance from an infinite straight boundary.

Draw the streamlines and plot the velocity distribution on the boundary when $K = \pi$. (U. of L.)

18. The velocity components of a two-dimensional inviscid incompressible flow are given by

$$u = 2y - \frac{y}{(x^2 + y^2)^{\frac{1}{2}}}, \quad v = -2x - \frac{x}{(x^2 + y^2)^{\frac{1}{2}}}$$

Find the stream function, and the vorticity, and sketch the streamlines.

$\left(Ans. \; \psi = x^2 + y^2 + (x^2 + y^2)^{\frac{1}{2}}, \; \zeta = -\left[4 + \dfrac{1}{(x^2 + y^2)^{\frac{1}{2}}} \right] \right)$ (U. of L.)

CHAPTER 11

THE COMPLEX POTENTIAL FUNCTION AND CONFORMAL TRANSFORMATION

11.1. The complex potential function. The *stream function* gives a mathematical 'picture' of a flow pattern in terms of the streamlines of the flow, and the *velocity potential* can sometimes give an alternative interpretation of the same flow pattern.

Graphically these streamlines and lines of constant potential can be combined to give a complete representation of the pattern, an orthogonal mapping of the stream in which every point can be represented by a Stream Function, value ψ, and a Velocity Potential, value ϕ (Fig. 11.1).

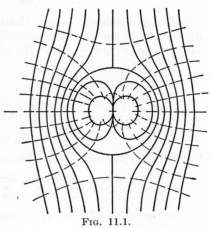

Analytically the velocity potential and the stream function are combined in a new function called the *complex potential function*, by introducing the complex variable $z = x + iy$.

FIG. 11.1.

11.1.1. Complex variables.* Let $z = x + iy$.

Then z indicates a position P (say) in the complex plane xOy (Fig. 11.2).

Let w be some function of z.

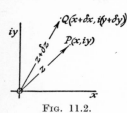

FIG. 11.2.

$$w = f(z)$$

and, since $z = x + iy$,

$$w = f(x + iy)$$

and thus for every point P in the plane a value of w obtains.

Let the value of the complex function $f(x + iy)$ be w at $P(x, iy)$, where point P is given by $z = x + iy$ and let an adjacent point

$$Q[x + \delta x, i(y + \delta y)]$$

provide a value of $w + \delta w$ for the complex function.

Then these adjacent points P and Q given by z and $z + \delta z$ respectively in the complex plane provide values of w and $w + \delta w$.

*See *Advanced Mathematics for Technical Students*, by H. V. Lowry and H. A. Hayden, Part II (Longmans, Green & Co.), for a fuller treatment of the functions of complex variables.

267

Now
$$\delta z = \delta x + i\delta y$$
$$= \delta s \cos \theta + i\delta s \sin \theta$$
$$= \delta s(\cos \theta + i \sin \theta) \qquad . \qquad . \qquad . \qquad (11.1)$$

$$\delta w = \frac{\partial w}{\partial x}\delta x + \frac{\partial w}{\partial y}\delta y$$

$$= \frac{\partial w}{\partial x}\delta s \cos \theta + \frac{\partial w}{\partial y}\delta s \sin \theta$$

$$= \delta s\left(\frac{\partial w}{\partial x}\cos \theta + \frac{\partial w}{\partial y}\sin \theta\right) \qquad . \qquad (11.2)$$

To find a meaning for dw/dz, the differential of the complex function w with respect to the complex variable, it is necessary to investigate the limit of $\delta w/\delta z$ as Q approaches the adjacent point P

i.e.,
$$\frac{dw}{dz} = \operatorname*{Lim}_{Q \to P}\frac{\delta w}{\delta z}$$

$$= \operatorname*{Lim}_{Q \to P}\frac{\left(\dfrac{\partial w}{\partial x}\cos \theta + \dfrac{\partial w}{\partial y}\sin \theta\right)}{\cos \theta + i \sin \theta}$$

which dividing top and bottom by $\cos \theta$ becomes:

$$\frac{dw}{dz} = \operatorname*{Lim}_{Q \to P}\left(\frac{\partial w}{\partial x} + \frac{\partial w}{\partial y}\tan \theta\right)\bigg/ 1 + i \tan \theta \qquad . \qquad (11.3)$$

Now the value of eqn. (11.2) depends upon θ, the angle at which Q approaches P *unless*

$$\frac{\partial w}{\partial x} = \frac{1}{i}\frac{\partial w}{\partial y} \text{ when on substituting } \frac{\partial w}{\partial y} = \frac{i\partial w}{\partial x}$$

eqn. (11.3) becomes:

$$\frac{dw}{dz} = \operatorname*{Lim}_{Q \to P}\frac{\dfrac{\partial w}{\partial x} + i\dfrac{\partial w}{\partial x}\tan \theta}{1 + i \tan \theta}$$

$$= \operatorname*{Lim}_{Q \to P}\frac{\partial w}{\partial x}$$

In general, then, the complex function w can have a unique or single value for its derivative dw/dz at a point only if

$$\frac{\partial w}{\partial x} = \frac{1}{i}\frac{\partial w}{\partial y} \quad \text{or} \quad \frac{\partial w}{\partial y} = i\frac{\partial w}{\partial x}$$

It is then called a monogenic function.

Now in general the complex function w will consist of a real and an imaginary part (w_1 and w_2 respectively)

$$w = f(z) = f(x + iy) = w_1 + iw_2 = f_1(x, y) + i f_2(x, y)$$

and if it is a monogenic function

$$\frac{dw}{dz} = \frac{\partial w}{\partial x} = \frac{\partial w_1}{\partial x} + i\frac{\partial w_2}{\partial x} \qquad . \qquad . \qquad . \qquad (11.4)$$

but

$$\frac{\partial w}{\partial x} = \frac{1}{i}\frac{\partial w}{\partial y} = \frac{1}{i}\left(\frac{\partial w_1}{\partial y} + i\frac{\partial w_2}{\partial y}\right)$$

$$= -i\frac{\partial w_1}{\partial y} + \frac{\partial w_2}{\partial y} \qquad . \qquad . \qquad (11.5)$$

and equating real and imaginary terms in eqns. (11.4) and (11.5)

$$\frac{\partial w_1}{\partial x} = \frac{\partial w_2}{\partial y} \quad \text{and} \quad \frac{\partial w_1}{\partial y} = -\frac{\partial w_2}{\partial x}$$

These are the Cauchy–Riemann *relations.*

11.1.2. The Complex Potential Function.

In eqn. (11.6) above, w_1 and w_2 are functions of the two independent variables x and y, in general, and if $w = w_1 + iw_2$ is a monogenic function, as above, and w_1 and w_2 are real functions of x and y, then w_1 and w_2 are called conjugate functions. Now ϕ and ψ are real functions of x and y and are related similarly to w_1 and w_2 because they satisfy the Cauchy–Riemann relations.

Thus, putting $w_1 = \phi$ and $w_2 = \psi$,

$$\left.\begin{array}{l} \dfrac{\partial \phi}{\partial x} = u = \dfrac{\partial \psi}{\partial y} \\[2mm] \dfrac{\partial \phi}{\partial y} = v = -\dfrac{\partial \psi}{\partial x} \end{array}\right\} \begin{array}{l} \text{The velocity components of} \\ \text{the flow at any point.} \end{array}$$

and

Then

$$w = \phi + i\psi = f(z) = f(x + iy)$$

and this complex function using the velocity potential as real part and stream function as imaginary part is the *Complex Potential Function.*

Substitution for w_1 and w_2 in eqn. (11.4) gives

$$\frac{dw}{dz} = \frac{\partial \phi}{\partial x} + i\frac{\partial \psi}{\partial x}$$

$$= u - iv \qquad . \qquad . \qquad . \qquad (11.6)$$

the real and imaginary parts thus giving values for the local velocity components of the flow.

The modulus of $u - iv$ is

$$|u - iv| = \sqrt{u^2 + v^2} = q$$

the magnitude of the local flow velocity and the argument of $u - iv$ is arc tan $(-v/u)$ and gives the direction of the local velocity relative to the reference axes.

Briefly, then, in *one* complex function w a complete picture of a flow pattern consisting both of streamlines and equipotentials can be portrayed. Moreover the complex function w can be treated as a function of a single variable z.

The flow cases which were dealt with in the previous chapter can now be re-written in their complex form.

11.1.3. Uniform stream flowing in any direction.

$$w = \phi + i\psi = (Ux + Vy) + i(Uy - Vx)$$
$$= U(x + iy) - V(ix - y)$$
$$= U(x + iy) - iV(x + iy)$$
$$w = (U - iV)z \quad \text{where } z = x + iy \qquad . \qquad (11.7)$$

Note that for a horizontal stream from left to right

$$w = Ux + iUy = Uz \qquad . \qquad . \qquad . \qquad (11.7a)$$

for a vertical stream upwards

$$w = Vy - iVx = -iVz \ . \qquad . \qquad . \qquad (11.7b)$$

and by combining these two for any uniform stream having components U and V

$$w = (U - iV)z \qquad . \qquad . \qquad . \qquad (11.7)$$

11.1.4. Source (sink) at the origin.

$$\phi = \frac{m}{2\pi} \log_e \frac{r}{r_0} \; ; \; \psi = \frac{m}{2\pi} \theta$$

$$w = \phi + i\psi = \frac{m}{2\pi}\left(\log_e \frac{r}{r_0} + i\theta \right)$$

$$= \frac{m}{2\pi}\left(\log_e \frac{r}{r_0} + \log_e e^{i\theta} \right) = \frac{m}{2\pi} \log_e \frac{r}{r_0} e^{i\theta}$$

but

$$re^{i\theta} = x + iy = z$$

Therefore

$$w = \frac{m}{2\pi} \log_e \frac{z}{r_0} = \frac{m}{2\pi} \log_e z \quad \text{when } r_0 = 1 \quad . \quad (11.8)$$

11.1.5. A source in a uniform horizontal stream.

By combining (11.8) and (11.7a)

$$w = \frac{m}{2\pi} \log_e \frac{z}{r_0} + Uz \qquad . \qquad . \qquad . \qquad (11.9)$$

11.1.6. Straight line vortex (axis normal to the plane of the flow at the origin).

$$\phi = \frac{K}{2\pi}\theta \; ; \; \psi = -\frac{K}{2\pi} \log_e \frac{r}{r_0}$$

$$w = \phi + i\psi = \frac{K}{2\pi}\left(\theta - i \log_e \frac{r}{r_0} \right)$$

$$= -\frac{iK}{2\pi}\left(-\frac{\theta}{i} + \log_e \frac{r}{r_0} \right) = -\frac{iK}{2\pi}\left(i\theta + \log_e \frac{r}{r_0} \right)$$

$$= -\frac{iK}{2\pi}\left(\log_e \frac{r}{r_0} + \log e^{i\theta} \right) = -\frac{iK}{2\pi}\left(\log_e \frac{r}{r_0} e^{i\theta} \right)$$

$$w = -\frac{iK}{2\pi} \log_e \frac{z}{r_0} = -i\frac{K}{2\pi} \log_e z \quad \text{when } r_0 = 1 \qquad . \qquad (11.10)$$

11.1.7. Doublet at origin with axis along Ox.

$$\phi = -\frac{\mu}{2\pi r} \cos \theta \; ; \; \psi = \frac{\mu}{2\pi r} \sin \theta$$

$$w = \phi + i\psi = -\frac{\mu}{2\pi r}(\cos \theta - i \sin \theta)$$

$$= -\frac{\mu}{2\pi} \frac{e^{-i\theta}}{r} = -\frac{\mu}{2\pi r e^{i\theta}} = -\frac{\mu}{2\pi z} \quad . \quad . \quad (11.11)$$

11.1.8. For a doublet in a uniform horizontal stream (R to L).

Combining eqns. (11.7a) and (11.11)

$$w = -Uz - \frac{\mu}{2\pi z} = -U\left(z + \frac{a^2}{z}\right) \quad . \quad . \quad (11.12)$$

where $a = \sqrt{\dfrac{\mu}{2\pi U}}$

is the radius of the streamline $\psi = 0$.

11.1.9. It is useful here to consider the approach to the reverse problem. This is where the complex potential function is known and the typical flow pattern it represents has to be determined.

Example 11.1. Show that part of the flow given by the complex potential function $w = $ arc cosh z/c can represent irrotational flow in a convergent divergent channel of constant depth.   (U. of L.)

$$w = \cosh^{-1} \frac{z}{c}$$

rearranging, $\dfrac{z}{c} = \cosh w$

and in the usual notation,

$$x + iy = c \cosh (\phi + i\psi)$$

on expanding,

$$x + iy = c[\cosh \phi \cosh i\psi + \sinh \phi \sinh i\psi]$$

when equating real and imaginary parts

$$x = c \cosh \phi \cos \psi \quad . \quad . \quad (11.13)$$

$$y = c \sinh \phi \sin \psi \quad . \quad . \quad (11.14)$$

From (11.13) $\cosh^2 \phi = \left(\dfrac{x}{c \cos \psi}\right)^2$

From (11.14) $\sinh^2 \phi = \left(\dfrac{y}{c \sin \psi}\right)^2$

but $\cosh^2\phi - \sinh^2 \phi = 1$

Therefore $\left(\dfrac{x}{c \cos \psi}\right)^2 - \left(\dfrac{y}{c \sin \psi}\right)^2 = 1 . \quad . \quad . \quad (11.15)$

The streamlines are lines of constant ψ by definition. Thus the equations to the streamlines are:

$$\frac{x^2}{A^2} - \frac{y^2}{B^2} = 1 \qquad . \qquad . \qquad . \qquad . \qquad (11.16)$$

where A and B are constants depending upon the magnitude of ψ.

Eqns. (11.16) are equations of con-focal hyperbolae so that the streamlines are con-focal hyperbolae, any pair of which can be taken to represent a solid boundary, for example the walls of a converging diverging channel (Fig. 11.13). The flow is two-dimensional and confined to the Oxy plane which is very nearly reproduced in a channel of constant depth.

To find the shape of the equipotentials the ψ terms can be eliminated from eqns. (11.13) and (11.14) thus:

From (11.13) $\cos^2 \psi = \left(\dfrac{x}{c \cosh \phi}\right)^2$

From (11.14) $\sin^2 \psi = \left(\dfrac{y}{c \sinh \phi}\right)^2$

but $\cos^2 \psi + \sin^2 \psi_2 = 1$

Therefore $\left(\dfrac{x}{c \cosh \phi}\right)^2 + \left(\dfrac{y}{c \sinh \phi}\right)^2 = 1 \qquad . \qquad . \qquad . \qquad (11.17)$

which for lines of constant ϕ (equipotentials) gives an equation of the form

$$\frac{x^2}{\alpha^2} + \frac{y^2}{\beta^2} = 1 \qquad . \qquad . \qquad . \qquad . \qquad (11.18)$$

where α and β are constants depending upon the magnitude of ϕ.

The eqns. (11.18) represent con-focal ellipses (shown in Fig. 11.3) which meet the hyperbolae (streamlines) everywhere at right angles.

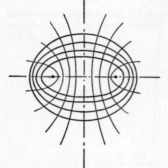

Example 11.2. Show that a faired entry to a long parallel-sided channel can be derived from the complex potential function $z = w + e^w$.

(U. of L.)

$$z = w + e^w \quad \text{but} \quad z = x + iy$$
$$w = \phi + i\psi$$

Therefore

$$x + iy = \phi + i\psi + e^{\phi + i\psi}$$
$$= \phi + i\psi + e^\phi (\cos \psi + i \sin \psi)$$
$$= \phi + e^\phi \cos \psi + i (\psi + e^\phi \sin \psi).$$

FIG. 11.3.—Hyperbolae and ellipses on the same foci obtained from $w = \cosh^{-1} z/c$.

Therefore

$$x = \phi + e^\phi \cos \psi . \qquad . \qquad (11.19)$$

and $y = \psi + e^\phi \sin \psi . \qquad . \qquad . \qquad . \qquad (11.20)$

From (11.19) $x - \phi = e^\phi \cos \psi$

From (11.20) $y - \psi = e^\phi \sin \psi$

Therefore dividing, $\tan \psi = \dfrac{y - \psi}{x - \phi} \quad \text{giving} \quad \phi = x - \dfrac{y - \psi}{\tan \psi}$

substituting for ϕ in (11.20)

$$y = \psi + e^{x - \frac{y + \psi}{\tan \psi}} \sin \psi \qquad . \qquad . \qquad . \qquad (11.21)$$

when ψ is constant, eqn. (11.21) is of the form
$$y = a + be^{x+cy+d}$$
where a, b, c and d are constant, or putting $\psi = C = $ constant
$$y = C + \sin C . e^{x - \frac{y}{\tan C} + \frac{C}{\tan C}} \qquad . \qquad . \qquad . \qquad (11.22)$$
which is the equation of the flow pattern.

Putting $\psi = C = \pm \pi/2$ gives a possible boundary of the flow as $y = \pi/2 + e^x$.

The significant points on this boundary are given by:

(a) putting $x = -\infty$ when $y = \pm \pi/2$

(b) putting $x = 0$, $y = \pi/2 = 1$, etc.

i.e., for $\psi = $ constant less than $\pi/2$ gives streamlines with boundary lines shaped like a faired entry into a long parallel-sided channel (Fig. 11.4).

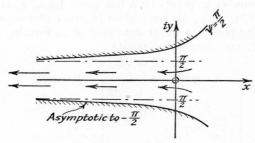

FIG. 11.4 $z = w + e^w$.

Further, eqns. (11.19) and (11.20) show that when
$$\psi = \pi, \quad x = \phi - e^\phi, \quad y = \pi$$
i.e., $\phi = -\infty, \quad x = -\infty$
$$\frac{dx}{d\phi} = 1 - e^\phi = 0 \text{ when } \phi = 0, \quad \text{i.e., when } x = -1$$

This indicates that the limiting streamlines are the branches of $y = \pm \pi$ between $x = -1$ and $x = -\infty$.

The remaining streamlines, two of which have been chosen to illustrate the solution above, emerge from these parallel lines.

11.2. Conformal transformation.

The subject of conformal transformation is the study of methods whereby an orthogonal geometric pattern (plane 1) comprised of certain shaped elements can be transformed into an entirely different pattern (plane 2) whilst the elements retain their distinctive form and proportion (Fig. 11.5).

11.2.1. The basic principles.

As shown in the figure the elements will, in the limit, retain their similar geometric form. For this to be true the angles between intersecting lines in plane 1 must remain the same when the two lines are transformed to plane 2.

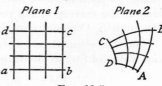

FIG. 11.5.

In plane 1 (Fig.11.6), any point p is located by $z = x + iy$ (with respect

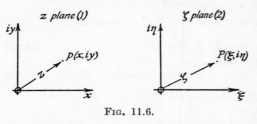

to the origin O and a pair of reference axes Ox and Oy) and in the transformed plane, the corresponding point P is given by $\zeta = \xi + i\eta$ (with respect to the origin O and a pair of reference axes $O\xi$ and $O\eta$), the relation between z and ζ

Fig. 11.6.

being a particular specified function of z. That is $\zeta = f(z)$. This function is known as the *Transformation Function*.

Consider a number of points on a line given by z_1, z_2, etc. in the Oxy plane 1 (Fig. 11.7). p_1, p_2 are very close together and separated by δz. The corresponding points in the transformed plane forming the line P_1P_2 are given by $\zeta_1\zeta_2$, etc. Now for all points

$$\zeta = f(z) \qquad . \qquad . \qquad . \qquad . \qquad (11.23)$$

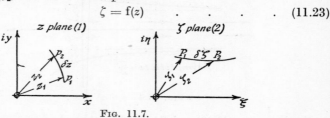

Fig. 11.7.

and differentiating with respect to z

$$d\zeta = f'(z)\, dz \qquad . \qquad . \qquad . \qquad . \qquad (11.24)$$

In the limit as $p_1 \rightarrow p_2$, $\delta z \rightarrow dz$ and $P_1 \rightarrow P_2$, $\delta\zeta \rightarrow d\zeta$. Then from eqn. (11.24) $d\zeta$ becomes 'the vector dz' multiplied by 'the vector $f'(z)$,'

i.e., $d\zeta = (\text{vector } dz) \times (\text{vector } f'(z))$

Now to understand this operation of the multiplication of vectors, consider $f'(z)$ rewritten in its exponential form, i.e.,

$$f'(z) = re^{i\theta} \quad \text{where } r = \text{modulus of } f'(z)$$

Then $$|\, d\zeta \,| = |\, dz \,|\, . r$$

and is in the direction of dz after it has been rotated through θ, the 'angular displacement' of $f(z)$. That is, the transformed element equals the original element rotated through θ and multiplied by r. The location of the element is given by P_1P_2 and not by eqn. (11.24).

Consider two intersecting lines ab and cd, cutting each other at p in the z plane. At p the angle of intersection is β (Fig. 11.8). In the transformed plane 2, the corresponding point is P and the lines AB, CD intersecting with angle β. Consider now the actual elements of intersection.

Since the elements are at the same point p they will be affected by the same value of $f'(z)$ in the transformation

$$\therefore \quad \overrightarrow{P_1P_2} = p_1p_2 . r, \quad \text{and rotated through } \theta$$

$$\overrightarrow{P_3P_4} = p_3p_4 . r, \quad \text{and rotated through } \theta$$

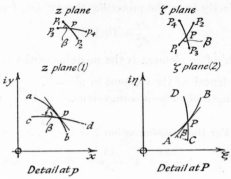

FIG. 11.8.

where $f'(z) = re^{i\theta}$. Since both elements of the intersection are rotated through the *same angle*, the angle of intersection must remain unchanged during the transformation,

i.e., $$\beta = \beta$$

Again this method can be used to show that a small element *abcd* in plane 1 (Fig. 11.9), is transformed to a geometrically similar element *ABCD* in plane 2.

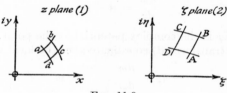

FIG. 11.9.

This type of transformation then, satisfies the condition required for conformal transformation. It is essentially of the vector type

$$\zeta = f(z) \quad \text{where } z = x + iy, \quad \zeta = \xi + i\eta$$

A general form of the equation of transformation is

$$\zeta = A_0 + A_1 z + A_2 z^2 + \ldots A_n z^n + \frac{B_1}{z} + \frac{B_2}{z^2} + \frac{B_3}{z^3} + \ldots \frac{B_n}{z^n}$$

where A_0, A_1, A_2, etc., B_1, B_2, B_3, etc. are constants, vectors or combinations of constants and vectors.*

11.2.2. Length ratios between corresponding elements in transformed planes.

The length ratio of corresponding elements in planes 1

* The account of conformal transformation in this section largely follows that in *Aerodynamic Theory*, Vol. I, Editor-in-Chief W. F. Durand (Julius Springer), to which further reference should be made for a more detailed explanation.

and 2 is given directly from the preceding theory, i.e., from eqn. (11.24)

$$\frac{dz}{d\zeta} = f'(z)$$

The actual 'length' of an element is the modulus of the vector δz.

Thus $$\frac{\text{the length of the element in plane 2}}{\text{the length of corresponding element in 1}} = \left| \frac{d\zeta}{dz} \right| \qquad (11.25)$$

Example 11.3. For the transformation $\zeta = z + \dfrac{b^2}{z}$, b = constant,

$$\frac{d\zeta}{dz} = 1 - \frac{b^2}{z^2} = 1 - \frac{b^2}{r^2}e^{2i\theta} \quad \text{since } z = re^{i\theta}$$

$$= 1 - \frac{b^2}{r^2}(\cos 2\theta - i \sin 2\theta)$$

$$\therefore \left| \frac{d\zeta}{dz} \right| = \left\{ \left(1 - \frac{b^2}{r^2} \cos 2\theta \right)^2 + \left(\frac{b^2}{r^2} \sin 2\theta \right)^2 \right\}^{\frac{1}{2}}$$

$$= \left\{ 1 - \frac{2b^2}{r^2} \cos 2\theta + \frac{b^4}{r^4} \right\}^{\frac{1}{2}} . \qquad . \qquad . \qquad . \qquad (11.26)$$

Velocity ratios between corresponding points in transformed planes. The velocity q_z at any point p in plane 1 is given by

$$\frac{dw}{dz} = u - iv$$

where $w = \phi + i\psi$ is the complex potential at the point. But with reference to the new (transformed) coordinate axes the local velocity at P

$$= q_\zeta = \frac{dw}{d\zeta} = \bar{u} - i\bar{v}$$

Thus for corresponding points, considering magnitudes only,

$$\frac{\text{the velocity in transformed plane 2}}{\text{the velocity in original plane 1}} = \left| \frac{dw}{d\zeta} \right| \bigg/ \left| \frac{dw}{dz} \right| = \left| \frac{dz}{d\zeta} \right| . \qquad (11.27)$$

or, the velocity ratio between corresponding points is the inverse of the length ratios.

Example 11.4. For the transformation $\zeta = z + \dfrac{b^2}{z}$, b = constant, it was shown that

$$\left| \frac{d\zeta}{dz} \right| = \left\{ 1 - \frac{2b^2}{r^2} \cos 2\theta + \frac{b^4}{r^4} \right\}^{\frac{1}{2}}$$

From eqn. (11.26),

Therefore $$\left| \frac{dz}{d\zeta} \right| = \left\{ 1 - \frac{2b^2}{r^2} \cos 2\theta + \frac{b^4}{r^4} \right\}^{-\frac{1}{2}}$$

or $$|q_\zeta| = \frac{|q_z|}{\left\{ 1 - \dfrac{2b^2}{r^2} \cos 2\theta + \dfrac{b^4}{r^4} \right\}^{\frac{1}{2}}} . \qquad . \qquad . \qquad (11.28)$$

Alternatively if when transforming an element of line from one plane to another it has its length *increased* by $\left|\dfrac{d\zeta}{dz}\right|$ the local velocity of flow at the element must by continuity of flow be *decreased* by $\dfrac{1}{\left|\dfrac{d\zeta}{dz}\right|} = \left|\dfrac{dz}{d\zeta}\right|$

Singularities. The relationship between corresponding elements is adequately defined by eqn. (11.24).

Thus $d\zeta = f'(z)\, dz$, and in most situations the correspondence between elements is the modulus and argument of the vector $f'(z) = d\zeta/dz$, as outlined in the previous sections.

This arrangement clearly breaks down where $f'(z) = d\zeta/dz$ is zero or infinite.

In both cases the *conformality* of the transformation is lost. The points at which $d\zeta/dz = 0$ or ∞ in any transformation are known as singular points commonly abbreviated to singularities.

Nearly all transformation functions contain singularities but the points at which they occur may be of no importance in the problems considered. In § 11.2.3 the transformation $\zeta = 1/z$ is considered. This gives $d\zeta/dz = -1/z^2$ which is infinite at $z = 0$. Equally $d\zeta/dz = -1/z^2 = 0$ at $z = \infty$. Now z at ∞ transforms to $\zeta = 0$, i.e., to the origin in the ζ-plane. From Fig. 11.10, all the streamlines concentrate on this singular point.

In § 11.3 $\zeta = z + b^2/z$ is considered and from above $d\zeta/dz = 1 - b^2/z^2$ which is clearly zero when $z = \pm b$. This gives two singular points where $f'(z)$ equals zero, and where the elements dz in the z-plane transform to points in the ζ-plane, and where the rotation of dz to form $d\zeta$ ceases to have any meaning. The point in the ζ-plane corresponding to $z = -b$ has particular significance in § 11.3 and illustrates the generality that a smooth curve through such a singular point in the z plane transforms to a curve with a sharp corner at the corresponding point in the ζ-plane.

11.2.3. Transformation of a flow pattern.

Any flow pattern can be conveniently considered to consist of a pattern of lines (streamlines and/or equipotentials). Thus the transformation of a flow pattern becomes the transformation of a series of lines, whilst the transformation of individual lines implies the transformation of a number of points, e.g., a point p in plane (1) given by $z = x + iy$ is transformed to P in plane (2) given by $\zeta = \xi + i\eta$ using the transformation formula $\zeta = f(z)$.

Methods of performing a transformation. Expand $\zeta = f(z) = \xi + i\eta$ and by equating real and imaginary parts, find functions of ξ and η in terms of x and y.

That is $\xi = f_1(x, y)$ and $\eta = f_2(x, y)$. Thus any point $p(x, iy)$ gives point $P(\xi, i\eta)$.

Example 11.5. Using the transformation $\zeta = 1/z$

$$\zeta = \frac{1}{z} = \frac{1}{x+iy} = \frac{x-iy}{x^2+y^2} = \frac{x}{x^2+y^2} - \frac{iy}{x^2+y^2}$$
$$= \xi + i\eta$$

Therefore
$$\left.\begin{array}{c} \xi = \dfrac{x}{x^2+y^2} \\[2mm] \eta = \dfrac{-y}{x^2+y^2} \end{array}\right\} \qquad . \qquad . \qquad . \qquad . \quad (11.29)$$

Then from any point in any desired flow pattern in plane (1) values of x, y can be substituted in the eqns. (11.29) to give the corresponding point ξ, η in plane (2).

By analytical means. From the flow pattern in plane (1) the lines in the pattern give individual equations.

For example $f(x, y) = \psi = $ constant, and again expanding $\zeta = f(z)$ three equations are obtained,

$$\left.\begin{array}{c} \psi = \text{constant} = f(x, y) \\[2mm] \xi = f_1(x, y) \quad \text{and} \quad \eta = f_2(x, y) \end{array}\right\} \qquad . \qquad . \quad (11.30)$$

From these equations, ξ and η can be isolated to give an equation for the transformed line by eliminating x, y.

Example 11.6. Using the transformation $\zeta = 1/z$ as before

$$\zeta = f(z) = \frac{x}{x^2+y^2} - \frac{iy}{x^2+y^2}$$
$$\xi = \frac{x}{x^2+y^2} \qquad \eta = \frac{-y}{x^2+y^2}$$

Taking the flow pattern of plane (1) to be that due to uniform flow parallel to the Ox axis say:

$$Uy = \psi = \text{constant} \quad \text{or} \quad y = \frac{\psi}{U} = k$$

$$y = k \text{ (i)} \quad \xi = \frac{x}{x^2+y^2} \text{ (ii)} \quad \eta = \frac{-y}{x^2+y^2} \text{ (iii)}$$

From (iii)
$$x = \sqrt{\frac{-y}{\eta} - y^2}$$

subs. in (ii)
$$\xi = \frac{\sqrt{\dfrac{-y}{\eta} - y^2}}{\dfrac{-y}{\eta}}$$

then putting $y = k$
$$\xi^2 = \frac{\dfrac{-k}{\eta} - k^2}{\dfrac{k^2}{\eta^2}}$$

or rearranging
$$\xi^2 + \eta^2 + \eta/k = 0 \qquad . \qquad . \qquad . \qquad . \quad (11.31)$$

which is the equation to a circle of radius $1/2k$ and centre at $(0, -1/2k)$.

Thus the horizontal streamline in (1) transforms using ($\zeta = 1/z$) to circles of radius $1/2k$ and centre at $(0, -1/2k)$ (Fig. 11.10).

This particular case shows streamlines of a uniform stream transformed to the streamlines of a simple doublet with its axis parallel to Ox at the origin.

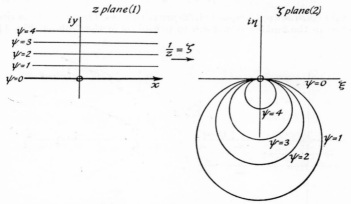

FIG. 11.10.—The conformal transformation of uniform streamlines parallel to x axis in z plane to circular streamlines in ζ plane (doublet flow).

By graphical means: Briefly, a point p is given by z and from it $\zeta = f(z)$ is constructed to locate the transformed point (see § 11.6).

11.2.4. Examples of simple transformations.

The main use of conformal transformation in aerodynamics is to reduce a complicated flow arrangement to a simpler one or one more amenable to simpler mathematical treatment. The problem in the original case is always to find the best transformation formula to do the operation required. This is beyond the scope of this book and one of the most established transformations of accepted use in aerodynamics will be considered as the main subject of the chapter.

This is the Kutta–Zhukovsky transformation which produces a family of aerofoil shaped curves, with their associated flow patterns, by applying a certain transformation to the flow about a circular cylinder (see § 11.3).

Before attempting this transformation it will be as well to consider a simpler conformal transformation to consolidate the theory given in the previous pages.

Example 11.7. Apply the transformation formula $\zeta = z^2$ to a uniform flow parallel to Ox.

$$\zeta = z^2 = (x + iy)^2 = x^2 - y^2 + 2ixy = \xi + i\eta$$
$$\therefore \ \xi = x^2 - y^2$$
$$\eta = 2xy$$

The stream function for uniform flow parallel to Ox is given by $\psi = Uy$ giving the third equation

$$\frac{\psi}{U} = k = y \quad \text{and} \quad x = \frac{\eta}{2y}$$

which on substitution gives

$$\xi = \frac{\eta^2}{4y^2} - y^2 = \frac{\eta^2}{4k^2} - k^2$$

$$\therefore \ \eta = 2k\sqrt{\xi + k^2} \ . \quad . \quad . \quad . \quad . \quad (11.32)$$

Then for constant ψ/U, eqns. (11.32) are parabolas. Therefore the horizontal streamlines in the z-plane transform to parabolas in the ζ-plane (Fig. 11.11).

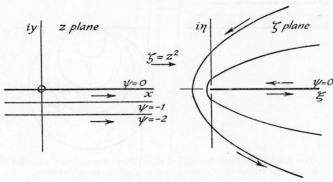

FIG. 11.11.

It should be noted that the halves of the z-plane above or below the Ox axis each transform to occupy the whole of the ζ-plane and must be treated separately.

In this case the lower z-plane (i.e., y negative) will be taken. With the flow streaming from left to right the streamlines are given by $\psi = Uy$ where y is always negative. Thus the stream function is negative here.

Example 11.8. Apply the transformation formula $\zeta = z^2$ to downward uniform flow parallel to Oy axis.

The stream function for uniform flow parallel Oy downwards is:

$$\psi = Vx$$
$$\xi = x^2 - y^2$$
$$\eta = 2xy$$
$$\frac{\psi}{V} = k = x$$

Then $y = \eta/2x$ and substituting for x in $\xi = x^2 - \eta^2/4x^2$, $x = k$.

$$\eta = 2k\sqrt{k^2 - \xi} \ . \quad . \quad . \quad . \quad (11.33)$$

Thus again the streamlines become parabolas but reversed to the previous case (Fig. 11.12).

Here the two halves of the z-plane on either side of the Oy axis now *each* transform to occupy the *whole* of the ζ-plane so that once again only one side can be considered. With the flow streaming upwards with velocity V, the streamlines are $\psi = $ constant $= -Vx$ and here x and y are positive.

The General Case of transformation of uniform flow in any direction (α say) to the Ox axis, using $\zeta = z^2$, lies between the two previous Examples.

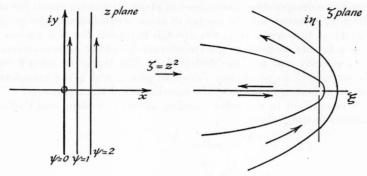

FIG. 11.12.

The flow transforms to parabolas with a common axis which makes an angle 2α to the Ox axis (Fig. 11.13).

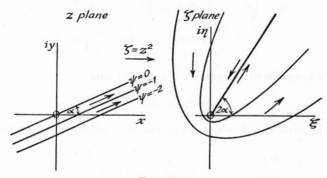

FIG. 11.13.

11.3. The Kutta–Zhukovsky transformation.

The Kutta–Zhukovsky transformation is the simplest of all the transformations producing aerofoil shaped contours. These derived sections suffer severe disadvantages as practical aerofoils and many other sections of more direct use have been obtained. All, however, require more complicated transformations to control the added parameters.

Kutta used this transformation to study circular arc wing sections while Zhukovsky showed how it could be extended to produce sections with thickness as well as camber. Here the transformation will be applied in 'easy stages' before obtaining the end product—the wing section.

Another simplification made is to confine the study to the actual contour of the circle and show how its shape changes on transformation. It should be remembered that the circle is only one streamline of the flow in the original plane (1), although a very important one, and the corresponding shape in the transformed plane (2) is the corresponding streamline. Further, the transformation can be applied to all the other streamlines to

T

produce the corresponding streamlines in plane (2) flowing round the aerofoil. Rarely, however, are the shapes of these streamlines or the pressure or velocity of flow away from the aerofoil required. For this reason this analysis is largely confined to the transformation of the *contour* streamline with its velocity and pressure distribution. The transformation formula can be expanded as previously shown to give ξ and η the transformed ζ-plane coordinates, in terms of the coordinates of the z-plane.

It is convenient to use polar coordinates in the z-plane and Cartesian coordinates in the ζ-plane.

$$\zeta = z + \frac{b^2}{z} = re^{i\theta} + \frac{b^2}{re^{i\theta}}$$

$$= re^{i\theta} + \frac{b^2}{r}e^{-i\theta}$$

$$= r(\cos\theta + i\sin\theta) + \frac{b^2}{r}(\cos\theta - i\sin\theta)$$

$$\xi + i\eta = \left(r + \frac{b^2}{r}\right)\cos\theta + i\left(r - \frac{b^2}{r}\right)\sin\theta$$

giving
$$\xi = \left(r + \frac{b^2}{r}\right)\cos\theta, \quad \eta = \left(r - \frac{b^2}{r}\right)\sin\theta \qquad . \quad (11.34)$$

11.3.1. To transform a circle to a straight line

$$\left(\text{using } \zeta = z + \frac{b^2}{z}\right)$$

Now for the circle of radius a to transform to a straight line a must equal b.

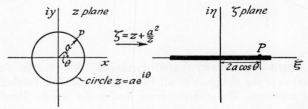

FIG. 11.14.

Further, the centre of the circle must be at the origin (Fig. 11.14). Therefore substituting $r = a = b$ in eqn. (11.34),

$$\xi = 2a\cos\theta, \quad \eta = 0$$

The transformed line in the ζ-plane is thus confined to the $O\xi$ axis, and as θ varies from 0 to $\pi/2$ to π, P moves from $+2a$ to 0 to $-2a$.

The 'chord' of the locus of P is thus $4a$.

11.3.2. To transform a circle to an ellipse

$$\left(\text{using } \zeta = z + \frac{b^2}{z}\right)$$

Here the circle must still have its centre at the origin of the z-plane and $a > b$. Eqns. (11.34) become, on substituting a for r

$$\xi = \left(a + \frac{b^2}{a}\right)\cos\theta, \quad \eta = \left(a - \frac{b^2}{a}\right)\sin\theta \qquad (11.35)$$

θ can be easily eliminated

$$\cos^2\theta = \left(\frac{\xi}{a + \frac{b^2}{a}}\right)^2$$

$$\sin^2\theta = \left(\frac{\eta}{a - \frac{b^2}{a}}\right)^2$$

and adding $\qquad \sin^2\theta + \cos^2\theta = 1$

Therefore $\qquad \left(\dfrac{\xi}{a + \dfrac{b^2}{a}}\right)^2 + \left(\dfrac{\eta}{a - \dfrac{b^2}{a}}\right)^2 = 1 \qquad . \qquad . \quad (11.36)$

and this is the equation to an ellipse whose major and minor axes lie along the ξ and η axes respectively (Fig. 11.15).

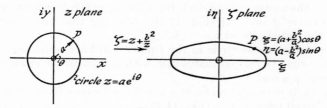

FIG. 11.15.

The magnitudes of the major and minor axes are given by eqn. (11.36) as:

$$\text{the chord of ellipse (major axis)} = 2\left(a + \frac{b^2}{a}\right)$$

$$\text{maximum thickness of ellipse (minor axis)} = 2\left(a - \frac{b^2}{a}\right)$$

$$\text{fineness ratio} = \frac{\text{chord}}{\text{maximum thickness}} = \frac{a + \dfrac{b^2}{a}}{a - \dfrac{b^2}{a}}$$

$$= \frac{a^2 + b^2}{a^2 - b^2} = \frac{\left(\dfrac{a}{b} + \dfrac{b}{a}\right)}{\left(\dfrac{a}{b} - \dfrac{b}{a}\right)}$$

Clearly any ellipse may be obtained by varying the ratio a/b.

11.3.3. The transformation of a circle (of radius a) into a symmetrical aerofoil profile.
Here the centre of the circle is no longer located at the origin of the z-plane but is shifted a very small distance along the Ox axis.

The 'fractional shift' of the origin of the circle to be transformed is of great importance in the following transformations as it is the quantity responsible for the 'asymmetry' of the various profiles derived.

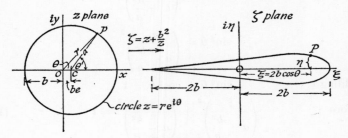

Fig. 11.16.

Let the horizontal 'fractional shift' or 'eccentricity' be e. The actual distance of the centre c of the circle from the origin O is be, whilst the radius a of the circle is $(b + be)$ (Fig. 11.16), ensuring that the circle passes through the singularity at $z = -b$.

Any point p on the circle in the z-plane will have ordinates r, θ with respect to origin O, *and* ordinates a, θ' with respect to the circle centre c. Therefore $r \neq a$ and $\theta \neq \theta'$.

If the angle between r and a at p is γ it can be seen from the geometry of the enlarged triangle Ocp (Fig. 11.17) that $r = be \cos\theta + a \cos\gamma$.

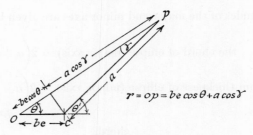

Fig. 11.17.

Now since e is very small γ is small so that $\cos\gamma \doteqdot 1$,

whence $\qquad\qquad\qquad r = be \cos\theta + a$

and on substituting $\qquad\quad a = b + be$

$$\frac{r}{b} = 1 + e + e \cos\theta$$

Also, since e is small, e^2 and higher powers may be neglected as an approximation, so that to the first order

$$\frac{b}{r} = [1 + e(1 + \cos\theta)]^{-1} = \left[1 - e(1 + \cos\theta) + \frac{e^2}{2!}(1 + \cos\theta)^2 \cdots\right]$$

$$= [1 - e - e\cos\theta]$$

Thus r and b can be expressed in terms of the horizontal shift of the centre of the circle of transformation

$$\frac{r}{b} = 1 + e + e\cos\theta, \quad \frac{b}{r} = 1 - e - e\cos\theta \qquad . \quad (11.37)$$

Now expanding the Zhukovsky transformation $\zeta = z + b^2/z$ as before:

$$\zeta = z + \frac{b^2}{z} = re^{i\theta} + \frac{b^2}{r}e^{-i\theta}$$

$$\zeta = r(\cos\theta + i\sin\theta) + \frac{b^2}{r}(\cos\theta + i\sin\theta)$$

$$\zeta = \left(r + \frac{b^2}{r}\right)\cos\theta + i\left(r - \frac{b^2}{r}\right)\sin\theta$$

$$\zeta = b\left(\frac{r}{b} + \frac{b}{r}\right)\cos\theta + ib\left(\frac{r}{b} - \frac{b}{r}\right)\sin\theta$$

and on substituting for r/b and b/r from eqn. (11.37)

$$\zeta = 2b\cos\theta + i2be(1 + \cos\theta)\sin\theta$$
$$= \xi + i\eta$$

thus giving the ordinates of points in the transformed plane as:

$$\xi = 2b\cos\theta$$
$$\eta = 2be(1 + \cos\theta)\sin\theta \qquad . \qquad . \qquad . \qquad . \quad (11.38)$$

Plotting values of ξ and η as θ varies from $0 \longrightarrow \pi \longrightarrow 2\pi$ gives a symmetrical profile as shown in Fig. 11.16. This symmetrical form has a chord of length $4b$ (by putting $\theta = 0$ and π in $\xi = 2b\cos\theta$) and has a maximum thickness at the quarter chord point.

The thickness chord ratio. The maximum thickness occurs where $d\eta/d\theta = 0$.

From eqn. (11.38)

$$\eta = 2be(1 + \cos\theta)\sin\theta$$

$$\therefore \frac{d\eta}{d\theta} = 2be\{(1 + \cos\theta)\cos\theta - \sin\theta\sin\theta\} = 0$$

or
$$\cos^2\theta - \sin^2\theta + \cos\theta = 0$$

simplifying to
$$2\cos^2\theta + \cos\theta - 1 = 0$$

or
$$(2\cos\theta - 1)(\cos\theta + 1) = 0$$

giving two solutions:

(a) $\qquad \cos \theta = \frac{1}{2} \quad \therefore \ \theta = \dfrac{\pi}{3} = 60°$ gives a maximum

(b) $\qquad \cos \theta = -1 \quad \theta = \pi$ gives a minimum.

Then on substituting $\theta = \pi/3$ for the position of the maximum thickness in eqn. (11.38)

$$\xi = 2b \cos \frac{\pi}{3} = b \qquad . \qquad . \qquad . \qquad (11.39)$$

that is, maximum thickness is at the quarter chord point. Maximum thickness t, equals $2\eta_{\max}$

$$= 2 \times 2be\left(1 + \cos \frac{\pi}{3}\right) \sin \frac{\pi}{3}$$

$$= 4be \frac{3}{2} \frac{\sqrt{3}}{2} = 3\sqrt{3}be$$

Giving the thickness/chord ratio of the profile as

$$\frac{3\sqrt{3}be}{4b} = 1{\cdot}299e \doteqdot 1{\cdot}3e \qquad . \qquad . \qquad (11.40)$$

From eqn. (11.39) it can be seen that the position of the maximum thickness is independent of the magnitude of the 'fractional shift' e. This value serves only to fix the fineness ratio of the profile.

For example, a 20% thick section would require

$$e = \frac{0{\cdot}2}{1{\cdot}3} = 0{\cdot}154$$

11.3.4. The transformation of a circle into a cambered aerofoil profile.
In this case the circle is displaced vertically as well as horizontally from the origin of the Oxy plane (Fig. 11.18).

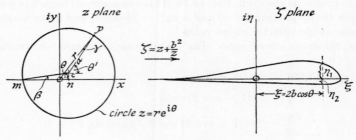

Fig. 11.18.

Let the horizontal shift $On = be$, as before, whilst the vertical shift $cn = h$. As h is small, angle β defined as $\angle cmn$ is small so that $\cos \beta \doteqdot 1$. Also $\cos \gamma \doteqdot 1$. $\therefore$ vertical shift $h = a \sin \beta = b(1 + e)\beta \doteqdot b\beta$ to the first order of small quantities.

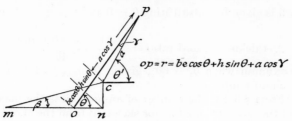

$$op = r = be\cos\theta + h\sin\theta + a\cos\gamma$$

FIG. 11.19.

By dropping perpendiculars on to Op from n and c it can readily be seen (Fig. 11.19) that

$$OP = r = a\cos\gamma + h\sin\theta + be\cos\theta$$

when on substituting for $a = b + be$ and $h = b\beta$

$$r = b + be + be\cos\theta + b\beta\sin\theta$$

when

$$\left.\frac{r}{b} = 1 + e + e\cos\theta + \beta\sin\theta\right\}$$

and

$$\left.\frac{b}{r} = 1 - e - e\cos\theta - \beta\sin\theta\right\} \qquad . \qquad . \quad (11.41)$$

(since e^2 and β^2 and higher powers are assumed to be negligible).

Again expanding the Zhukovsky transformation as before

$$\zeta = z + \frac{b^2}{z} = b\left(\frac{r}{b} + \frac{b}{r}\right)\cos\theta + ib\left(\frac{r}{b} - \frac{b}{r}\right)\sin\theta$$

and on substituting for r/b and b/r from (11.41)

$$\zeta = 2b\cos\theta + i2b(e + e\cos\theta + \beta\sin\theta)\sin\theta$$
$$= \xi + i\eta$$

The circle of centre c thus transforms into a cambered aerofoil section given in the ζ-plane by

$$\left.\begin{array}{l} \xi = 2b\cos\theta \\ \eta = 2be(1 + \cos\theta)\sin\theta + 2b\beta\sin^2\theta \end{array}\right\} \qquad . \qquad . \quad (11.42)$$

When β is zero, i.e., when no vertical shift is made, the previous symmetrical case occurs. The additional term in the η equation alters the shape of the section since it is always a positive addition to the η ordinate. The trailing edge is still sharp and the maximum thickness is at the quarter chord point.

The thickness chord ratio. The thickness (t) at any section is given by $\eta = \eta_1 - \eta_2$ where η_1 and η_2 are the vertical ordinates of the upper and lower surfaces respectively (Fig. 11.19).

$$\eta_1 = 2be(1 + \cos\theta_1)\sin\theta_1 + 2b\beta\sin^2\theta_1$$
$$\eta_2 = 2be(1 + \cos\theta_2)\sin\theta_2 + 2b\beta\sin^2\theta_2$$

but since η_1 and η_2 are at the same ξ ordinate $\theta_2 = -\theta_1$,

$$\therefore \ \eta_1 - \eta_2 = 4be(1 + \cos\theta_1)\sin\theta_1 = t$$

The chord is given by substituting $\theta = 0$ and π in $\xi = 2be \cos \theta$, when chord $= 4b$.

$$\therefore \text{ thickness/chord ratio} = \frac{4be(1 + \cos \theta_1) \sin \theta_1}{4b}$$

This is a maximum when $\theta_1 = 60°$, giving $(t/c)_{max} \fallingdotseq 1\cdot3e$ as before, at the quarter chord point.

Camber. From § 5.2.1, the camber of an aerofoil is the maximum displacement of the *mean camber line* (or skeleton) from the chord. The *mean camber line* is the locus of mid-points of lines drawn perpendicular to the chord.

Here, this is given by $\frac{1}{2}(\eta_1 + \eta_2)_{max}$. Making this non-dimensional by dividing by the chord, the camber is quoted as a fraction of the chord.

$$\text{Percentage Camber} = \frac{(\eta_1 + \eta_2)_{max}}{2 \times \text{chord}} \cdot 100\%$$

From above $\qquad (\eta_1 + \eta_2) = \frac{(4b\beta \sin^2 \theta)_{max}}{2 \times 4b} = \frac{\beta}{2}(\sin^2 \theta)_{max}$

$\sin^2 \theta$ is a maximum when $\theta = \pi/2$, i.e., at mid-chord,

$$\therefore \text{ Percentage Camber} = \frac{\beta}{2} \cdot 100\% \qquad . \qquad . \quad (11.43)$$

i.e., the vertical shift above is responsible for the camber of the aerofoil, the horizontal shift determining the thickness chord ratio.

11.3.5. The transformation of a circle into a circular arc boundary.

For completeness, consider the effect of raising the centre of the circle of radius a a vertical distance h along the Oy axis from the origin (Fig. 11.20).

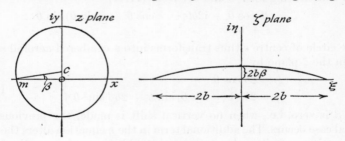

Fig. 11.20.

On transformation using Zhukovsky's transformation $\zeta = z + b^2/z$, a circular arc results of camber/chord ratio $\frac{1}{2} \tan \beta$, or since β is small, of percentage camber $\beta/2 . 100\%$. This is the extreme case of a thin Zhukovsky profile and is treated in more detail in § 12.3.2.

Summary. For convenience the various Zhukovsky transformations are shown together in Fig. 11.21.

11.4. The lift of the Zhukovsky aerofoil section.

The Zhukovsky hypothesis relates directly the lift generated by the two-dimensional aero-

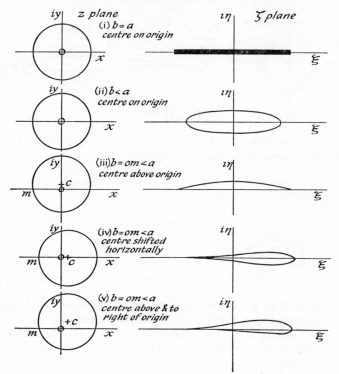

Fig. 11.21.—Zhukovsky's transformation $\zeta = z + \dfrac{b^2}{z}$ applied to a circle of radius a.

foil to its incidence, as well as indicating the significance of the thickness chord ratio and camber.

The lift arises as a consequence of the circulation in the system, and providing the conditions at infinity in the original plane and its corresponding transformed plane are the same, the lift force (circulation impressed on uniform stream) arising in one remains in the other. Equally, if no circulation exists in the first plane there will be none in the second. This makes it easy to consider the relationship between the strength of circulation $(l = \rho U K)$ and the incidence, by referring to the transformed planes.

It has been shown that, applying the transformation $\zeta = z + b^2/z$ to an offset circle, a rudimentary aerofoil shape is obtained. If the remaining streamlines of the flow are also transformed they will be distorted in the transformed plane to the shape of the streamlines round the aerofoil and Fig. 11.22 shows this on a symmetrical section.

Now tilt the stream so that it approaches the circle at some incidence α but continues to transform about the original axes. The circle goes into the aerofoil shape but the streamlines now are inclined to the aerofoil (Fig. 11.23) and the stagnation points move on the aerofoil to the lower and

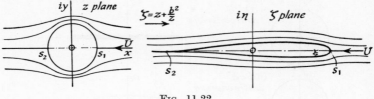

Fɪɢ. 11.22.

Fɪɢ. 11.22.

upper surfaces near the front and trailing edges respectively. Fig. 11.23 shows this for a general section with camber.

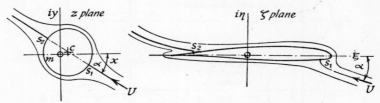

Fɪɢ. 11.23.—Transformation of streamlines *without* circulation.

As mentioned in § 6.8.5 this regime is not sustained, although it is initiated every time an aerofoil starts from rest. In practice the generation of the starting vortex brings the rear stagnation point to the trailing edge. As the process develops (this takes place very quickly) the circulation about the section is generated and the aerofoil lifts. The 'amount' of circulation generated is sufficient only to persuade the rear stagnation point down to the trailing edge. Now in the z plane the rear stagnation point on the cylinder must have now been depressed to the corresponding point to the trailing edge M, which on the circle is m (Fig. 11.24), and this permits the evaluation of the magnitude of the circulation.

At the same time the front stagnation point on the circle with circulation has been depressed a corresponding amount to n, the angular displacement being $\alpha + \beta$ since (by simple geometry)

$$\angle s_2 cm = (\alpha + \beta) = \angle s_1 cn.$$

The velocity at any point p on the cylinder, with θ_c measured from the diameter $s_2 c s_1$ is

$$q_c = 2U \sin \theta_c + \frac{K}{2\pi a} \qquad . \qquad . \qquad . \quad (11.44)$$

a being the radius of the circle.

Note: θ_c is *not* the angle of transformation.

Now at n the velocity is zero, and $\theta_c = -(\alpha + \beta)$.

Therefore at n, $\quad q_c = 0 = 2U \sin \{-(\alpha + \beta)\} + \dfrac{K}{2\pi a}$

giving $\qquad K = 4\pi U a \sin (\alpha + \beta) \qquad . \qquad . \qquad . \qquad . \quad (11.45)$

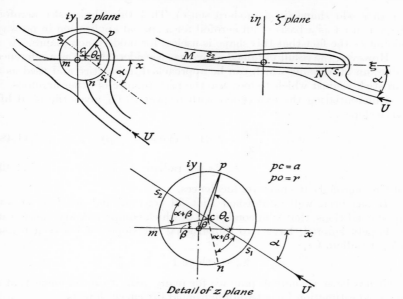

FIG. 11.24.—Transformation of streamlines with circulation sufficient to bring the rear stagnation point to trailing edge of aerofoil.

and substituting back in the expression for q_c

$$q_c = 2U\{\sin\theta_c + \sin(\alpha + \beta)\} \qquad . \qquad . \qquad (11.46)$$

The lift per unit span
$$l = \rho U K$$
$$= \rho U . 4\pi U a \sin(\alpha + \beta)$$
$$= 4\pi\rho U^2 a \sin(\alpha + \beta)$$

But another expression is $l = C_L \frac{1}{2}\rho U^2 c$

Equating and putting chord $c = 4b$

$$C_L = 2\pi\frac{a}{b}\sin(\alpha + \beta) \quad \text{but} \quad \frac{a}{b} = (1 + e)$$

$$\therefore C_L = 2\pi(1 + e)\sin(\alpha + \beta) \qquad . \qquad . \qquad . \qquad (11.47)$$

At first sight eqn. (11.47) gives an expression for the lift coefficient of a two-dimensional aerofoil in terms of the thickness chord ratio ($t/c = 1.299e$) and the percentage camber ($100.\beta/2$), but it is essential to remember the restrictions imposed on the formula, as an expression for general use, by the limitations of the theory.

To begin with, it has been assumed throughout that the fluid was ideal, significantly simplifying the mathematics. This means that the effects of viscosity have been ignored, although in the real process of creating circulation and hence lift on an aerofoil, it is important.

Secondly, one of the simplest transformation functions has been used so that the results really only apply to a particular family of aerofoils of a rather odd shape (in a modern sense). That this Zhukovsky aerofoil shape is used as a basis of an aerofoil for a special application in no way minimizes the fact that this shape is useless for modern aeroplanes.

However, the result obtained above has considerable use as a reference value; an ideal value which can be approached in practice and used as a yardstick against which to measure the performance of other aerofoils.

Differentiating the expression with respect to C_L gives the ideal lift curve slope $a_{\infty I}$

$$a_{\infty I} = \frac{\partial C_L}{\partial \alpha} = 2\pi(1 + e) \cos(\alpha + \beta) \quad . \quad . \quad (11.48)$$

$$\fallingdotseq 2\pi \text{ per radian} \quad . \quad . \quad . \quad (11.49)$$

for thin aerofoils at moderate incidences.

It has been well established that all conventional aerofoils in low speed conditions, that is in conditions in which compressibility effects can be largely ignored, have two dimensional lift slopes of between 6 and 5·5 per radian. Or,

$$a_{\infty} = k2\pi \quad \text{where } 1 > k > \tfrac{7}{8}$$

It has been a common practice for many years to recommend that a practical estimation for a two-dimensional lift curve slope is

$$a_{\infty} = 5·73 \text{ per radian} \quad . \quad . \quad . \quad (11.50)$$

the sole advantage being that a_{∞} then becomes $a_{\infty} = 0·1$ per degree of incidence, which is easy to remember and think of when estimating in performance problems, etc.

11.4.1. The velocity and pressure distribution on the Zhukovsky aerofoils.
The velocity anywhere on the 'circle with circulation' in the z-plane corresponding to the lifting cambered section in the ζ-plane of the previous transformation was given in eqn. (11.46) as

$$q_c = 2U\{\sin \theta_c + \sin(\alpha + \beta)\}$$

The velocity at the corresponding point on the aerofoil q_a is obtained directly by applying the velocity ratio between transformed planes from eqn. (11.28).

$$q_a = \frac{q_c}{\left\{1 - \dfrac{2b^2}{r^2}\cos 2\theta + \left(\dfrac{b}{r}\right)^4\right\}^{\frac{1}{2}}}$$

or

$$q_a = 2U \cdot \frac{\sin \theta_c + \sin(\alpha + \beta)}{\left\{1 - \dfrac{2b^2}{r^2}\cos 2\theta + \left(\dfrac{b}{r}\right)^4\right\}^{\frac{1}{2}}} \quad . \quad . \quad (11.51)$$

As previously emphasized θ_c does *not* equal θ the transformation variable.

From Fig. 11.24,

$$\theta_c = \alpha + \arcsin\left[\frac{r}{a}\sin\theta\right]$$

and

$$\frac{r}{a} = \frac{b + be + be\cos\theta + b\beta\sin\theta}{b + be}$$

$$= 1 + \frac{e\cos\theta + \beta\sin\theta}{1 + e}$$

$$q_a = 2U \cdot \frac{\left[\sin\alpha + \sin(\alpha + \beta) + \sin\theta + \dfrac{e}{1 + e}\sin\theta\cos\theta + \dfrac{\beta}{1 + e}\sin^2\theta\right]}{\left\{1 - \dfrac{2b^2}{r^2}\cos 2\theta + \left(\dfrac{b}{r}\right)^4\right\}^{\frac{1}{2}}}$$

while substituting $r/b = 1 + e + e\cos\theta + \beta\sin\theta$ further simplification can be made especially with continuing use of the basic approximation that powers of e higher than unity are negligible.

The resulting equation is however somewhat unwieldy for obtaining and plotting numerous values of local velocity round the profile. The further reflection that the local pressure anywhere on the aerofoil is related to the square of the local velocity (i.e., from Bernoulli's Equation the pressure coefficient $C_p = 1 - (q_a/U)^2$ makes it clear that the plotting of a comprehensive pressure distribution on the aerofoil is a long and tedious process. Added to this is the ever-present thought that an approximation has been made which becomes progressively more unreal as thicker and more cambered sections are required.

The use of approximations is only justified in general if they produce significant simplifications at the expense of acceptable small deviations from the exact. In the present case the utility of the approximate method largely ceases after the profile eqns. (11.42) have been obtained and for velocity and pressure distributions the exact numerical solution is no more tedious a process by 'hand' and has the advantage of lending itself to rapid solution on a computer.

11.5. The exact Zhukovsky transformation process and its numerical solution.

Taking the cambered section again, the transformation formula is

$$\zeta = z + \frac{b^2}{z}$$

or

$$\xi + i\eta = x + iy + \frac{b^2}{x + iy}$$

which, rationalized and separated into real and imaginary parts, gives the ordinates of the aerofoil section:

$$\xi = x\left\{1 + \frac{b^2}{x^2 + y^2}\right\}, \quad \eta = y\left\{1 - \frac{b^2}{x^2 + y^2}\right\} \qquad . \quad (11.52)$$

Referring back to Fig. 11.19

$$x = a \cos \theta' + be$$
$$y = a \sin \theta' + b\beta(1 + e)$$

and with $a = b + be$

$$x = (b + be) \cos \theta' + be$$
$$y = (b + be) \sin \theta' + b\beta(1 + e)$$

For given aerofoil parameters e and β representing thickness and camber, values of x and y can be found for given values of angle θ' round the circle from $0 \rightarrow 2\pi$, and substituted in eqn. (11.52) to give the aerofoil coordinates ξ and η.

This method may be used with both singularities within the circle when

$$x = a \cos \theta' + be$$
$$a = b(1 + e)$$
$$e \leqslant l$$

Table 11.1 shows a typical arrangement of column headings, given b, e and β.

TABLE 11.1

Column headings for exact Zhukovsky transformation

(1)	(2)	(3)	(4)	(5)	(6)
θ'	$\cos \theta'$	$\sin \theta'$	$(b + be) \cos \theta'$	$(b + be) \sin \theta'$	$x = (4) + be$

(7)	(8)	(9)	(10) $= \xi$	(11) $= \eta$
$y = (5) + b\beta(1 + e)$	$(6)^2 + (7)^2$	$\dfrac{b^2}{(8)}$	$(6)\{1 + (9)\}$	$(7)\{1 - (9)\}$

11.5.1. The velocity and pressure distribution. For the velocity on the aerofoil, it is necessary to relate the incidence to the circulation, as discussed in the previous section. This is done by applying Zhukovsky's Hypothesis, and noting for completeness, in the present case, that in practical aerodynamics the full Zhukovsky circulation, i.e., that required to bring the rear stagnation on to the point of the trailing edge, is not realized. This is due to the combination of two 'practical' realities, (a) that air is viscous and the flow near the trailing edge of an aerofoil is modified by the presence of the boundary layers and wake, and (b) that the trailing edge must be rounded to some degree of curvature which allows the rear stagnation point to deviate from the position given in the 'ideal' case. So if K is the full Zhukovsky circulation it can be assumed that a practical value is kK where k is a constant less than unity.

Reference to the previous section will show that the velocity anywhere on the circle q_c is given in terms of the free stream velocity by

$$\frac{q_c}{U} = 2\{\sin \theta_c + \mathrm{k} \sin (\alpha + \beta)\}$$

and q_a can be found by use of the ratio

$$\frac{q_c}{q_a} = \left| \frac{dz}{d\zeta} \right|$$

Now $\dfrac{d\zeta}{dz} = 1 - \dfrac{b^2}{z^2}$

$$= 1 - \frac{b^2}{x^2 - y^2 + 2ixy}$$

$$= \left\{ 1 - \frac{b^2(x^2 - y^2)}{(x^2 + y^2)^2} \right\} + i . \left\{ \frac{2b^2xy}{(x^2 + y^2)^2} \right\}$$

$$\equiv A + iB$$

$$\therefore \left| \frac{d\zeta}{dz} \right| = \{A^2 + B^2\}^{\frac{1}{2}}$$

$$\therefore \frac{q_a}{U} = \frac{\dfrac{q_c}{U}}{\sqrt{A^2 + B^2}} = \frac{2\{\sin \theta_c + \mathrm{k} \sin (\alpha + \beta)\}}{(A^2 + B^2)^{\frac{1}{2}}}$$

It is now simple arithmetic to continue the table of the previous section to obtain q_a/U at the values of θ' taken, since $\theta_c = \theta' + \alpha$,

i.e., $\dfrac{q_a}{U} = \dfrac{2\{\sin (\theta' + \alpha) + \mathrm{k} \sin (\alpha + \beta)\}}{(A^2 + B^2)^{\frac{1}{2}}}$.   .   (11.53)

e.g., continuing the table above with α and k as given data in Table 11.2, (20) gives q_a/U at points round the profile given by the ordinates ξ and η of columns (10) and (11).

TABLE 11.2

Continuation of Table 11.1 to obtain velocity and pressure distribution

(12)	(13)	(14)	(15) $= A$	(16) $= B$
$(6)^2 - (7)^2$	$(6) \times (7)$	$\dfrac{b^2(12)}{(8)^2}$	$1 - (14)$	$\dfrac{2b^2(13)}{(8)^2}$
(17) $= \left\| \dfrac{d\zeta}{dz} \right\|$	(18)	(19)	(20) $= \dfrac{q_a}{U}$	
$\{(15)^2 + (16)^2\}^{\frac{1}{2}}$	$\theta' + \alpha$	$\sin (\theta' + \alpha)$	$\dfrac{2}{(17)} \{(19) + \mathrm{k} \sin (\alpha + \beta)\}$	

11.5.2. The pressure distribution. The pressure coefficient

$$C_p = \frac{p - p_0}{\frac{1}{2}\rho U^2} = 1 - \left(\frac{q_a}{U}\right)^2$$

is found by the simple addition to the table of two columns (21) and (22):—

(21)	(22) = C_p
$(20)^2$	$1 - (20)^2$

The authors consider that the above process is no longer and much more straightforward than the analytic method previously given, when it is necessary to generate a profile or obtain theoretical distributions for comparison with experimental results.

Moreover, the method lends itself to simple programming on a digital computer and it was found that only a few minutes' running time was necessary to produce the complete pressure distribution around an ellipto-Zhukovsky aerofoil at each of several incidences and values of k. A typical selection of these is given in Table 11.3 and Fig. 11.25.

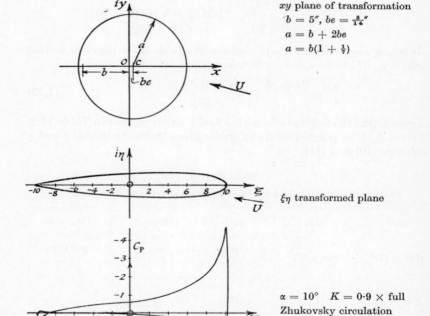

xy plane of transformation
$b = 5''$, $be = \frac{5}{14}''$
$a = b + 2be$
$a = b(1 + \frac{1}{7})$

$\xi\eta$ transformed plane

$\alpha = 10°$ $K = 0.9 \times$ full Zhukovsky circulation

FIG. 11.25.—Ellipto-Zhukovsky aerofoil.

These results are for the case of an ellipto-Zhukovsky symmetrical profile found from the transformation $\zeta = z + b^2/z$ applied to a circle of radius a shifted horizontally only *half* the necessary distance to produce the Zhukovsky symmetrical section. This has the combined advantages of rounding off the trailing edge and moving back the point of maximum thickness.

Here $\qquad b = 5$ in., $\quad e = \frac{1}{14}, \quad a = (1 + \frac{1}{7})b.$

The approximate formula gives chord $= 4b$ which, in this case, is 20 in. The correct result is chord $= 20\cdot2138$ in., showing the approximation to underestimate the chord by slightly over 1%.

The velocity profile and pressure distribution are given in Table 11.3

TABLE 11.3

Pressure distribution around an ellipto-Zhukovsky aerofoil

(10) ξ	(11) η	(22) C_p	(20) q_a/U	
$-10\cdot0238$	$+0\cdot0000$	$+0\cdot9273$	$-0\cdot2696$	⎫ —Trailing
$-9\cdot8841$	$-0\cdot1165$	$-0\cdot0084$	$-1\cdot0042$	⎟ edge
$-9\cdot4699$	$-0\cdot2381$	$-0\cdot0020$	$-1\cdot0010$	
$-8\cdot7954$	$-0\cdot3686$	$+0\cdot0229$	$-0\cdot9885$	
$-7\cdot8835$	$-0\cdot5100$	$+0\cdot0403$	$-0\cdot9796$	
$-6\cdot7638$	$-0\cdot6612$	$+0\cdot0519$	$-0\cdot9737$	
$-5\cdot4715$	$-0\cdot8184$	$+0\cdot0604$	$-0\cdot9693$	
$-4\cdot0454$	$-0\cdot9754$	$+0\cdot0681$	$-0\cdot9654$	
$-2\cdot5259$	$-1\cdot1236$	$+0\cdot0775$	$-0\cdot9604$	
$-0\cdot9542$	$-1\cdot2536$	$+0\cdot0915$	$-0\cdot9532$	⎬ Lower
$+0\cdot6295$	$-1\cdot3558$	$+0\cdot1129$	$-0\cdot9419$	surface
$+2\cdot1869$	$-1\cdot4214$	$+0\cdot1455$	$-0\cdot9244$	
$+3\cdot6820$	$-1\cdot4430$	$+0\cdot1936$	$-0\cdot8980$	
$+5\cdot0818$	$-1\cdot4158$	$+0\cdot2628$	$-0\cdot8586$	
$+6\cdot3565$	$-1\cdot3373$	$+0\cdot3597$	$-0\cdot8002$	
$+7\cdot4802$	$-1\cdot2081$	$+0\cdot4927$	$-0\cdot7123$	
$+8\cdot4305$	$-1\cdot0314$	$+0\cdot6687$	$-0\cdot5755$	
$+9\cdot1889$	$-0\cdot8131$	$+0\cdot8777$	$-0\cdot3497$	
$+9\cdot7410$	$-0\cdot5616$	$+0\cdot9965$	$+0\cdot0593$	
$+10\cdot0765$	$-0\cdot2868$	$+0\cdot2542$	$+0\cdot8636$	⎭
$+10\cdot1890$	$-0\cdot0000$	$-3\cdot2064$	$+2\cdot0510$	—Leading
$+10\cdot0765$	$+0\cdot2868$	$-4\cdot7367$	$+2\cdot3951$	edge
$+9\cdot7410$	$+0\cdot5616$	$-3\cdot7015$	$+2\cdot1683$	⎫
$+9\cdot1889$	$+0\cdot8131$	$-2\cdot7950$	$+1\cdot9481$	⎟
$+8\cdot4305$	$+1\cdot0314$	$-2\cdot1918$	$+1\cdot7866$	
$+7\cdot4802$	$+1\cdot2081$	$-1\cdot7721$	$+1\cdot6650$	
$+6\cdot3565$	$+1\cdot3373$	$-1\cdot4591$	$+1\cdot5682$	
$+5\cdot0818$	$+1\cdot4158$	$-1\cdot2117$	$+1\cdot4872$	
$+3\cdot6820$	$+1\cdot4430$	$-1\cdot0075$	$+1\cdot4168$	
$+2\cdot1869$	$+1\cdot4214$	$-0\cdot8336$	$+1\cdot3541$	
$+0\cdot6295$	$+1\cdot3558$	$-0\cdot6827$	$+1\cdot2972$	Upper
$-0\cdot9542$	$+1\cdot2536$	$-0\cdot5499$	$+1\cdot2450$	⎬ surface
$-2\cdot5259$	$+1\cdot1236$	$-0\cdot4324$	$+1\cdot1968$	
$-4\cdot0454$	$+0\cdot9754$	$-0\cdot3277$	$+1\cdot1523$	
$-5\cdot4715$	$+0\cdot8184$	$-0\cdot2341$	$+1\cdot1109$	
$-6\cdot7638$	$+0\cdot6612$	$-0\cdot1494$	$+1\cdot0721$	
$-7\cdot8835$	$+0\cdot5100$	$-0\cdot0704$	$+1\cdot0346$	
$-8\cdot7954$	$+0\cdot3686$	$+0\cdot0092$	$+0\cdot9954$	
$-9\cdot4699$	$+0\cdot2381$	$+0\cdot1083$	$+0\cdot9443$	
$-9\cdot8841$	$+0\cdot1165$	$+0\cdot3218$	$+0\cdot8235$	
$-10\cdot0238$	$+0\cdot0000$	$+0\cdot9273$	$-0\cdot2696$	⎭ —Trailing edge

U

for the case when $\alpha = 10°$ and the circulation is $0·9$ of that required by Zhukovsky's hypothesis.

11.6. Graphical generation of a Zhukovsky profile. Producing the profile streamline of a Zhukovsky transformation is a relatively easy process, though somewhat lengthy. This is because the original streamline is a simple geometrical shape, a circle, the ordinates of which can be easily absorbed as the controlled variables in the numerical process (e.g., in the above, a and θ').

For other adjacent streamlines the process is more complicated, and a speedier picture can often be obtained by a graphical process of transformation.

A point p in plane (1) is defined by the vector $z = x + iy$, which when acted on by the transformation function f(z) produces the corresponding point P in plane (2) defined by another vector $\zeta = \xi + i\eta$.

In other words the final vector ζ is the vector sum of components of the transformation function which in the case here is

$$\zeta = z + \frac{b^2}{z}$$

This, written in the exponential form, is

$$\zeta = re^{i\theta} + \frac{b^2}{r}e^{-i\theta}$$

or more fully in words:

The transformed point P is given by the vector ζ which is the vector sum of (a) the vector of 'length' r and argument θ and (b) the vector of 'length' b^2/r and argument $-\theta$.

The graphical addition is made in the usual way (Fig. 11.26) by drawing the vector Op (of length r, and θ degrees round from Ox), the vector op' (of length b^2/r, and $-\theta$ degrees round from Ox), and constructing the parallelogram $op'pP$ to give the location of the transformed point P.

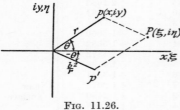

FIG. 11.26.

This construction, which is quite simple and quick, is the least difficult part of the graphical method. The problem lies in obtaining the moduli and arguments of the vectors to be summed, i.e., the lengths and angles of the lines op and op'.

Once again elegant geometrical methods can be used when the original streamline lends itself, but it has been found more convenient in the general case to construct the streamline in plane (1) and consider each point along it separately for graphical transformation.

Before going on to do a worked example it should be noted that a similar graphical method is available for plotting the velocity distribution in the transformed plane. A detailed description of this is not given here;

it is the authors' view that the average student could apply the above method to any vector addition (which is all q_a is) when it is necessary.

Example 11.10. Develop the section of a Zhukovsky aerofoil of chord = 6 in., thickness/chord ratio = 15% and 5% camber, and draw in a few adjacent streamlines when the aerofoil is developing full Zhukovsky Lift at 10° incidence in a wind of 60 ft/sec.

The solution to this problem requires several stages.

Stage I. The construction of the circle in the appropriate uniform stream.

Stage II. The addition of the correct magnitude of circulation to the circle to conform with the Zhukovsky hypothesis.

Stage III. The transformation of this circle and its adjacent streamlines, about an axis inclined at 10° to the undisturbed wind, to give the required aerofoil section and the solution of the problem.

The first two stages follow the procedure outlined in the previous chapter for superpositioning of streamlines. The third stage is the point by point transformation.

Stage I. It is first necessary to find the strength of the doublet required to produce the required circle for transformation. This implies obtaining the radius a.

From the data: chord = 6 in. = $4b$, $\therefore$ b = 1·5 in. and the transformation function then is

$$\zeta = z + \frac{2\cdot 25}{z}$$

where x, y and r, ξ and η are in inches.

The thickness/chord ratio = 0·15 = 1·299e, giving e = 0·1155.

Further, from previous work,

$$a = b + be = b(1 + e)$$
$$= 1\cdot 5(1\cdot 1155) = 1\cdot 673 \text{ in.}$$

i.e.,   radius a = 1·673 in.

From § 10.2.12 the strength of the doublet is $\mu = 2\pi a^2 U$, where U is 60 ft/sec and a must be in feet.

$$= 2\pi \times \frac{1\cdot 673^2}{12^2} \times 60$$

$$\mu = 7\cdot 35 \text{ ft}^3/\text{sec}$$

The streamlines due to a doublet in a uniform stream are given by

$$\psi = \left[\frac{\mu}{2\pi} \cdot \frac{1}{x^2 + y^2} - U\right]y$$

or $$\psi = 1\cdot 167\frac{y}{x^2 + y^2} - 60y \qquad . \qquad . \qquad . \quad (11.54)$$

(ft²/sec, when y is in feet)

This flow, given by eqn. (11.54), can be obtained by plotting the uniform stream, $-Uy$, and superimposing on it the streamlines due to the doublet which are pairs of eccentric circles meeting in the origin with centres on the y-axis.

Therefore, putting $x = 0$ in the first term of eqn. (11.54) gives the diameter and hence the centre of the circle since the origin is in the circumference of each doublet streamline.

i.e.,   radius of streamlines due to doublet = $r_{\text{doublet}} = \dfrac{1\cdot 167}{2\psi}$ ft . (11.55)

For the uniform horizontal streamlines the vertical ordinate $y_{u/s}$ can be obtained from

$$y_{u/s} = -\frac{\psi}{60} \text{ ft} = -\frac{\psi}{5} \text{ in.} \qquad . \qquad . \qquad . \qquad (11.56)$$

(since $U = -60$ ft/sec, i.e., from right to left).

Choosing values of ψ and making up a simple table gives the values of $y_{u/s}$ and r_d in inches (see Table 11.4).

TABLE 11.4

$\pm\psi$	0	1	2	3	4	5	6	7	8
r_d (ft) . . .	∞	0·583	0·292	0·194	0·146	0·117	0·097	0·083	0·073
r_d (in.) . .	∞	7·00	3·50	2·33	1·75	1·40	1·17	1·00	1·88
$\mp y_{u/s}$ (in.) .	0	0·2	0·4	0·6	0·8	1·0	1·2	1·4	1·6

The circles and straight lines can be drawn on the same sheet and the points of constant value ψ joined up by smooth curves to complete Stage I.

As a check the circle $\psi = 0$ should be of radius 1·673 in.

Stage II. To obtain the streamlines due to a spinning cylinder generating circulation K in a uniform stream the streamlines due to a vortex of strength K at the centre of the circle must be superimposed on to those of Stage I.

From the Zhukovsky hypothesis

$$K = 4\pi a U \sin (\alpha + \beta)$$

From the data $\alpha = 10°$, camber $= \beta/2 = 0\cdot05$ radians. $(\alpha + \beta) = 15\cdot73°$ and if this, being a depression of the stagnation points, is reckoned negative, then

$$K = 4\pi.(-60).\frac{1\cdot673}{12} \sin (-15\cdot73°)$$

$$K = +28\cdot5 \text{ ft}^2/\text{sec}$$

The streamlines due to the vortex outside the circle of radius a are given by

$$\psi_v = -\frac{K}{2\pi} \log_e \frac{r_v}{a}$$

$$= -\frac{28\cdot5}{2\pi} \times 2\cdot3 \times \log_{10} \frac{r_v}{a}$$

$$= -10\cdot42 \log_{10} r_v + 10\cdot42 \log_{10} a$$

rearranging, $\qquad 0\cdot096\psi = -\log_{10} r_v + \log_{10} a$

$$\log_{10} r_v = \log_{10} a - 0\cdot096 \psi$$

giving Table 11.5 for the vortex streamline radii r_v.

TABLE 11.5

ψ	$-0\cdot096\psi$	$\log_{10} r_v$	r_v (ft)	r_v (in.)
0	0	$-0\cdot8554$	0·139	1·67
-1	0·096	$-0\cdot7594$	0·174	2·095
-2	0·192	$-0\cdot6634$	0·217	2·61
-3	0·288	$-0\cdot5674$	0·271	3·26
-4	0·384	$-0\cdot4714$	0·338	4·07
-5	0·480	$-0\cdot3754$	0·422	5·08
-6	0·576	$-0\cdot2794$	0·526	6·34
-7	0·672	$-0\cdot1834$	0·656	7·90
-8	0·768	$-0\cdot0874$	0·819	9·85

These circles drawn on streamlines of Stage I and the points of constant total ψ connected by smooth lines give the stream pattern of Stage II (Fig. 11.27).

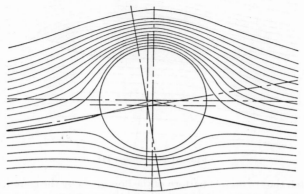

FIG. 11.27.—Stage II.

Stage III. Stage II provides the streamline pattern due to a section of rotating circular cylinder in a horizontal uniform stream and it must now be transformed with reference to the origin and inclined axes of transformation. The ξ axis of transformation (the chord line) is inclined at 10° (the incidence) to the horizontal stream and the origin is offset by a distance $b\beta = 0.15$ in. normal, and a distance $be = 0.173$ in. parallel, to the $O\xi$ axis.

Any point p can now be selected, giving r and θ the radial and angular displacements from the $O\xi$ axis. The length of Op' can be calculated from $2.25/r$ and drawn in at $-\theta$ to the $O\xi$ axis, and the parallelogram $Opp'P$ completed to give the point P on Fig. 11.28.

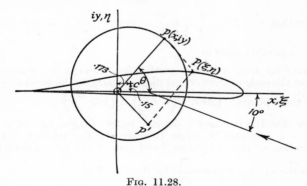

FIG. 11.28.

Stage III has been completed and the appropriate streamlines drawn in on Fig. 11.29 (p. 302).

EXERCISES

1. Show that the function $w = \cosh z$ represents the irrotational flow of an incompressible fluid within a 'semi-infinite' rectangular enclosure of width 2π, and sketch the form of the streamlines. (N.C.A.T.)

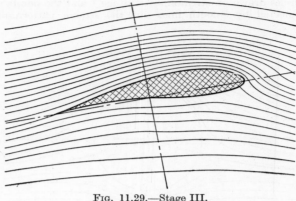

Fig. 11.29.—Stage III.

2. Sketch the streamline pattern of the flow given by the complex potential function $w = Az^2$ where A is a constant and the other symbols have their usual meaning.

Find the magnitude and direction of the velocity of the stream at the point $x = 1$, $y = 2$, when $A = 10$. (*Ans.* 44·67 ft/sec, $-63°\ 26'$) (N.C.A.T.)

3. Find the potential function for a two-dimensional source of strength m whose axis lies at a distance c from an infinite plane wall. Show that some of the lines of constant velocity potential are closed curves lying in the fluid whilst others terminate on the plane wall.

Find also the magnitude and direction of the force on the wall if the pressure behind it is constant and equal to the stagnation pressure.

$$\left(Ans.\ \frac{m^2}{4\pi c}\right) \qquad \text{(U. of L.)}$$

4. Show that $w = Uz + \dfrac{h}{4} \coth \dfrac{\pi z}{h}$ represents the flow past an oval midway between parallel walls at $\pm \dfrac{h}{2}$

Determine the horizontal and vertical diameters of the oval and find the velocities on the ends of the vertical diameter and on the walls directly above and below these points. $\left(Ans.\ U\!\left(1 + \dfrac{\pi}{2}\right),\ U\!\left(1 + \dfrac{\pi}{4}\right)\right)$ (U. of L.)

5. Show that the real and imaginary parts of a function of the complex variable $z = x + iy$ can be taken to represent the velocity potential and stream function of the two-dimensional flow of an incompressible inviscid fluid.

Discuss the motion represented by the function

$$w = \phi + i\psi = z + 2z^{\frac{1}{2}}$$

Draw the streamline $\psi = 0$ and sketch in some others. (U. of L.)

6. Show that the flow from a point source past a circular cylinder (section) may be obtained from a suitable distribution of sources and sinks. Find an approximate expression for the pressure force acting on the cylinder of radius a if the distance R of the source from the centre of the cylinder is large compared with a. $\left(Ans.\ \text{Force towards source} = \dfrac{1}{2}\dfrac{m^2a^2}{\pi r^3}\right)$ (U. of L.)

7. Investigate the flow given by $w = i\left(z - \dfrac{a^2}{z}\right)$ and calculate the direction and magnitude of the velocity at the point $z = a\left(1 + \dfrac{i}{2}\right)$.

Sketch without proof the flow in the ζ-plane on applying the transformation $\zeta = z + \dfrac{b^2}{z}$.   (*Ans.* 1·615, $-66°\ 30'$)   (N.C.A.T.)

8. Show that the solution $w = f(z)$ of a problem of irrotational motion of a fluid in two dimensions can be used to obtain solutions of other problems by transformations of the form $\zeta = f(z)$.

Use an example in your demonstration, e.g., $\zeta = e^{\frac{\pi}{a}z}$.   (N.C.A.T.)

9. Sketch the circle in the z-plane which, by use of the Zhukovsky transformation, may be used to yield a circular arc aerofoil. Given that the equation of this aerofoil is

$$\xi^2 + \left[\eta + a\left(\frac{1}{\beta} - \beta\right)\right]^2 = a^2\left[4 + \left(\frac{1}{\beta} - \beta\right)^2\right]$$

and $\eta = 2a\beta \sin^2 \theta$ where a is the constant in the transformation

$$\zeta = z + \frac{a^2}{z}$$

calculate the aerofoil camber.

A section of this type is placed in a wind stream at an incidence such that the stagnation points occur at the leading and trailing edges. If the section has 7% camber, estimate the lift coefficient.   (*Ans.* $C_L = 0·887$)   (N.C.A.T.)

10. A long elliptic cylinder of thickness/chord ratio $= \frac{1}{7}$ is set in, and with its major axis parallel to, a uniform irrotational stream of 116 ft/sec. Calculate the pressure difference between pressure holes set in the nose, and at the point of maximum thickness.   (*Ans.* 20·9 lb/ft²)   (N.C.A.T.)

11. Show that when the transformation $\zeta = z^2$ is applied to a field of uniform flow parallel to the Oy axis the transformed streamlines are parabolas about the $O\xi$ axis. Plot any transformed streamline.   (N.C.A.T.)

12. Calculate the velocity just outside the boundary layer at the $\frac{3}{4}$ chord point of a symmetrical Zhukovsky aerofoil of thickness/chord ratio 0·2, set at zero incidence in a stream of undisturbed velocity 150 ft/sec.   (*Ans.* 162 ft/sec)   (N.C.A.T.)

13. Show that a straight line of length $4a$ can be obtained from the conformal transformation of a circle of radius a.

A flat plate is inclined at 3° to a uniform stream. Working from first principles and using the Zhukovsky hypothesis calculate the lift coefficient of the plate.   (*Ans.* $C_L = 0·3288$)   (N.C.A.T.)

14. A long strut of elliptic section and fineness ratio 4 is set with the major axis of the section at zero incidence to an irrotational stream of undisturbed velocity 100 ft/sec. Calculate the stream velocity just outside the boundary layer at a point of maximum thickness.   (*Ans.* 125 ft/sec)   (N.C.A.T.)

15. Calculate the theoretical lift coefficient of a Zhukovsky aerofoil having thickness ratio 0·2, and 2% camber, set at 4° incidence in a two-dimensional irrotational flow.

Derive your formula for the lift coefficient.   (*Ans.* $C_L = 0·795$)   (N.C.A.T.)

16. Prove that the thickness ratio of a symmetrical Zhukovsky aerofoil is approximately $1·3 \left(\dfrac{a}{b} - 1\right)$ where b is the constant of transformation and a the radius of the circle from which the aerofoil is derived.

Explain briefly why a Zhukovsky aerofoil is not satisfactory from the point of view of modern requirements. (N.C.A.T.)

17. A small symmetrical Zhukovsky aerofoil has a thickness ratio of 10 in. and is fitted with pressure holes on both surfaces at 12% of the chord behind the leading edge so that it can be used as a yaw-meter. Estimate the pressure difference which would be found when it is set at $1\frac{1}{2}°$ incidence to the flow. Assume two-dimensional conditions and express the result in terms of the pressure rise at the stagnation point. (*Ans.* 0·33) (U. of L.)

18. An elliptic cylinder has a fineness ratio 9 and is set at an angle of incidence of 5° in an airstream flowing at 200 ft/sec. Find the resultant velocity and its direction at a point one chord ahead of the centre of the cylinder measured along the major axis. Assume that the circulation generated is 2/3 of that required to bring the rear stagnation point to the end of the major axis. (*Ans.* 196 ft/sec, 8°·1). (U. of L.)

19. An elliptic cylinder with a thickness ratio 15% has its major axis lying horizontally along the direction of the undisturbed flow of velocity V. Assuming incompressible inviscid flow obtain a general expression for the velocity of the flow crossing the vertical axis of symmetry. Show that the velocity on this line is everywhere greater than V and that a maximum value of $1·15V$ occurs on the elliptic boundary. Find also the distance from this boundary at which the velocity is $1·1V$. (*Ans.* 3·16 × semi-minor axis) (U. of L.)

20. A 20% Zhukovsky aerofoil set with its chord at zero incidence to a two-dimensional irrotational airstream of 100 ft/sec has a lift coefficient of 0·3. Estimate the lift coefficient at 5° incidence and the velocity of the airflow just outside the boundary layer at the nose at this attitude. (*Ans.* 0·93, 84 ft/sec) (U. of L.)

21. In the z-plane the boundary consists of a vertical wall defined by $x = a$ where a is a positive constant. Show that the transformation $\zeta = z^2$ maps the region to the right of this boundary into an area lying outside a parabolic boundary in the ζ-plane. If the potential function in the z-plane is $w = V(z-a)^2$ sketch a few streamlines of the flow in the ζ-plane and show that the velocity on the parabolic boundary is everywhere less than V. (U. of L.)

22. Show that the Zhukovsky transformation

$$z = \zeta + \frac{l^2}{\zeta} \text{ transforms the circle } |\zeta| = l$$

in the ζ-plane into a section of a flat plate of chord length $4l$ in the z-plane.

Show that the circle in the ζ-plane with centre $(-\delta, 0)$ and of radius $(l + 2\delta)$ where $\delta \ll l$ is transformed into an oval curve in the z-plane and that except near its ends the equation of the oval is

$$y = 4\delta\left(1 - \frac{x}{4l}\right)\left[1 - \left(\frac{x}{2l}\right)^2\right]^{\frac{1}{2}}$$

(U. of L.)

CHAPTER 12

THIN AEROFOIL THEORY

12.1. The development of the theory. The aerodynamic characteristics of an aerofoil are simply predicted from classical hydrodynamic
theory if the aerofoil is a shape easily obtained by conformal transformation. The Zhukovsky transformation of a lifting circle into an aerofoil at
incidence has been shown in Chapter 11. The main limitation is that this
theory applies only to the Zhukovsky family of aerofoil sections. A similar
argument could apply to the families of aerofoil profiles obtained by other
transformations; that is, that the shape of the aerofoil is obtained almost
as a by-product of the derivation of the characteristics.

Recognizing that most aerofoils could be classed as thin, Munk* produced an aerofoil theory which was refined by Glauert in *R. and M.*† 910
(1924). Although not quite in its final form the analysis did succeed in
relating the shape to the aerofoil characteristics.

Taking account of the fact that the transformation $\zeta = z + a^2/z$
applied to a circle in a uniform stream gave a straight line rudimentary
aerofoil (see § 11.3.1), the theory assumed that the general thin aerofoil
could be replaced by its camber line, which is assumed to be only a slight
distortion of a straight line. Consequently the shape from which it was to
be transformed would be a similar slight distortion from the original circle
(Fig. 12.1). The original circle could be found by transforming the slightly
distorted shape (dotted). This transformation function defines the distortion, or change of shape, of the circle, and hence by implication the distortion (or camber) of the straight line aerofoil.

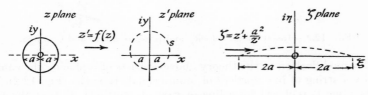

FIG. 12.1.

Fig. 12.1 gives pictorially the transformation sequence, viz. circle
($z = ae^{i\theta}$) to shape S using the transformation $z' = f(z)$, and then shape S
to aerofoil camber line via

$$\zeta = z' + \frac{a^2}{z'} = f(z) + \frac{a^2}{f(z)}$$

* *N.A.C.A. Rep.* No. 142.
† *Reports and Memoranda* of the Aeronautical Research Council.

It is evident that the transformation $z' = f(z)$ defines the shape of the camber and Glauert used a series expression

$$z' = z\left[1 + i \sum A_x \frac{a^x}{z^x}\right]$$

for this.

Using potential theory and the Zhukovsky hypothesis the lift and moment on the aerofoil section was found in terms of the coefficients A_x, that is in terms of the shape parameter.

The usefulness of the theory lay in the fact that the aerofoil characteristics could be quoted in terms of functions of the coefficients A_x, which in turn could be found by graphical integration methods from any camber line shape.

The results obtained by the 'Zhukovsky in reverse' method above are identical in every way to those obtained by the modified theory more generally used today and which is the subject of this chapter. It is however interesting to note that the numerical and analytical examples quoted as illustrating the modified theory* were taken directly from the examples used in *R. and M.* 910 to illustrate the 'reverse' theory.

12.2. The general theory. The essential assumptions of size and shape are retained. These are that the aerofoil is thin so that its shape is effectively that of its camber line, and also that the camber line shape deviates only slightly from the chord line. A corollary of the second assumption is that the theory should be restricted to low angles of incidence.

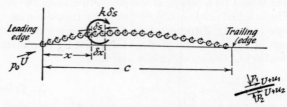

FIG. 12.2.—Insert shows velocity and pressure above and below δs.

The modification to the theory above consists of replacing the camber line by a string of line vortices of infinitesimal strengths (Fig. 12.2). The camber line is replaced by a line of variable vorticity so that the total circulation about the chord is the sum of the vortex elements.

Thus
$$K = \int_0^c k \, ds \qquad . \qquad . \qquad . \qquad (12.1)$$

where k is the distribution of vorticity over the element of camber line δs and circulation is taken positive in the clockwise direction.

There should be no difficulty in accepting this idealized concept. Previous chapters have indicated that a lifting wing may be replaced by, and

* *Aerofoil and Airscrew Theory*, H. Glauert.

produces forces and disturbances identical to, a vortex system and Chapter 13 presents the classical theory of finite aerofoils in which the idea of a bound vortex system is fully exploited. A wing replaced by a sheet of spanwise vortex elements (Fig. 13.9) will have a section which is essentially that of the replaced camber line above.

Using the notation put forward by Glauert the leading edge is taken as the origin of a pair of coordinate axes x and y, Ox along the chord, and Oy normal to it. The basic assumptions of the theory permit the variation of vorticity along the camber line to be assumed the same as the variation along the Ox axis, i.e., δs differs negligibly from δx, so that eqn. (12.1) above becomes

$$K = \int_0^c k \, dx \qquad . \qquad . \qquad . \qquad (12.2)$$

Hence for unit span of this section the lift is given by

$$l = \rho U K = \rho U \int_0^c k \, dx \qquad . \qquad . \qquad (12.3)$$

Eqn. (12.3) could be written with $\rho U k = p$

$$l = \int_0^c \rho U k \, dx = \int_0^c p \, dx \qquad . \qquad . \qquad (12.4)$$

Now considering unit spanwise length, p has the units of intensity of force per unit area or pressure and the moment of these chordwise pressure forces about the leading edge or origin of the system is simply

$$M_{\text{L.E.}} = -\int_0^c px \, dx = -\rho U \int_0^c kx \, dx \qquad . \qquad (12.5)$$

(Pitching 'nose up' is positive.)

The thin wing section has thus been replaced for analytical purposes by a line discontinuity in the flow in the form of a vorticity distribution. This gives rise to an overall circulation, as does the aerofoil, and produces a chordwise pressure variation.

For the aerofoil in a wind of undisturbed velocity U and pressure p_0, the insert to Fig. 12.2 shows the static pressures p_1 and p_2 above and below the element δs where the local velocities are $U + u_1$ and $U + u_2$ respectively.

The overall pressure difference p is $p_2 - p_1$. By Bernoulli

$$p_1 + \tfrac{1}{2}\rho(U + u_1)^2 = p_0 + \tfrac{1}{2}\rho U^2$$
$$p_2 + \tfrac{1}{2}\rho(U + u_2)^2 = p_0 + \tfrac{1}{2}\rho U^2$$

and subtracting

$$p_2 - p_1 = \tfrac{1}{2}\rho U^2 \left[2\left(\frac{u_1}{U} - \frac{u_2}{U}\right) + \left(\frac{u_1}{U}\right)^2 + \left(\frac{u_2}{U}\right)^2 \right]$$

and with the aerofoil thin and at small incidence the perturbation velocity ratios u_1/U and u_2/U will be so small compared with unity that $(u_1/U)^2$ and $(u_2/U)^2$ are neglected compared with u_1/U and u_2/U respectively.

Then $\qquad\qquad\qquad p = p_2 - p_1 = \rho U(u_1 - u_2)$. $\qquad$. $\qquad$ (12.6)

The equivalent vorticity distribution indicates that the circulation due to element δs is $k\,\delta x$ (δx because the camber line deviates only slightly from the Ox axis). Evaluating the circulation around δs and taking clockwise as positive in this case, by taking the algebraic sum of the flow of fluid along the top and bottom of δs, gives

$$k\,\delta x = + (U + u_1)\,\delta x - (U + u_2)\,\delta x = (u_1 - u_2)\,\delta x \qquad (12.7)$$

Comparing (12.6) and (12.7) shows that $p = \rho U k$ as introduced in (12.4) above.

A further condition presents itself, namely the flow direction on the surface of the aerofoil (camber line). This clearly must be tangential to the surface everywhere and make the angle arc tan dy/dx, or since the aerofoil is thin, the angle dy/dx, to Ox (Fig. 12.3).

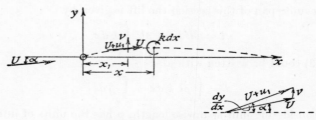

Velocities at x_1 from O
$U + u_1$ resultant tangential to camber line
v induced by chordwise variation in circulation
U free stream velocity inclined at α to Ox

Fig. 12.3.

The velocity on the surface at x_1 from the leading edge is the vector sum of the induced component arising from elements of circulation (or vortices) along the camber line and the free stream velocity U inclined at α to the Ox axis.

Resolving vertical velocity components

$$(U + u_1)\frac{dy}{dx} = v + U\alpha$$

and ignoring second order quantities the important relationship is obtained:

$$U\left(\frac{dy}{dx} - \alpha\right) = v \qquad\qquad (12.8)$$

The induced velocity is found by considering the effect of the elementary circulation $k\,\delta x$ at x, a distance $x - x_1$ from the point considered.

Circulation $k\,\delta x$ induces a velocity at the point x_1 equal to $\dfrac{1}{2\pi}\dfrac{k\,\delta x}{x - x_1}$ from eqn. (13.12).

The effect of all such elements of circulation along the chord is the induced velocity v where

$$v = \frac{1}{2\pi} \int_0^c \frac{k\,dx}{x - x_1}$$

and introducing this in eqn. (12.8) gives

$$U\left[\frac{dy}{dx} - \alpha\right] = \frac{1}{2\pi} \int_0^c \frac{k\,dx}{x - x_1} \qquad . \qquad . \qquad . \qquad (12.9)$$

The solution for $k\,dx$ which satisfies eqn. (12.9) for a given shape of camber line (defining dy/dx) and incidence can be introduced in eqns. (12.4) and (12.5) to obtain the lift and moment for the aerofoil shape. The characteristics C_L and $C_{M\,\text{L.E.}}$ follow directly and hence k_{cp} and the angle for zero lift.

12.3. The solution of the general equation.

The problem in the general case is the solution of eqn. (12.9) direct giving k as some expression in terms of the camber line shape.

Another method of finding $k\,dx$ is to utilize the method of eqn. (12.7) above, where simple expressions can be found for the velocity distribution round skeleton aerofoils.

The present approach is to work up to the general case through particular skeleton shapes that do provide such simple expressions, and then to apply the general case to some practical considerations.

12.3.1. Thin symmetrical flat plate aerofoil.

In this first simple case the camber line is straight along Ox, and $dy/dx = 0$.

The general equation becomes, on changing the sign,

$$U\alpha = \frac{1}{2\pi} \int_0^c \frac{k\,dx}{-x + x_1} \qquad . \qquad . \qquad . \qquad (12.10)$$

It is convenient in what follows to change the variable x to θ,

(through $\qquad x = \frac{c}{2}(1 - \cos\theta))$, and x_1 to θ_1,

then the limits change $\left.\begin{array}{l} \theta \sim 0 \to \pi \\ x \sim 0 \to c \end{array}\right\}$ and $dx = \frac{c}{2}\sin\theta\,d\theta$
as

Eqn. (12.10) becomes

$$U\alpha = \frac{1}{2\pi} \int_0^\pi \frac{k\sin\theta\,d\theta}{(\cos\theta - \cos\theta_1)} \qquad . \qquad . \qquad (12.11)$$

A value of k which satisfies (12.11) is

$$k = 2U\alpha\frac{(1 + \cos\theta)}{\sin\theta}$$

as can be shown by substitution.

$$-\frac{1}{2\pi}\int_0^\pi \frac{2U\alpha \sin\theta(1 + \cos\theta)\, d\theta}{(\cos\theta - \cos\theta_1)\sin\theta}$$

$$= \frac{U\alpha}{\pi}\int_0^\pi \frac{1 + \cos\theta}{\cos\theta - \cos\theta_1}d\theta$$

$$= \frac{U\alpha}{\pi}[\pi]$$

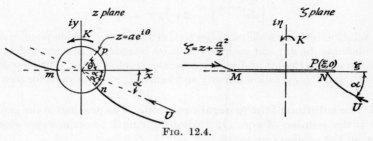

FIG. 12.4.

A more direct method for k is found as follows: transforming the circle $z = ae^{i\theta}$ through the Zhukovsky transformation $\zeta = z + a^2/z$ to a lifting flat plate section (Fig. 12.4) at incidence α requires by Zhukovsky hypothesis (see § 12) that sufficient circulation be imposed to bring the rear stagnation point down to m on the cylinder where the velocity at a general point (a, θ) is

$$q_c = 2U \sin(\theta + \alpha) + \frac{K}{2\pi a}$$

Equating this to zero at m gives $K = 4\pi a U \sin\alpha$ whence

$$q_c = 2U \sin(\theta + \alpha) + 2U \sin\alpha$$

The velocity at the corresponding point P ($\xi = 2a \cos\theta, \eta = 0$) on the aerofoil is

$$q_a = \frac{q_c}{\left|\dfrac{d\zeta}{dz}\right|} = \frac{2U[\sin(\theta + \alpha) + \sin\alpha]}{\left|1 - \dfrac{a^2}{z^2}\right|}$$

Now

$$\left|1 - \frac{a^2}{z^2}\right| = |\,1 - \cos 2\theta + i \sin 2\theta\,|$$

$$= [(1 - \cos 2\theta)^2 + (\sin 2\theta)^2]^{\frac{1}{2}}$$

$$= [1 - 2\cos 2\theta + 1]^{\frac{1}{2}} = 2\sin\theta$$

whence

$$q_a = 2U\frac{\sin(\theta + \alpha) + \sin\alpha}{2\sin\theta}$$

rearranging this gives

$$\frac{q_a}{U} = \left[\frac{\sin\theta\cos\alpha + \sin\alpha\cos\theta + \sin\alpha}{\sin\theta}\right]$$

$$= \cos\alpha + \frac{\sin\alpha}{\sin\theta}(1 + \cos\theta) \qquad . \qquad . \qquad . \quad (12.12)$$

$$= \cos \alpha + \frac{\sin \alpha . 2 \cos^2 \theta/2}{2 \sin \theta/2 . \cos \theta/2}$$

$$\frac{q_a}{U} = \left[\cos \alpha + \sin \alpha \cot \frac{\theta}{2} \right] \quad . \qquad . \qquad . \qquad . \quad (12.13)$$

For the purposes of thin aerofoil theory α is small so that eqn. (12.13) becomes

$$\frac{q_a}{U} = \left(1 + \alpha \cot \frac{\theta}{2} \right) \qquad . \qquad . \qquad . \quad (12.14)$$

Eqn. (12.14) has been given for completeness, but the equation in θ (eqn. (12.12)) is of more interest here. This gives, for small values of α,

$$\frac{q_a}{U} = \left[1 + \alpha . \frac{1 + \cos \theta}{\sin \theta} \right] \qquad . \qquad . \qquad . \quad (12.15)$$

and in eqn. (12.15) θ is the same variable as that used in the general eqn. (12.11). This can be easily shown by shifting the axes in the right-hand sketch of Fig. 12.4 to the leading edge and measuring x rearwards, when with $c = 4a$

$$x = \frac{c}{2} - \xi = \frac{c}{2} - \frac{c}{2} \cos \theta = \frac{c}{2}(1 - \cos \theta)$$

Then taking $k = q_{a1} - q_{a2}$ from (12.7) where q_{a1} is the velocity at the point where $\theta = \theta_1$ and q_{a2} is the velocity at the same point on the other side of the aerofoil where $\theta = -\theta_1$

$$k = U\left[1 + \alpha \frac{(1 + \cos \theta_1)}{\sin \theta_1} \right] - U\left[1 + \alpha \frac{(1 + \cos (-\theta_1))}{\sin (-\theta_1)} \right]$$

$$k = 2U\alpha \frac{1 + \cos \theta_1}{\sin \theta_1}$$

so that in general at any point on the flat plate

$$k = 2U\alpha \frac{1 + \cos \theta}{\sin \theta} \qquad . \qquad . \qquad . \quad (12.16)$$

which has been shown to satisfy eqn. (12.11).

The aerodynamic coefficients for a flat plate. The expression for k can now be put in the appropriate equations for lift and moment by using the 'pressure'

$$p = \rho U k = 2\rho U^2 \alpha \frac{1 + \cos \theta}{\sin \theta} . \qquad . \qquad . \quad (12.17)$$

It should be noted that the full Zhukovsky circulation is involved in k. Indeed k vanishes at the trailing edge, $x = c$, $\theta = \pi$, and this must necessarily be so for the velocity at the trailing edge to be finite.

The lift per unit span

$$l = \rho U \int_0^\pi 2U\alpha \left(\frac{1 + \cos \theta}{\sin \theta} \right) \frac{c}{2} \sin \theta \, d\theta$$

and using the usual substitution:

$$x = \frac{c}{2}(1 - \cos \theta)$$

$$dx = \frac{c}{2} \sin \theta \, d\theta$$

$$l = \alpha \rho U^2 c \int_0^\pi (1 + \cos \theta) \, d\theta$$

$$l = \pi \alpha \rho U^2 c = C_L \tfrac{1}{2} \rho U^2 c \, . \, 1 \text{ for unit span}$$

whence $\qquad\qquad C_L = 2\pi\alpha$. $\quad$. $\quad$. $\quad$. $\quad$. $\quad$. (12.18)

The moment about the leading edge per unit span

$$M_{\text{L.E.}} = -\int_0^c px \, dx$$

Changing the sign

$$- M_{\text{L.E.}} = 2\rho U^2 \alpha \int_0^\pi \frac{(1 + \cos \theta)}{\sin \theta} \cdot \frac{c}{2}(1 - \cos \theta)\frac{c}{2} \sin \theta \, d\theta$$

$$= \tfrac{1}{2}\rho U^2 \alpha c^2 \int_0^\pi (1 - \cos^2 \theta) \, d\theta = - C_{M \, \text{L.E.}} \tfrac{1}{2}\rho U^2 c^2 \, . \, 1 \text{ for unit span}$$

$$\therefore \, - C_{M \, \text{L.E.}} = \alpha \int_0^\pi \left(\tfrac{1}{2} - \frac{\cos 2\theta}{2}\right) d\theta$$

$$- C_{M \, \text{L.E.}} = \alpha \frac{\pi}{2} \quad . \quad . \quad . \quad . \quad . \quad (12.19)$$

Comparing eqns. (12.19) and (12.18) shows that

$$C_{M \, \text{L.E.}} = - \frac{C_L}{4} \quad . \quad . \quad . \quad . \quad (12.20)$$

The centre of pressure coefficient k_{cp} is given for small angles of incidence approximately by

$$k_{cp} = \frac{- C_{M \, \text{L.E.}}}{C_L} = \frac{1}{4} \quad . \quad . \quad . \quad (12.21)$$

and this shows a fixed centre of pressure coincident with the aerodynamic centre.

12.3.2. The circular arc aerofoil. In this case also, the use of the direct method of finding the distribution of k is the logical method to adopt, since the circular arc skeleton aerofoil is derived from a circle by the Zhukovsky transformation.

Further, it can be anticipated that the difference in k distribution between the circular arc aerofoil below and the flat plate above will give a pointer to a more general distribution for any camber line shape.

Consider the transformation of a circle of radius a, with centre at the

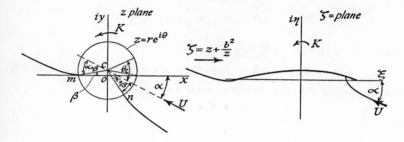

Further details of circle

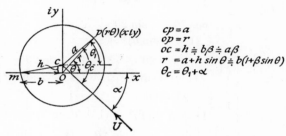

FIG. 12.5.

point $y = h = a \sin \beta$ in the z-plane (Fig. 12.5) to the ζ-plane via the transformation $\zeta = z + b^2/z$ where $b = a \cos \beta$. The circle transforms to a circular arc of camber $\tan \beta/2$. Kutta originated these circular arc aerofoils in 1902. With the aerofoil generating circulation according to the Zhukovsky hypothesis the stagnation point on the originating circle is depressed to m. By the process adopted above and in Chapter 11, the velocity on the circle

$$q_c = 2U \sin \theta_c + \frac{K}{2\pi a} = 0, \quad \text{when } \theta_c = -(\alpha + \beta)$$

Thus $\qquad q_c = 2U[\sin \theta_c + \sin (\alpha + \beta)] \qquad . \qquad . \qquad . \qquad . \qquad (12.22)$

Within the limitations of the theory, $\sin (\alpha + \beta) \doteqdot \alpha + \beta$ and the geometry of Fig. 12.5 gives $\theta_c = \theta_1 + \alpha$. Therefore $\sin \theta_c = \sin \theta_1 + \alpha \cos \theta_1$ which substituted in eqn. (12.22) gives

$$q_c = 2U(\sin \theta_1 + \alpha \cos \theta_1 + \alpha + \beta)$$

From $\qquad y = a \sin \theta_1 + b\beta = r \sin \theta; \quad \sin \theta_1 = \frac{r}{b} \sin \theta - \beta$

and $\qquad x = a \cos \theta_1 = r \cos \theta; \qquad \cos \theta_1 = \frac{r}{b} \cos \theta$

since $a \doteqdot b$.

x

Then $\qquad q_c = 2U\left(\dfrac{r}{b}\sin\theta - \beta + \alpha.\dfrac{r}{b}\cos\theta + \alpha + \beta\right)$

and since $r/b \fallingdotseq (1 + \beta \sin\theta)$ and $\alpha\beta \fallingdotseq \beta^2 \fallingdotseq 0$

$$q_c = 2U[\sin\theta(1 + \beta\sin\theta) + \alpha(1 + \cos\theta)] \qquad . \quad (12.23)$$

The corresponding velocity on the circular arc aerofoil is

$$q_a = \frac{q_c}{\left|\dfrac{d\zeta}{dz}\right|}$$

where

$$\left|\frac{d\zeta}{dz}\right| = \left|1 - \frac{b^2}{z^2}\right| = \left|1 - \frac{b^2}{r^2}e^{-i2\theta}\right|$$

$$= \left|1 - \frac{\cos 2\theta - i\sin 2\theta}{(1 + \beta\sin\theta)^2}\right|$$

$$\left|\frac{d\zeta}{dz}\right| = \left[\left\{1 - \frac{\cos 2\theta}{(1 + \beta\sin\theta)^2}\right\}^2 + \left\{\frac{\sin 2\theta}{(1 + \beta\sin\theta)^2}\right\}^2\right]^{\frac{1}{2}}$$

$$= \left[1 - \frac{2\cos 2\theta}{(1 + \beta\sin\theta)^2} + \frac{1}{(1 + \beta\sin\theta)^4}\right]^{\frac{1}{2}}$$

$$= [(1 + \beta\sin\theta)^2 - 2\cos 2\theta + (1 + \beta\sin\theta)^{-2}]^{\frac{1}{2}}(1 + \beta\sin\theta)^{-1}$$

Now within the limits of the theory, β is small so that

$$(1 + \beta\sin\theta)^2 \fallingdotseq 1 + 2\beta\sin\theta$$

$$(1 + \beta\sin\theta)^{-2} \fallingdotseq 1 - 2\beta\sin\theta$$

which on substituting in the above expression gives

$$\left|\frac{d\zeta}{dz}\right| = (2 - 2\cos 2\theta)^{\frac{1}{2}}(1 + \beta\sin\theta)^{-1}$$

$$= \frac{2\sin\theta}{(1 + \beta\sin\theta)} \qquad . \qquad . \qquad . \qquad . \qquad . \quad (12.24)$$

Therefore the velocity on the aerofoil $q_a \equiv \dfrac{\text{eqn. (12.23)}}{\text{eqn. (12.24)}}$.

$$q_a = 2U\left[\frac{\sin\theta(1 + \beta\sin\theta) + \alpha(1 + \cos\theta)}{2\sin\theta(1 + \beta\sin\theta)^{-1}}\right]$$

$$= U\left[(1 + \beta\sin\theta)^2 + \alpha\frac{(1 + \cos\theta)}{\sin\theta}(1 + \beta\sin\theta)\right]$$

Again for α and β small, $\alpha\beta \fallingdotseq \beta^2 \fallingdotseq 0$.

$$\therefore \frac{q_a}{U} = \left[1 + 2\beta\sin\theta + \alpha\left(\frac{1 + \cos\theta}{\sin\theta}\right)\right]$$

Once again θ is the same variable as used in the general eqn. (12.12) and taking $k = q_{a1} - q_{a2}$ from eqn. (12.7)

$$k = U\left[1 + 2\beta \sin \theta_1 + \alpha\left(\frac{1 + \cos \theta_1}{\sin \theta_1}\right)\right]$$
$$- U\left[1 + 2\beta \sin (-\theta_1) + \alpha\frac{(1 + \cos (-\theta_1))}{\sin (-\theta_1)}\right]$$
$$= 2U\left[2\beta \sin \theta_1 + \alpha\left(\frac{1 + \cos \theta_1}{\sin \theta_1}\right)\right]$$

and hence for any position θ

$$k = 2U\left[2\beta \sin \theta + \alpha\left(\frac{1 + \cos \theta}{\sin \theta}\right)\right] \qquad . \qquad (12.25)$$

Eqn. (12.16) may now be compared directly with eqn. (12.25). They refer to the k distribution along a flat plate, and a circular arc aerofoil respectively.

Rewriting them for comparison

$$k \text{ (for flat plate)} = 2U\alpha\frac{1 + \cos \theta}{\sin \theta} \qquad . \qquad (12.16)$$

$$k \text{ (for circular arc)} = 2U\left[\alpha\frac{1 + \cos \theta}{\sin \theta} + 2\beta \sin \theta\right] \quad (12.25)$$

It is apparent that the effect of the camber of this circular arc aerofoil is to increase the k distribution by $2U . 2\beta \sin \theta$ over that of the flat plate, and that the distribution for the cambered aerofoil can be expressed as the sum of two parts.

Thus $\qquad k = k_{(a)} + k_{(b)}$

where $\qquad k_{(a)} = 2U\alpha\frac{1 + \cos \theta}{\sin \theta}$

arises from the incidence of the aerofoil alone,

and $\qquad k_{(b)} = 4U\beta \sin \theta$

arises from the effect of the camber alone.

A final point to note is that this distribution satisfies the Kutta–Zhukovsky hypothesis (it should, since it was derived on that basis) by allowing k to vanish at the trailing edge where $\theta = \pi$.

Lift and moment coefficient and k_{cp} for a circular arc aerofoil. The same process as that adopted in the case of the flat plate can now be followed,

i.e., $\qquad p = \rho Uk; \quad l = C_L\frac{1}{2}\rho U^2 c = \int_0^c \rho Uk \, dx$

and $\qquad M_{\text{L.E.}} = C_{M \text{ L.E.}} \frac{1}{2}\rho U^2 c^2 = \int_0^c \rho Ukx \, dx$ etc.

Directly from (12.25)

$$p = 2\rho U^2\left[\alpha\frac{1 + \cos \theta}{\sin \theta} + 2\beta \sin \theta\right] \qquad . \qquad (12.26)$$

with the usual substitution $x = (c/2)(1 - \cos \theta)$, etc.

$$l = \int_0^\pi 2\rho U^2 \left[\alpha \frac{(1 + \cos \theta)}{\sin \theta} + 2\beta \sin \theta \right] \frac{c}{2} \sin \theta \, d\theta$$

$$= \rho U^2 c \int_0^\pi [\alpha(1 + \cos \theta) + 2\beta \sin^2 \theta] \, d\theta$$

$$= \pi \rho U^2 c(\alpha + \beta)$$

$$\therefore \; C_L = 2\pi(\alpha + \beta) \qquad . \qquad . \qquad . \qquad . \qquad . \qquad . \qquad (12.27)$$

and $\qquad \dfrac{dC_L}{d\alpha} = 2\pi$

There are two deductions from eqn. (12.27). The first is that the aerofoil will, at zero incidence, produce a lift coefficient of magnitude $C_L = 2\pi\beta$, which is due entirely to the camber.

The second—a corollary of the first—is that zero lift is obtained at a negative incidence given by $-\beta$.

The aerodynamic moment about the leading edge is given by

$$M_{\text{L.E.}} = - \int_0^c px \, dx = - 2\rho U^2 \int_0^\pi \left[\alpha \frac{(1 + \cos \theta)}{\sin \theta} + 2\beta \sin \theta \right]$$

$$\frac{c}{2}(1 - \cos \theta) \cdot \frac{c}{2} \sin \theta \, d\theta$$

$$= - 2\rho U^2 \left(\frac{c}{2}\right)^2 \int_0^\pi [\alpha(1 - \cos^2 \theta) + 2\beta \sin^2 \theta(1 - \cos \theta)] \, d\theta$$

$$\therefore \; - C_{M \text{ L.E.}} \tfrac{1}{2}\rho U^2 c^2 = \tfrac{1}{2}\rho U^2 c^2 \left[\frac{\pi}{2}\alpha + \frac{2\pi}{2}\beta \right]$$

$$C_{M \text{ L.E.}} = - \frac{\pi}{2}[\alpha + 2\beta] \qquad . \qquad . \qquad . \qquad . \qquad . \qquad . \qquad (12.28)$$

Comparing this with eqn. (12.19) shows that the camber of the circular arc decreases the moment about the leading edge by $\pi\beta$ so that compared with (12.20)

$$C_{M \text{ L.E.}} = - \frac{C_L}{4} - \pi\beta \qquad . \qquad . \qquad . \qquad (12.29)$$

The centre of pressure coefficient k_{cp} becomes

$$k_{cp} = - \frac{C_{M \text{ L.E.}}}{C_L} = \tfrac{1}{4} + \frac{\pi\beta}{C_L} \qquad . \qquad . \qquad . \qquad (12.30)$$

The effect of the camber is thus to set back the centre of pressure by an amount which decreases with increasing incidence or lift.

At zero lift the centre of pressure is an infinite distance behind the aerofoil, which means that there is a moment on the aerofoil but no resultant lift force. This cannot apply to the flat plate aerofoil.

12.3.3. The general thin aerofoil section.

As suggested in the previous section, the general camber line can be replaced by a chordwise distribution of circulation, made up of two components. One component defines the distribution due to the equivalent flat plate section and accommodates the incidence variable, and the other component defines the distribution, resulting from any deviation from the straight line, present in the camber line shape.

Thus, as before $k = k_{(a)} + k_{(b)}$. The $k_{(a)}$ component is of the same form as the distribution over the flat plate but must contain a constant (A_0) to absorb any difference between the 'equivalent' flat plate and the actual chord line.

Then
$$k_{(a)} = 2UA_0\left(\frac{1 + \cos \theta}{\sin \theta}\right) \qquad . \qquad . \qquad . \qquad (12.31)$$

Note the Kutta–Zhukovsky condition is satisfied since $k_{(a)} = 0$ when $\theta = \pi$ (i.e., $x = c$).

The component, $k_{(b)}$, is conveniently represented by a Fourier series. Providing $0 < \theta < \pi$, the end conditions are satisfied, and any variation in shape accommodated if it is a sine series; thus

$$k_{(b)} = 2U\{A_1 \sin \theta + A_2 \sin 2\theta + A_3 \sin 3\theta + A_4 \sin 4\theta \ldots\}$$

or $\quad k_{(b)} = 2U\sum_1^\infty A_n \sin n\theta$. $\qquad . \qquad . \qquad . \qquad . \qquad . \qquad (12.32)$

This gives

$$k = 2U\left\{A_0\left(\frac{1 + \cos \theta}{\sin \theta}\right) + \sum_1^\infty A_n \sin n\theta\right\} \qquad . \qquad . \qquad . \qquad (12.33)$$

Note that for the circular arc of the previous section $k_{(b)} = 2UA_1 \sin \theta$.

The coefficients $A_0, A_1, A_2 \ldots A_n$ can be found by substituting for k in the general eqn. (12.9) suitably converted with regard to units.

E.g., $\qquad U\left[\dfrac{dy}{dx} - \alpha\right] = \dfrac{1}{2\pi}\displaystyle\int_0^c \dfrac{k\,dx}{x - x_1}$ (eqn. (12.9))

substituting

$$x = \frac{c}{2}(1 - \cos \theta); \quad dx = \frac{c}{2}\sin \theta\,d\theta; \quad x = c \text{ when } \theta = \pi$$

$$U\left[\frac{dy}{dx} - \alpha\right] = -\frac{1}{2\pi}\int_0^\pi \frac{k \sin \theta\,d\theta}{\cos \theta - \cos \theta_1}$$

and substituting from eqn. (12.33)

$$U\left[\frac{dy}{dx} - \alpha\right] = -\frac{2U}{2\pi}\int_0^\pi\left\{\frac{A_0(1 + \cos \theta)}{\sin \theta} + \sum_1^\infty A_n \sin n\theta\right\}\frac{\sin \theta\,d\theta}{\cos \theta - \cos \theta_1}$$

At the point x_1 (or θ_1) on the aerofoil

$$\frac{dy}{dx} - \alpha = -\frac{A_0}{\pi}\int_0^\pi \frac{(1 + \cos \theta)\,d\theta}{\cos \theta - \cos \theta_1} - \frac{1}{\pi}\int_0^\pi \sum \frac{A_n \sin n\theta \sin \theta\,d\theta}{\cos \theta - \cos \theta_1}$$

Reducing $\qquad\qquad \sum A_n \sin n\theta \sin \theta$

to $\qquad\qquad\qquad \sum A_n \tfrac{1}{2}(\cos (n - 1)\theta - \cos (n + 1)\theta)$

the expression reduces to

$$\frac{dy}{dx} - \alpha = - \left\{ \frac{A_0}{\pi}G_{(0)} + \frac{A_0}{\pi}G_{(1)} + \sum \frac{A_n}{2\pi}G_{(n-1)} - \sum \frac{A_n}{2\pi}G_{(n+1)} \right\}$$

where $G_{(n)}$ signifies the integral $\displaystyle\int_0^\pi \frac{\cos n\theta \, d\theta}{\cos \theta - \cos \theta_1}$

which has the solution $\dfrac{\pi \sin n\theta_1}{\sin \theta_1}$. (See § 13.3.4)

$$\frac{dy}{dx} - \alpha = - \frac{A_0}{\pi}\pi - \sum A_n \frac{\sin (n - 1)\theta_1 - \sin (n + 1)\theta_1}{2 \sin \theta_1}$$

and for the general point $x = (c/2)(1 - \cos \theta)$ on the aerofoil

$$\frac{dy}{dx} - \alpha = - A_0 + \sum A_n \cos n\theta$$

or rearranging

$$\frac{dy}{dx} = - A_0 + \alpha + \sum A_n \cos n\theta \qquad . \qquad . \quad (12.34)$$

On integrating both sides with respect to θ from 0 to π the third term on the right-hand side vanishes leaving

$$\int_0^\pi \frac{dy}{dx}d\theta = \int_0^\pi (\alpha - A_0) \, d\theta = (\alpha - A_0)\pi$$

$$\therefore \; A_0 = \alpha - \frac{1}{\pi} \int_0^\pi \frac{dy}{dx}d\theta \qquad . \qquad . \qquad . \qquad . \quad (12.35)$$

Multiplying both sides of eqn. (12.34) by $\cos m\theta$, where m is an integer, and integrating with respect to θ

$$\int_0^\pi \frac{dy}{dx}\cos m\theta \, d\theta = \int_0^\pi (\alpha - A_0) \cos m\theta \, d\theta$$

$$+ \int_0^\pi \sum A_n \cos n\theta \cos m\theta \, d\theta$$

$\displaystyle\int_0^\pi A_n \cos n\theta \cos m\theta \, d\theta = 0 \quad$ except when $m = n$.

Then the first term on the right-hand side vanishes, and also the second term, except for $n = m$, i.e.,

$$\int_0^\pi \frac{dy}{dx} \cos n\theta = \int_0^\pi A_n \cos^2 n\theta = \frac{\pi}{2} A_n$$

whence $\qquad\qquad A_n = \frac{2}{\pi} \int_0^\pi \frac{dy}{dx} \cos n\theta \, d\theta \qquad . \qquad . \qquad . \quad (12.36)$

The lift, moment and centre of pressure coefficients for a general thin aero-foil. From the equations above

$$k = 2U\left[A_0\frac{(1 + \cos\theta)}{\sin\theta} + \sum_1^\infty A_n \sin n\theta\right]$$

From eqn. (12.4)

$$l = \int_0^c \rho Uk\, dx = \int_0^\pi \rho U\frac{c}{2}k \sin\theta\, d\theta$$

$$= 2\rho U^2\frac{c}{2}\int_0^\pi\left[A_0(1 + \cos\theta) + \sum_1^\infty A_n \sin n\theta \sin\theta\right]d\theta$$

$$= 2\rho U^2\frac{c}{2}\left[\pi A_0 + \frac{\pi}{2}A_1\right] = C_L\tfrac{1}{2}\rho U^2 c$$

since $\displaystyle\int_0^\pi \sin n\theta \sin\theta\, d\theta = 0$ when $n \neq 1$,

giving
$$C_L = 2\pi A_0 + \pi A_1 \qquad . \qquad . \qquad . \qquad (12.37)$$

As a check
$$C_L = 2\pi\left[A_0 + \frac{A_1}{2}\right]$$

can be compared with eqn. (12.27) which gives the C_L for a circular arc. Once again the lift coefficient is increased by the product of π and the *first term* of the Fourier sine series describing the camber.

From eqn. (12.5)

$$-M_{\text{L.E.}} = \rho U\int_0^c kx\, dx = \frac{-C_{M\,\text{L.E.}}}{\tfrac{1}{2}\rho U^2 c^2}$$

With the usual substitution

$$-C_{M\,\text{L.E.}} = \frac{2\rho U^2(c/2)^2}{\tfrac{1}{2}\rho U^2 c^2}\int_0^\pi\left[A_0\frac{(1 + \cos\theta)}{\sin\theta} + \sum_1^\infty A_n \sin n\theta\right]$$
$$\sin\theta\,(1 - \cos\theta)\, d\theta$$

$$= \int_0^\pi A_0(1 - \cos^2\theta)\, d\theta + \int_0^\pi\sum_1^\infty A_n \sin n\theta \sin\theta\, d\theta$$

$$-\int_0^\pi\sum A_n \sin n\theta \cos\theta \sin\theta\, d\theta$$

$$= \frac{\pi}{2}A_0 + \frac{\pi}{2}A_1 - \frac{\pi}{4}A_2$$

since $\displaystyle\int_0^\pi \sin n\theta \sin m\theta\, d\theta = 0$ when $n \neq m$,

or
$$C_{M\,\text{L.E.}} = -\frac{\pi}{2}\left[A_0 + A_1 - \frac{A_2}{2}\right] \qquad . \qquad . \qquad (12.38)$$

In terms of the lift coefficient, $C_{M\,\text{L.E.}}$ becomes

$$C_{M\,\text{L.E.}} = -\frac{C_L}{4}\left[1 + \frac{A_1 - A_2}{C_L/\pi}\right]$$

Then the centre of pressure coefficient is

$$k_{cp} = -\frac{C_{M\,\text{L.E.}}}{C_L} = \frac{1}{4} + \frac{\pi}{4C_L}(A_1 - A_2) \quad . \qquad (12.39)$$

and again the C.P. moves as the lift or incidence is changed.

Now, from § 6.5.2
$$k_{cp} = -\frac{C_{M\,1/4}}{C_L} + \frac{1}{4} \qquad . \qquad . \qquad . \qquad (12.40)$$

and comparing eqns. (12.38) and (12.39) gives

$$-C_{M\,1/4} = \frac{\pi}{4}(A_1 - A_2) \qquad . \qquad . \qquad . \qquad (12.41)$$

This shows that, theoretically, the pitching moment about the quarter chord point for a thin aerofoil is constant, depending on the camber parameters only, and the quarter chord point is therefore the aerodynamic centre.

It is apparent from this analysis that no matter what the camber line shape, only the first two terms of the sine series describing that shape have any influence on the usual aerodynamic characteristics. This is indeed the case, but the terms corresponding to $n > 2$ contribute to the pressure distribution over the chord.

Owing to the quality of the basic approximations used in the theory it is found that the theoretical chordwise pressure distribution p does not agree closely with experimental data, especially near the leading edge and near stagnation points where the small perturbation theory, for example, breaks down. Any local inaccuracies tend to vanish in the overall integration processes, however, and the aerofoil coefficients are found to be reliable theoretical predictions.

12.4. The flapped aerofoil. Thin aerofoil theory lends itself very readily to aerofoils with variable camber such as flapped aerofoils.

The distribution of circulation along the camber line for the general aerofoil has been found to consist of the sum of a component due to a flat plate at incidence and a component due to the camber line shape. It is sufficient for the assumptions in the theory to consider the influence of a flap deflection as an addition to the two components above. Fig. 12.6 shows

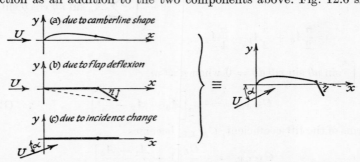

FIG. 12.6.—Subdivision of lift contributions to total lift of cambered flapped aerofoil.

how the three contributions can be combined. In fact the deflection of the flap about a hinge in the camber line effectively alters the camber so that the contribution due to flap deflection is the effect of an additional camber line shape.

The problem is thus reduced to the general case of finding a distribution to fit a camber line made up of the chord of the aerofoil and the flap chord deflected through η (see Fig. 12.7).

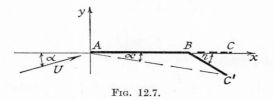

FIG. 12.7.

If the camber line is now ABC', the x axis must be taken along the 'new' chord AC' which is inclined at an effective incidence $\alpha + \alpha'$ to the wind stream (Fig. 12.8).

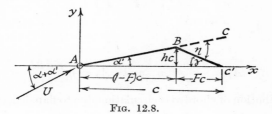

FIG. 12.8.

With the camber defined as hc the slope of the part AB of the aerofoil is $h/(1-F)$, and that of the flap $-h/F$. To find the coefficients of k for the 'flap camber' substitute these values of slope in eqns. (12.35) and (12.36) but with the limits of integration confined to the parts of the aerofoil over which the slopes occur. Thus

$$A_0 = \alpha + \alpha' - \left\{ \frac{1}{\pi} \int_0^\phi \frac{h}{1-F} d\theta + \frac{1}{\pi} \int_\phi^\pi \frac{-h}{F} d\theta \right\} \quad . \quad (12.42)$$

where ϕ is the value of θ at the hinge,

i.e., $$(1-F)c = \frac{c}{2}(1 - \cos \phi)$$

whence $\cos \phi = 2F - 1$.

Evaluating the integral

$$A_0 = \alpha + \alpha' - \frac{1}{\pi} \left[\frac{h}{1-F} \phi - \frac{h}{F}(\pi - \phi) \right]$$

$$A_0 = \alpha + \alpha' + \frac{h}{F} - \frac{\phi}{\pi}\left(\frac{h}{1-F} + \frac{h}{F} \right) \quad . \quad . \quad (12.43)$$

For α' and η to be small enough to satisfy the theory, Fig. 12.3 shows that

$$\eta = \alpha' + \gamma = \frac{h}{1-F} + \frac{h}{F} \qquad . \qquad . \quad (12.44)$$

and

$$\alpha' + \frac{h}{F} = \eta \qquad . \qquad . \qquad . \qquad . \quad (12.45)$$

which substituted in eqn. (12.43) above gives

$$A_0 = \alpha + \eta - \frac{\phi}{\pi}(\eta)$$

i.e.,

$$A_0 = \alpha + \eta\left(1 - \frac{\phi}{\pi}\right) \qquad . \qquad . \quad (12.46)$$

Similarly from (12.36)

$$A_n = \frac{2}{\pi}\left\{\int_0^\phi \frac{h}{1-F}\cos n\theta \, d\theta + \int_\phi^\pi -\frac{h}{F}\cos n\theta \, d\theta\right\}$$

$$= \frac{2}{n\pi}\left\{\frac{h}{1-F}\sin n\phi - \frac{h}{F}[\sin n\pi - \sin n\phi]\right\}$$

$$= \frac{2}{n\pi}.\sin n\phi\left[\frac{h}{1-F} + \frac{h}{F}\right]$$

$$A_n = \frac{2\sin n\phi}{n\pi}.\eta \qquad . \qquad . \qquad . \qquad . \quad (12.47)$$

Thus

$$A_1 = \frac{2\sin\phi}{\pi}.\eta \quad \text{and} \quad A_2 = \eta.\frac{\sin 2\phi}{\pi}$$

The distribution of chordwise circulation due to flap deflection becomes

$$k = 2U\alpha\frac{1+\cos\theta}{\sin\theta} + 2U\left[\left(1 - \frac{\phi}{\pi}\right)\frac{1+\cos\theta}{\sin\theta}\right.$$

$$\left. + \sum_1^\infty \frac{2\sin n\theta}{n\pi}\sin n\theta\right].\eta \qquad . \qquad . \quad (12.48)$$

and this for a constant incidence α is a linear function of η, as is the lift coefficient,

e.g., from eqn. (12.37)

$$C_L = 2\pi A_0 + \pi A_1$$

$$C_L = 2\pi\alpha + 2\pi\eta\left(1 - \frac{\phi}{\pi}\right) + 2\eta\sin\phi$$

giving

$$C_L = 2\pi\alpha + 2[(\pi - \phi + \sin\phi)].\eta \qquad . \qquad . \quad (12.49)$$

Likewise the moment coefficient $C_{M \text{ L.E.}}$ from eqn. (12.38) is

$$-C_{M \text{ L.E.}} = \frac{\pi}{2}\alpha + \frac{\pi}{2}\left[\eta\left(1 - \frac{\phi}{\pi}\right) + \frac{2\sin\phi}{\pi}.\eta - \frac{\sin 2\phi}{2\pi}.\eta\right]$$

$$C_{M \text{ L.E.}} = -\frac{\pi}{2}\alpha - \frac{1}{2}[\pi - \phi + \sin\phi(2 - \cos\phi)].\eta \quad . \quad (12.50)$$

In both eqns. (12.49) and (12.50) ϕ is given by

$$c(1 - F) = \frac{c}{2}(1 - \cos \phi)$$

Note that a positive flap deflection, i.e., a downwards deflection, *decreases* the moment coefficient, tending to pitch the main aerofoil nose down and vice versa.

The hinge moment coefficient. A flapped aerofoil characteristic, which is of great importance in stability and control calculations, is the aerodynamic moment about the hinge line, shown as H in the Fig. 12.9.

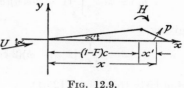

FIG. 12.9.

Taking moments of elementary pressures p, acting on the flap, about the hinge

$$H = - \int_{\text{hinge}}^{\text{trailing edge}} px' \, dx \qquad \begin{array}{l} \text{where } p = \rho U k \\ \text{and } \quad x' = x - (1 - F)c \end{array}$$

putting $\quad x' = \dfrac{c}{2}(1 - \cos \theta) - \dfrac{c}{2}(1 - \cos \phi) = \dfrac{c}{2}(\cos \phi - \cos \theta)$

and k from eqn. (12.48)

$$H = - \int_{\phi}^{\pi} 2\rho U^2 \left[\left\{ \alpha + \eta \left(1 - \frac{\phi}{\pi} \right) \right\} \frac{(1 + \cos \theta)}{\sin \theta} \right.$$
$$\left. + \eta \sum_{1}^{\infty} \frac{2 \sin n\phi}{n\pi} \sin n\theta \right] \frac{c}{2}(\cos \phi - \cos \theta) . \frac{c}{2} \sin \theta \, d\theta$$

Substituting $H = C_H \frac{1}{2}\rho U^2 (Fc)^2$ and cancelling

$$- C_H F^2 = \alpha \int_{\phi}^{\pi} (1 + \cos \theta)(\cos \phi - \cos \theta) \, d\theta$$
$$+ \eta \left\{ \left(1 - \frac{\theta}{\pi} \right) \cos \phi \, I_1 - \left(1 - \frac{\phi}{\pi} \right) I_2 \right.$$
$$\left. + \sum_{1}^{\infty} \frac{2 \sin n\phi}{n\pi} \cos \phi \, I_3 + \sum_{1}^{\infty} \frac{2 \sin n\phi}{n\pi} I_4 \right\} \qquad . \quad (12.51)$$

where

$$I_1 = \int_{\phi}^{\pi} (1 + \cos \theta) \, d\theta = \pi - \phi - \sin \phi$$

$$I_2 = \int_{\phi}^{\pi} (1 + \cos \theta) \cos \theta \, d\theta = \left[\frac{\pi - \phi}{2} \sin \phi - \frac{\sin 2\phi}{4} \right]$$

$$I_3 = \int_{\phi}^{\pi} \sin n\theta \, \sin \theta \, d\theta = \frac{1}{2} \left[\frac{\sin (n + 1)\phi}{n + 1} - \frac{\sin (n - 1)\phi}{n - 1} \right]$$

$$I_4 = \int_{\phi}^{\pi} \sin n\theta \, \sin \theta \, \cos \theta \, d\theta = \frac{1}{2} \left[\frac{\sin (n + 2)\phi}{n + 2} - \frac{\sin (n - 2)\phi}{n - 2} \right]$$

In the usual notation $C_H = b_1\alpha + b_2\eta$,

where $$b_1 = \frac{\partial C_H}{\partial \alpha} \quad \text{and} \quad b_2 = \frac{\partial C_H}{\partial \eta}$$

From eqn. (12.51),

$$b_1 = -\frac{1}{F^2}\int_\phi^\pi (1 + \cos\theta)(\cos\phi - \cos\theta)\,d\theta$$

giving

$$b_1 = -\frac{1}{4F^2}\{2(\pi - \phi)(2\cos\phi - 1) + 4\sin\phi - \sin 2\phi\}. \quad (12.52)$$

Similarly from eqn. (12.51),

$$b_2 = \frac{\partial C_H}{\partial \eta} = \frac{1}{F^2} \times \text{coefficient of } \eta \text{ in eqn. (12.51)}$$

This somewhat unwieldy expression reduces to*

$$b_2 = -\frac{1}{4\pi F^2}\{(1 - \cos 2\phi) - 2(\pi - \phi)^2(1 - 2\cos\phi) + 4(\pi - \phi)\sin\phi\}$$
$$(12.53)$$

The parameter $a_1 = \partial C_L/\partial \alpha$ is 2π and $a_2 = \partial C_L/\partial \eta$ from
eqn. (12.49)

becomes $$a_2 = 2(\pi - \phi + \sin\phi) \quad . \quad . \quad . \quad (12.54)$$

Thus thin aerofoil theory provides an estimate of all the parameters of a flapped aerofoil.

Note that aspect ratio corrections have not been included in this analysis which is essentially two-dimensional. Following the conclusions of the finite aerofoil theory in Chapter 13 the parameters a_1, a_2, b_1 and b_2 may be suitably corrected for 'end effects'. In practice, however, they are always determined from exhaustive tunnel tests.

12.5. The jet flap. Considering the jet flap as a high-velocity sheet of air issuing from the trailing edge of an aerofoil at some downward angle τ to the chord line of the aerofoil, an analysis can be made by replacing the jet stream as well as the aerofoil by a vortex distribution.†

The flap contributes to the lift on two accounts. Firstly the downward deflection of the jet efflux produces a lifting component of reaction, and secondly the jet affects the pressure distribution on the aerofoil in a similar manner to that obtained by an addition to the circulation round the aerofoil.

The jet is shown to be equivalent to a band of spanwise vortex fila-

* See *R. and M.* No. 1095 for the complete analysis.
† D. A. Spence, 'The lift coefficient of a thin, jet flapped wing', *Proc. Roy. Soc. A.*, No. 1212, Dec. 1956. D. A. Spence, 'The lift on a thin aerofoil with jet augmented flap', *Aeronautical Quarterly*, Aug. 1958.

ments which for small deflection angles τ can be assumed to lie along the Ox axis (Fig. 12.10). In the analysis, which will not be proceeded with here, both components of lift are considered in order to arrive at the expression for C_L,

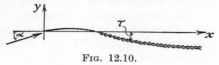

FIG. 12.10.

$$C_L = 4\pi A_0 \tau + 2\pi(1 + 2B_0)\alpha \qquad . \qquad . \quad (12.55)$$

where A_0 and B_0 are the initial coefficients in the Fourier series associated with the deflection of the jet and the incidence of the aerofoil respectively and which can be obtained in terms of the momentum (coefficient) of the jet.

It is interesting to notice that in experimental work on jet flaps at N.G.T.E. Pyestock, good agreement was obtained with the theoretical C_L even at large values of τ.

12.6.* The normal force and pitching moment derivatives due to pitching. $(Z_q)(M_q)$ *wing contributions.* Thin aerofoil theory can be used as a convenient basis for the estimation of these important derivatives. Although the use of derivatives is beyond the general scope of this volume, some moment velocity and moment rotary derivatives are introduced in Chapter 14, and no text on thin aerofoil theory is complete without some reference to this common use of the theory.

FIG. 12.11.   FIG. 12.12.

When an aeroplane is rotating with pitching velocity q about an axis through the C.G. normal to the plane of symmetry on the chord line produced (see Fig. 12.11), the aerofoil effective incidence is changing with time as also, as a consequence, are the aerodynamic forces and moments.

The rates of change of these forces and moments with respect to the pitching velocity q are two of the Aerodynamic Quasi-static Derivatives which are in general commonly abbreviated to Derivatives.

Here the rate of change of normal force on the aircraft (i.e., resultant force in the normal or Z direction) with respect to pitching velocity is, in the conventional notation, $\partial Z/\partial q$. This is symbolized by Z_q.

Similarly the rate of change of M with respect to q is $\partial M/\partial q = M_q$.

In common with other aerodynamic forces and moments these are reduced to non-dimensional or coefficient form by dividing through in this case by $\rho V l_t$ and $\rho V l_t^2$ respectively, to give the non-dimensional normal

* It is suggested that this section be omitted from general study until the reader is familiar with these derivatives and their use.

force derivative due to pitching z_q, and the non-dimensional pitching moment derivative due to pitching m_q.

The contributions to these two, due to the mainplanes, can be considered by replacing the wing by the equivalent thin aerofoil. In Fig. 12.12 the centre of rotation (C.G.) is a distance hc behind the leading edge where c is the chord.

At some point x from the leading edge of the aerofoil the velocity induced by the rotation of the aerofoil about the C.G. is $v' = -q(hc - x)$. Due to the vorticity replacing the camber line a velocity v is induced. The incident wind stream is V inclined at α to the chord line, and from the condition that the local velocity at x must be tangential to the aerofoil (camber line), see § 12.2, eqn. (12.8) becomes for this case

$$V\left(\frac{dy}{dx} - \alpha\right) = v - v'$$

or

$$\frac{dy}{dx} - \alpha = \frac{v}{V} - \frac{q}{V}(hc - x) \qquad . \qquad . \qquad (12.56)$$

and with the substitution $x = \frac{c}{2}(1 - \cos \theta)$

$$\frac{dy}{dx} - \alpha = \frac{v}{V} - \frac{qc}{V}\left(h - \frac{1}{2} + \frac{\cos \theta}{2}\right)$$

From the general case in steady straight flight eqn. (12.34)

$$\frac{dy}{dx} - \alpha = -A_0 + \sum A_n \cos n\theta \qquad . \qquad . \qquad (12.57)$$

but in the pitching case the loading distribution would be altered to some general form given by

$$\frac{v}{V} = -B_0 + \sum B_n \cos n\theta \qquad . \qquad . \qquad (12.58)$$

where the coefficients are changed because of the relative flow changes, while the camber line *shape* remains constant, i.e., the form of the function remains the same but the coefficients change.

Thus in the pitching case

$$\frac{dy}{dx} - \alpha = -B_0 + \sum B_n \cos n\theta - \frac{qc}{V}\left(h - \frac{1}{2} + \frac{\cos \theta}{2}\right) \qquad . \qquad (12.59)$$

Eqns. (12.57) and (12.59) give:

$$B_0 = A_0 + \frac{qc}{V}\left(\frac{1}{2} - h\right),$$

$$B_1 = A_1 + \frac{qc}{2V}, \quad \text{and} \quad B_n = A_n$$

The lift coefficient in terms of the general distribution

$$k = 2V\left[B_0\left(\frac{1 + \cos \theta}{\sin \theta}\right) + \sum B_n \sin n\theta\right]$$

is, from § 12.3.3,

$$C_L = 2\pi B_0 + \pi B_1 = 2\pi\left\{A_0 + \frac{A_1}{2} + \left(\frac{3}{4} - h\right)\frac{qc}{V}\right\} \qquad . \qquad (12.60)$$

It should be remembered that this is for a two-dimensional wing. However, the effect of the curvature of the trailing vortex sheet is negligible in three dimensions, so it remains to replace the ideal $\partial C_L/\partial\alpha = 2\pi$ by a reasonable value, a, which accounts for the aspect ratio change (see Chapter 13). The lift coefficient of a pitching rectangular wing then becomes

$$C_L = a\left\{A_0 + \frac{A_1}{2} + \left(\frac{3}{4} - h\right)\frac{qc}{V}\right\} \qquad . \qquad (12.61)$$

Similarly the pitching moment coefficient about the leading edge is found from eqn. (12.38)

$$C_{M\text{ L.E.}} = \frac{\pi}{4}(B_2 - B_1) - \frac{C_L}{4}$$

$$= \frac{\pi}{4}(A_2 - A_1) - \frac{\pi qC}{8V} - \frac{1}{4}C_L \qquad . \qquad (12.62)$$

which for a rectangular wing becomes on substituting for C_L

$$C_{M\text{L.E.}} = \frac{\pi}{4}(A_2 - A_1) - \frac{\pi}{8}\frac{c}{V}q - \frac{a}{4}\left\{A_0 + \frac{A_1}{2} + \left(\frac{3}{4} - h\right)\frac{qc}{V}\right\} \qquad . \qquad (12.63)$$

The moment coefficient of importance in the derivative is that about the C.G. and this is found from

$$C_{M\text{ C.G.}} = C_{M\text{ L.E.}} + hC_L \qquad . \qquad . \qquad . \qquad (12.64)$$

and substituting appropriate values

$$C_{M\text{ C.G.}} = \frac{\pi}{4}(A_2 - A_1) - \frac{2\pi}{16}\frac{qc}{V} + (h - \tfrac{1}{4})\,a\left[A_0 + \frac{A_1}{2} + \left(\frac{3}{4} - h\right)\frac{qc}{V}\right]$$

which can be rearranged in terms of a function of coefficients A_n plus a term involving q thus

$$C_{M\text{ C.G.}} = \mathrm{f}(A_n) - \left[\frac{a}{4}(1 - 2h)^2 + \frac{2\pi - a}{16}\right]\frac{qc}{V} \qquad . \qquad (12.65)$$

The contribution of the wings to Z_q or z_q thus becomes

$$Z_q = \frac{\partial Z}{\partial q} = -\frac{\partial L}{\partial q} = -\frac{\partial C_L}{\partial q}\frac{1}{2}\rho V^2 S$$

$$= -\frac{1}{2}\rho V^2 S a\left(\frac{3}{4} - h\right)\frac{c}{V}$$

by differentiating eqn. (12.61) with respect to q.

Therefore for a rectangular wing, defining z_q by $Z_q/\rho VSl_t$

$$z_q = \frac{-a}{2}\left(\frac{3}{4} - h\right)\frac{c}{l_t} \qquad . \qquad . \qquad (12.66)$$

For other than rectangular wings an approximate expression can be obtained by using the strip theory,

e.g.,
$$Z_q = -\rho V \int_{-s}^{s} \frac{a}{2}\left(\frac{3}{4} - h\right)c^2 \, dy$$

giving
$$z_q = \frac{-1}{Sl_t} \int_{-s}^{s} \frac{a}{2}\left(\frac{3}{4} - h\right)c^2 \, dy \quad . \qquad . \qquad . \quad (12.67)$$

In a similar fashion the contribution to M_q and m_q can be found by differentiating the expression for $M_{\text{C.G.}}$ with respect to q,

i.e.,
$$M_q = \frac{\partial M_{\text{C.G.}}}{\partial q} = \frac{\partial C_{M\text{C.G.}}}{\partial q}\frac{1}{2}\rho V^2 Sc$$

$$M_q = -\frac{1}{2}\rho V^2 Sc\left\{\frac{a}{4}(1 - 2h)^2 + \frac{2\pi - a}{16}\right\}\frac{c}{V} \quad \text{from eqn. (12.65)}$$

$$M_q = -\left[\frac{a}{8}(1 - 2h^2) + \frac{2\pi - a}{32}\right]VSc^2 \quad . \qquad . \qquad . \qquad . \quad (12.68)$$

giving for a rectangular wing

$$m_q = \frac{M_q}{\rho VSl_t^2} = -\left[\frac{a}{8}(1 - 2h)^2 + \frac{2\pi - a}{32}\right]\frac{c^2}{l_t^2} \quad . \quad (12.69)$$

For other than rectangular wings the contribution becomes, by strip theory,

$$M_q = -\rho V \int_{-s}^{s}\left\{\frac{a}{8}(1 - 2h)^2 + \frac{2\pi - a}{32}\right\}c^3 \, dy \quad . \quad (12.70)$$

and
$$m_q = -\frac{1}{Sl_t^2}\int_{-s}^{s}\left\{\frac{a}{8}(1 - 2h)^2 + \frac{2\pi - a}{32}\right\}c^3 \, dy \quad . \quad (12.71)$$

For the theoretical estimation of z_q and m_q, of the complete aircraft, the contributions of the tailplane must be added. These are given here for completeness.

$$\left.\begin{aligned} z_{q\text{ tail}} &= -\frac{1}{2}\frac{S'}{S}\left(\frac{\partial C_L{'}}{\partial \alpha'} + C_D{'}\right)\\ m_{q\text{ tail}} &= -\frac{1}{2}\frac{S'}{S}\left(\frac{\partial C_L{'}}{\partial \alpha'} + C_D{'}\right) \end{aligned}\right\} \quad . \qquad . \quad (12.72)$$

where the terms with dashes refer to tailplane data.

12.7. Particular camber lines.

Previous sections in this chapter have shown that quite general camber lines may be used in the theory satisfactorily and reasonable predictions of the aerofoil characteristics obtained. The reverse problem may be of more interest to the aerofoil designer who wishes to obtain the camber line shape to produce certain desirable characteristics. The general design problem is more comprehensive than this simple statement suggests and the theory so far dealt with is capable of considerable extension involving the introduction of 'thickness' functions to give shape to the camber line.* This allows an aerofoil shape to be designed for a given pressure distribution.

* L. M. Milne-Thomson, *Theoretical Aerodynamics.*

12.7.1. Cubic camber lines.

Starting with a desirable aerodynamic characteristic the simpler problem will be considered here. Numerous authorities* have taken a cubic equation as the general shape and evaluated the coefficients required to give the aerofoil the characteristic of a fixed centre of pressure. The resulting camber line has the reflex trailing edge which is the well-known feature of this characteristic.

Example 12.1. Find the cubic camber line which will provide zero pitching moment about the quarter chord point for a given camber.

The general equation for a cubic can be written as $y = a'x(x + b')(x + d')$ with the origin at the leading edge.

For convenience the new variables $x_1 = x/c$ and $y_1 = y/\delta$ can be introduced. δ is the camber.

The conditions to be satisfied are:

That

(i) $y = 0$ when $x = 0$, i.e., $y_1 = x_1 = 0$ at leading edge.

(ii) $y = 0$ when $x = c$, i.e., $y_1 = 0$ when $x_1 = 1$.

(iii) $\dfrac{dy}{dx} = 0$ and $y = \delta$, i.e., $\dfrac{dy_1}{dx_1} = 0$ when $y_1 = 1$ (when $x_1 = x_0$).

(iv) $C_{M\,1/4} = 0$, i.e., $A_1 - A_2 = 0$.

Rewriting the cubic in the 'dimensionless' variables x_1 and y_1

$$y_1 = ax_1(x_1 + b)(x_1 + d). \qquad . \qquad . \qquad . \qquad (12.73)$$

this satisfies condition (i).

To satisfy condition (ii) $(x_1 + d) = 0$ when $x_1 = 1$, $\therefore d = -1$, giving

$$y_1 = ax_1(x_1 + b)(x_1 - 1). \qquad . \qquad . \qquad . \qquad (12.74)$$

or multiplying out

$$y_1 = ax_1{}^3 + a(b - 1)x_1{}^2 - abx_1 \qquad . \qquad . \qquad (12.75)$$

Differentiating (12.75) to satisfy (iii)

$$\frac{dy_1}{dx_1} = 3ax_1{}^2 + 2a(b - 1)x_1 - ab = 0 \text{ when } y_1 = 1 \quad . \quad (12.76)$$

and if x_0 corresponds to the value of x_1 when $y_1 = 1$, i.e., at the point of maximum displacement from the chord the two simultaneous equations are

$$\left.\begin{array}{l} 1 = ax_0{}^3 + a(b - 1)x_0{}^2 - abx_0 \\ 0 = 3ax_0{}^2 + 2a(b - 1)x_0 - ab \end{array}\right\}. \qquad . \qquad . \qquad (12.77)$$

To satisfy (iv) above, A_1 and A_2 must be found. dy_1/dx_1 can be converted to expressions suitable for introducing in eqn. (12.36) by writing

$$x = \frac{c}{2}(1 - \cos\theta) \quad \text{or} \quad x_1 = \frac{1}{2}(1 - \cos\theta)$$

$$\frac{dy_1}{dx_1} = \frac{3}{4}a(1 - 2\cos\theta + \cos^2\theta) + a(b - 1) - a(b - 1)\cos\theta - ab$$

$$= \left(\frac{3}{4}a + ab - a - ab\right) - \left(\frac{3}{2}a + ab - a\right)\cos\theta + \frac{3}{4}a\cos^2\theta$$

$$\frac{dy_1}{dx_1} = \frac{3}{4}a\cos^2\theta - \left(\frac{a}{2} + ab\right)\cos\theta - \frac{a}{4} \quad . \qquad . \qquad . \qquad . \qquad (12.78)$$

---

* H. Glauert, *Aerofoil and Airscrew Theory.* N. A. V. Piercy, *Aerodynamics,* etc.

Y

From eqn. (12.36)

$$A_1 = \frac{2}{\pi} \int_0^\pi \left(\frac{dy}{dx}\right) \cos\theta \, d\theta = \frac{2}{\pi} \int_0^\pi \frac{\delta}{c} \frac{dy_1}{dx_1} \cos\theta \, d\theta$$

$$= \frac{2}{\pi} \cdot \frac{\delta}{c} \int_0^\pi \left(\frac{3}{4}a\cos^3\theta - \left(\frac{a}{2}+ab\right)\cos^2\theta - \frac{a}{4}\cos\theta\right) d\theta$$

$$A_1 = -\left(\frac{a}{2}+ab\right)\frac{\delta}{c}$$

Again,

$$A_2 = \frac{2}{\pi} \cdot \frac{\delta}{c} \int_0^\pi \left(\frac{dy_1}{dx_1}\right) \cos 2\theta \, d\theta$$

$$= \frac{2}{\pi} \cdot \frac{\delta}{c} \int_0^\pi \left(\frac{dy_1}{dx_1}\right)(2\cos^2\theta - 1) \, d\theta$$

$$= \frac{2}{\pi} \cdot \frac{\delta}{c} \int_0^\pi \left(\frac{3}{2}a\cos^4\theta - 2\left(\frac{a}{2}+ab\right)\cos^3\theta - \frac{a}{2}\cos^2\theta - \frac{3}{4}a\cos^2\theta \right.$$
$$\left. + \left(\frac{a}{2}+ab\right)\cos\theta + \frac{a}{4}\right) d\theta$$

$$= \frac{2}{\pi} \cdot \frac{\delta}{c} \cdot \frac{a}{4} \int_0^\pi (6\cos^4\theta - 5\cos^2\theta + 1) \, d\theta = \frac{\delta}{c} \cdot a \cdot \frac{3}{8}$$

Thus to satisfy (iv) above, $A_1 = A_2$,

i.e. $\qquad\qquad -\left(\frac{a}{2}+ab\right)\frac{\delta}{c} = a \cdot \frac{3}{8} \cdot \frac{\delta}{c} \quad$ giving $b = -\frac{7}{8}$ . . (12.79)

The quadratic in eqn. (12.77) gives for x_0 on cancelling a,

$$x_0 = \frac{-2(b-1) \pm \sqrt{2^2(b-1)^2 + 4 \times 3b}}{6} = \frac{(1-b) \pm \sqrt{b^2+b+1}}{3}$$

From eqn. (12.79), $b = -\frac{7}{8}$

giving $\qquad\qquad x_0 = \dfrac{22 \cdot 55}{24} \quad$ or $\quad \dfrac{7 \cdot 45}{24}$

i.e., taking the smaller value since the larger only gives the point of reflexure near the trailing edge,

$$y = \delta \quad \text{when} \quad x = 0 \cdot 31 \times \text{chord}$$

Substituting $x_0 = 0 \cdot 31$ in the cubic of eqns. (12.77) gives

$$a = \frac{1}{0 \cdot 121} = 8 \cdot 28$$

The camber line equation then is

$$\left. \begin{aligned} y &= 8 \cdot 28\delta . x\left(x - \frac{7}{8}\right)(x-1) \\ y &= 8 \cdot 28\delta\left(x^3 - \frac{15}{8}x^2 + \frac{7}{8}x\right) \end{aligned} \right\} \qquad . \quad (12.80)$$

or

This cubic camber line shape is shown plotted on Fig. 12.13 and the ordinates given on the inset table.

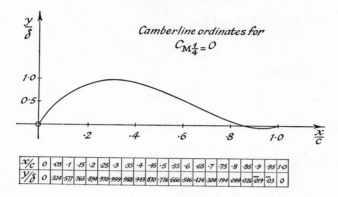

x/c	0	·05	·1	·15	·2	·25	·3	·35	·4	·45	·5	·55	·6	·65	·7	·75	·8	·85	·9	·95	1·0
y/δ	0	·324	·577	·765	·894	·970	·999	·988	·943	·870	·776	·666	·546	·424	·304	·194	·099	·026	⁻·019	⁻·03	0

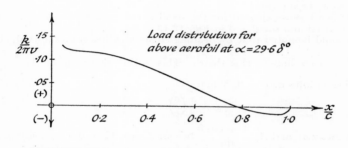

x/c	0	·05	·1	·15	·2	·25	·3	·35	·4	·45	·5	·55	·6	·65	·7	·75	·8	·85	·9	·95	1·0
$k/2\pi v$	∞	·127	·123	·121	·118	·112	·105	·096	·087	·076	·065	·053	·042	·030	·019	·009	·006	⁻·008	⁻·013	⁻·014	0

Fig. 12.13.

Lift coefficient. The lift coefficient is given from eqn. (12.38) by

$$C_L = 2\pi\left(A_0 + \frac{A_1}{2}\right)$$

and from eqn. (12.35)

$$A_0 = \alpha - \frac{1}{\pi}\int_0^\pi \frac{dy}{dx}.d\theta$$

$$A_0 = \alpha - \frac{1}{\pi}\cdot\frac{\delta}{c}\int_0^\pi \frac{dy_1}{dx_1}.d\theta$$

$$= \alpha - \frac{1}{\pi}\frac{\delta}{c}\int_0^\pi\left(\frac{3}{4}a\cos^2\theta - \left(\frac{a}{2}+ab\right)\cos\theta - \frac{a}{4}\right)d\theta$$

$$= \alpha - \frac{1}{\pi}\frac{\delta}{c}\left(\frac{3}{4}a\cdot\frac{\pi}{2} - \frac{a}{4}\pi\right)a$$

Thus

$$A_0 = \alpha - \frac{\delta}{c}\cdot\frac{a}{8} \qquad\qquad\qquad\qquad (12.81)$$

and

$$C_L = 2\pi\left[\alpha - \frac{a}{8}\cdot\frac{\delta}{c} + - \left(\frac{a}{2}+ab\right)\frac{\delta}{c}\right]$$

Substituting for $a = 8\cdot28$ and $b = -\dfrac{7}{8}$

$$C_L = 2\pi\left(\alpha + 2\cdot07\frac{\delta}{c}\right)$$

giving a no lift angle

$$\alpha_0 = -2\cdot07\frac{\delta}{c} \text{ radians}$$

or with $\qquad \beta = \text{the percentage camber} = \dfrac{100\delta}{c}$

$$\alpha_0 = 1\cdot2\beta \text{ degrees}$$

The load distribution. From eqn. (12.33),

$$k = 2U\left\{\left(\alpha - \frac{1\cdot04\delta}{c}\right)\frac{1 + \cos\theta}{\sin\theta} + \frac{3\cdot12\delta}{c}\sin\theta + \frac{3\cdot12\delta}{c}\sin 2\theta\right\}$$

for the first three terms.

This has been evaluated for the incidence $\alpha° = 29\cdot6(\delta/c)$ and the result shown plotted and tabulated in Fig. 12.13.

It should be noted that the leading edge value has been omitted, since it is infinite according to this theory. This is due to the term $A_0.\dfrac{1 + \cos\theta}{\sin\theta}$ becoming infinite at $\theta = 0$. When

$$\alpha = \frac{a}{8}\left(\frac{\delta}{c}\right) = 1\cdot04\frac{\delta}{c}$$

A_0 becomes zero and $A_0.\dfrac{1 + \cos\theta}{\sin\theta}$ becomes zero. Then the intensity of circulation at the leading edge is zero, and the stream flows smoothly on to the camber line at the leading edge, the leading edge being a stagnation point. This is the 'Theodorsen' condition, and the appropriate C_L is the ideal, optimum, or design lift coefficient, $C_{L\text{ opt}}$.

Example 12.2. A thin aerofoil has a camber line defined by the relation $y = kx(x - 1)(x - 2)$ where x and y are its coordinates expressed in terms of unit chord and the origin is at the leading edge.

If the maximum camber is 2% of the chord, determine the low-speed two-dimensional pitching moment coefficient at 3° incidence. (U. of L.)

If (x_0, δ) is the point of maximum camber two equations result directly

$$\delta = kx_0(x_0 - 1)(x_0 - 2) = 0\cdot02$$

$$\frac{dy}{dx} = k[3x_0{}^2 - 6x_0 + 2] = 0$$

From the quadratic

$$x_0 = \frac{+6 \pm \sqrt{36 - 24}}{6} = 1 \pm 0\cdot578$$

$$= 0\cdot4225$$

Substituting back in the cubic

$$\frac{0\cdot02}{k} = 0\cdot4225 \times -0\cdot578 \times -1\cdot578 = 0\cdot385$$

giving $\qquad k = \underline{0\cdot0520.}$

Changing the variable, $\dfrac{dy}{dx}$ becomes on substituting $x = \dfrac{1 - \cos\theta}{2}$

$$\frac{dy}{dx} = k\left[\frac{3}{4}(1 - \cos\theta)^2 - \frac{6}{2}(1 - \cos\theta) + 2\right]$$

$$\frac{dy}{dx} = \frac{k}{4}[3\cos^2\theta + 6\cos\theta - 1]$$

$$A_0 = \alpha - \frac{1}{\pi}\int_0^\pi \frac{dy}{dx}d\theta = \alpha - \frac{1}{\pi}\int_0^\pi \frac{k}{4}[3\cos^2\theta + 6\cos\theta - 1]\,d\theta$$

$$A_0 = \alpha - \frac{k}{8}$$

$$A_1 = \frac{2}{\pi}\int_0^\pi \frac{dy}{dx}\cos\theta\,d\theta = \frac{2}{\pi}\int_0^\pi \frac{k}{4}[3\cos^3\theta + 6\cos^2\theta - \cos\theta]\,d\theta = \frac{3}{2}k$$

$$A_2 = \frac{2}{\pi}\int_0^\pi \frac{dy}{dx}\cos 2\theta\,d\theta = \frac{2}{\pi}\int_0^\pi \frac{k}{4}(3\cos^2\theta\cos 2\theta + 6\cos\theta\cos 2\theta - \cos 2\theta)\,d\theta = \frac{3}{8}k$$

$$C_L = 2\pi\left[A_0 + \frac{A_1}{2}\right] = 2\pi\left[\alpha - \frac{k}{8} + \frac{3}{4}k\right]$$

$$\alpha = \frac{3}{51\cdot 3}\text{ rads.}\quad k = 0\cdot 052$$

$$C_L = \underline{0\cdot 535.}$$

$$C_{M\frac{1}{4}} = -\frac{\pi}{4}(A_1 - A_2) = -\frac{\pi}{4}\left(\frac{9}{8}k\right) = -\frac{\pi}{4}\cdot\frac{9}{8}\cdot 0\cdot 052$$

$$C_{M\frac{1}{4}} = \underline{-0\cdot 046.}$$

EXERCISES

1. A flat plate of chord 2 units is placed at an angle α in a stream of velocity V. Determine the vorticity distribution over the surface of the plate, assuming the Kutta–Zhukovsky value of circulation. Describe briefly how thin aerofoil theory can generalize this vorticity distribution to account for camber.

2. A thin two-dimensional aerofoil of chord c operating at its ideal lift coefficient C_{Li} has linear loading falling to zero at the trailing edge. Show that its shape is given by

$$\frac{y}{c} = \frac{C_{Li}}{4\pi}\left[\frac{x}{c}\left(\frac{x}{c} - 2\right)\log\frac{x}{c} - \left(1 - \frac{x}{c}\right)^2\log\left(1 - \frac{x}{c}\right)\right]$$

(U. of L.)

3. A thin two-dimensional flat plate aerofoil is fitted with a trailing edge flap whose chord is $100E$ per cent of the aerofoil chord. Show that the flap effectiveness a_2/a_1 is approximately $(4/\pi)\sqrt{E}$ for small chord flaps in incompressible flow.

4. Show how the moment coefficient of a thin aerofoil can be estimated from the shape of its camber line.

Derive expressions giving the moment coefficient in terms of a Fourier series defining the slope of the camber line. (U. of L.)

5. A thin aerofoil has a circular arc camber line with a maximum camber of $2\frac{1}{2}\%$. Determine the theoretical low-speed pitching moment coefficient about a point one quarter of the chord behind the leading edge and indicate briefly methods by which this could be reduced without changing the maximum camber.

The camber line may be approximated to by a relation of the form

$$y = k\left[\frac{1}{4} - \left(\frac{x}{c}\right)^2\right]$$ where the origin for x is taken at the mid-point of the chord

line of length c. (U. of L.)

6. The camber line of a circular arc aerofoil is given by

$$\frac{y}{c} = 4h\frac{x}{c}\left(1 - \frac{x}{c}\right)$$

Find the load distribution at incidence α. Show that the zero lift angle α_0 is equal to $-2h$ and sketch the load distribution at this incidence showing clearly the separate effects of camber and incidence. Compare the lift curve of this aerofoil with that of a flat plate. (U. of L.)

FINITE AEROFOIL THEORY

A great step forward in Aeronautics came with the Vortex Theory of a lifting aerofoil by Lanchester and the subsequent development of this work by Prandtl. Previously, all aerofoil data had to be obtained from experimental work and fitted to other aspect ratios, planforms, etc., by empirical formulae based on past experience with other aerofoils. The development of the Lanchester–Prandtl theory of aerofoils permitted, among other uses, prediction of aerofoil characteristics whatever their shape and geometry. It is this derivation of aerodynamic coefficients of monoplanes of conventional shape that is the concern of this chapter.

13.1. The vortex system.   Lanchester's contribution was essentially the replacement of the lifting wing by a system of vortices which imparted to the surrounding air a motion similar to the actual flow, and which sustained a force equivalent to the lift known to be created. The vortex system can be divided into three main parts: the Bound Vortex system, the Starting Vortex, and the Trailing Vortex system. Each of these may be treated separately but it should be remembered that they are all component parts of one whole. The last two have been fully explained in § 6.8.5.

13.1.1. The bound vortex system.   Both the starting vortex and the trailing system of vortices are physical entities which can be explored and discerned, and sometimes seen if conditions are right. The bound vortex system, on the other hand, is a hypothetical arrangement of vortices which replace the real physical wing in every way except that of thickness, in the theoretical treatments given in this chapter. This is the essence of finite wing theory. It is largely concerned with developing the *equivalent* bound vortex system which simulates accurately, at least a little distance away, all the properties, effects, disturbances, force systems, etc., due to the real aerofoil.

Consider an aerofoil in steady flight. What effect has it on the surrounding air, and how will changes in basic aerofoil parameters such as span, planform, aerodynamic or geometric twist, etc., alter these disturbances? The replacement bound vortex system must create the same disturbances, and this mathematical model must be sufficiently flexible to allow for the effects of the changed parameters.

From § 6.8.5 it is noted that a real aerofoil produces a trailing vortex system. The hypothetical bound vortex must do the same.

A consequence of the tendency to equalize the pressures acting on the top and bottom surfaces of an aerofoil is for the lift force per unit span to fall off towards the tips. The bound vortex system must produce the same grading of lift along the span.

335

For complete equivalence, the bound vortex system should consist of a large number of spanwise vortex elements of differing spanwise lengths all turned backwards at each end to form a pair of the vortex elements in the trailing system. The varying spanwise lengths accommodate the grading of the lift towards the wing-tips, the ends turned back produce the trailing system and the two physical attributes of a real aerofoil are thus simulated.

For partial equivalence the aerofoil can be considered to be replaced by a single bound vortex of strength equal to the mid-span circulation. This, bent back at each end, forms the trailing vortex pair. This concept provides adequate facilities for good estimations of aerofoil effects at distances greater than about two chord lengths from the centre of pressure.

13.1.2. The horseshoe vortex.

The total vortex system associated with an aerofoil, plus its replacement bound vortex system, forms a complete vortex ring which satisfies all physical laws. The starting vortex, however, is soon left behind and the trailing pair stretches effectively to infinity as steady flight proceeds. For practical purposes the system consists of the

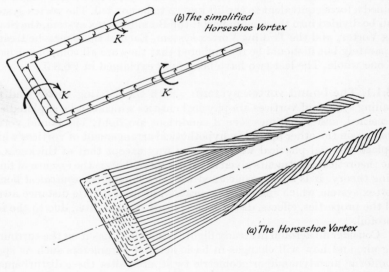

(b) The simplified Horseshoe Vortex

(a) The Horseshoe Vortex

FIG. 13.1.

bound vortices and the trailing vortex on either side close to the aerofoil. This three-sided vortex has been called the *horseshoe vortex* (Fig. 13.1 (a)).

Study of the 'complete equivalence' bound system and its trail is largely confined to investigating aerofoil effects in close proximity to the aerofoil. For estimation of distant phenomena the system is simplified to a single bound vortex and trailing pair known as the *simplified horseshoe vortex* (Fig. 13.1 (b)). See § 13.5.

13.2. Fundamental laws of vortex motion.

In the analysis of the vortex, in Chapter 10, it was considered to be a string of rotating particles surrounded by fluid at large moving irrotationally under the influence of the rotating particles. Further, the flow investigation was confined to a plane section normal to the 'length' or 'axis' of the vortex.

A more general definition is that a vortex is a flow system in which a finite area in a normal section plane contains vorticity. Fig. 13.2 shows the section area S of a vortex so called because S possesses vorticity. The axis of the vortex (or of the vorticity, or spin) is clearly always normal to the two-dimensional flow plane considered previously and the influence of the so-called line vortex is the influence, in a section plane, of an infinitely long straight line vortex of vanishingly small area.

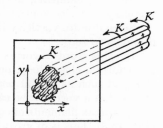

FIG. 13.2.—The vorticity of a section of vortex tube.

In general the vortex axis will be a curve in space and area S will have finite size. It is convenient to assume that S is made up of several elemental areas, or alternatively, that the vortex consists of a bundle of elemental vortex lines or filaments. Such a bundle is often called a *vortex tube* (cf. a *stream tube* which is a bundle of streamlines), being a tube bounded by vortex filaments.

Since the vortex is a curve winding about within the fluid, capable of flexure and motion as a whole, the estimation of its influence on the fluid at large is somewhat complex and beyond the present intentions of the chapter. All the vortices of significance to the present theory (a) are fixed relative to some axes in the system or free to move in a very controlled fashion and (b) can be assumed to be linear. None the less the vortices will not all be of infinite length and therefore some three-dimensional or end influence must be accounted for.

In spite of the above provisions the vortices conform to laws of motion appropriate to their behaviour. A rigorous treatment of these is precluded from a text of this standard but should not be beyond the average capacity with additional study of the basic references.*

13.2.1. Helmholtz's Theorems.

The four fundamental theorems of vortex motion in an inviscid flow are named after their author, Helmholtz.

The first theorem has been discussed in part in § 10.1, and refers to a fluid particle in general motion possessing all or some of the following: linear velocity, vorticity and distortion.

The second theorem demonstrates the constancy of strength of a vortex along its length. This is sometimes referred to as the equation of vortex 'continuity'. It is not difficult to prove that the strength of a vortex cannot grow or diminish along its axis or length. The strength of a vortex is the

---

* Lamb, *Hydrodynamics*. Milne-Thomson, *Theoretical Hydro- and Aerodynamics*, Vols. I and II.

magnitude of the circulation around it and this is equal to the product of the vorticity ζ and area S.

Thus
$$K = \zeta . S$$

It follows from the second theorem that $\zeta . S$ is constant along the vortex tube (or filament), so that if the section area diminishes, the vorticity increases and vice versa.

Since infinite vorticity is unacceptable the cross-section area S cannot diminish to zero.

In other words a vortex cannot end in the fluid. In practice the vortex must form a closed loop, or originate (or terminate) in a discontinuity in the fluid such as a solid body or a surface of separation. A refinement of this is that a vortex tube cannot change in strength between two sections unless vortex filaments of equivalent strength join or leave the vortex tube (Fig. 13.3). This is of great importance to the vortex theory of lift.

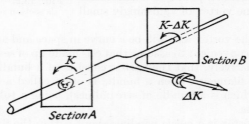

FIG. 13.3.

The third and fourth theorems demonstrate respectively that a vortex tube consists of the same particles of fluid, i.e., that there is no fluid interchange between tube and surrounding fluid, and that the strength of a vortex remains constant as the vortex moves throughout the fluid confines.

The theorem of most consequence to the present chapter is theorem two, although the third and fourth are tacitly accepted as the development proceeds. See § 13.3 below.

13.2.2. The Biot–Savart Law. This law relates the intensity of magnetic field close to an electric current carrying conductor to the magnitude of the current. It is mathematically identical to, and capable of interpreting, the basically similar concept of relating intensity of flow in the fluid close to a 'vorticity carrying' vortex tube to the strength of the vortex tube.

To minimize confusion the fluid motion aspect only is explained here.

Allow a vortex tube of strength K, consisting of an infinite number of vortex filaments, to terminate in some point P. The total strength of the vortex filaments will be spread over the surface of a spherical boundary of radius R (say) (Fig. 13.4), as the filaments diverge from the point P in all directions. The vorticity in the spherical surface will thus have the total strength K.

Due to symmetry the velocity of flow in the surface of the sphere will be tangential to the circular line of intersection of the sphere with a plane normal to the axis of the vortex. Moreover the direction will be in the sense of the circulation about the vortex. Fig. 13.5 shows such a circle ABC of radius r subtending a conical angle of 2θ at P.

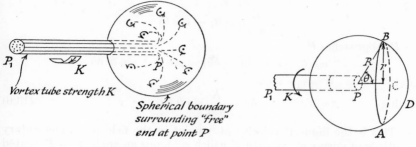

Vortex tube strength K

Spherical boundary
surrounding "free"
end at point P

FIG. 13.4.

FIG. 13.5.

If the velocity on the sphere at R, θ from P is v ft/sec, then the circulation round the circuit ABC is K' where

$$K' = 2\pi R \sin \theta . v \qquad . \qquad . \qquad . \qquad (13.1)$$

Putting r = radius of circuit = $R \sin \theta$, eqn. (13.1) becomes

$$K' = 2\pi r v \qquad . \qquad . \qquad . \qquad . \qquad (13.2)$$

Now the circulation round the circuit is equal to the strength of the vorticity in the contained area. This is on the cap $ABCD$ of the sphere.

Since the distribution of the vorticity is constant over the surface

$$K' = \frac{\text{surface area of cap}}{\text{surface area of sphere}} . K = \frac{2\pi R^2 (1 - \cos \theta)}{4\pi R^2} . K$$

$$\therefore K' = \frac{K}{2}(1 - \cos \theta) \qquad . \qquad . \qquad . \qquad . \qquad . \qquad (13.3)$$

Equating (13.2) and (13.3) gives

FIG. 13.6.

$$v = \frac{K}{4\pi r}(1 - \cos \theta) . \qquad . \qquad (13.4)$$

Now let the length of the vortex decrease until it is very short, $P_1 P$ (Fig. 13.6). The circle ABC is now influenced by the opposite end P_1. Working through eqns. (13.1), (13.2) and (13.3) shows that the induced velocity due to P_1 is now

$$- v_1 = \frac{- K}{4\pi r}(1 - \cos \theta_1) \qquad . \qquad . \qquad . \qquad (13.5)$$

since $r = R_1 \sin \theta_1$ and the sign of the vorticity is reversed on the sphere of radius R_1 as the vortex elements are now *entering* the sphere to congregate on P_1.

The nett velocity in the circuit ABC is the sum of eqns. (13.4) and (13.5)

$$v - v_1 = \frac{K}{4\pi r}[1 - \cos \theta - (1 - \cos \theta_1)]$$

$$= \frac{K}{4\pi r}(\cos \theta_1 - \cos \theta)$$

as P_1 approaches P

$$\cos \theta_1 \to \cos (\theta - \delta\theta) = \cos \theta + \sin \theta . \delta\theta$$

and $\qquad v - v_1 \to \delta v$

giving $\qquad\qquad\qquad \delta v = \frac{K}{4\pi r} \sin \theta\, \delta\theta$.   .   .   . (13.6)

This is the induced velocity at a point in the field of an elementary length δs of vortex of strength K which subtends an angle $\delta\theta$ at P located by the ordinates r, θ from the element, and since $\delta s = r\,\delta\theta$ it is more usefully quoted as

$$\delta v = \frac{K}{4\pi r^2} \sin \theta . \delta s \qquad . \qquad . \qquad . \quad (13.7)$$

13.2.3. Special cases of the Biot–Savart Law.

Eqn. 13.6 above needs further treatment before it yields working equations. This treatment, of integration, varies with the length and shape of the finite vortex being studied. The vortices of immediate interest are all nearly linear and so no shape complexity arises. They will vary only in their overall length.

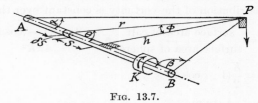

FIG. 13.7.

A linear vortex of finite length AB. Fig. 13.7 shows a length AB of vortex with an adjacent point P located by the angular displacements α and β from A and B respectively.

Point P has, further, coordinates r and θ with respect to any elemental length δs of the length AB which may be defined as a distance s from the foot of the perpendicular h.

From eqn. (13.7) the velocity at P induced by the elemental length δs is

$$\delta v = \frac{K}{4\pi r^2} \sin \theta\, \delta s . \qquad . \qquad . \qquad . \quad (13.8)$$

in the sense shown, i.e., normal to the plane APB.

To find the velocity at P due to the length AB the sum of induced velocities due to all such elements is required. Before integrating, how-

ever, all the variables must be quoted in terms of a single variable. A convenient variable is ϕ (see Fig. 13.7) and the limits of the integration are

$$\phi_A = -\left(\frac{\pi}{2} - \alpha\right) \quad \text{to} \quad \phi_B = +\left(\frac{\pi}{2} - \beta\right)$$

since ϕ passes through zero when integrating from A to B.

$$\sin \theta = \cos \phi, \quad r^2 = h^2 \sec^2 \phi$$
$$ds = d(h \tan \phi) = h \sec^2 \phi \, d\phi$$

The integration of eqn. (13.8) is thus

$$v = \int_{-\left(\frac{\pi}{2} - \alpha\right)}^{+\left(\frac{\pi}{2} - \beta\right)} \frac{K}{4\pi h} \cos \phi \, d\phi = \frac{K}{4\pi h}\left[\sin \left(\frac{\pi}{2} - \beta\right) + \sin \left(\frac{\pi}{2} - \alpha\right)\right]$$

$$v = \frac{K}{4\pi h}(\cos \alpha + \cos \beta) \quad . \qquad . \qquad . \qquad . \qquad . \qquad . \qquad . \qquad (13.9)$$

This result is of the utmost importance in what follows and is so often
required that it is best committed to memory.

All the values for induced velocity now to be used in this chapter are
derived from this eqn. (13.9), which is limited to a *straight* line vortex of
length AB.

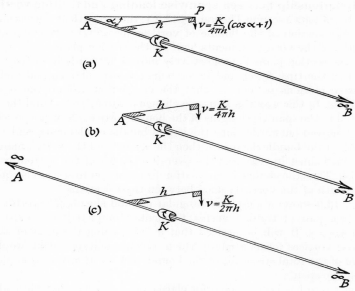

FIG. 13.8.

The influence of a 'semi-infinite' vortex (Fig. 13.8 (a)). If one end of the
vortex stretches to infinity (end B say), then $\beta = 0$ and $\cos \beta = 1$, so that
eqn. (13.9) becomes

$$v = \frac{K}{4\pi h}(\cos \alpha + 1) \qquad . \qquad . \qquad . \qquad (13.10)$$

When the point P is opposite the end of the vortex (Fig. 13.8 (b)), so that $\alpha = \pi/2$, $\cos \alpha = 0$ and eqn. (13.9) becomes

$$v = \frac{K}{4\pi h} \qquad . \qquad . \qquad . \qquad . \qquad (13.11)$$

The influence of an infinite vortex (Fig. 13.8 (c)) follows by putting $\alpha = \beta = 0$ when eqn. (13.9) gives

$$v = \frac{K}{2\pi h} \qquad . \qquad . \qquad . \qquad . \qquad (13.12)$$

and this will be recognized as the familiar expression for velocity in the vicinity of the line vortex of § 10.2.10. Note that this is twice the velocity induced by a semi-infinite vortex, a result which can be seen intuitively.

Theory for finite aerofoils

The wing has been replaced for purposes of analysis by a bundle of bound vortex filaments each of different length in the spanwise direction and turned back into two trailing vortex filaments.

13.3. Relationship between spanwise loading and trailing vorticity.
From Helmholtz's second Theorem, § 13.2.1, the strength of the circulation round any section of the bundle of vortices (or wing) is the sum of the strengths of the vortex filaments 'cut' by the section plane.

As the section plane is progressively moved outwards from the centre section to the tips, fewer and fewer bound vortex filaments are left for successive sections to 'cut' so that the circulation around the sections diminishes. In this way the spanwise change in circulation round the wing is related to the spanwise lengths of the bound vortices. Now as the section plane is moved outwards along the bound bundle of filaments, and as the strength of the bundle decreases, then the strength of the vortex filaments so far shed must increase, as the overall strength of the system cannot diminish. Thus the change in circulation from section to section is equal to the strength of the vorticity shed between these sections.

Fig. 13.9 shows a simple rectangular aerofoil shedding a vortex trail with each pair of trailing vortex filaments 'completed' by a spanwise bound vortex. It will be noticed that a line joining the ends of all the spanwise vortices forms a curve which, given a suitable scale, would be a curve of the total strengths of the bound vortices at any section plotted against the span.

This curve has been erected for clarity on a spanwise line through the centre of pressure of the aerofoil and is a plot of (chordwise) circulation (K) measured on a vertical ordinate, against spanwise distance from the centre-line measured on the horizontal ordinate.

Thus at a section y from the centre-line sufficient hypothetical bound vortices are cut to produce a chordwise circulation around that section equal to K ft²/sec. At a further section $y + \delta y$ from the centre-line the circulation has fallen to $K - \delta K$, indicating that between sections y and $y + \delta y$ trailing vorticity to the strength of δK has been shed.

If the circulation curve can be described as some function of y, $\mathrm{f}(y)$ say, then the strength of circulation shed

$$\delta K = \frac{-\,d\mathrm{f}(y)}{dy}\,.\,\delta y$$

or $$\delta K = -\,\mathrm{f}'(y)\,\delta y \ . \qquad . \qquad . \qquad . \quad (13.13)$$

Now at any section the lift per unit span is given by

$$l = \rho V K$$

and for a given flight speed and air density, K is thus proportional to l. But l is the local intensity of lift or lift grading, which is either known or is the required quantity in the analysis. In either case it can be adequately described.

The substitution of the aerofoil by a bound system is therefore a means to an end and not one to be rigorously accepted. The idea allows a relation to be built up between the physical load distribution on the aerofoil, which depends, as shall be shown, on the aerofoil geometric and aerodynamic parameters, and the trailing vortex system.

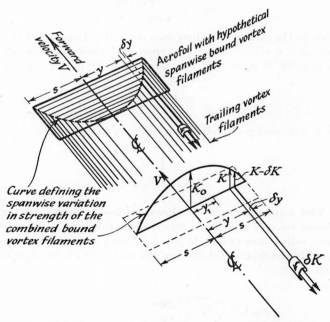

FIG. 13.9.—The relation between spanwise load variation and trailing vortex strength.

Fig. 13.9 illustrates two further points:

(a) It will be noticed from the leading sketch that the trailing filaments are closer together when they are shed from a rapidly diminishing or changing distribution curve. Where the filaments are closer the strength of the vorticity is greater. Near the tips, therefore, the shed vorticity is the most strong, and at the centre where the distribution curve is flattened out the shed vorticity is weak to infinitesimal.

(b) An aerofoil infinitely long in the spanwise direction, or in two-dimensional flow, will have constant spanwise loading. The bundle will have filaments all of equal length and none will be turned back to form trailing vortices. Thus there is *no* trailing vorticity associated with two-dimensional aerofoils. This is capable of deduction by a more direct process, viz., as the aerofoil is infinitely long in the spanwise direction the lower surface (high) and upper surface (low) pressures cannot tend to equalize by spanwise components of velocity so that the streams of air meeting at the trailing edge after sweeping under and over the aerofoil have no opposite spanwise motions but join up in symmetrical flow in the direction of motion. Again no trailing vorticity is formed.

13.3.1. Downwash.   Consider now the influence of the trailing vortex filaments of strength δK shed from the section at y. At some other point y_1 (Fig. 13.9) along the span an induced velocity equal to

$$\delta w_{y_1} = \frac{-\,\mathrm{f}'(y)\,dy}{4\pi(y - y_1)}$$

will be felt in the downwards direction, according to eqn. (13.11). All elements of shed vorticity along the span add their contribution to the induced velocity at y_1 so that the total influence of the trailing system at y_1 is

$$w_{y_1} = \frac{-1}{4\pi} \int_{-s}^{s} \frac{\mathrm{f}'(y)\,dy}{(y - y_1)}$$

where w is reckoned positively downwards, or more usually,

$$w_{y_1} = \frac{-1}{4\pi} \int_{-s}^{s} \frac{\left(\dfrac{dK}{dy}\right) dy}{y - y_1} \qquad . \qquad . \qquad . \quad (13.14)$$

13.3.2. The consequences of downwash—Trailing vortex drag.
The induced velocity at y_1 is, in general, in a downwards direction and is sometimes called downwash. It has two very important consequences which modify the flow about the aerofoil and alter its aerodynamic characteristics.

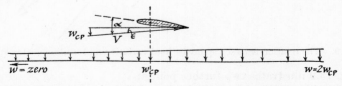

Fig. 13.10.—Variation in magnitude of downwash in front of and behind an aerofoil.

Firstly, the downwash which has been obtained for the particular point y_1 is felt to a lesser extent ahead of y_1 and to a greater extent behind (see Fig. 13.10), and has the effect of tilting the resultant wind at the aerofoil (or anywhere else within its influence) through an angle

$$\varepsilon = \tan^{-1}\frac{w}{V} \doteqdot \frac{w}{V}$$

where w is the local downwash. This *reduces* the effective incidence so that for the *same lift* as the equivalent infinite or two-dimensional aerofoil at incidence α_∞ an incidence $\alpha = \alpha_\infty + \varepsilon$ is required at that section on the finite aerofoil.

This is illustrated in Fig. 13.11, which in addition shows how the 'two-dimensional' lift L_∞ is normal to the resultant velocity V_R, and is, therefore, tilted back against the actual direction of motion of the aerofoil V. The 'two-dimensional' lift L_∞ is resolved into the aerodynamic forces L and D_v respectively, normal to and against the direction of the forward velocity of the aerofoil.

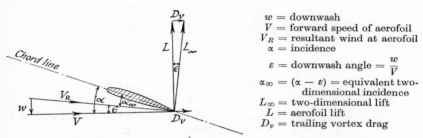

w = downwash
V = forward speed of aerofoil
V_R = resultant wind at aerofoil
α = incidence
ε = downwash angle = $\dfrac{w}{V}$
$\alpha_\infty = (\alpha - \varepsilon)$ = equivalent two-dimensional incidence
L_∞ = two-dimensional lift
L = aerofoil lift
D_v = trailing vortex drag

FIG. 13.11.—The influence of downwash on aerofoil velocities and forces.

Thus the second important consequence of downwash emerges. This is the generation of a drag force D_v. This is so important that the sequence will be explained in an alternative way.

A section of an aerofoil generates a circulation of strength K. This circulation superimposed on an apparent wind velocity V_∞ produces a lift force $L_\infty = \rho V_\infty K$ according to Zhukovsky's Theorem, which is normal to the apparent wind direction. The apparent wind 'felt' by the aerofoil section is the resultant of the forward velocity and the downward induced velocity arising from the trailing vortices. Thus the aerodynamic force L_∞ produced by the combination of K and V_∞ appears as a lift force L normal to the forward motion and a drag force D_v against the normal motion. This drag force is called *trailing vortex drag*, abbreviated to *vortex drag* or commonly in the past *induced drag* (see § 6.6).

Considering for a moment the aerofoil as a whole moving through air at rest at infinity, two-dimensional wing theory suggests that, taking air as being of small to negligible viscosity, the static pressure of the free stream ahead is recovered behind the aerofoil. This means roughly that the kinetic energy induced in the flow is converted back to pressure energy

z

and zero drag results. The existence of a thin boundary layer and narrow wake is ignored but this does not modify the argument.

In addition to this motion of the airstream, a finite aerofoil spins the airflow near the tips into what eventually become two trailing vortices of considerable core size. The generation of these vortices requires a quantity of kinetic energy which is *not* recovered by the aerofoil system and which in fact is *lost* to the aerofoil by being left behind. This constant expenditure of energy appears to the aerofoil as the *trailing vortex drag*. In what follows, a third explanation of this important consequence of downwash will be of use. Fig. 13.12 shows the two velocity components of the relative wind superimposed on the circulation produced by the aerofoil. The forward wind velocity produces the lift and the downwash produces the vortex drag per unit span.

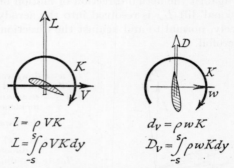

$$l = \rho VK$$
$$L = \int_{-s}^{s} \rho VK \, dy$$

$$d_v = \rho wK$$
$$D_v = \int_{-s}^{s} \rho wK \, dy$$

FIG. 13.12.—Circulation superimposed on forward wind velocity and downwash to give lift and vortex drag (induced drag) respectively.

Thus the lift per unit span of finite aerofoil (l) (or the load grading) is, by Zhukovsky's Theorem,

$$l = \rho VK \qquad . \qquad . \qquad . \qquad . \qquad (13.15)$$

The total lift being

$$L = \int_{-s}^{s} \rho VK \, dy \qquad . \qquad . \qquad . \qquad . \qquad (13.16)$$

The vortex drag per unit span (d_v), or the vortex drag grading, again by Zhukovsky's Theorem is

$$d_v = \rho wK \qquad . \qquad . \qquad . \qquad . \qquad (13.17)$$

and by similar integration over the span

$$D_v = \int_{-s}^{s} \rho wK \, dy \qquad . \qquad . \qquad . \qquad . \qquad (13.18)$$

This expression for D_v shows conclusively that if w is zero all along the span then D_v is zero also. Clearly, if there is no trailing vorticity then there will be no vortex drag. This condition arises when an aerofoil is working under two-dimensional conditions, or if all sections are producing zero lift.

As a consequence of the trailing vortex system, which is produced by the basic lifting action of a (finite span) aerofoil, the aerofoil characteristics are considerably modified, almost always adversely, from those of the equivalent two-dimensional aerofoil of the same section.

Equally an aerofoil whose flow systems more nearly approach the two-dimensional case will have better aerodynamic characteristics than one where the 'end-effects' are conspicuous. It seems therefore that an aerofoil which is large in the spanwise dimension, i.e., large aspect ratio, is a better (i.e., nearer the ideal) aerofoil than a short span aerofoil of the same section.

It would thus appear that an aerofoil of large aspect ratio will have better aerodynamic characteristics than one of the same section with a lower aspect ratio.

The analytical demonstration of this fundamental quality of finite aerofoils forms a large part of this chapter.

13.3.3. The characteristics of a simple symmetric loading—elliptic distribution.

In order to demonstrate the general method of obtaining the aerodynamic characteristics of an aerofoil from its loading distribution the simplest load expression for symmetric flight is taken, that is, a semi-ellipse. In addition it will be found to be a good approximation to many (mathematically) more complicated distributions and is thus suitable for use as first predictions in performance estimates (see § 13.5).

The spanwise variation in circulation is taken to be represented by a semi-ellipse having the span ($2s$) as major axis and the circulation at mid-span (K_0) as the semi-minor axis (Fig. 13.13).

From the general expression for an ellipse

$$\frac{K^2}{K_0{}^2} + \frac{y^2}{s^2} = 1$$

or

$$K = K_0\sqrt{1 - \left(\frac{y}{s}\right)^2} . \qquad . \qquad . \qquad (13.19)$$

This is the expression $K = f(y)$ which can now be substituted in eqns. (13.16), (13.14) and (13.18) to find the lift, downwash, and vortex drag, on the aerofoil.

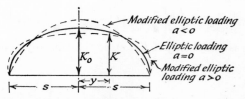

Fig. 13.13.—Elliptic and modified elliptic loadings for the same total lift, i.e. for the same enclosed area. $K = K_0\sqrt{1 - \left(\frac{y}{s}\right)^2}\left(1 + a\left(\frac{y}{s}\right)^2\right)$

Lift for elliptic distribution. From eqn. (13.16)

$$L = \int_{-s}^{s} \rho VK \, dy = \int_{-s}^{s} \rho VK_0 \sqrt{1 - \left(\frac{y}{s}\right)^2} \, dy$$

$$L = \rho VK_0 \pi \frac{s}{2} \qquad \qquad (13.20)$$

whence

$$K_0 = \frac{L}{\frac{1}{2}\rho V \pi s}$$

or introducing

$$L = C_L \tfrac{1}{2} \rho V^2 S$$

$$K_0 = \frac{C_L VS}{\pi s} \qquad \qquad (13.21)$$

giving the mid-span circulation in terms of the overall aerofoil lift coefficient and geometry.

Downwash for elliptic distribution. Here

$$\frac{dK}{dy} = -K_0 \frac{2y}{s^2}\left[1 - \left(\frac{y}{s}\right)^2\right]^{-\frac{1}{2}} \cdot \tfrac{1}{2} = -K_0 \frac{1}{s}\frac{y}{\sqrt{s^2 - y^2}}$$

Substituting this in eqn. (13.14),

$$w_{y_1} = \frac{K_0}{2\pi s} \int_{-s}^{s} \frac{y \, dy}{\sqrt{s^2 - y^2}(y - y_1)}$$

Adding $y_1 - y_1$ to the numerator,

$$w_{y_1} = \frac{K_0}{2\pi s} \int_{-s}^{s} \frac{(y - y_1) + y_1 \, dy}{\sqrt{s^2 - y^2}(y - y_1)}$$

$$= \frac{K_0}{2\pi s}\left[\int_{-s}^{s} \frac{dy}{\sqrt{s^2 - y^2}} + y_1 \int_{-s}^{s} \frac{dy}{\sqrt{s^2 - y^2}(y - y_1)}\right]$$

Evaluating the first integral which is standard and writing I for the second

$$w_{y_1} = \frac{K_0}{4\pi s} \cdot \left[\frac{\pi}{1} + y_1 I\right] \qquad (13.22)$$

Now as this is a symmetric flight case, the shed vorticity is the same from each side of the wing and the value of the downwash at some point y_1 is identical to that at the corresponding point $-y_1$ on the other wing.

So substituting for $\pm y_1$ in (13.22) and equating

$$w_{\pm y_1} = \frac{K_0}{4\pi s}\left[\frac{\pi}{1} + y_1 I\right] = \frac{K_0}{4\pi s}\left[\frac{\pi}{1} - y_1 I\right]$$

This identity is satisfied only if $I = 0$, so that for any point $y = y_1$ along the span

$$w = \frac{K_0}{4s} \qquad \qquad (13.23)$$

This is an important result, the importance being that the downwash is constant along the span.

Vortex drag (induced drag) for elliptic distribution. From eqn. (13.18)

$$D_v = \int_{-s}^{s} \rho w K \, dy = \int_{-s}^{s} \rho \frac{K_0}{4s} . K_0 \sqrt{1 - \left(\frac{y}{s}\right)^2} \, dy$$

whence

$$D_v = \frac{\pi}{8} \rho K_0{}^2 \qquad . \qquad . \qquad . \qquad . \qquad . \qquad . \qquad . \qquad (13.24)$$

Introducing

$$D_v = C_{D_v} \tfrac{1}{2} \rho V^2 S$$

and from eqn. (13.21)

$$K_0 = \frac{C_L V S}{\pi s}$$

Eqn. (13.24) gives

$$C_{D_v} \tfrac{1}{2} \rho V^2 S = \left(\frac{C_L V S}{\pi s}\right)^2 \frac{\pi}{8} \rho$$

or

$$C_{D_v} = \frac{C_L{}^2}{\pi \mathcal{R}} \qquad . \qquad . \qquad . \qquad . \qquad (13.25)$$

since

$$\frac{4s^2}{S} = \frac{\text{span}^2}{\text{area}} = \text{aspect ratio } (\mathcal{R})$$

This expression entails the provisions discussed in the previous sections and shows that at zero lift in symmetric flight C_{D_v} is zero and the other condition that as $\mathcal{R}$ increases (to infinity for two-dimensional flow) C_{D_v} decreases (to zero).

13.3.4. Aerofoil characteristics with a more general distribution.

The elliptic distribution above is a particular distribution which produces simple and convenient expressions for C_L, C_{D_v} and w. A more general distribution must satisfy the end conditions that $K = 0$ at $y = \pm s$, that is, at the tips. For the symmetric flight case of a simple aerofoil with no irregularities, e.g. engine nacelles or fuselages, the spanwise distribution will also reach a maximum at mid-span where $y = 0$. Any mathematical expression which satisfies these conditions can conceivably be used to evaluate the characteristics. It is found, however, that for plain rectangular or slightly tapered aerofoils the spanwise distribution does not depart radically from the simple elliptic distribution of the previous section, and that this departure can be adequately described by the so-called modified elliptic loading.

$$K = K_0 \sqrt{1 - \left(\frac{y}{s}\right)^2} \left(1 + a\left(\frac{y}{s}\right)^2\right)$$

The constant (a) can vary positively or negatively and so change the shape, but the end and centre conditions are satisfied (Fig. 13.13).

The lift for modified elliptic loading. From eqn. (13.16)

$$L = \int_{-s}^{s} \rho V K \, dy = \int_{-s}^{s} \rho V K_0 \sqrt{1 - \left(\frac{y}{s}\right)^2} \left(1 + a\left(\frac{y}{s}\right)^2\right) dy$$

Since the distribution is symmetrical

$$L = 2\rho V K_0 \int_{0}^{s} \sqrt{1 - \left(\frac{y}{s}\right)^2} \left(1 + a\left(\frac{y}{s}\right)^2\right) dy$$

It is convenient to effect the substitution $y = s \sin \phi$ and hence

$$dy = s \cos \phi \, d\phi$$

and the limits become 0 and $\pi/2$.

Thus the lift

$$L = 2\rho V K_0 s \int_0^{\frac{\pi}{2}} \cos^2 \phi (1 + a \sin^2 \phi) \, d\phi$$

writing $a = 4\lambda$

$$L = 2\rho V K_0 s \int_0^{\frac{\pi}{2}} (\cos^2 \phi + 4\lambda \cos^2 \phi \sin^2 \phi) \, d\phi$$

These are standard forms integrable by Wallis's Rule to give

$$L = 2\rho V K_0 s \left[\frac{\pi}{4} + 4\lambda \frac{\pi}{16} \right]$$

$$L = \rho V K_0 s \frac{\pi}{2} (1 + \lambda) \quad . \qquad . \qquad . \qquad . \quad (13.26)$$

and

$$C_L = \frac{\pi K_0 s}{VS} (1 + \lambda) \qquad . \qquad . \qquad . \qquad . \quad (13.27)$$

Comparing this with eqn. (13.20) for the same lift from the equivalent elliptically loaded aerofoil with mid-span circulation K_E say,

$$\rho V K_0 s \frac{\pi}{2} (1 + \lambda) = \rho V K_E s \frac{\pi}{2}$$

showing that

$$K_E = K_0 (1 + \lambda) = K_0 \left(1 + \frac{a}{4} \right) \qquad . \qquad . \quad (13.28)$$

Thus a distribution which diminishes fairly rapidly from the mid-span sections would have a (or λ) negative, while for 'flattish' distributions a is positive.

The downwash for modified elliptic loading.

$$w_{y\,1} = -\frac{1}{4\pi} \int_{-s}^{s} \frac{\left(\dfrac{dK}{dy} \right) dy}{y - y_1}$$

Again for ease of manipulation put $a = 4\lambda$ but this time the variable change is more convenient when $y = -s \cos \theta$, then $y_1 = -s \cos \theta_1$, $dy = s \sin \theta \, d\theta$ and the limits range from 0 at $y = -s$ to π at $y = +s$.

$w_{y\,1}$ becomes

$$w_{\theta\,1} = \frac{1}{4\pi s} \int_0^{\pi} \frac{\left(\dfrac{dK}{d\theta} \right) d\theta}{\cos \theta - \cos \theta_1} \qquad . \qquad . \quad (13.29)$$

and

$$K = K_0 \sqrt{1 - \cos^2 \theta (1 + 4\lambda \cos^2 \theta)}$$

$$\frac{dK}{d\theta} = K_0 \{ \cos \theta [1 + 4\lambda \cos^2 \theta] + - 8\lambda \sin^2 \theta \cos \theta \}$$

$$= K_0 \{ (1 - 8\lambda) \cos \theta + 12\lambda \cos^3 \theta \}$$

Putting $\cos^3 \theta = \dfrac{3 \cos \theta + \cos 3\theta}{4}$

$$\frac{dK}{d\theta} = K_0[(1 + \lambda) \cos \theta + 3\lambda \cos 3\theta]$$

and substituting this in eqn. (13.29) gives

$$w_{\theta\,1} = \frac{K_0}{4\pi s} \int_0^\pi \left\{ \frac{(1 + \lambda) \cos \theta}{\cos \theta - \cos \theta_1} + \frac{3\lambda \cos 3\theta}{\cos \theta - \cos \theta_1} \right\} d\theta$$

Now these integrals cannot be solved by direct methods because the integrand becomes infinite when $\theta = \theta_1$. Integrals of the type

$$G_n = \int_0^\pi \frac{\cos n\theta}{\cos \theta - \cos \theta_1} d\theta$$

can be solved by integrating over two ranges 0 to $(\theta_1 - \varepsilon)$ and $(\theta_1 + \varepsilon)$ to π and taking the limits as ε tends to zero,

thus $\quad G_n = \underset{\varepsilon \longrightarrow 0}{\text{Lim}} \left\{ \int_0^{\theta_1 - \varepsilon} \frac{\cos n\theta \, d\theta}{\cos \theta - \cos \theta_1} + \int_{\theta_1 + \varepsilon}^\pi \frac{\cos n\theta \, d\theta}{\cos \theta - \cos \theta_1} \right\}$

or by contour integration (see Appendix 3).

The former treatment is fully explained in the reference,[*] and elsewhere, the integrals becoming

$$G_n = \int_0^\pi \frac{\cos n\theta \, d\theta}{\cos \theta - \cos \theta_1} = \frac{\pi \sin n\theta_1}{\sin \theta_1}$$

for all values of $n > 0$. When $n = 0$, $G_0 = 0$, as can be deduced from the first appearance of this type of integral in the previous downwash case (elliptic loading.) (See § 12.3.3 and 13.3.3.)

Introducing this solution into the downwash expression gives

$$w_{\theta\,1} = \frac{K}{4\pi s} \left[(1 + \lambda) \frac{\pi \sin \theta_1}{\sin \theta_1} + 3\lambda \frac{\pi \sin 3\theta_1}{\sin \theta_1} \right]$$

Now $\dfrac{\sin 3\theta_1}{\sin \theta_1}$ reduces to $(4 \cos^2 \theta_1 - 1)$

$$\therefore \quad w_{\theta\,1} = \frac{K_0}{4s} \{(1 + \lambda) + 3\lambda(4 \cos^2 \theta_1 - 1)\}$$

For the point $y_1 = -s \cos \theta_1$

$$w_{y\,1} = \frac{K_0}{4s} \left\{ (1 + \lambda) + 12\lambda \left(\frac{y_1}{s}\right)^2 - 3\lambda \right\}$$

or equally for any point y along the span the downwash is

$$w = \frac{K_0}{4s} \left\{ 1 - 2\lambda + 12\lambda \left(\frac{y}{s}\right)^2 \right\}. \qquad . \qquad . \quad (13.30)$$

It can now be seen that the downwash in the general case will vary in magnitude along the span, and may even become negative and give an

[*] H. Glauert, *The Elements of Aerofoil and Airscrew Theory*.

upwash near the tips if $\lambda < -0.1$. If w is negative near the tips d_v is negative and that region of wing gives a thrust. This is, however, compensated by a greater drag grading over the central regions of the wing.

The vortex drag (induced drag) for modified loading. From eqn. (13.18)

$$D_v = \int_{-s}^{s} \rho w K \, dy \quad \text{and on substituting for } K \text{ and } w$$

$$D_v = \int_{-s}^{s} \frac{\rho K_0}{4s}\left\{1 - 2\lambda + 12\lambda\left(\frac{y}{s}\right)^2\right\} K_0 \sqrt{1 - \left(\frac{y}{s}\right)^2}\left(1 + 4\lambda\left(\frac{y}{s}\right)^2\right) dy$$

or since it is symmetrical, it is twice the value from 0 to s.

Then changing the variable to $y = s \sin \phi$, $dy = s \cos \phi \, d\phi$,

$$D_v = \frac{2\rho K_0^2}{4}\int_0^{\frac{\pi}{2}}(1 - 2\lambda + 12\lambda \sin^2 \phi)\cos^2 \phi(1 + 4\lambda \sin^2 \phi)\, d\phi$$

which multiplied out becomes

$$D_v = \frac{\rho K_0^2}{2}\int_0^{\frac{\pi}{2}}[(1 - 2\lambda)\cos^2 \phi + (16\lambda - 8\lambda^2)\sin^2 \phi \cos^2 \phi$$
$$+ 48\lambda^2 \sin^4 \phi \cos^2 \phi]\, d\phi$$

These again are standard integrals which solve to give

$$D_v = \frac{\rho K_0^2}{2}\left[(1 - 2\lambda)\frac{\pi}{4} + (16\lambda - 8\lambda^2)\frac{\pi}{16} + 48\lambda^2\frac{\pi}{32}\right]$$

$$D_v = \frac{\pi\rho K_0^2}{8}[1 + 2\lambda + 4\lambda^2] \quad . \quad . \quad . \quad . \quad . \quad (13.31)$$

Defining the vortex drag coefficient

$$C_{D_v} = \frac{D_v}{\frac{1}{2}\rho V^2 S}$$

and substituting for K_0 from the lift coefficient eqn. (13.27),

$$C_{D_v} = \frac{\pi\rho C_L^2 V^2 S^2[1 + 2\lambda + 4\lambda^2]}{8\pi^2 s^2(1 + \lambda)^2}$$

$$C_{D_v} = \frac{C_L^2}{\pi \mathcal{R}}\left[1 + \frac{3\lambda^2}{(1 + \lambda)^2}\right] \quad . \quad . \quad . \quad (13.32)$$

or writing

$$\delta = 3\left(\frac{\lambda}{1 + \lambda}\right)^2$$

$$C_{D_v} = \frac{C_L^2}{\pi \mathcal{R}}[1 + \delta] \quad . \quad . \quad . \quad (13.33)$$

Minimum vortex drag condition. Comparing this with the vortex drag coefficient for the elliptic case, eqn. (13.25), it can be seen that modifying the spanwise distribution away from the elliptic increases the drag coefficient by the fraction δ which is *always positive* as it contains λ^2 terms only. It follows that for the vortex drag to be a minimum δ must be zero and hence so must λ (or a) so that the distribution for minimum vortex drag is the semi-ellipse. It will also be noted that the minimum drag distribution produces a constant downwash along the span while all other distributions produce a spanwise variation in induced velocity. This is no mere coincidence. It is part of the physical explanation of why elliptic distribution should have minimum vortex drag.

Consider two aerofoils (a) and (b) (Fig. 13.14), of equal span with spanwise distributions in downwash velocity $w = w_0 =$ constant along (a) and $w = f(y)$ along (b). Without altering the latter downwash variation it can be expressed as the sum of two distributions w_0 and $w_1 = f_1(y)$ as shown in Fig. 13.14 (c).

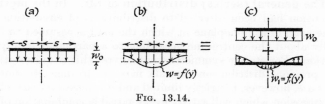

FIG. 13.14.

(a) Elliptic distribution gives constant downwash and minimum drag.
(b) Non-elliptic distribution gives varying downwash.
(c) Equivalent variation for comparison purposes.

If the lift due to both aerofoils is the same under given conditions, the rate of change of vertical momentum in the flow is the same for both.

Thus for (a)
$$L \propto \int_{-s}^{s} \dot{m} w_0 \, dy \qquad . \qquad . \qquad . \qquad . \qquad (13.34)$$

and for (b)
$$L \propto \int_{-s}^{s} \dot{m}(w_0 + f_1(y)) \, dy \qquad . \qquad . \qquad . \qquad (13.35)$$

where $\dot{m}$ is a representative mass flow meeting unit span.

Since L is the same on each wing
$$\int_{-s}^{s} \dot{m} f_1(y) \, dy = 0 \qquad . \qquad . \qquad . \qquad (13.36)$$

Now the energy transfer or rate of change of the kinetic energy of the representative mass flows is the vortex drag (or induced drag).

For (a),
$$D_{v(a)} \propto \tfrac{1}{2}\dot{m} \int_{-s}^{s} w_0^2 \, dy \qquad . \qquad . \qquad . \qquad . \qquad (13.37)$$

For (b),
$$D_{v(b)} \propto \tfrac{1}{2}\dot{m} \int_{-s}^{s} (w_0 + f_1(y))^2 \, dy$$

$$\propto \tfrac{1}{2}\dot{m} \int_{-s}^{s} [w_0^2 + 2w_0 f_1 y + (f_1(y))^2] \, dy$$

and since $\int_{-s}^{s} \dot{m} f_1(y) = 0$ in eqn. (13.36)

$$D_{v(b)} \propto \left[\tfrac{1}{2}\dot{m} \int_{-s}^{s} w_0^2 \, dy + \tfrac{1}{2}\dot{m} \int_{-s}^{s} (f_1(y))^2 \, dy \right] \qquad . \qquad (13.38)$$

Comparing eqns. (13.37) and (13.38)

$$D_{v(b)} = D_{v(a)} + \tfrac{1}{2}m \int_{-s}^{s} f_1(y)^2 \, dy$$

and since $\int_{-s}^{s} f_1(y) \, dy = 0$ and $f_1(y)$ is an explicit function of y,

$$\int_{-s}^{s} (f_1(y))^2 > 0$$

since $(f_1(y))^2$ is always positive whatever the sign of $f_1(y)$.

Hence $D_{v(b)}$ is always greater than $D_{v(a)}$.

13.3.5. The general (series) distribution of lift.

In the previous section attention had been directed to distributions of circulation (or lift) along the span of a monoplane in which the load is assumed to fall symmetrically about the centre-line according to a particular family of load distributions. For steady symmetric manœuvres this is quite satisfactory and the previous distribution formula may be arranged to suit certain cases. Its use, however, is strictly limited and it is necessary to seek further for an expression which will satisfy every possible combination of aerofoil design parameter and flight manœuvre.

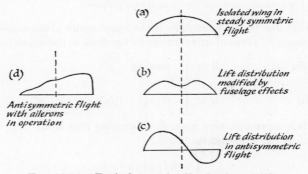

(a) Isolated wing in steady symmetric flight

(d) Antisymmetric flight with ailerons in operation

(b) Lift distribution modified by fuselage effects

(c) Lift distribution in antisymmetric flight

FIG. 13.15.—Typical spanwise distributions of lift.

For example, it has so far been assumed that the wing was an isolated lifting surface which in straight steady flight had a load distribution rising steadily from zero at the tips to a maximum at mid-span (Fig. 13.15 (a)). The general wing, however, will have a fuselage located in the centre sections which will modify the loading in that region (Fig. 13.15 (b)), and engine nacelles or other excrescences may deform the remainder of the curve locally.

The load distributions on both the isolated wing and the general aeroplane wing will be considerably changed in anti-symmetric flight. In rolling, for instance, the upgoing wing suffers a large decrease in lift, which may become negative at some incidences (Fig. 13.15 (c)). With ailerons in operation the curve of spanwise loading for a wing is no longer smooth and symmetrical but can be rugged and distorted in shape (Fig. 13.15 (d)).

It is clearly necessary to find an expression which will accommodate all these various possibilities. From previous work the formula $l = \rho V K$ for any section of span is familiar. Writing l in the form of the non-dimensional lift coefficient and equating to $\rho V K$,

$$K = \frac{C_L}{2} V c \qquad . \qquad . \qquad . \qquad . \qquad (13.39)$$

is easily obtained. This shows that for a given steady flight state the circulation at any section can be represented by the product of the forward velocity and the local chord. Now in addition the local chord can be expressed as a fraction of the semi-span s, and with this fraction absorbed in a new number and the numeral 4 introduced for later convenience, K becomes:

$$K = m.4Vs$$

where m is a dimensionless quantity which will vary similarly to K across the span.

In other words, m is the shape parameter or variation of the K curve and being dimensionless it can be expressed as the Fourier sine series $\sum_1^\infty A_n \sin n\theta$ in which the coefficients A_n represent the amplitudes, and the sum of the successive harmonics describes the shape. The sine series was chosen to satisfy the end conditions of the curve reducing to zero at the tips where $y = \pm s$. These correspond to the values of $\theta = 0$ and π. It is well understood that such a series is unlimited in angular measure but the portions beyond 0 and π can be disregarded here. Further, the series can fit any shape of curve, but in general, for rapidly changing distributions as shown by a rugged curve, for example, many harmonics are required to produce a sum which is a good representation.

In particular the series is simplified for the symmetrical loading case when the even terms disappear (Fig. 13.16 (II)). For the symmetrical case a maximum or minimum must appear at the mid-section. This is only possible for sines of odd values of $\pi/2$. That is, the symmetrical loading must be the sum of symmetrical harmonics. Odd harmonics are symmetrical. Even harmonics, on the other hand, return to zero again at $\pi/2$ where in addition there is always a change in sign. For any asymmetry in the loading one or more even harmonics are necessary.

With the number and magnitude of harmonics effectively giving all generalities the spanwise loading can be expressed as

$$K = 4sV \sum_1^\infty A_n \sin n\theta \qquad . \qquad . \qquad . \qquad (13.40)$$

In passing it should be noticed that since $l = \rho v K$ the spanwise lift distribution can be expressed as

$$l = 4\rho V^2 s \sum A_n \sin n\theta \qquad . \qquad . \qquad . \qquad (13.41)$$

the limits to the series being omitted for convenience.

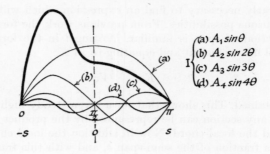

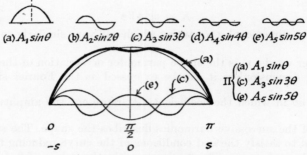

FIG. 13.16.—Loading make-up by selected sine series.

13.3.6. Aerodynamic characteristics for symmetrical general loading.
The operations to obtain lift, downwash and drag vary only in detail from the previous cases.

Lift on the aerofoil. $L = \int_{-s}^{s} \rho V K \, dy$ and changing the variable

$y = -s \cos \theta$, $L = \int_{0}^{\pi} \rho V K s \sin \theta \, d\theta$ and substituting for the general series expression

$$L = \int_{\rho}^{\pi} V . 4 V s^2 \sum A_n \sin n\theta \sin \theta \, d\theta$$

$$= 4s^2 \rho V^2 \int_{0}^{\pi} \sum \tfrac{1}{2} A_n (\cos (n-1)\theta - \cos (n+1)\theta) \, d\theta$$

$$= 4s^2 \rho V^2 \tfrac{1}{2} \left[\sum A_n \left(\frac{\sin (n-1)\theta}{n-1} - \frac{\sin (n+1)}{n+1} \right) \right]_{0}^{\pi}$$

The squared bracket equals zero for all values of n other than unity when it becomes

$$\left[\lim_{(n-1)\to 0} A_1 \frac{\sin (n-1)\theta}{n-1} \right]_{0}^{\pi} = A_1 \pi$$

Thus
$$L = A_1 \pi \tfrac{1}{2} \rho V^2 . 4s^2 = C_L \tfrac{1}{2} \rho V^2 S$$

and writing $\qquad$ Aspect Ratio $= \dfrac{4s^2}{S} = \mathcal{R}$

$$C_L = \pi . A_1 . \mathcal{R} \qquad . \qquad . \qquad . \quad (13.42)$$

This indicates the rather surprising result that the lift depends on the magnitude of the coefficient of the *first* term only, no matter how many more may be present in the series describing the distribution.

This is because the terms $A_3 \sin 3\theta$, $A_5 \sin 5\theta$, etc., provide positive lift on some sections and negative lift on others so that the overall effect of these is zero. These terms provide the characteristic variations in the spanwise distribution but do not affect the total lift of the whole which is determined solely from the amplitude of the first harmonic.

Thus $\qquad C_L = \pi \mathcal{R} . A_1$, and $\quad L = 2\pi \rho V^2 s^2 A_1$

Downwash. Changing the variable and limits of eqn. (13.14), the equation for the downwash is

$$w_{\theta\,1} = \frac{1}{4\pi s} \int_0^\pi \frac{\dfrac{dK}{d\theta} d\theta}{\cos\theta - \cos\theta_1} \quad \text{as before}$$

In this case $K = 4sV \sum A_n \sin n\theta$ and thus on differentiating

$$\frac{dK}{d\theta} = 4sV \sum n A_n \cos n\theta$$

Introducing this into the integral expression

$$w_{\theta\,1} = \frac{4sV}{4\pi s} \int_0^\pi \frac{\sum n A_n \cos n\theta}{\cos\theta - \cos\theta_1} d\theta$$

$$= \frac{V}{\pi} \sum n A_n G_n$$

and writing in $\qquad G_n = \dfrac{\pi \sin n\theta_1}{\sin \theta_1}$ from p. 351 or App. 3,

and reverting back to the general point θ,

$$w = V \frac{\sum n A_n \sin n\theta}{\sin \theta} \qquad . \qquad . \qquad . \quad (13.43)$$

This involves all the coefficients of the series, and will be symmetrically distributed about the centre line for odd harmonics.

Vortex drag (induced drag). The drag grading is given by $d_v = \rho w K$. Integrating gives the total vortex drag

$$D_v = \int_{-s}^s \rho w K \, dy \quad \text{or in the polar variable}$$

$$= \int_0^\pi \rho . \underbrace{\frac{V \sum n A_n \sin n\theta}{\sin \theta}}_{w} . \underbrace{4sV \sum A_n \sin n\theta}_{K} . \underbrace{s \sin \theta \, d\theta}_{dy}$$

$$D_v = 4\rho V^2 s^2 \int_0^\pi \sum n A_n \sin \theta \sum A_n \sin n\theta \, d\theta$$

The integral becomes $\sum n A_n^2 \dfrac{\pi}{2}$. This can be demonstrated by multiplying out the first three (say) odd harmonics, thus

$$I = \int_0^\pi (A_1 \sin \theta + 3A_3 \sin 3\theta + 5A_5 \sin 5\theta)(A_1 \sin \theta + A_3 \sin 3\theta + A_5 \sin \theta) \, d\theta$$

$$I = \int_0^\pi \{A_1{}^2 \sin^2 \theta + 3A_3{}^2 \sin^2 \theta + 5A_5{}^2 \sin^2 \theta + [A_1 A_3 \sin \theta \sin 3\theta \text{ and other}$$

like terms which are products of different multiples of θ]$\}$ $d\theta$

On carrying out the integration from 0 to π all terms other than the squared terms vanish leaving

$$I = \int_0^\pi (A_1{}^2 \sin^2 \theta + 3A_2{}^2 \sin^2 3\theta + 5A_5{}^2 \sin^2 5\theta + \ldots) \, d\theta$$

$$= \frac{\pi}{2}[A_1{}^2 + 3A_3{}^2 + 5A_5{}^2 + \ldots] = \frac{\pi}{2} \sum n A_n{}^2$$

This gives
$$D_v = 4\rho V^2 s^2 \frac{\pi}{2} \sum n A_n{}^2 = C_{D\,v} \tfrac{1}{2}\rho V^2 S$$

whence
$$C_{D\,v} = \pi \mathcal{R} \sum n A_n{}^2 \qquad . \qquad . \qquad . \qquad . \qquad \textbf{(13.44)}$$

From eqn. (13.42)

$$A_1{}^2 = \frac{C_L{}^2}{\pi^2 \mathcal{R}^2}$$

and introducing this into eqn. (13.44)

$$C_{D\,v} = \frac{C_L{}^2}{\pi \mathcal{R}} \sum n \left(\frac{A_n}{A_1}\right)^2$$

$$= \frac{C_L{}^2}{\pi \mathcal{R}}\left[1 + \left(\frac{3A_3{}^2}{A_1{}^2} + \frac{5A_5{}^2}{A_1{}^2} + \frac{7A_7{}^2}{A_1{}^2} + \ldots\right)\right]$$

Writing the symbol δ for the term $\left(\dfrac{3A_3{}^2}{A_1{}^2} + \dfrac{5A_5{}^2}{A_1{}^2} + \dfrac{7A_7{}^2}{A_1{}^2} + \ldots\right)$

$$C_{D\,v} = \frac{C_L{}^2}{\pi \mathcal{R}}[1 + \delta] \text{ (eqn. (13.33))}$$

As before δ is always a positive quantity because it consists of squared terms which must always be positive. $C_{D\,v}$ can be a minimum *only* when $\delta = 0$. That is when $A_3 = A_5 = A_7 = \ldots = 0$ and the only term remaining in the series is $A_1 \sin \theta$.

13.3.7. Aerodynamic characteristics of asymmetrical loading.

The sine series is capable of interpreting any variation over the range $0 - \pi$ providing sufficient terms are taken. As the previous section details, distributions in K which fall symmetrically about the mid-span sections involve only the odd terms, and produce vortex drag and downwash variations which also are symmetrical about the centre-line.

In the general case, where the loading or lift distribution is not symmetrical about mid-span sections, even terms appear in the distribution, and as a consequence of the asymmetry other aerofoil characteristics appear which have hitherto been zero in magnitude and tacitly ignored.

When the lift distribution is not symmetrically disposed about the centre-line one wing will have a greater lift force than the other and a net *rolling moment* about the longitudinal axis through the mid-sections will result.

Again, as the lift is not symmetrical, nor is the spanwise distribution of circulation, the downwash will vary across the span without symmetry about the centre-line and so will the vortex drag grading. Hence, more drag will be experienced on one wing (the one with more lift) than on the other and a net *yawing moment* will result about the vertical (or normal) axis through the mid-span sections.

In addition to these there will be the overall lift and vortex drag forces normal and parallel to the plane of the aerofoil in the plane of symmetry.

Lift on the aerofoil. It is pointless simply to repeat the identical work of the previous section, which gives this result.

The main steps are:

$$L = \int_{-s}^{s} \rho V K \, dy = \int_{0}^{\pi} \rho V 4 s V \sum A_n \sin n\theta \cdot s \sin \theta \, d\theta$$

$$= C_L \tfrac{1}{2} \rho V^2 S$$

giving $C_L = \pi . A_1 \mathcal{R}$ as before from eqn. (13.42).

Once again, and in the same way, no harmonics subsequent to the first, either odd or even, change the magnitude of the lift on the aerofoil as a whole. Indeed the overall lift may well be zero in the case of a wing with an asymmetric distribution and will be so if the series describing the distribution contains no terms in $\sin \theta$ (i.e., $A_1 = 0$). See Exercise No. 8.

Downwash. As derived in § 13.3.6 and given in eqn. (13.43)

$$w = \frac{V \sum n A_n \sin n\theta}{\sin \theta}$$

and this will no longer be symmetrical as it contains even harmonics in the same way as does the lift.

Vortex drag (induced drag) from the similar treatment for the symmetrical distribution but again allowing n to be any integer from 1 to ∞.

Eqn. 13.44 gives

$$C_{D_v} = \pi \mathcal{R} \sum n A_n^2$$

which can be expanded for clarity to

$$C_{D_v} = \pi \mathcal{R} [A_1^2 + 2A_2^2 + 3A_3^2 + 4A_4^2 + 5A_5^2 +] \quad . \quad (13.45)$$

and again shown as

$$C_{D\,v} = \frac{C_L{}^2}{\pi A}[1 + \delta] \quad \text{where } \delta > 0$$

Rolling moment. Chapter 14 defines the terms and notation used in defining the forces and moments acting on an aeroplane as a whole, and it may be confusing to insist on the standard symbol L for rolling moment in the present context as L has been successfully and commonly used for denoting the overall lift.

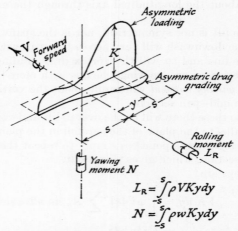

Asymmetric loading

Forward speed

K

Asymmetric drag grading

y

s

s

s

Rolling moment L_R

Yawing moment N

$$L_R = \int_{-s}^{s} \rho V K y \, dy$$

$$N = \int_{-s}^{s} \rho w K y \, dy$$

FIG. 13.17.—Asymmetric spanwise loading produces an asymmetric vortex drag grading.

This difficulty will be overcome here by denoting the rolling moment as L_R and the non-dimensional form, or rolling moment coefficient, as C_l. Fig. 13.17 shows a schematic representation of a rectangular wing with an asymmetric lift grading and the corresponding drag grading.

The lift on any section of spanwise length δy distance y from the centre-line or Ox axis will produce a negative increment of rolling moment equal to

$$\Delta L_R = -\, ly \,\delta y \quad . \qquad . \qquad . \qquad . \quad (13.46)$$

where l is the lift grading and $l = \rho V K$.

Thus integrating across the span for the total moment

$$L_R = -\int_{-s}^{s} ly \, dy = -\int_{-s}^{s} \rho V K y \, dy \quad . \qquad . \quad (13.47)$$

Inserting $K = 4sV \sum A_n \sin n\theta$ and changing the limits and variables as previously,

$$L_R = 4\rho s V^2 \int_{0}^{\pi} \sum A_n \sin n\theta \, . s \cos \theta \, . s \sin \theta \, d\theta$$

$$= 4\rho s^3 V^2 \int_0^\pi \tfrac{1}{2} \sum A_n \sin n\theta \sin 2\theta \, d\theta$$

$$= 2\rho s^3 V^2 \int_0^\pi \tfrac{1}{2} \sum A_n [\cos (n - 2)\theta - \cos (n + 2)\theta] \, d\theta$$

$$= \rho s^3 V^2 \left[\sum A_n \left(\frac{\sin (n - 2)\theta}{n - 2} - \frac{\sin (n + 2)\theta}{n + 2} \right) \right]_0^\pi$$

$$L_R = \rho s^3 V^2 A_2 . \pi = C_l \tfrac{1}{2}\rho V^2 Ss$$

giving $\quad C_l = \dfrac{\pi}{2} . Æ . A_2$ . . . . (13.48)

Yawing moment (N). The yawing moment arises as a result of the asymmetric drag grading across the span. Fig. 13.17 shows this in a stylized way. The contribution of the vortex drag of an element of span δy, y from the Oz axis is

$$\Delta N = d_v y \, \delta y \quad . \qquad . \qquad . \qquad . \quad (13.49)$$

where d_v is the vortex drag per unit span and $d_v = \rho w K$. Integration over the whole span gives

$$N = \int_{-s}^s d_v y \, dy = \int_{-s}^s \rho w K y \, dy$$

Inserting the series expressions for K and w and changing the limits and variable gives

$$N = - \int_0^\pi \rho V \frac{\sum n A_n \sin n\theta}{\sin \theta} . 4s V \sum A_n \sin n\theta . s \cos \theta s \sin \theta \, d\theta$$

$$= - 4\rho s^3 V^2 \int_0^\pi \sum n A_n \sin n\theta \sum A_n \sin n\theta \cos \theta \, d\theta$$

$$= C_N \tfrac{1}{2}\rho V^2 Ss$$

whence

$$C_N = 2Æ \int_0^\pi \sum n A_n \sin n\theta \sum A_n \sin n\theta \cos \theta \, d\theta$$

Multiplying out these two series for a few terms establishes the general solution

$$C_N = \frac{\pi}{2} Æ [3A_1 A_2 + 5A_2 A_3 + 7A_3 A_4 + \ldots + (2n+1)A_n A_{n+1}] \quad . \quad (13.50)$$

since all terms other than those with coefficients which are the products $A_1 A_2$, $A_2 A_3$, $A_3 A_4$, etc., vanish on integration.

13.4. Determination of the load distribution on a given wing.

This is the direct problem broadly facing a designer who wishes to predict the performance of a projected wing before the long and costly process of model tests begin. This does not imply that such tests need not be carried

A A

out. On the contrary, they are important steps in the design process towards a production aircraft.

The problem can be rephrased to suggest that a designer would wish to have some indication of how the aerofoil characteristics vary as, for example, the geometric parameters of the project aerofoil are changed. In this way he can balance the aerodynamic effects of his changing ideas against the basic specification—providing there is a fairly simple process relating the changes in design parameters to the aerodynamic characteristics.

Of course, this is stating one of the design problems in its baldest and simplest terms, but as in any design work, plausible theoretical processes yielding reliable predictions are very comforting.

Already the loading on the wing has been described in the most general terms available and the overall characteristics are immediately to hand in terms of the coefficients of the loading distribution (§ 13.3).

It remains to relate the coefficients (or the series as a whole) to the basic aerofoil parameters of planform and aerofoil section characteristics.

13.4.1. The general theory—the monoplane equation. A start is
made by considering the influence of the end effect, or downwash, on the lifting properties of an aerofoil section at some distance y from the centre-line of the wing.

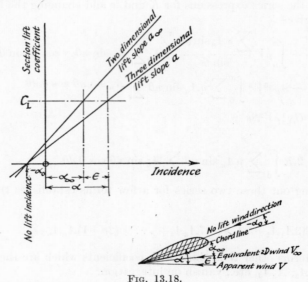

FIG. 13.18.

Fig. 13.18 shows the lift versus incidence curve for an aerofoil section of a certain profile (a) working two-dimensionally and (b) working in a flow regime influenced by end effects, i.e., working at some point along the span of a finite lifting wing.

Assuming that both curves are linear over the range considered (i.e., the working range) and that under both flow regimes the no lift incidence is the same, then

$$C_L = a_\infty[\alpha_\infty - \alpha_0] = a[\alpha - \alpha_0] \qquad . \qquad . \quad (13.51)$$

Taking the first equation with $\alpha_\infty = \alpha - \varepsilon$

$$C_L = a_\infty[(\alpha - \alpha_0) - \varepsilon] \qquad . \qquad . \qquad . \quad (13.52)$$

But equally
$$C_L = \frac{\text{lift per unit span}}{\frac{1}{2}\rho V^2 c . 1} = \frac{l}{\frac{1}{2}\rho V^2 c . 1}$$

$$= \frac{\rho V K}{\frac{1}{2}\rho V^2 c}$$

or
$$C_L = \frac{2K}{Vc} \qquad . \qquad . \qquad . \qquad . \qquad . \quad (13.53)$$

Equating eqns. (13.52) and (13.53) and rearranging,

$$\frac{2K}{ca_\infty} = V(\alpha - \alpha_0) - V\varepsilon$$

and since

$$V\varepsilon = w = -\frac{1}{4\pi} \int_{-s}^{s} \frac{\left(\dfrac{dK}{dy}\right) dy}{y - y_1} \quad \text{from eqn. (13.14)}$$

$$\frac{2K}{ca_\infty} = V(\alpha - \alpha_0) + \frac{1}{4\pi} \int_{-s}^{s} \frac{\left(\dfrac{dK}{dy}\right) dy}{y - y_1} \qquad . \qquad . \qquad . \quad (13.54)$$

This equation is the integral equation for the circulation K at any section along the span in terms of all the aerofoil parameters. These will be discussed when eqn. (13.54) is reduced to a form more amenable to numerical solution. To do this the general series expression for K is taken,

$$K = 4sV \sum A_n \sin n\theta$$

The previous section gives eqn. (13.43),

$$w = \frac{V \sum n A_n \sin n\theta}{\sin \theta}$$

which substituted in eqn. (13.54) gives together

$$2 . \frac{4sV \sum A_n \sin n\theta}{ca_\infty} = V(\alpha - \alpha_0) - \frac{V \sum n A_n \sin n\theta}{\sin \theta}$$

Cancelling V and collecting $ca_\infty/8s$ into the single parameter μ this equation becomes:

$$\mu(\alpha - \alpha_0) = \sum_{1}^{\infty} A_n \sin n\theta \left(1 + \frac{\mu n}{\sin \theta}\right) \qquad . \qquad . \quad (13.55)$$

Consider the solution of this equation. It cannot in general be solved identically, that is for all points along the span, but only at selected spanwise stations and at each end.

13.4.2. General solution of the monoplane equation.

This will be best understood if a particular value of θ, or position along the span, be taken in eqn. (13.55). Take for example the position $y = -0.5s$, which is midway between the mid-span sections and the tip.

From $\qquad y = -s \cos \theta, \ \theta = \cos^{-1}(+\tfrac{1}{2}) = 60°$

Then if the value of the parameter μ is μ_1 and the incidence from no lift is $(\alpha_1 - \alpha_{01})$ eqn. (13.55) becomes

$$\mu_1(\alpha_1 - \alpha_{01}) = A_1 \sin 60° \left[1 + \frac{\mu_1}{\sin 60°}\right] + A_2 \sin 120° \left[1 + \frac{2\mu_1}{\sin 60°}\right]$$

$$+ A_3 \sin 180° \left[1 + \frac{3\mu_1}{\sin 60°}\right] + \text{etc.}$$

This is obviously an equation with A_1, A_2, A_3, A_4, etc., as the only unknowns.

Other equations in which A_1, A_2, A_3, A_4, etc., are the unknowns can be found by considering other points y along the span, bearing in mind that the value of μ and of $(\alpha - \alpha_0)$ may also change from point to point. If it is desired to use, say, four terms in the series, an equation of the above form must be obtained at each of four values of θ, noting that normally the values $\theta = 0$ and π (i.e., the wing-tips) lead to the trivial equation $0 = 0$, and are therefore useless for the present purpose. Generally four coefficients are sufficient in the symmetrical case to produce a spanwise distribution which is insignificantly altered by the addition of further terms. In the case of symmetric flight the coefficients would be A_1, A_3, A_5, A_7, since the even harmonics do not appear. Also the arithmetic need only be concerned with values of θ between 0 and $\pi/2$ since the curve is symmetrical about the mid-span section.

If the spanwise distribution is irregular, more harmonics are necessary in the series to describe it adequately, and more coefficients must be found from the monoplane equation. This becomes quite a tedious and lengthy operation by 'long-hand', but being a simple mathematical procedure the simultaneous equations can be easily programmed for a computer.

The aerofoil parameters are contained in the expression

$$\mu = \frac{\text{chord} \times \text{two-dimensional lift slope}}{8 \times \text{semi-span}}$$

and the absolute incidence $(\alpha - \alpha_0)$.

μ clearly allows for any spanwise variation in the chord (i.e., change in plan shape) or in the two-dimensional slope of the aerofoil profile (i.e., change in aerofoil section). α is the local geometric incidence and will vary if there is any geometric twist present on the wing. α_0, the no-lift incidence, may vary if there is any aerodynamic twist present, i.e., if the aerofoil section is changing along the span.

Example 13.1. Consider a tapered aerofoil. For completeness in the example every parameter is allowed to vary in a linear fashion from mid-span to the wing-tips.

Mid-span Data		*Wing-tip Data*
10	Chord ft	5
5·5	$\left(\dfrac{\partial C_L}{\partial \alpha}\right)_\infty$ per radian	5·8
5·5	absolute incidence $\alpha°$	3·5
	Total span of wing is 40 ft.	

Obtain the aerofoil characteristics of the wing, the spanwise distribution of circulation, comparing it with the equivalent elliptic distribution for the wing flying straight and level at 200 m.p.h at low altitude.

From the data:

$$\text{Wing area } S = \frac{10 + 5}{2} \times 40$$
$$= 300 \text{ ft}^2$$
$$\text{Aspect Ratio } \mathcal{R} = \frac{\text{span}^2}{\text{area}} = \frac{40^2}{300} = \frac{16}{3} = 5·333$$

At any section y from the centre-line [θ from the wing-tip]

$$\text{chord } c = 10\left[1 - \frac{10 - 5}{10}\left(\frac{y}{s}\right)\right] = 10[1 + 0·5 \cos \theta]$$

$$\left(\frac{\partial C_L}{\partial \alpha}\right)_\infty = a_\infty = 5·5\left[1 + \frac{5·8 - 5·5}{5·5}\left(\frac{y}{s}\right)\right] = 5·5[1 - 0·05455 \cos \theta]$$

$$\alpha° = 5·5\left[1 - \frac{5·5 - 3·5}{5·5}\left(\frac{y}{s}\right)\right] = 5·5[1 + 0·36364 \cos \theta]$$

This gives at any section,

$$\mu = \frac{c a_\infty}{8s} = 0·34375(1 + 0·5 \cos \theta)(1 - 0·05455 \cos \theta)$$

and $\mu\alpha = 0·032995(1 + 0·5 \cos \theta)(1 - 0·05455 \cos \theta)(1 + 0·36364 \cos \theta)$

where α is now in radians.

For convenience eqn. (13.55) is rearranged to:

$$\mu\alpha \sin \theta = A_1 \sin \theta(\sin \theta + \mu) + A_3 \sin 3\theta(\sin \theta + 3\mu)$$
$$+ A_5 \sin 5\theta(\sin \theta + 5\mu) + A_7 \sin 7\theta(\sin \theta + 7\mu)$$

and since the distribution is symmetrical the odd coefficients only will appear. Four coefficients will be evaluated and because of symmetry it is only necessary to take values of θ between 0 and $\pi/2$, namely: $\pi/8$, $\pi/4$, $3\pi/8$, $\pi/2$.

TABLE 13.1

θ	$\sin \theta$	$\sin 3\theta$	$\sin 5\theta$	$\sin 7\theta$	$\cos \theta$
$\frac{1}{8}\pi$	0·38268	0·92388	0·92388	0·38268	0·92388
$\frac{1}{4}\pi$	0·70711	0·70711	−0·70711	−0·70711	0·70711
$\frac{3}{8}\pi$	0·92388	−0·38268	−0·38268	−0·92388	0·38268
π	1·00000	−1·00000	1·00000	−1·00000	0·00000

Table 13.1 gives values of $\sin\theta$, $\sin n\theta$, and $\cos\theta$ for the above angles and these substituted in the rearranged eqn. (13.55) lead to the following four simultaneous equations in the unknown coefficients.

$$0\cdot004739 = 0\cdot22079A_1 + 0\cdot89202A_3 + 1\cdot25100A_5 + 0\cdot66688A_7$$
$$0\cdot011637 = 0\cdot66319A_1 + 0\cdot98957A_3 - 1\cdot31595A_5 - 1\cdot64234A_7$$
$$0\cdot021665 = 1\cdot11573A_1 - 0\cdot67935A_3 - 0\cdot89654A_5 + 2\cdot68878A_7$$
$$0\cdot032998 = 1\cdot34375A_1 - 2\cdot03125A_3 - 2\cdot71875A_5 - 3\cdot40625A_7$$

These equations when solved give

$$A_1 = 0\cdot020329, \ A_3 = -0\cdot000955, \ A_5 = 0\cdot001029, \ A_7 = -0\cdot0002766$$

Thus

$$K = 4sV\ \{0\cdot020329\sin\theta - 0\cdot000955\sin 3\theta + 0\cdot001029\sin 5\theta - 0\cdot0002766\sin 7\theta\}$$

and substituting the values of θ taken above, the circulation attains the values of:

θ	0	$\pi/8$	$\pi/4$	$3\pi/8$	$\pi/2$
y/s . .	1	0·924	0·707	0·383	0
K ft²/sec .	0	181·5	308·6	433·6	529·5
K/K_0 . .	0	0·343	0·583	0·82	1·0

As a comparison, the equivalent elliptic distribution gives a series of values

K ft²/sec..	0	186·7	344·7	450·5	487·6

The aerodynamic characteristics follow from the equations given in § 13.3.4. Thus:

$$C_L = \pi\!R.A_1 = \underline{0\cdot3406}$$

$$C_{Dv} = \frac{C_L{}^2}{\pi\!R}[1 + \delta] = \underline{0\cdot007068}$$

since

$$\delta = 3\left(\frac{A_3}{A_1}\right)^2 + 5\left(\frac{A_5}{A_1}\right)^2 + 7\left(\frac{A_7}{A_1}\right)^2 = 0\cdot02073$$

i.e., the trailing vortex drag is 2% greater than the minimum.

For completeness the total lift and drag may be given

$$\text{Lift} = C_L\tfrac{1}{2}\rho V^2 S = 0\cdot3406 \times 31370\cdot5 = \underline{10{,}685\text{ lb}}$$

$$\text{Drag (vortex)} = C_{Dv}\tfrac{1}{2}\rho V^2 S = 0\cdot007068 \times 31370\cdot5 = \underline{221\cdot73\text{ lb}}$$

Example 13.2. A wing is untwisted and of elliptic planform with a symmetrical aerofoil section, and is rigged symmetrically in a wind-tunnel at incidence α_1 to a wind stream having an axial velocity V. In addition, the wind has a small uniform angular velocity ω, about the tunnel axis.

Show that the distribution of circulation along the wing is given by

$$K = 4sV[A_1\sin\theta + A_2\sin 2\theta]$$

and determine A_1 and A_2 in terms of the wing parameters. Neglect wind-tunnel constraints. (N.C.A.T.)

§ 13·4 gives the general monoplane equation

$$\mu(\alpha - \alpha_0) = \sum A_n \sin n\theta\left(1 + \frac{\mu n}{\sin\theta}\right)$$

In this case $\alpha_0 = 0$ and the effective incidence at any section y from the centre-line

$$\alpha = \alpha_1 + y\frac{\omega}{V} = \alpha_1 - \frac{\omega}{V}s\cos\theta$$

Also since the planform is elliptic and untwisted $\mu = \mu_0 \sin\theta$ (§ 13.4.3) and the monoplane equation becomes for this problem

$$\mu_0 \sin\theta\left[\alpha_1 - \frac{\omega}{V}s\cos\theta\right] = \sum A_n \sin n\theta\left(1 + \frac{\mu_0 n \sin\theta}{\sin\theta}\right)$$

Expanding both sides,

$$\mu_0\alpha_1\sin\theta - \frac{\mu_0\omega s}{V}\frac{\sin 2\theta}{2} = A_1\sin\theta(1+\mu_0) + A_2\sin 2\theta(1+2\mu_0)$$
$$+ A_3\sin 3\theta(1+3\mu_0) + \text{etc.}$$

Equating like terms,

$$\mu_0\alpha_1\sin\theta = A_1(1+\mu_0)\sin\theta$$

$$\frac{\mu_0 s\omega}{2V}\sin 2\theta = A_2(1+2\mu_0)\sin 2\theta$$

$$0 = A_3(1+3\mu_0)\sin 3\theta \text{ etc.}$$

Thus the spanwise distribution for this case is

$$K = 4sV[A_1\sin\theta + A_2\sin 2\theta^-]$$

and the coefficients are

$$A_1 = \left(\frac{\mu_0}{1+\mu_0}\right)\alpha_1$$

and

$$A_2 = \left(\frac{\mu_0}{2(1+2\mu_0)}\right)\cdot\frac{\omega s}{V}$$

13.4.3. Load distribution for minimum drag.

Minimum trailing vortex drag for a given lift will occur if C_{D_v} is a minimum and this will be so only if δ is zero, since δ is always a positive quantity. Since δ involves squares of all the coefficients other than the first, it follows that the minimum drag condition coincides with the distribution which provides $A_3 = A_5 = A_7 = A_n = 0$. Such a distribution is $K = 4sVA_1\sin\theta$ and substituting $y = -s\cos\theta$

$$K = 4sVA_1\sqrt{1 - \left(\frac{y}{s}\right)^2}$$

which is an elliptic spanwise distribution. These findings are in accordance with those of the previous section, 13.3.3.

This elliptic distribution can be pursued in an analysis involving the general monoplane eqn. (13.55) to give a far-reaching expression.

Putting $A_n = 0$, $n \neq 1$ in eqn. (13.55) gives

$$\mu(\alpha - \alpha_0) = A_1\sin\theta\left(1 + \frac{\mu}{\sin\theta}\right)$$

and rearranging

$$A_1 = \frac{\mu}{\sin\theta + \mu}\cdot(\alpha - \alpha_0) \qquad . \qquad . \qquad (13.56)$$

Now consider an untwisted wing producing an elliptic load distribution, and hence minimum vortex drag. By § 13.3.3 the downwash is constant along the span and hence the equivalent incidence ($\alpha - \alpha_0 - w/v$) anywhere along the span is constant. This means that the lift coefficient is constant.

Therefore in the equation

$$\text{lift per unit span } l = \rho V K = C_L \tfrac{1}{2} \rho V^2 c \quad . \qquad . \quad (13.57)$$

as l and K vary elliptically so must c, since on the right-hand side $C_L \tfrac{1}{2} \rho V^2$ is a constant along the span.

Thus
$$c = c_0 \sqrt{1 - \left(\frac{y}{s}\right)^2}$$
$$= c_0 \sin \theta$$

and the general inference emerges that for a spanwise elliptic distribution an untwisted wing will have an elliptic chord distribution, though the planform may not be a true ellipse. For example, the one-third chord line may be straight, whereas for a true ellipse, the mid-chord line would be straight.

It should be noted that an elliptic spanwise variation can be produced by varying the other parameters in eqn. (13.57). For example, eqn. (13.57) can be rearranged as

$$K = C_L \frac{V}{2} c$$

and putting
$$C_L = a_\infty [(\alpha - \alpha_0) - \varepsilon] \quad \text{from eqn. (13.52)}$$
$$K \propto c a_\infty [(\alpha - \alpha_0) - \varepsilon]$$

Thus to make K vary elliptically, geometric twist (varying $(\alpha - \alpha_0)$) or change in aerofoil section (varying a_∞ and/or α_0) may be employed in addition to, or instead of, changing the planform.

Returning to an untwisted elliptic planform, the important expression can be obtained by including $c = c_0 \sin \theta$ in μ to give

$$\mu = \mu_0 \sin \theta \quad \text{where } \mu_0 = \frac{c_0 a_\infty}{8s}$$

Then eqn. (13.56) gives

$$A_1 = \frac{\mu_0}{1 + \mu_0} \cdot (\alpha - \alpha_0) \qquad . \qquad . \qquad . \quad (13.58)$$

But
$$A_1 = \frac{C_L}{\pi \mathcal{R}} \quad \text{from eqn. (13.42)}$$

Now
$$\frac{C_L}{(\alpha - \alpha_0)} = a = \text{three-dimensional lift slope}$$

and
$$\mu_0 = \frac{c_0 a_\infty}{8s} = \frac{a_\infty}{\pi \mathcal{R}}$$

for an elliptic chord distribution, so that on substituting in eqn. (13.58) and rearranging

$$a = \frac{a_\infty}{1 + \dfrac{a_\infty}{\pi \mathcal{R}}} \qquad . \qquad . \qquad . \qquad . \qquad (13.59)$$

This equation gives the lift curve slope (a) for a given aspect ratio $(\mathcal{R})$ in terms of the two-dimensional slope of the aerofoil section used in the aerofoil. It has been derived with regard to the particular case of an elliptic planform producing minimum drag conditions and is strictly true only for this case. However, most practical aerofoils diverge so little from the elliptic in this respect that eqn. (13.59) and its inverse

$$a_\infty = \frac{a}{1 - \dfrac{a}{\pi \mathcal{R}}}$$

can be used with confidence in performance predictions, forecasting of wind-tunnel results and like problems.

13.5. The simplified horseshoe vortex. It was suggested in § 13.1.2 that a simplified system could replace the complete vortex system of a wing when considering the influence of the lifting system on distant points in the flow, etc. Many such problems do exist and simple solutions, although not all exact, can be readily obtained using the suggested simplification.

This necessitates replacing the wing by a single bound spanwise vortex of constant strength which is turned through 90° at each end to form the trailing vortices which extend effectively to infinity behind the wing.

The general vortex system and its simplified equivalent must have two things in common:

(i) each must provide the same total lift,

(ii) each must have the same value of circulation about the trailing vortices and hence the same circulation at mid-span.

These equalities provide for the complete definition of the simplified system.

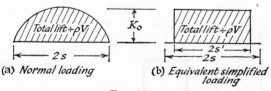

(a) *Normal loading*   (b) *Equivalent simplified loading*

FIG. 13.19.

The spanwise distributions created for the two cases of Fig. 13.1 are shown in Fig. 13.19. Both have the same mid-span circulation K_0 which is now constant along part of the span of the simplified equivalent case. For equivalence in area under the curve, which is proportional to the total lift, the span length of the single vortex must be less than that of the wing.

Thus $\qquad K_0 2s' =$ area under general distribution

$$= \frac{\text{lift}}{\rho V}$$

Hence $\qquad \dfrac{s'}{s} = \dfrac{\text{total lift}}{2s\rho V K_0}$ . . . . . . (13.60)

$2s'$ is the distance apart of the trailing vortex core centres.

From eqn. (13.42)

$$L = \rho V^2 s^2 2\pi A_1$$

and substituting also

$$K_0 = 4sV \sum A_n \sin n\frac{\pi}{2}$$

$$\frac{s'}{s} = \frac{\rho V^2 s^2 2\pi A_1}{2\rho V^2 . 4s^2 \sum A_n \sin n\dfrac{\pi}{2}}$$

$$= \frac{\pi}{4} \frac{A_1}{[A_1 - A_3 + A_5 - A_7]} \cdots$$

For the general case then,

$$\frac{s}{s'} = \frac{4}{\pi}\left[1 - \frac{A_3}{A_1} + \frac{A_5}{A_1} - \frac{A_7}{A_1} \cdots\right] \qquad . \qquad . \quad (13.61)$$

For the elliptic distribution,

$$A_3 = A_5 = A_7 = 0$$

$$s' = \frac{\pi}{4}s \qquad . \qquad . \qquad . \qquad . \quad (13.62)$$

In the absence of other information it is usual to assume that the separation of the trailing vortices is given by the elliptic case.

13.5.1. Formation flying effects.

Aircraft flying in close proximity experience mutual interference effects and good estimates of these influences are obtained by replacing each aircraft in the formation by its equivalent simplified horseshoe vortex.

Consider the problem shown in Fig. 13.20 where three identical aircraft are flying in a vee formation at a forward speed V ft/sec in the same horizontal plane. The total mutual interference is the sum of (i) that of the followers on the leader, (ii) that of the leader and follower (2) on

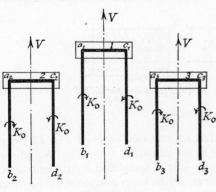

Fig. 13.20.

(3), and (iii) that of leader and follower (3) on (2). (ii) and (iii) are identical.

Consider (*i*). The leader is flying in a flow regime which has additional vertical flow components induced by the following vortices. Upward components appear from the bound vortices a_2c_2, a_3c_3, trailing vortices c_2d_2, a_3b_3 and downward components from the trailing vortices a_2b_2 and c_3d_3. The nett result is an upwash on the leader.

Consider (*ii*). These wings have additional influences to their own trails due to the leader and the other follower. Bound vortex a_1c_1 and trailing vortices a_1b_1, a_2b_2 produce downwashes. Again the nett influence is an upwash.

From these simple considerations it appears that each aircraft is flying in a regime in which upward components are induced by the presence of the others. The upwash components reduce the downward velocities induced by the aircraft's own trail and hence its trailing vortex drag. Because of the reduction in drag, less power is required to maintain the forward velocity and the well-known operational fact emerges that each aircraft of a formation has a better performance than when flying singly.

In most problems it is usual to assume that the wings have an elliptic distribution, and that the influence calculated for mid-span position is typical of the whole wing span. Also any curvature of the trails is neglected and the special forms of the Biot–Savart Law (§ 13.2.3) are used unreservedly.

13.5.2. Influence of the downwash on the tailplane.

On most aircraft the tailplane is between the trailing vortices springing from the mainplanes ahead and the flow around it is considerably influenced by these trails. Forces on aerofoils are proportional to the square of the velocity and the angle of incidence. Small velocity changes, therefore, have negligible effect unless they alter the incidence of the aerofoil, when they then have a significant effect on the force on the aerofoil.

Tailplanes work at incidences which are altered appreciably by the 'tilting' of the relative wind due to the large downward induced velocity components. This is illustrated in detail in § 14.7, where the downwash influence at the tail appears as the derivative $d\varepsilon/d\alpha$; that is the rate of change of downwash angle (or 'tilt' of relative wind vector) with respect to the mainplane incidence.

Each particular aircraft configuration will have its own geometry. The solution of a particular problem will be given here to show the method.

Example 13.3. Let the tailplane of a monoplane be x ft behind the wing centre of pressure and in the plane of the vortex trail (Fig. 13.21).

Assuming elliptic distribution, the span of the bound vortex is given by eqn. (13.62) as

$$s' = \frac{\pi}{4}s$$

The downwash at the mid-span point P of the tailplane caused by the wing is

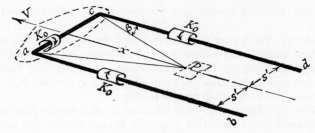

Fig. 13.21.

the sum of that caused by the bound vortex ac and that of each of the trailing vortices ab and cd. Using the special form of Biot–Savart Equations (§ 13.2.3)

$$w_p\downarrow = \frac{K_0}{4\pi x}\cdot 2\sin\beta + \frac{2K_0}{4\pi s'}(1+\cos\beta)$$

$$= \frac{K_0}{2\pi}\left[\frac{\sin\beta}{x} + \frac{1+\cos\beta}{s'}\right]$$

From the sketch $x = s'\cot\beta$ and $s' = (\pi/4)s$

$$w_p\downarrow = \frac{K_0}{2\pi}\left[\frac{\sin\beta}{s'\cot\beta} + \frac{1+\cos\beta}{s'}\right] = \frac{K_0}{2\pi s'}[1+\sec\beta]$$

$$w_p\downarrow = \frac{2K_0}{\pi^2 s}[1+\sec\beta]$$

Now from eqn. (13.21)

$$K_0 = \frac{C_L VS}{\pi s}$$

and downwash angle

$$\varepsilon = \frac{w_p}{V}$$

$$\varepsilon = \frac{2C_L VS}{\pi^3 s^2 V}[1+\sec\beta]$$

or

$$\varepsilon = \frac{8C_L}{\pi^3 \mathcal{R}}[1+\sec\beta]$$

The derivative

$$\frac{\partial\varepsilon}{\partial\alpha} = \frac{\partial\varepsilon}{\partial C_L}\cdot\frac{\partial C_L}{\partial\alpha} = a_1\frac{\partial\varepsilon}{\partial C_L}$$

thus

$$\frac{\partial\varepsilon}{\partial\alpha} = \frac{a_1 8}{\pi^3 \mathcal{R}}[1+\sec\beta] \quad . \qquad . \qquad . \qquad . \quad (13.63)$$

For cases when the distribution is non-elliptic or the tailplane is above or below the wing centre of pressure, the arithmetic of the problem is altered from that above, which applies only to this restricted problem. Again the mid-span point is taken as representative of the whole tailplane.

13.5.3. Ground effects.
In this section, the influence of solid boundaries on aeroplane (or model) performance is estimated and once again the wing is replaced by the equivalent simplified horseshoe vortex.

The influence of a plane boundary on a flow system is the same as that of an image flow system 'reflected' in the plane boundary.

In this case the boundary is the level ground and its influence on an aircraft h ft above is the same as that of the 'inverted' aircraft flying 'in formation' h ft below the ground level (Figs. 13.22 and 13.23).

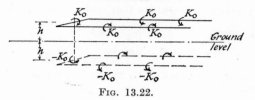

FIG. 13.22.

Before working out a particular problem, it is clear from the figure that the image system reduces the downwash on the wing and hence the drag and power required, as well as materially changing the downwash angle at the tail and hence the overall pitching equilibrium of the aeroplane.

Example 13.4. A monoplane of weight W and span $2s$ is flying horizontally near the ground at altitude h and speed V. Estimate the reduction in drag due to ground effect.

If $W = 20$ tons, $h = 50$ ft, $s = 45$ ft, $V = 100$ m.p.h, calculate the reduction in lb.   (U. of L.)

With the notation of Fig. 13.23, the change in downwash at y along the span is $\Delta w \uparrow$ where

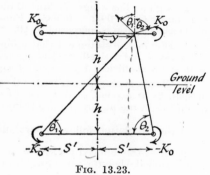

FIG. 13.23.

$$\Delta w \uparrow = \frac{K_0}{4\pi r_1} \cos \theta_1 + \frac{K_0}{4\pi r_2} \cos \theta_2$$

$$\Delta w = \frac{K_0}{4\pi}\left[\frac{s' + y}{r_1{}^2} + \frac{s' - y}{r_2{}^2}\right]$$

On a strip of span δy at y from the centre-line,

lift $l = \rho V K_0 \, \delta y$ and change in vortex drag

$$\Delta d_v = \frac{l \Delta w}{V}$$

$$\therefore \ \Delta d_v = \frac{\rho V K_0 \, \delta y \cdot \Delta w}{V} \qquad . \qquad . \qquad . \qquad . \qquad . \quad (13.64)$$

Total change in drag ΔD_v across the span is the integral of eqn. (13.64) from $-s'$ to s' (or twice that from 0 to s').

$$\therefore \ -\Delta D_v = 2 \int_0^{s'} \frac{\rho K_0{}^2}{4\pi}\left[\frac{s' + y}{r_1{}^2} + \frac{s' - y}{r_2{}^2}\right] dy$$

From the geometry, $r_1{}^2 = 4h^2 + (s' + y)^2$ and $r_2{}^2 = 4h^2 + (s' - y)^2$.

Making these substitutions and evaluating the integral

$$-\Delta D_v = \frac{\rho K_0{}^2}{4\pi} \cdot \left[\log_e \frac{4h^2 + (s' + y)^2}{4h^2 + (s' - y)^2}\right]_0^{s'}$$

$$-\Delta D_v = \frac{\rho K_0{}^2}{4\pi} \log_e \left[1 + \left(\frac{s'}{h}\right)^2\right]$$

With $W = \rho V K_0 \pi s$ and $s' = (\pi/4)s$ (assuming elliptic distribution),

$$\Delta D_v = \frac{W^2 \times 2\cdot303}{31 V^2 s^2} \log_{10}\left(1 + \frac{\pi^2}{16}\frac{s^2}{h^2}\right)$$

and substituting the values given

$$\Delta D_v = 253 \text{ lb}$$

A simpler approach is to assume that mid-span conditions are typical of the whole wing.

With this the case

$$\theta_1 = \theta_2 = \theta = \text{arc cos } \frac{s'}{\sqrt{s'^2 + 4h^2}}$$

and the change in drag is found to be 260 lb (a difference of about 3% from the first answer).

EXERCISES

1. A monoplane weighing 15,000 lb has elliptic wings 50 ft in span. For a speed of 200 m.p.h in straight and level flight at low altitude find (a) the vortex (induced) drag, (b) the circulation round sections halfway along the wings. (*Ans.* 280 lb, 475 ft²/sec) (U. of L.)

2. A glider has wings of elliptical planform of aspect ratio 6. The total drag is given by $C_D = 0\cdot02 + 0\cdot06 C_L{}^2$. Find the change in minimum angle of glide if the aspect ratio is increased to 10. (*Ans.* 5¼') 4·7' (N.C.A.T.)

3. Discuss the statement that minimum vortex (induced) drag of an aerofoil is associated with elliptic loading, and plot a curve of vortex drag coefficient against lift coefficient for a wing of aspect ratio 7·63. (N.C.A.T.)

4. Obtain an expression for the downward induced velocity behind a wing of span $2s$ at a point at distance y from the centre of span, the circulation around the wing at any point y being denoted by K.

If the circulation follows a parabolic law, i.e., $K = K_0\left(1 - \frac{y^2}{s^2}\right)$, calculate the value of the induced velocity w at mid-span, and compare this value with that obtained when the same total lift is distributed 'elliptically'. (U. of L.)

5. Discuss briefly the statement that minimum induced drag of an aerofoil is associated with 'elliptic loading'.

For an aerofoil with modified elliptic loading such that at distance y from centre of span, the circulation is given by

$$K = K_0\left(1 + \frac{1}{6}\cdot\frac{y^2}{s^2}\right)\sqrt{1 - \frac{y^2}{s^2}}$$

s being the semi-span, the downward induced velocity at y is

$$\frac{K_0}{4s}\left[\frac{11}{12} + \frac{1}{2}\cdot\frac{y^2}{s^2}\right]$$

Prove that for such an aerofoil of aspect ratio $Æ$ the vortex drag coefficient at lift coefficient C_L is

$$C_{Dv} = \frac{628}{625}\cdot\frac{C_L{}^2}{\pi.Æ}$$ (U. of L.)

6. If the distribution of circulation across the span of a wing is given by

$$K = 4sU \sum A_n \sin n\theta$$

state without proof the ~~equation~~ *IDENTITY* satisfied by the coefficients A_n. In this equation y is measured along the span of the wing from the centre section, s is the semi-span of the wing, U is the wind speed and $y = -s \cos \theta$.

If the wing is rectangular of aspect ratio 3, is untwisted, and the lift curve slope of the aerofoil section in two-dimensional flow is 6, determine approximately the circulation distribution by retaining only two coefficients and satisfying the equation at the stations $\theta = \pi/4, \pi/2$. (*Ans.* $A_1 = 0{\cdot}372\alpha$, $A_3 = 0{\cdot}0231\alpha$) (U. of L.)

7. A wing of symmetrical cross-section has an elliptical planform and is twisted so that when the incidence at the centre of the span is $2°$ the circulation K at a distance y from the wing root is given by

$$K = K_0[1 - (y/s)^2]^{3/2}$$

Find a general expression for the downwash velocity along the span and determine the corresponding incidence at the wing-tips. The wing aspect ratio is 7 and the lift curve slope for two-dimensional flow is 5·8. The integral

$$\int_0^\pi \frac{\cos n\theta \, d\theta}{\cos \theta - \cos \theta_1} = \frac{\pi \sin n\theta_1}{\sin \theta_1}$$

may be used without proof. (*Ans.* $\alpha_{\text{tip}} = 0{\cdot}566°$) (U. of L.)

8. If the distribution of the circulation along the span of an unswept wing of semi-span s in a stream of velocity V is given by the equation

$$K = 4sV \sum A_n \sin n\theta$$

where the distance from the centre-line is $y = -s \cos \theta$, derive the equation satisfied by the coefficients A_n.

The wing is flat and of elliptic planform and is rigged symmetrically in a wind-tunnel with its centre-line along the tunnel axis. If the air in the wind-tunnel has an axial velocity V and also has a small uniform angular velocity ω about its axis show that the distribution of circulation along the wing is given by

$$K = 4sVA_2 \sin 2\theta$$

and determine A_2 in terms of ω and the wing parameters. (The wind-tunnel boundary corrections should be ignored.). (U. of L.)

9. The spanwise distribution of circulation on an untwisted rectangular wing of aspect ratio 5 can be written in the form:

$$K = 4sV\alpha[0{\cdot}2524 \sin \theta + 0{\cdot}0289 \sin 3\theta + 0{\cdot}0078 \sin 5\theta + 0{\cdot}0011 \sin 7\theta]$$

Calculate the lift and vortex (induced) drag coefficients when the incidence α measured to no lift is $10°$. Compare the latter with that produced by the equivalent elliptic wing and give briefly the physical reasoning why elliptic loading produces minimum vortex (induced) drag. (*Ans.* $C_L = 0{\cdot}691$, $C_{Dv} = 0{\cdot}0317$) (N.C.A.T.)

10. A monoplane weighing 25 tons has a span of 112 ft and is flying at 90 m.p.h with its tailplane level with its wings and distant 20 ft above the ground. Calculate the change due to ground effect in the downwash angle at the tailplane, which is 60 ft behind the C.P. of the wings. (*Ans.* $3{\cdot}83°$) (N.C.A.T.)

11. Three monoplanes of the same type, having elliptical wings of $A = 6$, fly in 'V' formation at 150 m.p.h, with $C_L = 1{\cdot}2$. The followers keep a distance of one span length behind the leader and also the same distance apart from one another. Estimate the percentage saving in vortex (induced) drag due to flying in this formation. (*Ans.* 22%)

12. A 10-ton monoplane is 80 ft in span. Its tailplane which has a symmetrical section and is located 50 ft behind the C.P. of the wings is required to exert zero pitching moment at a speed of 150 m.p.h. Estimate the required tail-setting angle assuming elliptic loading on the wings. (*Ans.* 1° 58′)

(U. of L.)

13. Prove that for a monoplane, a rational formula for the downwash, in degrees, at the tailplane is $\varepsilon = $ constant $\times C_L/\cancel{R}$.

Determine the numerical value of the constant for a point on the centre-line of the machine $2s/3$ behind the centre of pressure, s being the semi-span.

(U. of L.)

14. A monoplane of 10 tons has a span of 64 ft and a wing-loading of 40 lb/ft². The wings are rather sharply tapered, having round the centre of span a circulation 10% greater than that for elliptic wings of the same span and lift. Determine the downwash angle ¼ span behind the centre of pressure, which is at the quarter-chord point, at a speed of 150 m.p.h, assuming the trailing vorticity to be completely rolled up just behind the wings. (*Ans.* 4·67°)

(U. of L.)

CHAPTER 14

AIRCRAFT STABILITY AND CONTROL

Preliminary basic definitions

In most of the analyses dealt with so far, the aircraft has been considered to be in some steady flight state, and usually only as a heavy aerodynamic 'force producing' element concentrated at the centre of gravity of the aeroplane. This is a perfectly legitimate assumption as it produces, in many performance problems, for example, adequate expressions for good estimates or predictions of the actual performance (Chapters 8 and 9).

14.1. The freedoms of motion of an aircraft. It is clear that an aeroplane, unlike most more familiar vehicles, is capable of performing any motion in the air in flight. For instance, a railway train, on a straight track, is permitted only to move along the direction of the track. It is said to have one degree of freedom. A pedestrian, standing upright and always facing the same way, can move forwards or sideways or both together on a surface. He has two degrees of freedom. Anywhere he goes on the surface, providing his body is upright and he is always facing in the same direction, he can only make use of these two translational or linear degrees of freedom. If he jumps up and down he is making use of the third linear degree of freedom, which is normal to the surface. But standing still he can sway his body sideways, i.e., rotate about an axis through his feet in the forwards direction (rolling), or turn right or left, i.e., rotate about a vertical axis through his body (yawing), or topple forwards or backwards about an axis through his feet going sideways (pitching). These are three degrees of freedom of *rotational* motion which combined with the three degrees of *translational* freedom produce the *complete* set of freedoms. Any motion of any complete body can be resolved into these six degrees of freedom. The flexibility of the pedestrian's body has been ignored in this analysis. That he is forked at the nether end and portions of him (legs) move independently of the motion of the trunk is a complexity that is introduced here to indicate that the simple analysis of his motion into the various degrees of freedom must assume that his body is rigid, or that his body 'in the main' does not distort or flex from some standard shape. This assumption may seem far-fetched at first, but returning attention to the aircraft it can be seen as the obvious first step. An aeroplane, missile, or other similar body is, to personal senses, a hard rigid structure, incapable of serious distortion under loadings considered normal to its performance. That the structure is made of elastic material and will deflect under any load system is a fact well understood by engineers, as is the additional fact that in general design and usage the deflections are small; too small materially to affect the overall performance or stability of the whole aircraft, except for special cases. To control and steer the aircraft destabilizers must be fitted, and these, for present purposes, can be considered to take the form of hinged flaps which effectively cause moments about the principal axes and hence persuade the aircraft into the required flight path. These primary controls are capable of movement relative to the aircraft as a whole and thus, in a way, the concept of rigidity is lost. This is not serious in preliminary investigations of aircraft stability, and in any case the 'fixing' of the controls in particular cases nullifies the fact that the controls are movable.

A more serious criticism of the rigidity assumption is that the light-weight structures of aircraft, though capable of sustaining large forces and moments, tend by the nature of the light alloys used to suffer from con-siderable deflections in an engineering sense. These deflections produce significant changes in local aerodynamic forces, forces materially different from those produced by the undeflected or rigid structure. As this is nearly always a dynamic (or changing) force and deflection system, the aircraft can be subject to an oscillating force system, which is independent of the motion of the whole. These Aero-Elastic Forces have considerable import-ance, for example, on high-speed aircraft which must have thin wings which sustain high force concentrations, and their study has become a separate science called Aero-Elasticity.

For the present it is assumed that the simple concept of a perfectly rigid body can apply. This will enable certain fundamentals to be studied without the introduction of too many complications.

The first assumption then, is that the aircraft can be treated as a rigid body subject to six degrees of freedom.

In discussing the ideas of the freedoms of motion using the pedestrian as the rigid body the directions forwards, sideways, up and down were used. In order to describe a motion, some reference direction had to be taken, to which we could relate the motion of the body. The vague defini-tion 'forwards', though fairly accurate for common use, is insufficient as a reference by itself and must be precisely defined in order to describe an aircraft's motion adequately.

14.2. Aircraft axes.   The set of three mutually perpendicular axes of a body so complicated geometrically as an aeroplane, can be defined in almost any way relative to the body, but it is usual to restrict the number of ways to three. These three are sufficient to produce convenient systems for most problems. They all have as origin (O) the centre of gravity of the aircraft (the C.G.) and all take a roughly forward, sideways (to the right), and downward direction as the three positive axes of linear motion OX, OY, OZ respectively, reckoned when the aircraft is in normal flight (Fig. 14.1). The important thing to remember here is that, whichever system is used, these axes are 'fixed' to the aircraft and move with the aircraft as it carries out the manœuvres or motions being studied. They are usually called Body Axes.

The principal axes. Here, the axes are the principal axes of inertia of the aircraft. The forward OX axis, or longitudinal axis, for most aircraft

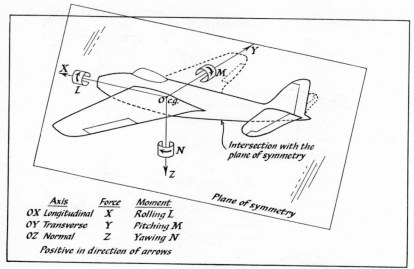

Axis		Force	Moment
OX	Longitudinal	X	Rolling L
OY	Transverse	Y	Pitching M
OZ	Normal	Z	Yawing N

Positive in direction of arrows

FIG. 14.1.—Aircraft axes and notation. (See also Fig. 6.2.)

approximates to the centre-line of the fuselage. The axes are fixed relative to the mass distribution or geometrical distribution of the aeroplane and stay so fixed whatever the subsequent motion (Fig. 14.2).

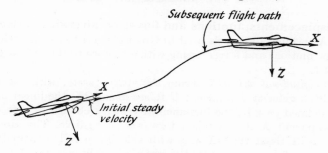

FIG. 14.2.—Principal axes.

The wind axes. The forward axis is taken to be the direction of forward flight in the steady state, before the disturbance of the motion to be studied occurs, and remains fixed relative to the aircraft during the motion. The forward (OX) axis is thus *initially* at incidence α to the mainplane's datum (Fig. 14.3). With this system the aerodynamic lift force is in the negative OZ axis and the drag force in the negative OX axis.

The ground axes (or gravity axes). During the initial steady state the OX and OY axes are taken as horizontal, and the OZ axis vertical. In this case there are no components of aircraft weight along OX and OY at the initiation of the motion. In the subsequent motion the axes remain fixed to the aircraft and rotate and move with it (Fig. 14.4).

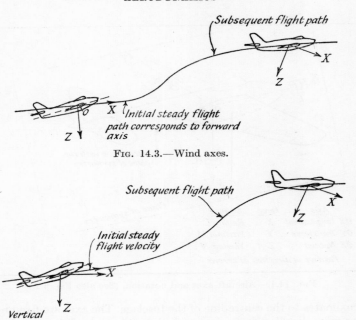

Fig. 14.3.—Wind axes.

Fig. 14.4.—Ground or gravity axes.

14.3. Displacements, motions and forces on aircraft relative to the axes.
A system of symbols used in Great Britain to distinguish all the moments, motions and forces acting with reference to the axes is given in Table 14.1.

The longitudinal axis OX. From the steady state, with the aircraft flying with a velocity component U ft/sec along OX, the linear displacement is defined as x ft, the incremental velocity change as u ft/sec and force component X lb, all taken forwards as positive. The aircraft, in addition, rolls about the OX axis with velocity p rad/sec, producing a displacement of ϕ radians under the action of a rolling moment L lb ft, all taken positive in the clockwise sense when 'looking' along OX from O.

The transverse or lateral axis OY. From steady forward flight, a sideslip velocity v ft/sec produces a sideways displacement y ft, the side force component being Y lb. In pitching about this axis with angular velocity q rad./sec an angular displacement of θ rad. is produced and a pitching moment M lb ft. All are taken positive in the 'nose up' sense, or the clockwise sense of rotation about OY 'looking' along OY from O.

The normal axis OZ. A downwards change in displacement of z ft arises from an increment of downwards velocity w ft/sec with a downwards force component of Z lb, downwards being positive. About the normal axis, the aircraft yaws with angular velocity r rad./sec, causing angular displacement ψ rad. and a yawing moment N lb ft. All are taken positive in the

TABLE 14.1

Axes	Displacements		Velocities	
	Linear	Angular	Linear*	Angular
OX longitudinal	x	ϕ bank	U, u	p
OY transverse	y	θ pitch	V, v	q
OZ normal	z	ψ yaw	W, w	r

Axes	Forces	Moments	Inertia	
			Moments of Inertia	Products of Inertia
OX longitudinal . . .	X	L	$A = \Sigma\, m(y^2 + z^2)$	$D = \Sigma\, myz$
OY transverse . . .	Y	M	$B = \Sigma\, m(z^2 + x^2)$	$E = \Sigma\, mzx$
OZ normal	Z	N	$C = \Sigma\, m(x^2 + y^2)$	$F = \Sigma\, mxy$

* Note that upper case symbols are used for steady velocities and lower case symbols for varying velocities or for perturbation velocities. Also in some cases, e.g. performance studies, V is used for the velocity parallel to OX when there is no velocity component parallel to OZ.

clockwise sense when looking down. For example, positive yaw means right wing *back*.

Accelerations of the moving axes, relative to axes fixed in space, are symbolized by the dot notation. For example, the normal acceleration of the C.G. (along OZ) is $\dot{w}$ and the angular acceleration of roll is $\dot{p}$. (Sometimes when p is written $\dot{\phi}$ the angular rolling acceleration is written $\ddot{\phi}$.)

14.4. Equations of equilibrium. The steady *unaccelerated* flight state of the aircraft in any type of motion or manœuvre, climb, glide or bank, is adequately described if the forces and moments acting on it with reference to some system of axes, are in equilibrium. For this to be so, the six equilibrium equations must apply:

$$\left. \begin{array}{ll} \sum X = 0 & \sum L = 0 \\ \sum Z = 0 & \sum Y = 0 \\ \sum M = 0 & \sum N = 0 \end{array} \right\} \qquad . \qquad . \qquad (14.1)$$

This is usually the first step in any stability analysis.

In a uniformly *accelerated* flight, the eqns. (14.1) can be applied, when the right-hand sides become constants instead of zeros.

In *unsteady* flight the right-hand sides are functions of time.

14.4.1. The symmetric group of equations. The first column of three refer to the *longitudinal* steady motion of the aircraft and simply mean that (a) the algebraic sum of all force components along OX is zero, thus indicating no acceleration in that direction, (b) the algebraic sum of force components in the OZ direction is zero and likewise (c) the sum of all pitching moments about the C.G. is zero, and there is no tendency for the aircraft to accelerate in any of these senses. The common feature of all three, as their collective name implies, is that they are confined to the plane containing OX and OZ, the so-called plane of symmetry of the aircraft (Fig. 14.1). No motion in any of these senses, that is along OX, OZ or about OY, will cause the plane of symmetry to move. Motions or disturbances in these directions are called symmetric motions. Simple climbing, gliding, and looping are symmetric motions.

14.4.2. The anti-symmetric group. The second group refer to steady *lateral* motions of the aircraft, or as they are sometimes called, the anti-symmetric movements. The side force (Y force) and moments L (rolling) and N (yawing) referred to are all out of the plane of symmetry, and such lateral movements so produced cause the plane of symmetry to move. Turning flight, spins, etc., are types of lateral motions.

14.4.3. The relation between symmetric and anti-symmetric groups. A great simplification to stability analysis is the separation of the longitudinal and lateral groups of motion. It is found that for changes in any of the longitudinal motions the lateral motions are unaltered, the reverse being true only for small changes. This is fairly simple to comprehend in the first case. Let the aircraft be flying straight and level in unaccelerated flight when, through some elevator control adjustment, or change in forward wind direction or speed, for example due to a gust, it acquires a change in forward velocity, and small downward and pitching velocities. Since the change in forward velocity (along OX) is the same for both wings, the change in lift force is the same for both wings and no rolling moment is produced because of the symmetric change in speed. For the same reason the change in drag force is the same on both sides and no yawing moment is produced. As both the downward and pitching velocities are the same on both sides of the plane of symmetry, the same argument applies and no anti-symmetric motion, e.g., yaw, roll or sideslip, can accrue from a change in a symmetric motion.

The basis of this argument is that the aircraft is truly symmetrical about its centre-line. This is not exactly the case (to a smaller or greater degree depending on the type and design), but again common sense dictates that to the order of accuracy expected in the basic study of a rigid aeroplane, the aircraft is symmetrical and the above argument holds.

The reverse case, the variation of longitudinal motion with lateral changes, has to be approached slightly differently. Again suppose the aircraft to be on steady straight and level flight. This time, for some reason, let it sideslip to starboard (to the right) with some small velocity v. The aeroplane will, apart from a tendency to roll and yaw, which are anti-symmetric motions anyway, pitch and acquire changes in forward and downward velocities. In other words a change in v produces increments in q, u and w.

Now let the aircraft again be flying straight and let it sideslip to port with the same velocity v (now negative in sign). Again the nose comes up, and the forward and downward velocities change but the changes are in the same direction as in the previous case. This means that whether the aeroplane sideslips to right or left the changes in symmetric motion are the same. It follows that these changes in q, u and w must arise from the square of the sideslip velocity because the longitudinal increments of u, w and q have a sign independent of the sign of v. Therefore if v is so small that v^2 can be neglected, it can be considered that small lateral changes of motion produce insignificant changes in longitudinal motion. Similar arguments can apply to small changes in yawing and rolling velocity.

To sum up the results of the above discussion: it can be stated that for *small* deviations in motion no coupling exists between the longitudinal and lateral groups of motion. For this reason it is customary and simpler to restrict the study of the stability of aircraft at any one time to the longitudinal or lateral cases separately.

It should be noted that for some high-speed aircraft of small wing span and large fins small lateral deviations do produce significant deviations in the longitudinal mode.

14.5. Stability.

In aerodynamics, aircraft stability is subdivided into two main types. The first refers to the changes of forces and moments on an aircraft due to a slight displacement and is termed *static stability*. The second, involving the subsequent history of the motion and the changing values of forces and moments, is termed *dynamic stability*. Both of these apply to deviations in any motion, longitudinal or lateral, and refer to the behaviour of an aircraft in a disturbance without the interference of pilot-operated control surfaces. In other words an aeroplane, to be defined stable, must possess inherent stability according to the following definitions without the aid of an external agency in the form of an independent control.

14.5.1. Static stability.

An aircraft is defined as statically stable when a small change in motion produces a force and/or moment system which *tends* to return the aircraft to its undisturbed state. If the tendency is in the opposite sense and the force/moment system helps the disturbance, the aircraft is statically *unstable*. *Neutral* stability is distinguished by the fact that a small disturbance produces no force or moment system either stabilizing or destabilizing.

Static stability, then, implies the growth of a force system tending to return the aircraft to the undisturbed condition, and whether the subsequent motion brings this about or not does not influence its definition.

14.5.2. Dynamic stability.

If the steady flight state of an aircraft is disturbed, the subsequent motion will either cause the aircraft to regain its initial steady state, or not. These are the two alternatives and in the former case the aircraft is dynamically stable, in the latter case dynamically unstable. The definition is as simple as that. No time is specified; the disturbed motion can be quickly overcome, or take many minutes. The criterion for dynamic stability is that after a disturbance from some steady flight case the aircraft will *eventually* return to the undisturbed state. The type of motion involved in the disturbance is not important to the definition, providing a steady state can be regained.

Take as an example the behaviour of an aircraft in a simple rolling disturbance. Static stability of the aeroplane as a whole will be assumed.

The aircraft flying steady, straight and level is so disturbed that the right wing drops. In dropping the relative wind incidence on the downward going wing is increased, and hence the lift force is increased to a greater amount than that of the upward going wing, which has had its angle of attack decreased. This produces a righting rolling moment against the disturbance. The aircraft is thus naturally resistant to rolling since the force system produced by the disturbance reacts against the motion. This is a rolling moment tending to damp out the motion. Now investigating the motion subsequent to the disturbance, it is clear that as the rolling moment dies away under the action of the righting moment, so does the righting moment, since it arises from the actual rolling velocity itself. The aeroplane's rolling velocity and reacting moment cease together with the aircraft displaced some angle ϕ about the OX axis. There is no righting moment tending to return the aircraft to level flight arising from the displacement, so the aeroplane is neutrally stable in this mode.

The elementary explanation of the general behaviour of the aircraft in this disturbance is as follows:

When the aeroplane rolls from the straight and level flight conditions, a drag increase is experienced on the downgoing wing, in addition to the lift increase providing the damping moment. There is a similar decrease of drag on the upgoing wing. This produces a yawing moment about the normal axis tending to pull the downgoing wing rearwards and turn the aeroplane into the direction of the roll. Having rolled through some angle ϕ, the lift force is now inclined at ϕ to the vertical and no longer balances the weight and the aeroplane sideslips with the lower wing leading, under the action of the resultant of the lift and weight (Fig. 14.5).

The leading wing receives a greater proportion of the lifting force than

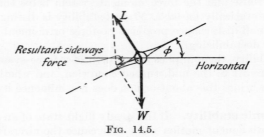

FIG. 14.5.

the follower because of dihedral (if any), planform and wing-body combination (§ 14.15), and hence a righting rolling moment is maintained
while the sideslip persists. This rolls the aircraft back towards the horizontal flight path again. A yawing moment in the same sense as that above
arises for precisely the same reason, but the yawing moment caused by
the directional stability of the aeroplane through its fin and rudder is of
greater additional effect (see § 14.16). This tends to turn the aeroplane into
the sideslip.

To simplify the following explanation of the possible motions leading
to dynamic stability or otherwise following a simple disturbance, the
yawing components have been largely omitted. The several possible
(simplified) motions may be best considered with the aid of the graphs in
Fig. 14.6. This shows the rolling displacement ϕ (radians) plotted against
time t (seconds) for the various possibilities. The graphs describe the
motions starting with the aeroplane in the displaced position, that is,
having been disturbed into a rolling velocity which has been damped out
by the wings.

The graphs also show the subsequent rolling velocity p at any instant, this being the slope of the graph at the point considered (i.e.,
$p = d\phi/dt = \dot{\phi}$). The rate at which the slopes change from point to point
along the curves indicates the magnitude of the rolling acceleration.

Case (*i*), given by the first curve in Fig. 14.6, shows the displacement
rapidly diminishing, indicating that the righting rolling moment due to

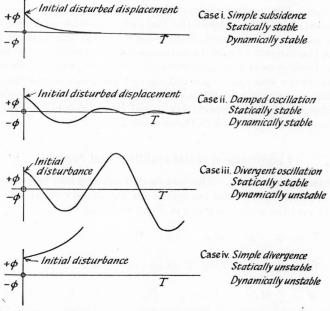

FIG. 14.6.—Rolling displacement ϕ plotted against time T for the possible motion
following a lateral disturbance.

sideslip is considerable. This type of curve describes a dead-beat or aperiodic oscillation. This motion is dynamically stable.

Case (ii) shows a motion which, although dynamically stable, takes longer to complete. Here the righting rolling moment is less powerful compared with the inertia of the aircraft so that the aircraft is rolled back through the equilibrium position to produce a (negative) displacement on the other side. This causes the aeroplane to sideslip in that direction, a righting rolling moment to be produced in the other sense, which repeats the process, pushing the aircraft back through the equilibrium condition again and again. Now if the alternative negative and positive displacements grow successively smaller, the motion will eventually die out, with the aircraft back in the steady flight state. It is thus a dynamically stable motion. This particular type of motion, consisting as it does of a roll, yaw to sideslip, roll back to overshoot the equilibrium position, yaw to sideslip on the other side and so on, is called a Dutch Roll and is physically unpleasant to pilots and passengers. It poses a considerable problem to designers, who can damp out this motion, only at the expense of spiral stability. It is of interest to note that it is usual to accede to comfort; most pilots prefer a degree of spiral instability to the discomfort of a lightly damped long period Dutch Roll.

Case (iii) is the motion of case (ii) above but one in which the damping is insufficient to reduce the amplitude of successive rolls. The consequence is that as the motion continues the displacements, velocities and accelerations become greater so that were it allowed to persist the aircraft would destroy itself. This motion is dynamically unstable.

Case (iv). For completeness the statically unstable and dynamically unstable motion is considered. Here there is no righting moment tending to return the aircraft to initial conditions. On the contrary, the tendency is for the force system produced to assist the disturbance, so the roll gets larger and larger and the graph of ϕ against t shows a simple divergence.

Deviations in yaw and pitch, indicating directional (or weathercock) and pitching stabilities respectively, could have been taken and similar types of oscillation obtained in those modes.

Longitudinal static stability and control

14.6. General equations. The first step in any stability calculation is to write down the equilibrium equations for the steady flight case. Using wind axes and the notation given in Figs. 14.7 and 14.8,

$$\sum X = T \cos (\alpha - \gamma) - D_W - D_B - W \sin \theta = 0 \qquad . \qquad . \qquad (14.2)$$

$$\sum Z = W \cos \theta - L - L' - T \sin (\alpha - \gamma) = 0 \qquad . \qquad . \qquad (14.3)$$

$$\sum M = M_{AC} + M_{FN} + (L \cos \alpha + D_W \sin \alpha)(h - h_0)\bar{c}$$
$$- L l_t (\cos \alpha') = 0 \qquad . \qquad . \qquad (14.4)$$

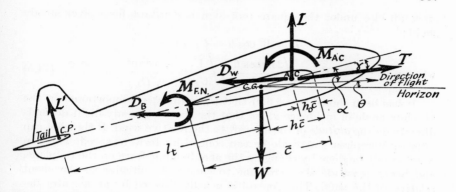

Forces and moments

W All up weight acting through C.G.

L Lift of wings acting through aerodynamic centre (normal to direction of flight)

L' Lift of tail plane acting through tail C.P. (normal to mean relative wind at tail)

D_W Drag of wings acting through aerodynamic centre

D_B Drag of remainder of body acting through centre of body drag

T Thrust of engines / propellers

M_{AC} Pitching wing moment about the aerodynamic centre

$M_{F.N.}$ Pitching moment due to fuselage & nacelles

Angular measure

θ Angle of climb – between flight path & horizontal

α Angle of wing incidence – between chord line & flight path

γ Angle between thrust line & chord line

Linear measure

$\bar{c}$ Aerodynamic mean chord

$h\bar{c}$ Distance of C.G. aft of leading edge of a.m.c.

$h_0\bar{c}$ Distance of aerodynamic centre aft of leading edge

l_t Distance of tail centre of pressure aft of centre of gravity

Fig. 14.7.—Major forces and moments on an aircraft in steady climbing flight.

neglecting tail forces and moments other than lift, for a symmetric, purely longitudinal, motion.

After the elimination of small quantities for easy handling, eqns. (14.2) and (14.3) have been met and discussed in Chapter 8. In particular, eqn. (14.3) becomes in its simplified form, $L = W \cos \theta$, when $T \sin \gamma$ and L' are taken as small compared with the lift force produced by the wings and the A.U.W.

On writing the lift in coefficient form and isolating the velocity it can be seen that the velocity of flight V is inversely proportion to $\sqrt{C_L}$

since all else under the square root sign is constant for a given steady flight:

$$L = W \cos \theta = C_L \tfrac{1}{2} \rho V^2 S$$

whence $$V = \sqrt{\frac{2W \cos \theta}{\rho S}} \cdot \sqrt{\frac{1}{C_L}} = \frac{\text{constant}}{\sqrt{C_L}} \qquad . \qquad . \quad (14.5)$$

It has been shown (see § 6.9) that C_L is directly proportional to the absolute angle of incidence α_∞ so that the speed of steady flight depends directly on the *attitude* of the aircraft to the relative wind. If the pilot can alter his aeroplane's attitude he can control his forward speed. This can most simply be done by changing the aerodynamic force on the tailplane, and hence persuade the aeroplane to change its pitching displacement relative to the wind. This control is usually effected by an elevator deflection. The elevator, together with its tab, is the pilot's only means of control of the flight speed.

Change in flight speed along a certain course may necessitate changes in engine power, which is controlled by the throttle.

In passing it should be noted that other means are in current use for changing the tail load, notably the 'all flying tailplane' which being pivoted has its incidence α' altered by changing the tail setting angle α_t. The pivoted tailplane has been used in the past as a trimming device in conjunction with a conventional elevator but high-speed practice demands a tail control which will not influence the shock pattern unduly, as does the trailing flap method. In conjunction with power assistance in manipulation, the all flying tailplane has become standard practice on supersonic aircraft (see § 14.20.1).

Other feasible methods are available for changing the pitching of the aeroplane without interfering with the tail unit. None have gained the currency of the fixed tailplane, hinged elevator and tab for subsonic aircraft or the hinged tailplane and elevator as a trim tab for supersonic aircraft.

The 'conventional' former case will be analysed in detail here. The latter case has a similar treatment with different angular variables.

14.7. The longitudinal equilibrium equation.

The equation of importance in estimating the static longitudinal equilibrium is (14.4). Before simplifying this further it is noted that some force effects have been omitted. Apart from the drag of the tailplane which is ignored except for its contribution to extra-to-wing drag in performance problems, the moments due to the offset of the thrust line, and the offset of the centre of body drag about the C.G. have been omitted from eqn. (14.4). It is found convenient to omit the effects of thrust of propellers, jets or rockets entirely from initial stability considerations and to consider these separately at a later stage for inclusion in the final stability estimations. The effect of the body drag is absorbed in the Fuselage Moment. Potential theory for flow about a solid of revolution, while denying the existence of a drag force, yields equations for fuselage and nacelle moments. These are modified by tunnel tests which must of course include the additional effects of the drag, as well as those of geometry.

Eqn. (14.4) symbolizes the requirement that the algebraic sum of pitching moments is zero in steady flight. Now if the aeroplane is disturbed in pitch the moments will not sum to zero and a resultant pitching moment M about the C.G. is produced.

In this case the equation is

$$M = M_{AC} + M_{FN} + (L \cos \alpha + D \sin \alpha)(h - h_0)\bar{c} - L'l_t. \quad (14.6)$$

A simplifying approximation is to put $(L \cos \alpha + D \sin \alpha) = L$, the error of the approximation reducing as α becomes smaller, giving

$$M = M_{AC} + M_{FN} + L\bar{c}(h - h_0) - L'l_t \qquad . \quad (14.7)$$

Rewriting eqn. (14.7) in coefficient form by substituting for the moments $M = C_M\frac{1}{2}V^2\bar{c}S$, for the lift $L = C_L\frac{1}{2}\rho V^2S$ and for the tail lift $L' = C'_L\frac{1}{2}\rho V_1^2S'$ (where V is the aircraft's speed through the air and V_1 the relative wind speed at the tailplane) and cancelling where appropriate:

$$C_M = C_{M\,AC} + C_{M\,FN} + C_L(h - h_0) - \frac{S'l_t}{S\bar{c}} \cdot C'_L \cdot \frac{\frac{1}{2}\rho V_1^2}{\frac{1}{2}\rho V^2} \qquad . \quad (14.8)$$

In eqn. (14.8) the term $S'l_t/S\bar{c}$ is the ratio of the tail 'volume' (the product of tailplane area and lever arm) to the wing 'volume' (the product of wing area and mean chord) and is called the tail volume ratio, symbolized by $\bar{V}$.

The term $\frac{1}{2}\rho V_1^2/\frac{1}{2}\rho V^2$ is called the tail efficiency (η_t). Because it is working in the disturbed air of the mainplanes and fuselage(s) the effective wind velocity at the tail is often less than that at the mainplanes, as well as being changed in direction, due to downwash. As a consequence η_t is usually less than unity, but can be greater than unity locally where the tail is in the slipstream of the airscrews. Therefore eqn. (14.8) becomes

$$C_M = C_{M\,AC} + C_{M\,FN} + C_L(h - h_0) - \bar{V}\eta_tC'_L \qquad . \quad (14.9)$$

The lift on the tailplane, and hence the value of C'_L, depends on the angle of tail incidence and the deflection of the elevator and tab (Fig. 14.8). The tailplane is an aerofoil, usually of symmetrical section and of smaller aspect ratio than the mainplane but none the less it follows the general pattern of aerofoils and has a fairly straight curve of lift versus incidence over the working range. This has a slope of $a'_1 = \partial C'_L/\partial \alpha'$. In addition it is found that at fixed working incidences the tailplane has a lift force depending on elevator and/or tab deflection, these curves having gradients

$$a'_2 = \frac{\partial C'_L}{\partial \eta} \quad \text{and} \quad a'_3 = \frac{\partial C'_L}{\partial \beta}$$

Thus putting

$$\alpha' = \alpha + \alpha_t - \varepsilon \quad \text{from Fig. 14.8}$$
$$C'_L = a'_1\alpha' + a'_2\eta + a'_3\beta$$
$$= a'_1(\alpha + \alpha_t - \varepsilon) + a'_2\eta + a'_3\beta$$

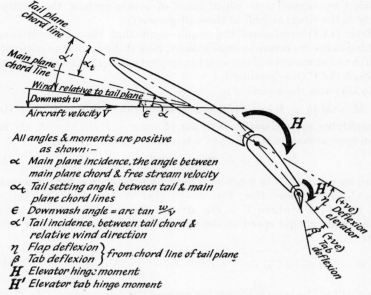

Fig. 14.8.—Tailplane configuration.

All angles & moments are positive as shown:—
α Main plane incidence, the angle between main plane chord & free stream velocity
α_t Tail setting angle, between tail & main plane chord lines
ε Downwash angle = arc tan $\frac{w}{V}$
α' Tail incidence, between tail chord & relative wind direction
η Flap deflexion
β Tab deflexion } from chord line of tailplane
H Elevator hinge moment
H' Elevator tab hinge moment

and introducing into eqn. (14.9)

$$C_M = C_{M\ AC} + C_{M\ FN} + C_L(h - h_0)$$
$$- \bar{V}\eta_t\{a_1'(\alpha + \alpha_t - \varepsilon) + a_2'\eta + a_3'\beta\} \qquad . \qquad . \quad (14.10)$$

Now the sum of the moments in eqn. (14.10) does not equal zero since the aircraft has been disturbed slightly from the equilibrium condition. For static stability the sum of these moments must act against the displacement. That is, the system set up by the disturbance must tend to reduce the disturbance. If the disturbance is a positive increment in pitching displacement about the C.G. the increment in moment coefficient produced by the disturbance must be negative for static stability. In other words, the rate of change of overall pitching moment (coefficient) with incidence or with wing lift (coefficient) must be negative for static stability.

This is usually written as

$$\frac{\partial C_M}{\partial \alpha} \quad \text{or} \quad \frac{\partial C_M}{\partial C_L} < 0$$

Differentiating each side of eqn. (14.10) with respect to C_L gives

$$\frac{\partial C_M}{\partial C_L} = \frac{\partial C_{M\ AC}}{\partial C_L} + \frac{\partial C_{M\ FN}}{\partial C_L} + (h - h_0)$$
$$- \bar{V}\eta_t\left\{a_1'\frac{\partial(\alpha + \alpha_t - \varepsilon)}{\partial C_L} + a_2'\frac{\partial\eta}{\partial C_L} + a_3'\frac{\partial\beta}{\partial C_L}\right\}$$

and putting $\qquad a_1 = \dfrac{\partial C_L}{\partial \alpha}$ and $\dfrac{\partial C_{M\ AC}}{\partial C_L} = 0$

$$\frac{\partial C_M}{\partial C_L} = \frac{\partial C_{M\ FN}}{\partial C_L} + (h - h_0)$$

$$- \bar{V}\eta_t \left\{ \frac{a_1'}{a_1}\left(1 - \frac{\partial \varepsilon}{\partial \alpha}\right) + \frac{a_2'}{a_1}\frac{\partial \eta}{\partial \alpha} + a_3'\frac{\partial \beta}{\partial C_L} \right\} \quad . \quad (14.11)$$

Before considering the effect of each term of eqn. (14.11) on the stability or otherwise of the aircraft in the longitudinal symmetric motion it will be realized that two distinct cases can apply. These concern the elevator and tab controls. The development of eqn. (14.11) depends on whether the controls can be assumed locked in the pre-disturbed position during the subsequent motion, or are allowed to float free under the action of the aerodynamic forces arising from the motion.

14.8. Longitudinal static stability (stick fixed). The elevator angle η and the tab angle β are constant in the motion so that the last terms of the braced quantity in eqn. (14.11) disappear, leaving

$$\frac{\partial C_M}{\partial C_L} = \frac{\partial C_{M\ FN}}{\partial C_L} + (h - h_0) - \bar{V}\eta_t\frac{a_1'}{a_1}\left(1 - \frac{\partial \varepsilon}{\partial \alpha}\right) \quad . \quad (14.12)$$

and the right-hand side must sum to a negative quantity for static stability.

Fuselage influence. Taking the first term of eqn. (14.12), potential flow theory predicts and experiment shows, that when a solid of revolution is inclined to an airstream, a moment is set up tending to turn the body broadside to the wind. In other words, a destabilizing moment is produced as α (or C_L) is increased. The term $\partial C_{M\ FN}/\partial C_L$ is positive and is for small displacements assumed constant. It is in fact considerable in magnitude, so that a general design requirement is that if a fuselage is to be included in the project design some powerful stabilizing influence must be added to counteract the destabilizing of the fuselage and nacelles. This is usually provided by the tail unit which also serves to stabilize the usually de-stabilizing wing contribution.

Influence of C.G. position. The term $(h - h_0)$ is the non-dimensional C.G. chordwise position relative to the aerodynamic centre, and is the most important parameter in preliminary design processes. The C.G. position can never remain constant in practice because of the removal during flight of the disposable load, for example fuel, bombs, etc., or the change from flight to flight of the cargo/passenger arrangements. It is the designer's initial problem so to arrange the siting of his disposal items and the like, that under no circumstances can the position of the C.G. move out of a small range which is defined below.

$(h - h_0)$ is clearly positive when $h > h_0$. That is, with the aerodynamic centre in front of the centre of gravity the contribution of the wing forces to the whole is destabilizing. Now if a tailless aeroplane is projected, the 3rd term, the tail term, vanishes and the resulting aeroplane will be stable only if the C.G. is ahead of the A.C. Thus an isolated wing can be made stable by arranging the C.G. to be forward of the A.C.

The influence of the tailplane. To make $\partial C_M/\partial C_L$ negative the requirement from eqn. (14.12) is that the term

$$-\left\{\bar{V}\eta_t\frac{a_1'}{a_1}\left(1-\frac{\partial\varepsilon}{\partial\alpha}\right)\right\}$$

retains its negative sign, and is of sufficient magnitude to control the sign of the algebraic sum of the moments. The retention of the negative sign is assured by considering the items in the term individually: $\bar{V}$ and η_t are numbers, a_1 and a_1' are both of the same sign, and same order of magnitude with $a_1' < a_1$, so that $a_1'/a_1 < 1$ but positive. It remains for the rate of change of downwash with mainplane incidence ($\partial\varepsilon/\partial\alpha$) to be a positive quantity less than unity or negative for the tail to be a stabilizing unit. $\partial\varepsilon/\partial\alpha$ is *always* positive and usually less than unity (see Example 13.3) so the sign of the whole term

$$-\left\{\bar{V}\eta_t\frac{a_1'}{a_1}\left(1-\frac{\partial\varepsilon}{\partial\alpha}\right)\right\}$$

is assured in most cases.

Except for a_1', a_1 and $\partial\varepsilon/\partial\alpha$, which are only very slightly changed in magnitude by large design rearrangements, the only variable capable of significant alteration by the aeroplane designer in the preliminary design is the tail volume ratio $\bar{V}$. The magnitude of this ratio, which is the main parameter involving the tail arm l_t and the tailplane area S_t, is determined by the geometry of the initial layout of the design, and the designer must use his art and knowledge to arrange the tail unit so that its power is sufficient for stability, but not so much that the aircraft is unresponsive to normal control movements. This and similar problems in the other modes are the essence of aeroplane design for stability.

The neutral point (stick fixed). Returning to eqn. (14.12) and considering it as a whole, it is seen that the only variable is h, the dimensionless C.G. position.

It is theoretically possible so to arrange the weight distribution that the C.G. moves behind the A.C. sufficient for the term $(h - h_0)$ to assist the fuselage influence in overcoming the stabilizing effect of the tail. If the critical condition of $\partial C_M/\partial C_L = 0$ be considered, the C.G. is said to be at the neutral point (stick fixed) and $h = h_n$.

So substituting in eqn. (14.12) gives

$$0 = \frac{\partial C_{M\ FN}}{\partial C_L} + (h_n - h_0) - \bar{V}\eta_t\frac{a_1'}{a_1}\left(1-\frac{\partial\varepsilon}{\partial\alpha}\right)$$

or

$$-h_n = \frac{\partial C_{M\ FN}}{\partial C_L} - h_0 - \bar{V}\eta_t\frac{a_1'}{a_1}\left(1-\frac{\partial\varepsilon}{\partial\alpha}\right) \qquad . \qquad . \qquad (14.13)$$

and replacing the right-hand side of eqn. (14.13) by $-h_n$ in eqn. (14.12) gives

$$\left(\frac{\partial C_M}{\partial C_L}\right) = (h - h_n) \qquad . \qquad . \qquad . \qquad (14.14)$$

Both sides of eqn. (14.14) must be negative for stability. The quantity

$(h_n - h)$, $\left(\dfrac{\text{distance of C.G. ahead of N.P.}}{\text{aerodynamic mean chord}}\right)$,

is called the *static margin* stick fixed* and indicates the allowable margin of rearward movement of the C.G. before the critical condition is reached (stick fixed). It must therefore be always a positive quantity. In practice the C.G. is never allowed to approach the neutral point, stick fixed, for fear that it may pass through a more critical position given by consideration of stick free stability.

Elevator movement to trim. With the aircraft trimmed for steady level flight at a certain speed, the overall pitching moment C_M is zero. If the aircraft is required to fly at a different speed, implying a different incidence, the elevator setting must be changed to trim the aircraft for equilibrium at the new flight attitude. (Note that in order to trim, stick fixed, a statically stable aircraft at a positive lift coefficient it is necessary that C_M at $C_L = 0$ is a positive quantity. This is of particular significance in the design of tailless aircraft.)

Putting $C_M = 0$ in eqn. (14.10) and rearranging,

$$\eta = \frac{1}{a_2'}\left[\frac{1}{\bar{V}\eta_t}\{C_{M\ AC} + C_{M\ FN} + C_L(h - h_0)\}\right.$$
$$\left. - a_1'(\alpha + \alpha_t - \varepsilon) - a_3'\beta\right] \qquad . \quad (14.10a)$$

and with β fixed, and the C.G. position unalterable in any one flight case, η is seen to be a linear function of C_L with a slope given by

$$\frac{\partial \eta}{\partial C_L} = \frac{1}{a_2'\bar{V}\eta_t}\left\{(h - h_0) + \frac{\partial C_{M\ FN}}{\partial C_L} - \bar{V}\eta_t\frac{a_1'}{a_1}\left(1 - \frac{\partial \varepsilon}{\partial \alpha}\right)\right\}$$
$$= -\frac{1}{a_2'\bar{V}\eta_t}(h_n - h)$$

This shows that the value of the elevator deflection per flight C_L change is proportional to the static margin, stick fixed, and must be a negative quantity for a stable aeroplane.

It is usual to choose a value of α_t in design to make $\eta \doteqdot 0$ (in eqn. (14.10a)) at the cruising condition.

14.9. Longitudinal static stability (stick free).

When the aircraft flying straight and level in unaccelerated flight is given a small disturbance in pitch, the tail unit provides the stabilizing influence. In the previous case the tailplane elevator system was a fixture. In this case the elevator is free to rotate on its hinge under the action of the pressure distribution over it, until the hinge moment is zero. This is called *floating*. For a slight increase in incidence (that is, a positive pitching disturbance) the elevator will float up or down (or remain as if fixed) depending in the main on the effective position of the hinge line of the elevator (Fig. 14.9). The elevator

---

* An alternative term in common use is *C.G. margin*.

C C

will have, as a discrete aerodynamic body, a centre of the pressures arising from the air flow round it. If, for the displacement, the C.P. is aft or ahead of the hinge the free elevator will float up or down respectively until the pressure distribution alters enough to bring the elevator C.P. on to the hinge line. The elevator will then remain in equilibrium, at some negative or positive deflection from the initial steady flight deflection.

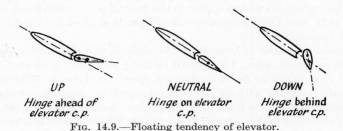

UP	*NEUTRAL*	*DOWN*
Hinge ahead of elevator c.p.	*Hinge on elevator c.p.*	*Hinge behind elevator c.p.*

Fig. 14.9.—Floating tendency of elevator.

This positive or negative elevator displacement for a given change in pitch ($\pm\ \partial\eta/\partial\alpha$) will increase or decrease the tail unit lift and so modify the equilibrium condition. The design operation of producing a given floating characteristic (Aerodynamic Balance) is a most powerful tool in the design of aircraft controls (see § 14.21).

Returning to the basic dimensionless equation of stability (eqn. (14.11)), which is reiterated for convenience:

$$\frac{\partial C_M}{\partial C_L} = \frac{\partial C_{M\ FN}}{\partial C_L} + (h - h_0) - \bar{V}\eta_t\left\{\frac{a_1'}{a_1}\left(1 - \frac{\partial\varepsilon}{\partial\alpha}\right) + \frac{a_2'}{a_1}\frac{\partial\eta}{\partial\alpha} + a_3'\frac{\partial\beta}{\partial C_L}\right\}$$

it can be seen that if the sign of $\partial\eta/\partial\alpha$ changes so that η decreases with increase in incidence a *reduction* in stability results when the stick is freed.

The tab is an irreversible control. That is, it is not capable of transmitting its message back to the pilot and cannot be deflected by its own aerodynamic force system. In other words, it cannot be freed and is unable to float like the elevator. Consequently the term $a_3'(\partial\beta/\partial C_L)$ is zero in the above equation. This is not so for a Geared Tab when the term must be included (§ 14.23).

Now $\partial\eta/\partial\alpha$ is an inconvenient quantity to obtain experimentally or analytically and it is usual to express it in terms of the hinge moment coefficient C_H' of the elevator where

$$C_H' = \frac{H'}{\frac{1}{2}\rho V_1^2 S_e c_e}$$

S_e and c_e being the area and chord of the elevator aft of the hinge.

The hinge moment, like the other aerodynamic characteristics of a flapped aerofoil system, is a function of the displacement of all the components of the system,

i.e., $$C_H' = \text{constant} + \frac{\partial C_H'}{\partial\alpha'}.\alpha' + \frac{\partial C_H'}{\partial\eta}.\eta + \frac{\partial C_H'}{\partial\beta}.\beta$$

or more usually

$$C'_H = b'_0 + b'_1\alpha' + b'_2\eta + b'_3\beta \qquad . \qquad . \qquad (14.15)$$

When the stick is freed and the elevator floats, the hinge moment is zero. Equating eqn. (14.15) to zero and rearranging

$$\eta = -\frac{1}{b'_2}(b'_0 + b'_1\alpha' + b'_3\beta) \qquad . \qquad . \qquad . \qquad (14.16)$$

and differentiating with respect to α

$$\frac{\partial\eta}{\partial\alpha} = -\frac{1}{b'_2}\left\{b'_1\frac{\partial\alpha'}{\partial\alpha}\right\}$$

since β and b'_0 are constant for symmetrical flaps and ungeared tabs, i.e.

$$\frac{\partial\eta}{\partial\alpha} = -\frac{b'_1}{b'_2}\left[1 - \frac{\partial\varepsilon}{\partial\alpha}\right] \quad \text{on substituting } \alpha' = (\alpha + \alpha_t - \varepsilon) \quad . \quad (14.17)$$

Distinguishing the stick free case by an index, the basic non-dimensional stability equation becomes for this case:

$$\frac{\partial C^1_M}{\partial C_L} = \frac{\partial C_{M\,FN}}{\partial C_L} + (h - h_0) - \frac{a'_1}{a_1}\bar{V}\eta_t\left(1 - \frac{\partial\varepsilon}{\partial\alpha}\right)\left(1 - \frac{a'_2 b'_1}{a'_1 b'_2}\right) \quad . \quad (14.18)$$

The neutral point (stick free). Equating (14.18) to zero gives the position of the C.G. for neutral stability. This position is $h^1_n \bar{c}$ aft of the leading edge of the aerodynamic mean chord and is called the neutral point (stick free). Equating (14.18) to zero,

$$- h^1_n = \frac{\partial C_{M\,FN}}{\partial C_L} - h_0 - \bar{V}\eta_t\left\{\left(\frac{a'_1}{a_1} - \frac{a'_2}{a_1}\frac{b'_1}{b'_2}\right)\left(1 - \frac{\partial\varepsilon}{\partial\alpha}\right)\right\} \quad (14.19)$$

which substituted back in eqn. (14.18) gives

$$+ \left(\frac{\partial C^1_M}{\partial C_L}\right) = + (h - h^1_n)$$

Again, eqn. (14.18) must be negative for static stability and the quantity $h^1_n - h$ is called the *static margin (stick free)*.

The static margin (stick free) can be greater or less than the static margin (stick fixed), eqn. (14.14), depending on the aerodynamic balance of the elevator.

By comparing eqns. (14.13) and (14.19) it can be seen that freeing the stick produces a decrease in static margin, and hence in static stability of

$$\bar{V}\eta_t\frac{a'_2}{a_1}\frac{b'_1}{b'_2}\left(1 - \frac{\partial\varepsilon}{\partial\alpha}\right) \qquad . \qquad . \qquad . \qquad (14.20)$$

the same result being obtained by substituting $\partial\eta/\partial\alpha$, eqn. (14.17), in the basic equation of equilibrium.

Examining the quantities in eqn. (14.20) b'_2 is usually negative, leaving the sign of b'_1 to determine the increase in stability (if any) on freeing the stick. b'_1 is negative if there is little or no aerodynamic balancing and positive if the control has much horn balance or has the hinge set well back. (See § 14.21.)

It is clear from eqn. (14.20) that a decrease in static margin on freeing the stick can vitiate the whole power of the tail unit if it is large enough. This must be watched in design. It is usual to try to balance out this decrease so that $-b_1'$ is nearly zero. This has the double effect of reducing the difference between fixed and free stabilities, as well as assisting in reducing the actual force required to operate the control in the manoeuvre case.

With b_1' negative, the static margin, stick free, is less than that stick fixed, and the neutral point, stick free, therefore is the aftermost allowable position of the C.G.

Stick free trim. With the stick free the aircraft is trimmed for steady straight flight by adjusting the tab angle β to give zero hinge moment on the elevator. The trim condition is represented by $C_M = 0$ in eqn. (14.10).

Isolating β from this equation, having substituted for η from eqn. (14.16),

$$\beta = \frac{1}{a_3'\left(1 - \frac{a_2'}{a_3'}\cdot\frac{b_3'}{b_2'}\right)}\left[\frac{1}{\bar{V}\eta_t}\{C_{M\ AC} + C_{M\ FN} + C_L(h - h_0)\}\right.$$
$$\left. - a_1'(\alpha + \alpha_t - \varepsilon)\left(1 - \frac{a_2'b_1'}{a_1'b_2'}\right)\right] \qquad . \quad (14.10b)$$

and a linear equation in C_L results with a slope given by

$$\frac{\partial\beta}{\partial C_L}\left(a_3' - a_2'\frac{b_3'}{b_2'}\right)\bar{V}\eta_t = \left\{h - h_0 + \frac{\partial C_{M\ FN}}{\partial C_L} - \bar{V}\eta_t\frac{a_1'}{a_1}\left(1 - \frac{\partial\varepsilon}{\partial\alpha}\right)\left(1 - \frac{a_2'b_1'}{a_1'b_2'}\right)\right\}$$
$$= -(h_n^1 - h), \text{ the static margin, stick free}$$

This equation shows that, for a stable aircraft, the slope of the tab angle to trim (β) against flight C_L will be positive, and increase with increase in static margin when, as is usual, the bracketed term on the left-hand side is negative.

If it is required to be able to trim the aircraft 'hands off' throughout the flight speed range, the C.G. position h and the range of tab deflections β available must be carefully considered.

14.10. Limit of forward C.G. travel.

It is shown in the previous section that with all the usual simplifying assumptions, an estimate can be made of the aftermost allowable position of the C.G. range. The effect of the major omission in the analysis, that of the propeller or engine thrust, is to bring the neutral point further forward. It is usual in prototypes to do exhaustive tunnel tests on models to which propellers, for example, are fitted, and later free flight trials to determine accurately the neutral point.

It would seem at first sight that if the C.G. position is well forward of the estimated neutral point, the small error between exact and estimated positions would be absorbed in the heavy static stability so produced. As already indicated, too much static stability is undesirable, for the reason that the pilot could not control the aircraft. Consider an aeroplane flying steadily at cruising speed. With a large static margin, that is with the C.G.

well ahead of the neutral point, the aeroplane will fly steadily, strongly resisting any disturbance trying to change its pitch. This is all right for that flight state. When the pilot wants the aircraft to land he must increase the incidence to decrease speed. He now wishes to alter the pitch, but the stabilizing forces are very large and he has to exert much force and control deflection to overcome the stabilizing of the tailplane. The stick force magnitudes are important design criteria for the designer since they must be neither too great to cause undue fatigue, nor so light as to permit the pilot to unwittingly engage on a vagrant manœuvre. The stick force required to bring the aeroplane to stalling attitude near the ground, where downwash effects at the tail are halved due to the presence of the ground, is one design criterion. This limits the control power available from the pilot via the gearing system, to overcome the static stability of the aeroplane in that attitude. The maximum permitted static margin is thus arrived at, and this indicates the most forward position of the C.G.

Lateral stability and control

The main aerodynamic force-producing surfaces of an aircraft, the wings and tail surfaces, make powerful contributions to pitching stability, largely because this mode involves changes of incidence, and aerofoils are very susceptible to incidence change. In other modes where incidence change occurs, equally high rates of change of force are to be expected, and such is indeed the case in the lateral motions of roll and sideslip. In yawing disturbance little or no incidence change is involved except on the fin and rudder which are then the main stabilizing agencies in directional stability.

In roll, most aircraft are very 'stiff', and to hold the aircraft in steady roll, powerful 'destabilizers' must be fitted to overcome the aerodynamic damping of the wings in rolling flight. These destabilizers usually take the form of flaps hinged at the trailing edges of the wings and geared in opposition so that one goes up when the other goes down. These flaps are called ailerons. The design of ailerons is one of the most demanding of all the design problems facing aeronautical engineers and has occupied much research and development time in all the major 'aeronautical' countries.

14.11. Lateral control. As mentioned above, an aerofoil disturbed about its longitudinal axis is very stiff, and large forces must be produced to overcome this damping. These forces must be capable of application with little effort from the pilot, who is physically incapable of exerting large forces sideways on a control column when seated. Wheel type controls permit more force to be applied but this is often insufficient. Aerodynamic balancing of the ailerons is thus called for, and sometimes additional aid from an auxiliary power system.

The aileron, when deflected up or down, alters appreciably the characteristics of the wing to which it is hinged. Briefly the upgoing aileron reduces the lift force on its wing, and the downgoing aileron increases the lift on its wing, thus creating a rolling moment about the longitudinal axis.

However, the reduction due to the upgoing aileron is not equal to the increase due to the same deflection of the downgoing aileron. The ailerons have an aerodynamic inequality which has to be removed, frequently by some form of differential gearing so that up and down movements are different in magnitude.

Unless carefully designed aerodynamically, the aileron, on deflection, will materially alter the drag force on the wing in addition to the desired change in lift force. The result is an inequality in drag force about the OZ axis which causes a yawing moment to be set up. This has to be minimized. The main design cases are: for aerodynamic balance of ailerons, the high-speed roll case, and for aileron movement the retention of control at high incidences near the ground. It should be remembered that lateral control is also necessary in other flight cases, notably to hold a sideslip with dihedral, and to take off cross wind.

14.12. Moment due to aircraft roll.

The natural damping of the wing in roll arises from the increase in incidence on the downgoing wing producing an increase in lift on that wing tending to stop the roll, and the equal and opposite effect taking place on the other wing.

In the steady roll state, the moment on the wings and tail surfaces tending to damp out the motion is counteracted and equalled by the extraneous moment arising from the deflections of the ailerons. This is the equation of equilibrium in the rolling case and can be written

$$L_{(roll)} + L_{(aileron)} = 0 \qquad . \qquad . \qquad . \qquad (14.21)$$

In the unsteady case when the rolling motion is being initiated or curtailed, eqn. (14.21) is equal to $A\dot{p}$, where $\dot{p}$ is the angular acceleration and A is the Moment of Inertia of the aircraft about OX defined in Table 14.1. The response to aileron control is so rapid, however, that the analysis assumes that the history of motion following an aileron control deflection is a short time lag of no change in flight attitude, followed instantaneously by the steady roll velocity p of the completed motion.

A method of obtaining aerodynamic data from wings, fins, tailplanes, etc., in rotating flight is the strip method. The results so obtained are usually first approximations only and are never used in final analyses. The method is interesting, however, as it develops from the fundamentals of the rotary motion investigated.

Consider the wing rolling moment $L_{(roll)}$. An element of span δy on the downgoing wing (Fig. 14.10) will have its effective wind velocity changed in direction by an increase in incidence $\Delta\alpha$, where

$$\Delta\alpha = \frac{py}{V} \text{ radians} \ . \qquad . \qquad . \qquad (14.22)$$

on the upgoing (the negative) wing

$$\Delta\alpha = -\frac{py}{V}$$

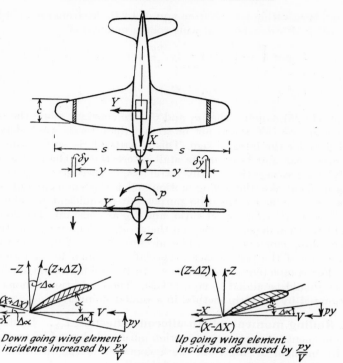

FIG. 14.10.—Nomenclature for strip theory of simple rolling (wing).

For the positive (downgoing) element the lift $(-Z)$ and drag $(-X)$ forces are increased by

$$- \Delta Z = a_1 \tfrac{1}{2} \rho V^2 c \, dy . \Delta \alpha \qquad . \qquad . \qquad . \quad (14.23)$$

and

$$- \Delta X = \frac{\partial C_D}{\partial \alpha} . \tfrac{1}{2} \rho V^2 c \, dy . \Delta \alpha$$

These forces are also rotated through $\Delta \alpha$ so that the lift is inclined *forwards* and drag *upwards*. The contribution of both of these to the rolling moment about the *wind OX* axis is

$$+ (Z + \Delta Z) \cos \Delta \alpha . y + (X + \Delta X) \sin \Delta \alpha . y$$

The contribution to the rolling moment about the *wind OX* axis due to the corresponding lift and drag forces on the *upgoing* wing which has had its lift and drag *decreased* and rotated *backwards* is

$$- (Z - \Delta Z) \cos \Delta \alpha . y + (X - \Delta X) \sin \Delta \alpha . y$$

The increment of rolling moment due to the elements at $\pm y$ on the wings is the sum of these two equations, viz.,

$$\Delta L = + (\Delta Z \cos \Delta \alpha + X \sin \Delta \alpha) 2y$$

Making the usual approximations for the small angle $\Delta \alpha$

$$\Delta L = + (\Delta Z + X \Delta \alpha) 2y \qquad . \qquad . \qquad . \quad (14.24)$$

when on substituting for ΔZ from eqn. (14.23), $\Delta \alpha$ from eqn. (14.22) and $- X = C_D \frac{1}{2} \rho V^2 c \, dy$, the total wing rolling moment is

$$L_{(p)} = \int_0^s - \left(a_1 \tfrac{1}{2} \rho V^2 c \, dy . \frac{py}{V} + C_D \tfrac{1}{2} \rho V^2 c \, dy . \frac{py}{V} \right) 2y$$

giving $\qquad L_{(p)} = - \, \rho . V . p (a_1 + C_D) \int_0^s c y^2 \, dy$ . . . (14.25)

Eqn. (14.25) assumes that a_1 and C_D are constant along the span. In the general case this would not be so and these terms would have to be included under the integral sign. This is particularly so for wing section incidences near and beyond the stall where the a_1 changes magnitude rapidly and goes negative. In this latter case $L_{(p)}$ becomes positive and the rolling moment aids the rolling motion and the phenomenon of *autorotation* occurs. For first estimation purposes it is sufficient to take a_1 with suitable correction for aspect ratio, and C_D as constant. The solution of eqn. (14.25) then depends solely on the aerofoil planform geometry.

The rolling moment of the whole aircraft about OX involves the righting moment of the tail surfaces, especially if a high fin and rudder are fitted. For completeness contributions to the rolling moments for these surfaces should be added to eqn. (14.25). These additional moments can be estimated by the strip method in a similar manner.

14.13. Rolling moment due to aileron deflection $L_{(\xi)}$.

In steady roll all the moments of the previous section must be balanced by an equal and opposite moment arising from the asymmetry of the spanwise lift distribution caused by the deflection of the ailerons.

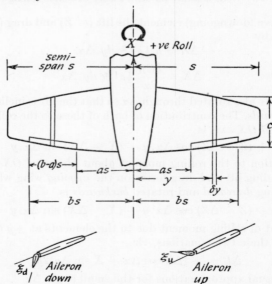

FIG. 14.11.—Nomenclature for aileron deflection.

Using strip theory again, it is assumed that the deflected aileron on each wing influences only the portion of the wing to which it is attached (see Fig. 14.11), i.e., between the spanwise stations as and bs. Consider a section of wing–aileron combination on the starboard (downgoing) wing, distant y from the OX axis. With $a_2 = \partial C_L/\partial \xi$, the change in lift coefficient due to an (up) deflection of $-\xi_u$ is $-a_2\xi_u$, producing a decrease of lift equal to $-a_2\xi_u\frac{1}{2}\rho V^2c\,\delta y$. This negative increment has a *positive* moment of

$$a_2\xi_u\tfrac{1}{2}\rho V^2cy\,\delta y \quad . \qquad . \qquad . \qquad . \qquad (14.26)$$

On the port (upgoing) wing, the corresponding element produces a moment in the *same* sense of

$$a_2\xi_d\tfrac{1}{2}\rho V^2cy\,\delta y \quad . \qquad . \qquad . \qquad . \qquad (14.27)$$

The total moment due to aileron deflection is the sum of moments due to eqns. (14.26) and (14.27) over the portion of wing affected by the ailerons:

$$L_{(\xi)} = \int_{as}^{bs} a_2\tfrac{1}{2}\rho V^2(\xi_u + \xi_d)cy\,dy$$

Now if there is no differential gearing, $\xi = \xi_u = \xi_d$, or if there is, it is usual to assume a representative deflection

$$\xi = \frac{\xi_u + \xi_d}{2}$$

The rolling moment due to aileron deflection becomes

$$L_{(\xi)} = a_2\rho V^2\xi \int_{as}^{bs} cy\,dy \qquad . \qquad . \qquad . \qquad (14.28)$$

14.14. Rolling moment derivatives. Eqn. (14.21) symbolized steady roll, that is

$$L_{(p)} + L_{(\xi)} = 0 \quad . \qquad . \qquad . \qquad . \qquad (14.21)$$

It is assumed that for small rates of roll (for small aileron deflections) $L_{(p)}$ varies linearly with p and $L_{(\xi)}$ linearly with ξ. Then eqn. (14.21) can be written

$$\left(\frac{\partial L_{(p)}}{\partial p}\right)\cdot p + \left(\frac{\partial L_{(\xi)}}{\partial \xi}\right)\cdot \xi = 0 \quad . \qquad . \qquad . \qquad (14.29)$$

$\partial L_{(p)}/\partial p$ is the rate of change of wing rolling moment with respect to rolling velocity and is termed a Moment-*rotary* derivative. $\partial L_{(\xi)}/\partial \xi$ is a Moment-*control* derivative indicating the rate of change of rolling moment with aileron deflection. Eqn. (14.30) gives the rolling velocity p for a given aileron deflection ξ,

$$p = -\left[\left(\frac{\partial L_{(\xi)}}{\partial \xi}\right)\Big/\left(\frac{\partial L_{(p)}}{\partial p}\right)\right]\cdot \xi \quad . \qquad . \qquad . \qquad (14.30)$$

and in this form shows the relative importance of the aileron power to the wing damping.

Aerodynamic derivatives are of considerable importance in stability analyses and are usually used in a non-dimensional form. For both the derivative and its non-dimensional form a standard notation is used which, in the United Kingdom, is the suffix system.

For example, let R stand for any component of aerodynamic force or couple on an aircraft and let s be any linear or angular velocity component. Then the derivative of R with respect to s is $\partial R/\partial s$ which is normally written R_s. In common with other force and moment systems it is made non-dimensional by dividing by a function of the size of the aircraft, velocity and air density.

In the non-dimensional form it is noted as r_s.

In this notation, eqn. (14.30) would be written

$$p = -\frac{L_\xi}{L_p}.\xi \qquad . \qquad . \qquad . \qquad (14.31)$$

14.15. Rolling moment due to sideslip. The evidence given in the previous section would suggest that an aeroplane is not statically stable in roll in the same sense as in pitch. In roll the reacting moment arises not from the angular displacement ϕ, but from the rate of displacement or angular velocity. Having damped out the rolling velocity, the aircraft has rolled through some angular displacement, and there is no aerodynamic force or moment available to tend to roll the aircraft back to its initial flight attitude. Equally there is no force tending to increase the displacement. In this simple mode then, the aircraft is neutrally, statically stable.

It was seen in the general discussion on stability in § 14.5, that the result of a displacement in bank about OX is to produce a sideslip velocity component v. An important effect of this sideslip is to induce a rolling moment tending to right the aircraft. This is one of the most important stabilizing aerodynamic effects available to the designer and the stability derivative L_v (or l_v), which is the rate of change of rolling moment with sideslip velocity, demands attention.

It is found that the total rolling moment of the aircraft due to sideslip can be assessed as the sum of separate sideslip effects, arising from the behaviour of the various components of the aircraft. These originate from:

(a) the dihedral of the wings,
(b) the fin and rudder combination,
(c) the planform of the wings,
(d) the wing–fuselage interference,
(e) flaps, nacelles, propellers, etc.

By far the greatest effect arises when the aeroplane possesses dihedral and the calculation of this is amenable to the strip method already discussed.

14.15.1. Wing contribution. For a small positive sideslip velocity v (to starboard) a sideslip angle of yaw ψ results where $\psi = v/U$, U being the initial forward velocity of the aircraft. The incidence at any section y from

OX on the leading wing will be increased by $\Delta\alpha = \psi\Gamma$ (Fig. 14.12), since the component of sideslip velocity *normal* to the plane of the wing is $v\Gamma$.

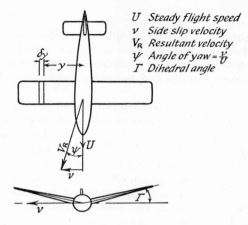

U Steady flight speed
v Side slip velocity
V_R Resultant velocity
ψ Angle of yaw $= \dfrac{v}{U}$
Γ Dihedral angle

Leading wing.
Increased incidence.

Trailing wing.
Decreased incidence.

Fig. 14.12.—Nomenclature and configuration for sideslip with dihedral.

Therefore
$$\Delta\alpha = \frac{v\Gamma}{U}$$

At the corresponding element of span on the trailing wing the incidence is decreased by a similar amount. The incidence changes at the elements due to sideslip produce aerodynamic force changes in exactly the same way as the incidence changes due to rolling in § 14.12. Substituting $v\Gamma/U$ for py/V in eqn. (14.25) gives the rolling moment due to dihedral $L_{(\Gamma)}$ as:

$$L_{(\Gamma)} = -\rho U v (a_1 + C_D) \int_0^s \Gamma c y \, dy \qquad . \qquad . \quad (14.31)$$

Again a_1 must be chosen to take account of the aspect ratio effect. Γ is included in the integral to allow for variable spanwise dihedral.

A tailplane with dihedral will also contribute and this addition can be obtained by a similar method to that above.

14.15.2. Contribution of fin and rudder combination to rolling moment in sideslip.

This arises from the off-set of the fin and rudder centre of pressure from the OX axis. The position of the centre of pressure varies with rudder deflection, and its contribution is usually obtained experimentally, or as a secondary estimate when investigating the main function of the fin and rudder as a stabilizer in the directional mode (see § 14.16).

14.15.3. Wing planform.

The contributions to l_v due to planform arise from the taper and sweep of the wings as well as the aspect ratio. Both of the former effects depend on the lift coefficient, being righting or negative moments for a positive sideslip and becoming more pronounced at low values of C_L.

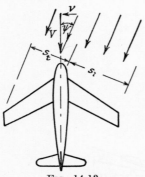

FIG. 14.13.

For moderate aspect ratios $(-l_v)$ increases with increase in sweepback, and also with increase in taper ratio $\dfrac{\text{tip chord}}{\text{root chord}}$ although the second effect is much smaller than the sweepback effect. The sweepback effect can be roughly explained by reference to Fig. 14.13. The relative wind in sideslip gives the leading wing an effective semi-span s_l which is greater than that of the trailing span s_t. The total lift on the leading wing is thus increased over that of the trailing wing and this produces the righting (negative) rolling moment.

Sweep forward, by the same argument, has a destabilizing moment.

14.15.4. Wing fuselage interference.

The influence of the fuselage on the flow round the wing in sideslip is significant and in some cases is sufficient to dispense with dihedral. If the wings are high, the sideflow of air from under the leading wing upwards over the fuselage and downwards again to beneath the trailing wing (Fig. 14.14) produces an effective inci-

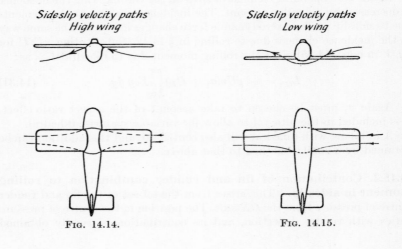

FIG. 14.14.   FIG. 14.15.

dence change. An increase of incidence on the leading wing and a decrease on the trailing wing produces the (righting) negative rolling moment.

The reverse is the case for a low wing aircraft (see Fig. 14.15) and a positive (destabilizing) moment is induced which requires in practice some dihedral in design to combat it.

For midwing aircraft the effect is not normally appreciable. All of the above effects apply only when the flow around the wing–body junction is smooth, that is when no separation of the flow occurs as is likely near the stall. When this happens the effects mentioned above are partially nullified.

14.15.5. Flaps and propellers. Each of these components has an influence on rolling in sideslip when in operation and must be accounted for. Little general theory is available on the effect of flaps but experiments and flight tests indicate that their influence is important. The effect of the propellers is caused almost entirely by the yawing of the slipstream, the trailing wing having a greater proportion of its surface in the slipstream and thereby having greater aerodynamic forces acting than the leader. This produces a destabilizing moment. It is usual, however, to neglect the effects of flaps, propellers and nacelles in stability estimates.

14.15.6. General remarks on rolling stability. The method used above for obtaining values of the rolling moment contributions of various aerodynamic surfaces has been the strip method. In modern design practice this method is never used except in an isolated example to check the order of magnitude of some other estimate.

A more accurate method is to use the lifting line theory with the spanwise loading suitably modified for aileron effects, and other geometrical parameters (see § 13.4). For many planforms, the results of applying this theory have been published in tabular or graphical form, which are available to the engineer. These data are published as *R.Ae.S. Data Sheets* in the United Kingdom.

Directional (or weathercock) stability and control

14.16. The equation of yawing moment. This section deals with the forces and moments arising on an aircraft caused by a small yawing displacement. If the aircraft is statically stable in this mode, it will tend to turn into the direction of the relative wind in the same way as a weather vane, which is always exceptionally stable, responds to any shift of the wind.

If an aircraft sideslips along a straight path the wind meets the OX axis at an angle which is also the angle of negative yaw of the aircraft. If the flight path is curved the sideslip angle will not in general be the angular rotation of the aircraft about the OZ axis which is the true definition of yaw. The former case is utilized in the present section and in Fig. 14.16, etc. This shows the plan view of an aeroplane which has suffered a small negative deviation about the OZ axis because of straight positive sideslip. This deviation will produce an overall yawing moment $N_{C.G.}$ about

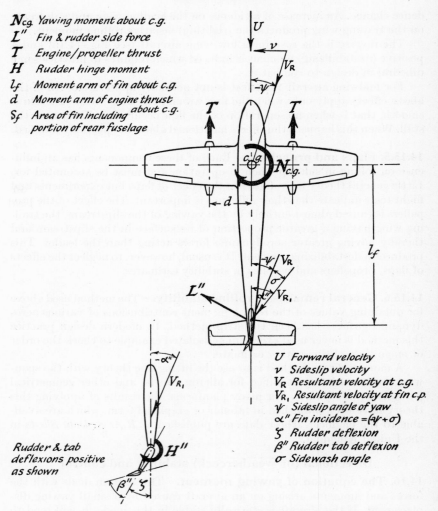

$N_{c.g.}$ Yawing moment about c.g.
L'' Fin & rudder side force
T Engine/propeller thrust
H Rudder hinge moment
l_f Moment arm of fin about c.g.
d Moment arm of engine thrust about c.g.
S_f Area of fin including portion of rear fuselage

U Forward velocity
v Sideslip velocity
V_R Resultant velocity at c.g.
V_{R_1} Resultant velocity at fin c.p.
ψ Sideslip angle of yaw
α'' Fin incidence $= (\psi + \sigma)$
ζ Rudder deflexion
β'' Rudder tab deflexion
σ Sidewash angle

Rudder & tab deflexions positive as shown

Fig. 14.16.—Nomenclature for directional stability and control.

the OZ axis, which if the aircraft is statically stable must be positive as shown; that is, tending to stop the motion. There are three main contributions to this moment and they are due to the wing, fuselage and fin–rudder combination. In symbols

$$N_{\text{C.G.}} = N_{\text{wing}} + N_{\text{fus.}} + N_{\text{F.R.}} \qquad . \qquad . \quad (14.32)$$

The wing contribution is small unless the planform has pronounced sweepback when N_{wing} is appreciable and stabilizing. It arises for the same reasons as the righting rolling moment due to sweepback in sideslip, § 14.15.3. The leading wing presents more 'span' to the wind and hence suffers more lift and drag. The former causes a rolling moment about OX, the latter a yawing moment about OZ tending to pull the aircraft round into wind.

For conventional planforms this yawing moment is small and is neglected below.

The fuselage contribution is destabilizing since it tends to turn the fuselage broadside on to the wind. A value for $-N_{\text{fus.}}$ (or its derivative $-\partial N_{\text{fus.}}/\partial\psi = -N_{\psi\,\text{fus.}}$) can be predicted from potential flow theory in a similar manner to that for the pitching moment contribution of the fuselage in pitch, but the process is simpler for this case and the values obtained closer to reality. This is because the flow on the OX, OY plane, meeting a yawed fuselage, has no large interference velocities due to wing up and down wash as has the flow in the OZ, OX plane meeting a fuselage at incidence, Fig. 14.17.

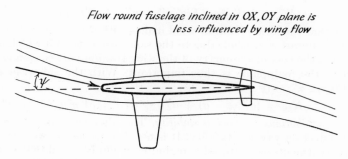

Flow round fuselage inclined in OX, OY plane is less influenced by wing flow

Flow round fuselage inclined in OX, OZ, plane below is influenced by wing flow

FIG. 14.17.

Fin and rudder contribution to yawing stability. The fin and rudder provides the main stabilizing moment to overcome the destabilizing of the fuselage. In addition it is the method of directional control via the rudder which is basically a flap hinged to the trailing edge of the fin. Deflecting the flap 'steers' the aircraft into the desired manœuvre.

With reference to Fig. 14.16 the wind is inclined at angle ψ' relative to the fin which therefore acts as a 'vertical' aerofoil which produces sideways 'lift' force L''. This provides a component $L''\cos\alpha'' \doteqdot L''$ normal to the OX axis through the fin centre of pressure l_f ft behind the C.G. of the aircraft.

L'' thus provides a moment $N_{\text{fin}} \doteqdot L''l_f$ tending to turn the aeroplane into the wind.

With
$$L'' = C_L'' \tfrac{1}{2}\rho V_{R\,1}^2 S_f, \quad a_1'' = \frac{\partial C_L''}{\partial \alpha''}, \quad a_2'' = \frac{\partial C_L''}{\partial \zeta}$$

and
$$a_3'' = \frac{\partial C_L''}{\partial \beta''} \text{ in the usual notation,}$$

$$N_{\text{fin}} = \tfrac{1}{2}\rho V_{R\,1}^2 S_f l_f (a_1'' \alpha'' + a_2'' \zeta + a_3'' \beta'')$$

Introducing a fin efficiency

$$\eta_f = \frac{\tfrac{1}{2}\rho V_{R\,1}^2}{\tfrac{1}{2}\rho V_R^2}$$

to take account of local velocity reductions in the neighbourhood of the fin due to wake effects of fuselage and wing

$$N_{\text{fin}} = \tfrac{1}{2}\rho V_R^2 \eta_f S_f l_f (a_1'' \alpha'' + a_2'' \zeta + a_3'' \beta'')$$

The angle that the local resultant wind makes with the fin, ψ', is less than that of the aircraft as a whole due to the sidewash at the fin which arises mainly from the lack of symmetry of the wing trailing vortex system. The position of the mainplane is thus important. With the sidewash angle denoted by σ, $\alpha'' = (\psi - \sigma)$,

$$\therefore\ N_{\text{fin}} = \{a_1''(\psi - \sigma) + a_2'' \zeta + a_3'' \beta''\}\tfrac{1}{2}\rho V_R^2 \eta_f S_f l_f \ . \quad (14.33)$$

Other contributions to yawing stability. The airscrew can have a considerable effect on yawing stability. It is usual to neglect power effects in the early treatments as discussed here, but it should be noted that a yawed propeller disc produces a side force in the *direction* of the relative side wind. This gives a pusher airscrew behind the C.G. a stabilizing effect whilst the opposite applies to a tractor airscrew set ahead of the C.G.

It is also found that the total effect of wing and fuselage is different from the simple sum, due to the interference in the flow between wing and body. This interference effect although very small is usually a stabilizing influence.

14.16.1. The condition for static directional stability.
Returning to eqn. (14.32) and introducing the signs and magnitudes of the various components

$$N_{\text{C.G.}} = N_{\text{wing}} - N_{\text{fus.}} + (\tfrac{1}{2}\rho V_R^2 \eta_f S_f l_f)\{a_1''(\psi - \sigma) + a_2'' \zeta + a_3'' \beta\}$$

Making non-dimensional by dividing through by the product of the dynamic pressure $(\tfrac{1}{2}\rho V^2)$, wing area and span the equation in coefficient form is

$$C_{N\,\text{C.G.}} = C_{N\,\text{wing}} - C_{N\,\text{fus.}} + \{a_1''(\psi - \sigma) + a_2'' \zeta + a_3'' \beta\}\left(\frac{V_R^2}{V^2}\eta_f \frac{S_f l_f}{S.2s}\right)$$

Now $V_R^2 \doteqdot V^2$ for most practical cases, and $S_f l_f/(S2s)$ is the fin volume ratio, $\bar{V}_f$, giving

$$C_{N\,\text{C.G.}} = C_{N\,\text{wing}} - C_{N\,\text{fus.}} + \eta_f \bar{V}_f\{a_1''(\psi - \sigma) + a_2'' \zeta + a_3'' \beta''\} \ . \quad (14.34)$$

For steady flight eqn. (14.34) must sum to zero and since the aeroplane is essentially symmetrical about the plane OX, OZ there are no yawing moments set up in steady straight flight and a rudder is theoretically unnecessary. In addition, with suitable combination of sweepback, pusher airscrews and no fuselage, an aeroplane could be statically stable without a fin and rudder. However, in the general case of steady curved flight some sideslip is required and to make eqn. (14.34) equate to zero with ψ in the third term an opposite value of rudder deflection (or trim tab deflection) is required. This means that some rudder power is required to hold an aeroplane in a sideslip or in a manœuvre requiring a sideslip.

When the condition for static stability is applied the rate of change of yawing moment with yawing deviation (of the relative wind) must be against the direction of deviation. Here $\partial C_N / \partial \psi$ must be positive since a negative deviation has been chosen in the derivation of the contributions.

Differentiating each term in eqn. (14.34) the condition is:

$$\frac{\partial C_{N \text{ C.G.}}}{\partial \psi} = \frac{\partial C_{N \text{ wing}}}{\partial \psi} - \frac{\partial C_{N \text{ fus.}}}{\partial \psi}$$

$$+ \eta_f \bar{V}_f \left\{ a_1'' \left(1 - \frac{\partial \sigma}{\partial \psi} \right) + a_2'' \frac{\partial \zeta}{\partial \psi} + a_3'' \frac{\partial \beta''}{\partial \psi} \right\} > 0 \quad . \quad (14.35)$$

With the possible exception for aircraft with highly swept wings, $\partial C_{N \text{ wing}} / \partial \psi$ is neglected and the simple equation for directional static stability becomes

$$\frac{\partial C_{N \text{ C.G.}}}{\partial \psi} = - \frac{\partial C_{N \text{ fus.}}}{\partial \psi} + \eta_f \bar{V}_f \left\{ a_1'' \left(1 - \frac{\partial \sigma}{\partial \psi} \right) + a_2'' \frac{\partial \zeta}{\partial \psi} + a_3'' \frac{\partial \beta''}{\partial \psi} \right\} > 0 \quad (14.36)$$

14.17. Pedal fixed directional static stability. In this case the rudder deflection ζ and tab deflection β'' are both fixed and eqn. (14.36) becomes

$$\frac{\partial C_{N \text{ C.G.}}}{\partial \psi} = - \frac{\partial C_{N \text{ fus.}}}{\partial \psi} + \eta_f \bar{V}_f a_1'' \left(1 - \frac{\partial \sigma}{\partial \psi} \right) > 0 \quad . \quad (14.37)$$

As the sidewash obviously reduces the directional stability by reducing the second (stabilizing) term, the rate of change of sidewash with yawing deviation must be carefully considered. The main preliminary design variable in eqn. (14.37) is the fin volume ratio $\bar{V}_f$ which increases with increase of fin and rudder 'effective' area, and distance of fin aft of the C.G. Both of these are designed to give the aircraft much directional stability as this is a quality which is demanded by most flyers of conventional aircraft. Some comment is called for on the 'effective' area of the fin and rudder. It is usual to incorporate some part of the fuselage area under the fin into this area, but the shape of the fin–fuselage combination from type to type varies so much that each case must be adjudged separately. So also with the estimation of the 'lift' curve slope for the fin, a_1''. A value can be obtained by assuming the fin to be a vertical aerofoil and making due allowance for its aspect ratio. Again, however, the proximity of the adjacent tail surfaces has an end effect on the fin which alters its effective aspect ratio.

D D

14.18. Pedal free directional static stability. Freeing the pedals will allow the rudder to float under the pressure distribution appropriate to the flight conditions. Any hinge moment created will be balanced out by the rudder deflecting until zero hinge moment condition is reached. The rudder will deflect either way depending upon the degree of aerodynamic balance incorporated in its design, in precisely the same way as the elevator in the pitching stability stick free case (§ 14.9). Here, for the positive sideslip (negative yaw) shown in Fig. 14.16 the rudder will float away from the sideslip (negative) and will reduce the static stability whilst a highly balanced rudder will float up (positive deflection) and increase the directional stability.

The rudder hinge moment coefficient C_H'' has contributions from fin, rudder and tab deflections.

$$C_H'' = \frac{\partial C_H''}{\partial \alpha''}\alpha'' + \frac{\partial C_H''}{\partial \zeta}\zeta + \frac{\partial C_H''}{\partial \beta''}\beta''$$

or in the usual notation

$$C_H'' = b_1''\alpha'' + b_2''\zeta + b_3''\beta'' \quad . \qquad . \qquad . \quad (14.38)$$

For zero hinge moment

$$\zeta = -\frac{1}{b_2''}\{b_1''\alpha'' + b_3''\beta''\}$$

and with $\alpha'' = \psi - \sigma$

$$\zeta = -\frac{1}{b_2''}\{b_1''(\psi - \sigma) + b_3''\beta''\} \qquad . \qquad . \quad (14.39)$$

substituting for ζ in the equation for directional equilibrium (eqn. (14.34)) and neglecting the wing term

$$C_{N\,\text{C.G.}} = -C_{N\,\text{fus.}}$$
$$+ \eta_f \bar{V}_f\left\{a_1''(\psi - \sigma) - \frac{a_2''}{b_2''}[b_1''(\psi - \sigma) + b_3''\beta''] + a_3''\beta''\right\} \quad (14.40)$$

Differentiating this with respect to ψ to obtain the static pedal free stability requirement, with rudder hinge moment trimmed out,

$$\frac{\partial C_{N\,\text{C.G.}}}{\partial \psi} = -\frac{\partial C_{N\,\text{fus.}}}{\partial \psi} + \eta_f \bar{V}_f a_1''\left(1 - \frac{a_2''b_1''}{a_1''b_2''}\right)\left(1 - \frac{\partial \sigma}{\partial \psi}\right) > 0 \quad (14.41)$$

Comparing eqn. (14.41) with the pedal fixed equation of the previous section eqn. (14.37) shows that freeing the pedals decreases the stability by an amount

$$\eta_f \bar{V}_f \frac{a_2''}{b_2''}.b_1''\left(1 - \frac{\partial \sigma}{\partial \psi}\right) \qquad . \qquad . \qquad . \quad (14.42)$$

$a_2'' = \dfrac{\partial C_L''}{\partial \zeta}$ is positive as is $b_1'' = \dfrac{\partial C_H''}{\partial \alpha''}$ and it is left to the sign of $b_2'' = \dfrac{\partial C_H''}{\partial \zeta}$

to determine the sign of the pedal free contribution to stability. The contribution will increase stability when b_2'' is negative.

14.19. Rudder power and design cases. It has been suggested above that an aeroplane could be designed statically stable without a fin and/or rudder. For adequate manœuvrability it is often necessary to hold an aircraft into a sideslip, for example, and it has been shown above that rolling an aeroplane produces a yawing moment which must be overcome. This latter case requires the rudder to maintain zero sideslip in a correctly banked turn, and this becomes critical at high lift coefficients (near the stall) with large aileron deflections. An aeroplane with 'stiff' directional stability will minimize the yaw due to roll.

In multi-engined aircraft the main rudder design criterion is that it should hold steady level flight with one engine cut out and the propeller windmilling. This power asymmetry produces a yawing moment equal to Td (see Fig. 14.16) plus an additional yawing moment due to the drag of the 'dead' airscrew. To maintain flight with zero sideslip requires that the rudder produce sufficient side force at the tail to overcome this asymmetric power condition. This is most critical at low air speeds and high engine powers, for example during take-off, since the thrust moment is large, while the rudder yawing moment produced by the aerodynamic force to the fin and rudder is small. This is usually the design criterion for multi-engined aircraft.

In common with the aileron the rudder design of an aeroplane demands considerable engineering ability. Purely theoretical reasoning produces estimates which, at their best, can be taken as rough guides and experimental data and flight tests of similar aircraft must then be studied.

The degree of stability and manœuvrability of an aeroplane depends on its purpose. Thus a civil air-liner requires to be stable about all axes, and only comparatively gentle manœuvres are called for. A fighter aircraft, on the other hand, needs to be highly manœuvrable and some small degree of static and dynamic instability is frequently accepted to achieve this manœuvrability.

Since many of the effects of the controls are interdependent, design of the complete control system of an aircraft is a complicated procedure, and evaluation of the success of the design is one of the main problems of flight testing.

Controls

14.20. General factors affecting controls. The design of an adequate control system for aircraft has never excited much general interest throughout the progress of aviation, nor have the problems encouraged organized research until the last two decades. This is somewhat paradoxical as it has been the invention of stability and control devices which has allowed the evolution of flight to develop. Each advance, from the initial powered leaps of A. V. Roe and the Wright Bros. at the turn of the century, to present-day vertical ascent vehicles and guided missiles, has been permitted only by significant solutions to stability and control problems.

It is not surprising that control systems tended to be designed for the aircraft, with the successful ones producing and confirming 'conventional' systems of control, since each aircraft type requires an individual control system. In so far as the specification for a prototype aircraft lays down the performance and manœuvrability requirements, then that specification designs the control system. With so many previous designs and data to call on, the designer of an aeroplane to standard specifications can, with fair certainty, put down on paper a control system which will not require serious modification when fitted to a prototype model.

It is the purpose of this section to review some of the methods of control which have gained almost universal currency in aeroplane design and note some of the less conventional which have, so far, restricted uses.

14.20.1. Longitudinal controls (pitching). The pilot's control of pitching, and hence forward speed, is the elevator–(fixed) tailplane combination with a trim device. This is the control system, in this mode, which is most common in aircraft designed to fly well below speeds at which compressibility effects would be felt.

With a fixed tailplane, the elevator must be sufficiently powerful to pull the aircraft up to stalling incidence at extreme ranges of C.G. position. Some light aircraft have undersized elevators to make the machine 'unstallable'. The elevator is essentially a flap, or pair of flaps, hinged at or near the nose to the trailing edge of the fixed horizontal stabilizing plane, or tailplane. When fitted as a pair, on either side of the fuselage say, they must be rigidly coupled so as to prevent any flutter between the two. The chord of the elevator is 30%–40% of the total chord of tailplane and elevator combined. The elevator should possess some aerodynamic balancing (see § 14.21) which is often achieved by horn balancing or setting the hinge back, or a combination of the two. Owing to the dependence of longitudinal trim on C.G. position which is variable, a trimming device of some kind, controllable by the pilot, should be fitted to allow the pilot to trim out any hinge moments set up by a C.G. position change or a forward velocity change, etc.

This trim device is usually a trim tab set in part of the trailing edge of the elevator, and connected to a control lever or wheel in the cockpit through an irreversible system which does not allow the tab to deflect in either way, relative to the elevator, unless operated from the cockpit.

Fixed trim tabs can be fitted, or some other permanent device having the same effect such as a strip of metal attached to the trailing edge and bent to the required deflection. Fixed trimmers can only effect one control position and are usually adjusted for the cruising position. Some aircraft have had the whole tailplane pivoted, and thus are capable of having the tail-setting angle altered at will by a trim control in the cockpit.

The adjustment of the tail incidence, relative to the fuselage, can be made into a very effective and powerful control in pitch, and it is known as the all flying, slab, or all moving tailplane.

The tailplane is hinged near the leading edge and the elevators are retained for special application, or in rudimentary form as trimmers, if at all. The aerodynamic moments about the pivot are extremely large, requiring power assistance in manipulation. Also the fuselage tailplane junction requires special attention in design to eliminate large drag losses. These two disadvantages prohibited the general use of this type of control until the advent of supersonic flight revealed inherent faults in the 'conventional' elevator. In supersonic aircraft and missiles, the rotating tailplane or stabilizer is almost universal. It can be made much more rigid and has a less disturbing effect on the shock pattern at the tail. The tailplane–fuselage interaction must still be most carefully studied.

Landing and take-off flaps, leading edge flaps and slats, are not controls in the sense meant here, but by their operation increase the lift and/or drag of the aircraft and are controllable by the pilot. They also have an influence on the pitching stability of the aeroplane but this is an undesirable attribute of their function (see § 9.2.2).

14.20.2. Lateral control.

This is most commonly effected by ailerons, which are a pair of flaps hinged near their leading edge, set at the trailing edges of the mainplanes and so coupled that they work in opposition. Thus, if one is deflected up the other goes down. The operation of the ailerons and the adverse yawing moment created by the operation of this control were described in § 14.11. It is called 'adverse' because the upgoing wing is retarded as a secondary effect of the aileron deflection, and this is opposite to the direction the upgoing wing is required to go, in a banked turn.

Apart from balance problems the design of ailerons has been concerned largely with eliminating the adverse yaw. Two ways have been extensively

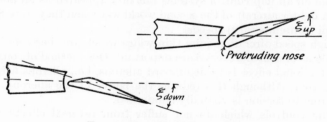

Fig. 14.18.—The Frise aileron.

used. The Frise aileron which, designed as a means of aerodynamic balance (Fig. 14.18), is arranged so that when the control is raised the 'offset' nose of the aileron protrudes into the airstream. This creates a localized region of low pressure and thus helps to balance the control and also to provide an addition to boundary layer drag on the *downgoing* wing. The nose of the downgoing aileron on the other side does *not* project into the airstream of the upgoing wing and no extra drag arises. Note that the ailerons are geared together so that any hinge moment felt by one is experienced by the system as a whole, so the balancing suction hinge moment is in the system as a whole, whilst the extra drag is on the wing of the up-deflected control only.

The other commonly used method of minimizing the adverse yaw is to gear the ailerons differentially so that, in the notation of Fig. 14.18, ξ_u does not equal ξ_d.

Ailerons are located towards the wing-tips by the necessity, in most aircraft, to utilize trailing edge flaps for landing and take-off. It can be argued that the further out the ailerons are placed the greater their 'moment arm' and hence their power. This is true in a sense, but to provide that power, ailerons of larger chord are required if their span is to be limited. Being set towards the tips of the wings, which are the most flexible part, helps the occurrence of *aileron reversal* and this is a serious condition.

Aileron reversal arises solely from the elasticity of the wing structure. In normal use an up-deflected aileron produces a twisting moment on the wing about the OY axis tending to increase the incidence of that part of the wing and this, in an elastic structure, will tend to nullify the action of the aileron and reduce the rolling moment. This twisting moment induced by an aerodynamic loading created by the control deflection increases as the square of the forward speed whilst the reacting torsional stiffness in the wing structure is constant. A flight speed is reached when the aileron deflections will not produce a rolling moment because the distortion of the main structure creates a main incidence change and hence aerodynamic force change sufficient to balance out that caused by the control deflection. This is a critical speed of flight which when exceeded produces the phenomenon of the aircraft rolling in opposition to a control deflection, i.e., the control is effectively reversed. This aeroelastic control reversal phenomenon is possible on all flap control systems but first appeared as an aileron reversal on fighter aircraft of the second world war when they were flown at very high (contemporary) speeds.

As high-speed aircraft require thin wings which are therefore less stiff the problems of control reversal are important. One method of counteracting this torsional effect is to fit inboard ailerons, i.e., ailerons fitted near the wing root. Although this reduces the power of the ailerons, control reversal due to torsion is virtually eliminated.

Rolling controls which do not suffer from reversal effects are 'lift spoilers'. Fitted on the upper surface of the wing forward of the quarter chord point these are essentially plates which protrude normal to the surface on one wing and violently disturb the flow over the wing and hence reduce the circulation and lift. The wing drops and the control is effected. The adverse yaw inherent in the motion is minimized by the large component of drag set up by the spoilers on the *downgoing* wing creating an opposing yawing moment. A further advantage to the use of this form of control is that being located in the wing to operate through the upper surface, the trailing edge is left free for full span flaps. The main disadvantage to this control type is that there is a delay between operation of control and response of aircraft. In addition there is no 'feed back' of sensitivity to the pilot who cannot feel the control although this can be introduced artificially.

Wings (or wing-tips) hinged near the quarter chord point, and allowed to alter their incidences in opposition through a simple power-assisted control system, would seem the logical control for high-speed aircraft, especially if the wings have to be rigid and thin, and of low aspect ratio.

14.20.3. Directional controls (yawing). Finless and rudderless aeroplanes can feasibly be designed but the general control criteria for flight demand a device for directional control. This is the rudder and it is probably the most familiar of all aircraft controls. It consists of a flap hinged near the leading edge and fixed to the trailing edge of the fin(s). It must be powerful in operation yet incapable of sensibly altering the directional stability of the aircraft when freed. This demands considerable aerodynamic balancing. Fins and rudders, like tailplanes and elevators, are usually of symmetrical streamline section, but in the case of single propeller-driven aircraft are sometimes offset, or of non-symmetrical section, to compensate for the rotation of the flow in the slipstream in which they are immersed. Single rudders are usually in the propeller slipstream and this is found to be a useful taxiing control. Multi-engined aircraft sometimes have twin fins and rudders set in the propellers' streams in order to obtain a measure of this control on the ground.

For multi-engined aircraft particularly, the rudder must be provided with very quick operating trimmers which must be sufficiently powerful to trim out the hinge moment associated with the design criterion of engine failure.

The action of the rudder, as that of all controls working in the wash of an aerodynamic surface, is susceptible to changes in flow regime over the fin. A stalled fin in a large sideslip can reverse the action of the rudder by causing it to take an adverse deflection and in severe cases can cause the rudder to 'lock on' beyond the control of the pilot. For some reason not yet fully explained a dorsal fin fairing at the junction of the top of the fuselage and the leading root edge of the fin alleviates or postpones severe fin stalling. Another method is to fit twin fins and rudders of smaller aspect ratio.

The necessity for landing with the OX axis nearly parallel to the ground surface results in fitting the fin and rudder to the top and rear of the fuselage, introducing a certain asymmetry to the whole tail unit. In future aircraft, landing with the OX axis vertical, designers will be able to arrange for a symmetrical tail unit in which the rudder and tailplane and their controls are identical. Further, if this cruciform tail system is turned so that the tail stabilizing planes are at 45° to the mainplanes, the elevating and steering function will be shared by each surface. This is a familiar design on some types of missile.

14.21. Aerodynamic balancing of controls. Previous discussion has shown that the control hinge moment has a considerable bearing on the power of the control and its ease of handling as well as on the static stability of the aircraft as a whole. Further investigation into the response characteristics of control surfaces and the dynamic stability of aircraft also shows

the importance of the hinge moment parameter. A basic design requirement is that over-large hinge moments must be reduced by balancing.
Care must be taken not to carry the process too far and overbalance the
control, which would then deviate from the neutral setting, if released
from the pilot's restraint.

Several methods of aerodynamic balancing are available to the designer
and it is not unusual for two or more methods to be used on a single control.
The methods discussed below have universal application and all could be
usefully employed on any of the controls, but those methods involving
asymmetric flaps, e.g., the Frise aileron which has a form of 'distorted' nose
balance, are most often used on aileron controls. For this reason the common symbolism of b_1, b_2, b_3, the slope of the curve of control hinge moment
coefficient with incidence, control deflection, and tab deflection respectively, is used here.

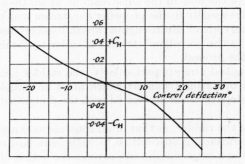

FIG. 14.19.

A complexity to be considered when comparing the utility of the types
of balance available is that the parameters b_1 and b_2 are themselves not
constant over the angles of incidence for deflections available to the control. An example of the change in slope is given in Fig. 14.19. The comments
given below will be confined to deflections near the neutral setting.

14.22. Methods of aerodynamic balance depending on control shape.

Horn balance. Part of the control surface is carried forward of the hinge
axis to protrude either within the fixed plane where it is then a *shielded*
horn or at the extremity of the fixed plane where it is *unshielded* (Fig.
14.20). Occasionally the horn is partly shielded. The portion forward of the
hinge-line will suffer aerodynamic forces causing a hinge moment in opposition to that of the trailing part of the control both when the incidence of
the whole is changed or when the control is deflected. The horn balance is
a powerful design tool which permits b_1 to be increased to zero or even made
positive without causing undue overbalance of b_2. For this reason horn
balance is mostly used on elevators and rudders. In general, the degree of
balance (or positive change in b_1 and b_2) is greater for increased area of horn,
relative to the control area, and increases as the aspect ratio of the horn

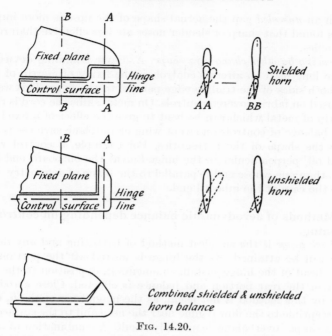

Fixed plane

Control surface

Hinge line

Shielded horn

AA   BB

Fixed plane

Control surface

Hinge line

Unshielded horn

Combined shielded & unshielded horn balance

FIG. 14.20.

decreases. The other parameters remain constant. For shielded and part shielded horns the nose shape of the horn has an effect, a blunter nose being more effective than a streamline or sharp nose.

Nose (shape) balance (sealed gap). The effect of change of nose shape is most marked when the gap between control and main surfaces is sealed by some flexible membrane so that lower surface flow conditions cannot communicate with the upper surface flow regime (Fig. 14.21). Further, with the gaps between the upper and lower control surfaces and main surfaces suitably restricted the pressures p_u and p_l acting over the nose portion will be appreciably constant and have no relation to the nose shape. The control nose will thus work as a 'lever' acted upon by the pressure difference $(p_l - p_u)$. The overall effect of the seal is somewhat diminished by the cut-outs necessary on the hinge structure. This allows the pressures to equalize in a region extending beyond that of the cut-out itself. In addition the leak from the lower to upper surface modifies the flow.

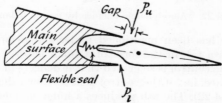

Gap P_u

Main surface

Flexible seal

P_l

FIG. 14.21.—Sealed gap (nose shape) aerodynamic balance.

With an *unsealed* gap the actual shape of the nose is more important and it is found that sharp or slender noses are less effective than round or bluff profiles.

Balancing by other changes in shape. A simple trimming device which has been long used on aircraft controls is the fixing of a strip of cord to one or both sides of the trailing edge parallel to the edge. This was commonly used on fabric-covered controls. On metal skins the cord is replaced by a strip of metal which can be bent to give the effect of a fixed tab.

The balance of controls on swept wing or tailplane surfaces is susceptible to the shape of the extremities. For example, a control which is 'finished off' perpendicular to the hinge-line at the outboard end is more positive than one whose end is parallel to the plane of symmetry. The reverse is the case at the inboard end.

14.23. Methods of aerodynamic balance depending on control positioning.

Set-back hinge is the simplest method of balancing and any degree of balance can be attained. As the hinge is moved aft the portion of the control ahead of the hinge sustains moments in opposition to the control moment of the rear portion and balance is effected. Close aerodynamic balance by this method is not usual, as the magnitude of the b_2 effect is very susceptible to the flow regime near the nose and to the surface condition and shape; overbalance can easily result. A combination of set-back hinge and horn balance in which overbalance can be avoided is often employed.

Gap. The gap between the control and fixed surface can have considerable influence on the working of the control by permitting a high-energy jet of air to leak from the lower surface to the upper, to re-energize the boundary layer and thus delay separation. The magnitude of the effect depends on the condition of the surfaces and the Reynolds number of the flow, and may vary appreciably. For sealed controls the vent gap size is important and the balance effectiveness falls off rapidly as the gap is increased.

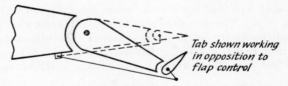

Tab shown working in opposition to flap control

FIG. 14.22.—Aerodynamic balance by geared balance tab.

Tab balancing has been mentioned under shape methods above. In some applications a tab in the form of a small flap set over part of the trailing edge of the control is so geared that it deflects in opposition to the main control surface, i.e., if the control deflects down the tab goes up and vice versa (Fig. 14.22). The tab produces a hinge moment on the control hinge-line which acts against the moment set up by the control and effects the balance. The gearing ratio of this type of tab is the important design feature. If necessary the linkage can be designed to allow the tab deflection to follow the flap. In this case it acts to increase the control hinge moment and thus provides 'anti-balance'.

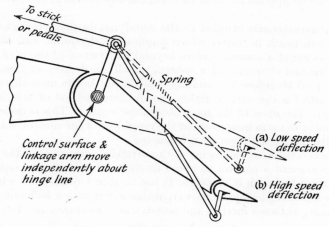

FIG. 14.23.—The spring tab.

Control surface deflection for identical *stick* or *pedal* movement at
(a) low speed—tab undeflected.
(b) high speed—tab aerodynamic hinge moment overcomes spring strength and control surface deflects an additional amount as the spring extends.

The *spring tab* is not a pure balancing device (Fig. 14.23). Its primary purpose is to relieve the high hinge moments and hence stick forces arising from the higher speed ranges of the aircraft's performance. Hinge moments are proportional to the square of the flight speed. Basically, the control linkage from the stick or pedals deflects the control through a stiff spring, and is continued to actuate the tab. At low speeds the aerodynamic forces are too weak to overcome the spring which acts as an inextensible link and the control surface deflects normally. At high speeds the forces on the tab extend the spring, the control surface moves under the action of these forces *independent* of the pilot's linkage since they both independently rotate about the hinge-line, and the tab is deflected relative to the control. Thus the tab deflection, which is geared to balance the hinge moment, arises in proportion to the hinge moment. The ratio between the two depends on the tab size gearing and spring strength.

14.24. Mass balancing. Although beyond the scope of the present volume mass balancing is mentioned here to distinguish it from aero-dynamic balance. Control surfaces, like other real bodies, possess mass and in all forms of motion exhibit inertial characteristics. It can be readily appreciated therefore that a flap hinged at its leading edge and possessing mass will resist accelerations in any form according to its inertia. For example, if the flap is an elevator and the aircraft begins to pitch nose up, the elevator, all aerodynamic considerations aside, will lag and deflect up if the centre of mass of the elevator is behind the hinge-line. Equally when in steady rotation about its hinge the elevator will have inertia $I\omega$ which will require an applied moment to bring the flap to rest in the new control position.

This characteristic coupled to the aerodynamic characteristics of the controls can result in flutter which implies the rhythmic, and often frequent, motion of a control surface beyond the control of the pilot.

The inertial character of a control, in all six degrees of freedom, or motion, must therefore be carefully considered. As the mass distribution of the control is the only variable the obvious method of solution is to redistribute the mass to the most innocuous location. This is done by the arrangement of extra masses about the hinge-line of the control, sometimes externally; hence the term *mass balancing*.

To reiterate; mass balancing is the artificial correction of the inertial characteristics of a control to avoid excessive flutter of the control and main surface to which it attaches. It has no direct connection with aerodynamic balancing except to the extent that aerodynamic balancing affects the coupling between inertial and aerodynamic moments and forces.

EXERCISES

1. Write down the equation for the longitudinal equilibrium of an aircraft. Applying the criterion for static stability discuss the influence of each term of your equation on the overall longitudinal stability, stick-fixed.

The following data relate to an aeroplane in which the tail volume ratio is 0·55, and the arm of the tailplane lift is 25 ft. For the wing, the area is 420 ft², and $\dfrac{\partial C_L}{\partial \alpha} = 4\cdot 6$. For the tailplane, the area is 50 ft²,

$$\frac{\partial C_L'}{\partial \eta}=1\cdot 9, \quad \frac{\partial C_H'}{\partial \alpha'} = -\,0\cdot 008, \quad \frac{\partial C_H'}{\partial \eta} = -\,0\cdot 013, \quad \text{and} \quad \frac{\partial \varepsilon'}{\partial \alpha} = 0\cdot 39$$

Assuming the tail efficiency to be 0·98 find the movement of the neutral point on freeing the stick. (*Ans.* 5·42 in. forwards) (U. of L.)

2. An aircraft has the following characteristics:

$$\frac{\partial C_L}{\partial \alpha} = 0\cdot 08, \quad b_1' = -0\cdot 006, \quad b_2' = -0\cdot 0035$$

in each case per degree.

The elevator chord is 3 ft, and the elevator area is 42 ft². Other geometry is such that

$$\frac{\partial \eta}{\partial \alpha} = -1\cdot 0 \quad \text{and} \quad \frac{\partial \varepsilon}{\partial \alpha} = 0\cdot 35$$

The elevators are trimmed for 'hands-off' flight at a speed of 300 ft/sec, when the lift coefficient is 0·167. Calculate the elevator hinge moment necessary for flight at 100 ft/sec, with no change in trim-tab deflection. (*Ans.* −11·25 lb ft) (N.C.A.T.)

3. The following data refer to an aeroplane in which the tail volume ratio is 0·55. For the wings $\dfrac{\partial C_L}{\partial \alpha} = 4\cdot6$, $C_{M\frac{1}{4}} = -\,0\cdot018$, and zero lift incidence is

$-2\cdot5°$. For the symmetrical tailplane and elevators

$$\frac{\partial C_L'}{\partial \alpha'} = 2\cdot9, \quad \frac{\partial C_L'}{\partial \eta} = 1\cdot4 \quad \text{and} \quad \frac{\partial \varepsilon}{\partial \alpha} = 0\cdot39$$

The C.G. of the aeroplane is at 0·29 of the mean chord.

For $C_L = 0\cdot4$ determine the tail-setting angle to give balance with eleva-tors neutral, and with the same tail-setting determine the elevator angle for balance at $C_L = 1\cdot2$ neglecting movement of the tail C.P. (*Ans.* $-1\cdot69°$ $-12\cdot7°$)
(U. of L.)

4. Distinguish between static and dynamic stability of an aeroplane.

An aeroplane weighing 21,000 lb has wings of aspect ratio 7 loaded to 30 lb/ft². For normal loading the C.G. coordinate is 18 in. behind the $\frac{1}{4}$ chord point of the wings. The tailplane is 60 ft² in area and has an aspect ratio of 4·8. The arm of the tailplane lift is 32 ft, the rate of change of downwash with wing incidence being 0·46. Is the aeroplane statically stable?

If not, what would you suggest to make it so. (*Ans.* No)

5. A small aircraft has the following characteristics:

Tail volume ratio	$\bar{V} = 0\cdot50$	
Total pitching moment coefficient about aero-dynamic centre at zero C_L . . .	$C_{M0} = -0\cdot05$	
For the wings	$C_L = 0\cdot08(\alpha + 2)$	
For the symmetrical tailplane . .	$C_L' = 0\cdot05\alpha' + 0\cdot017\eta$	

where the angles are in degrees.

At the tailplane	$\dfrac{\partial \varepsilon}{\partial \alpha} = 0\cdot35$
Tail efficiency	$\eta_t = 0\cdot90$
Wing loading	$w = 32 \text{ lb/ft}^2$

In this condition, the static margin is required to be 0·12.

On landing, flaps are used which give a stalling speed of 68 m.p.h, the operation of the flaps increasing the normal maximum lift coefficient by 1·15 at the same incidence. The corresponding increment in pitching moment coefficient is $-0\cdot13$.

Estimate the tail-setting angle required if the elevator deflection at the stalling speed is to be 10° up.

Also calculate, with this tail-setting angle, the elevator angle to trim when the aircraft is cruising at 250 m.p.h, T.A.S. at 10,000 ft ($\sigma = 0\cdot738$). Comment on the effect on pitching control of varying the static margin.

6. The lift curve of a light aeroplane wing of rectangular planform is prac-tically straight between the angle of no lift ($-3\cdot0$ degrees) and the incidence 10° at which $C_L = 1\cdot066$. The wing chord is 7 ft, the aspect ratio is 8·3 and the dihedral angle is 5°. Assuming that the speed of level flight is 135 m.p.h, calculate the rolling moment set up by a sudden yaw of 5°. (*Ans.* 9850 lb ft)
(N.C.A.T.)

7. A light aeroplane has a wing of approximately rectangular planform 42 ft span by 7 ft chord with a maximum lift coefficient of 1·5. The loading on the wing is 18 lb/ft². The machine is rolled through 90° in 1 sec when flying at 3 times its minimum flying speed. Estimate the rolling moment exerted by the ailerons assuming steady motion. (*Ans.* 109,500 lb ft)
(N.C.A.T.)

BIBLIOGRAPHY

BAIRSTOW, *Applied Aerodynamics* (Longmans).

DOMMASCH, *Principles of Aerodynamics* (Pitman).

DOMMASCH et al., *Airplane Dynamics* (Pitman).

DUNCAN, *The Principles of Control and Stability of Aircraft* (C.U.P.).

DURAND (Editor-in-Chief), *Aerodynamic Theory*, 6 vols. (Julius Springer).

GLAUERT, *The Elements of Airscrew and Aerofoil Theory* (C.U.P.).

MILLIKAN, *Aerodynamics of the Airplane* (Wiley, New York; Chapman & Hall, London).

MILNE-THOMSON, *Theoretical Aerodynamics* (Macmillan).

MORLEY, *Aircraft Propulsion* (Longmans).

PERKINS and HAGE, *Airplane Performance, Stability and Control* (Chapman & Hall).

PIERCY, *Elementary Aerodynamics* (E.U.P.).

PIERCY, *Aerodynamics* (E.U.P.).

POPE, *Basic Wing and Aerofoil Theory* (McGraw-Hill).

PRANDTL, *Essentials of Fluid Dynamics* (Blackie).

PRANDTL and TIETJENS, *Applied Hydro- and Aeromechanics* (McGraw-Hill).

RAUSCHER, *Introduction to Aeronautical Dynamics* (Chapman & Hall).

SHAPIRO, *Principles of Helicopter Engineering* (Temple Press).

SUTTON, *The Science of Flight* (Pelican Books).

APPENDIX I

SYMBOLS AND NOTATION

A — Moment of inertia about Ox. Aspect ratio (also $Æ$). Area. With suffices, coefficients in a Fourier series of sine terms, or a polynomial series in z.

A.F. — Activity factor of an airscrew.

a — Speed of sound. Axial inflow factor in airscrew theory. Radius of transformed circle. Lift curve slope, $dC_L/d\alpha$ (suffices denote particular values). Radius of vortex core. Acceleration or deceleration.

a.c. — Aerodynamic centre (also AC).

B — Number of blades on an airscrew.

b — Rotational interference factor in airscrew theory. Zhukovsky's transformation factor ($\zeta = z + b^2/z$). Total wing span ($= 2s$). Hinge moment coefficient slope.

C.G. — Centre of gravity.

C_D — Total drag coefficient.

C_{D_0} — Zero-lift drag coefficient.

C_{Dv} — Trailing vortex drag coefficient.

$C_{D\ L}$ — Lift-dependent drag coefficient. (Other suffices are used in particular cases.)

C_H — Hinge moment coefficient.

C_l — Rolling moment coefficient.

C_L — Lift coefficient.

C_M — Pitching moment coefficient.

C_N — Yawing moment coefficient.

C_P — Pressure coefficient. Power coefficient for airscrews.

C_R — Resultant force coefficient.

c — Wing chord. Specific fuel consumption. A distance.

$\bar{c}$ — Standard or geometric mean chord.

$\bar{\bar{c}}$ or $\bar{c}_A$ — Aerodynamic mean chord.

c_0 — Root chord.

c_T — Tip chord.

c_e — Elevator mean chord.

c_f — Fin mean chord.

$c_\mathrm{p}, c_\mathrm{v}$ — Specific heats at constant pressure and constant volume.

c.p. — Centre of pressure.

D — Drag (suffices denote particular values). Airscrew diameter. A length (occasionally).

d — Diameter, occasionally a length.

d_v — Spanwise trailing vortex drag grading ($= \rho w K$).

E — Kinetic energy.

e — Eccentricity factor.

F — Fractional flap chord. Force.

f — Mass of fuel.

f( ) — Function of the stated variables.

g — Acceleration due to gravity.

g( ) — Function of the stated variables.

H — Hinge moment. Total pressure. Momentum.

h — Fractional camber of a flapped plate aerofoil. Fractional position of C.G. Distance between plates in Maxwell's definition of viscosity. Vertical eccentricity factor. Altitude, or height generally.

h( ) — Function of the stated variables.

h_0 — Fractional position of the aerodynamic centre.

h_n — Fractional position of the neutral point, stick fixed.

h_n^1 — Fractional position of the neutral point, stick free.

423

I Momentum of rocket exhaust.

i   The imaginary operator, $\sqrt{-1}$.

J Advance ratio of an airscrew. Mechanical equivalent of heat (Joule's constant).

K Circulation. Modulus of bulk elasticity.

K_0 Circulation at mid-section of a wing.

k Chordwise variation of vorticity. Lift-dependent drag coefficient factor.

k_{cp} Centre of pressure coefficient.

k_T, k_Q Thrust and torque coefficients (airscrews).

L Lift. Dimension of length. Temperature lapse rate in the atmosphere.

L_R Rolling moment about Ox.

l Length.

l_{de} Effective disc loading of a helicopter.

l_t, l_f Tailplane and fin moment arms.

$l_p, l_\xi, l_v,$ etc.   Rolling moment derivatives.

M Dimension of mass. Mass of a rocket missile. Mach number. Pitching moment about Oy.

M_0 Initial mass of a rocket missile.

M_1 All-burnt mass of a rocket missile.

m Mass. Strength of a source (-sink). Ratio (flight speed / minimum drag speed). An index.

$\dot{m}$ Rate of mass flow. Rate of fuel consumption of a rocket missile.

N Yawing moment about Oz. r.p.m of an airscrew.

n Revolutions per second of an airscrew. Load factor in a turn. Frequency. Ratio (flight speed / minimum power speed). An index.

O Origin of coordinates.

P Power. The general point in space.

p Static pressure in a fluid. Angular velocity in roll about Ox.

Q Torque, or a general moment. Total velocity of a uniform stream.

q Angular velocity in pitch about Oy. Local resultant velocity. A coefficient in airscrew theory.

q_n, q_t Radial and tangential velocity components.

R Reynolds number. Resultant force. Characteristic gas constant. Force between ground and undercarriage. Range. Mass ratio (M_0/M_1) of a rocket missile. Radius of turn, or of a circle.

R.o.C.   Rate of climb.

r Angular velocity in yaw about Oz. Radius vector, or radius generally.

S Wing area. Vortex tube area. Area of actuator disc.

S' Tailplane area.

S_f Fin area.

S_e Elevator area.

s Semi-span $(= \frac{1}{2}b)$. Distance.

s' Spacing of each trailing vortex centre from aircraft centre-line.

T Dimension of time. Thrust. Temperature (suffices denote particular values).

T_0 Static thrust.

t Time. Aerofoil section thickness. A coefficient in airscrew theory.

U Velocity. Steady velocity parallel to Ox.

u Velocity component parallel to Ox.

V Velocity. Volume. Steady velocity parallel to Oy.

V_s Stalling speed.

V_E Equivalent air speed.

V_R Resultant speed.

$\bar{V}$ Tail volume ratio.

$\bar{V}_f$ Fin volume ratio.

v Velocity component parallel to Oy. Velocity. Velocity of exhaust relative to rocket motor. Rate of climb or descent.

W Weight. Steady velocity parallel to Oz.

w Wing loading. Downwash velocity. Complex potential function $(= \phi + i\psi)$. Velocity parallel to Oz.

X, Y, Z Components of aerodynamic or external force.

x, y, z Coordinates of the general point P.

x, X Distance.

z The complex variable $(= x + iy)$.

α Angle of incidence or angle of attack. An angle, generally.

α_t Tail-setting angle.

β An angle defining vertical shift in Zhukovsky's transformation. A factor in airscrew theory. Tab deflection. An angle generally.

Γ Half the dihedral angle; the angle between each wing and the Oxy plane.

γ Ratio of specific heats, c_p/c_v. Gliding angle $(= \text{arc cot } (L/D))$.

Δ Boundary layer thickness.

δ A factor. Camber of an aerofoil section.

δ_f Flap deflection. (High lift.)

ε Downwash angle. Surface slope.

ζ Vorticity. Complex variable in transformed plane $(= \xi + i\eta)$. Rudder deflection.

η Efficiency. Elevator deflection. Ordinate in ζ-plane.

θ Dimension of temperature. Angular displacement in pitch. Angle of climb. Polar angular coordinate. Blade helix angle (airscrews).

Λ Angle of sweepback or sweep-forward.

λ Taper ratio $(= c_T/c_0)$. A constant.

μ Strength of a doublet. Absolute coefficient of viscosity. Aerofoil parameter in lifting line theory.

ν Kinematic coefficient of viscosity.

ξ Aileron deflection. Abscissa in ζ-plane.

ρ Density. Radius of curvature.

Σ Summation sign.

σ Relative density. Blade or annular solidity (airscrews). Sidewash angle at fin.

τ Intensity of viscous traction.

τ_0 Intensity of surface friction.

ϕ Angular displacement in bank about Ox. Sweepback angle. Velocity potential. A polar coordinate. Angle of relative wind to plane of airscrew disc.

ψ Angular displacement in yaw, or sideslip angle. Angle turned through in circling flight. The stream function.

Ω Angular velocity of airscrew.

ω Angular velocity in general.

∇^2 Laplace's operator $(= \partial^2/\partial x^2 + \partial^2/\partial y^2)$.

Suffices

0 No lift. Standard sea-level. Straight and level flight. Undisturbed stream.

$\frac{1}{4}$ Quarter chord point.

1 Rates of change of aerodynamic characteristics with main surface incidence, or otherwise a particular value.

2 Rates of change of aerodynamic characteristics with flap or control deflection, or otherwise a particular value.

E E

3	Rates of change of aerodynamic characteristics with tab deflection, or otherwise a particular value.
∞	Infinity or two-dimensional conditions.
AC	Aerodynamic centre.
a	available.
FN	Fuselage-nacelle contribution.
fus.	Fuselage contribution.
f	Full scale or flight.
G	Gross.
g	Ground.
h	Horizontal.
i	Ideal.
in	Input.
L	Landing.
L.E.	Leading edge.
l	Local. Lower surface.
m	Model.
max	Maximum
min	Minimum.
md	Minimum drag.
mp	Minimum power.
m.r.	Maximum range.

N	Nett.
Na.	Nacelle contribution.
n	Denotes general term.
opt	Optimum.
out	Output.
p	Propulsive.
r	Required.
s	Stagnation or reservoir conditions. Slipstream. Stratosphere.
TO	Take-off.
T.E.	Trailing edge.
u	Upper surface.
v	Vertical.

Primes and superscripts

1	Stick free.
$'$	Tailplane.
$''$	Fin.
$*$	Throat (locally sonic) conditions.

The 'dot' notation is frequently used for differentials; e.g., $\dot{y} = dy/dx$, the rate of change of y with x.

APPENDIX 2

THE INTERNATIONAL STANDARD ATMOSPHERE

1. *Sea level conditions*

$T_0 = +15°C = +288·16°K$
$p_0 = 2116·216 \text{ lb/ft}^2$
$\rho_0 = 0·002378 \text{ slug/ft}^3$
$\mu_0 = 3·719 \times 10^{-7} \text{ slug/ft sec}$
$\nu_0 = 1·564 \times 10^{-4} \text{ ft}^2/\text{sec}$

2. *Relative values*

Altitude (ft)	Temperature $\theta = \dfrac{T}{T_0}$	Pressure $\tilde{\omega} = \dfrac{p}{p_0}$	Density $\sigma = \dfrac{\rho}{\rho_0}$	Viscosity $\tilde{\mu} = \dfrac{\mu}{\mu_0}$	Viscosity $\tilde{\nu} = \dfrac{\nu}{\nu_0}$
0	1	1	1	1	1
1000	0·99312	0·96439	0·97106	0·99457	1·0242
2000	0·98625	0·92981	0·94277	0·98912	1·0492
3000	0·97937	0·89624	0·91512	0·98365	1·0749
4000	0·97250	0·86366	0·88808	0·97816	1·1014
5000	0·96562	0·83205	0·86167	0·97266	1·1288
6000	0·95875	0·80138	0·83586	0·96714	1·1571
7000	0·95187	0·77163	0·81064	0·96160	1·1862
8000	0·94500	0·74278	0·78601	0·95604	1·2163
9000	0·93812	0·71481	0·76196	0·95046	1·2474
10,000	0·93125	0·68770	0·73848	0·94487	1·2795
11,000	0·92437	0·66143	0·71555	0·93925	1·3126
12,000	0·91750	0·63598	0·69317	0·93362	1·3469
13,000	0·91062	0·61133	0·67133	0·92796	1·3823
14,000	0·90374	0·58745	0·65002	0·92229	1·4189
15,000	0·89687	0·56434	0·62923	0·91660	1·4567
16,000	0·89000	0·54197	0·60896	0·91088	1·4958
17,000	0·88312	0·52032	0·58918	0·90515	1·5363
18,000	0·87624	0·49938	0·56991	0·89940	1·5781
19,000	0·86937	0·47912	0·55112	0·89362	1·6215
20,000	0·86249	0·45954	0·53280	0·88783	1·6663
21,000	0·85562	0·44061	0·51496	0·88202	1·7128
22,000	0·84874	0·42232	0·49758	0·87618	1·7609
23,000	0·84187	0·40464	0·48065	0·87032	1·8107
24,000	0·83499	0·38757	0·46416	0·86445	1·8624
25,000	0·82812	0·37109	0·44811	0·85855	1·9159
26,000	0·82124	0·35518	0·43249	0·85263	1·9714
27,000	0·81437	0·33983	0·41729	0·84669	2·0290
28,000	0·80749	0·32502	0·40250	0·84072	2·0888
29,000	0·80062	0·31073	0·38812	0·83474	2·1508
30,000	0·79374	0·29696	0·37413	0·82873	2·2151

427

2. *Relative values (contd.)*

Altitude (ft)	Temperature $\theta = \dfrac{T}{T_0}$	Pressure $\tilde{\omega} = \dfrac{p}{p_0}$	Density $\sigma = \dfrac{\rho}{\rho_0}$	Viscosity	
				$\tilde{\mu} = \dfrac{\mu}{\mu_0}$	$\tilde{\nu} = \dfrac{\nu}{\nu_0}$
31,000	0·78686	0·28369	0·36053	0·82270	2·2820
32,000	0·77999	0·27090	0·34731	0·81665	2·3514
33,000	0·77311	0·25858	0·33446	0·81058	2·4235
34,000	0·76624	0·24672	0·32199	0·80448	2·4985
35,000	0·75936	0·23530	0·30987	0·79836	2·5764
36,000	0·75249	0·22432	0·29810	0·79221	2·6575
36,089	0·75187	0·22336	0·29707	0·79166	2·6649
37,000	Constant in	0·21379	0·28435	Constant in	2·7841
38,000	Strato-	0·20376	0·27100	Strato-	2·9212
39,000	sphere	0·19420	0·25829	sphere	3·0650
40,000		0·18509	0·24617		3·2160
45,000		0·14555	0·19358		4·0896
50,000		0·11446	0·15223		5·2005
55,000		0·090005	0·11971		6·6133
60,000		0·070778	0·094136		8·4098
65,000	Constant in	0·055659	0·074027	Constant in	10·694
70,000	Strato-	0·043769	0·058213	Strato-	13·599
75,000	sphere	0·034419	0·045777	sphere	17·294
80,000		0·027066	0·035998		21·992
85,000		0·021284	0·028308		27·966
90,000		0·016738	0·022261		35·562
95,000		0·013162	0·017506		45·223
100,000		0·010350	0·013766		57·508

APPENDIX 3*

A SOLUTION OF INTEGRALS OF THE TYPE

$$G_n = \int_0^\pi \frac{\cos n\theta}{\cos \theta - \cos \theta_1} d\theta$$

In Chapters 12 and 13 much use is made of the integral

$$G_n = \int_0^\pi \frac{\cos n\theta}{\cos \theta - \cos \theta_1} d\theta$$

the result for which was quoted as

$$\pi \frac{\sin n\theta_1}{\sin \theta_1}$$

This may be proved, by contour integration, as follows.

In the complex plane, integrate the function

$$f(z) = \frac{z^n}{z^2 - 2z \cos \theta_1 + 1}$$

with respect to z round the circle of unit radius centred at the origin.

On this circle $z = e^{i\theta}$ and therefore

$$\int_C \frac{z^n \, dz}{z^2 - 2z \cos \theta_1 + 1} = \int_{-\pi}^{+\pi} \frac{e^{in\theta} \, i e^{i\theta} \, d\theta}{e^{2i\theta} - 2e^{i\theta} \cos \theta_1 + 1}$$

which, cancelling $e^{i\theta}$ from numerator and denominator, putting

$$e^{i\theta} = \cos \theta + i \sin \theta,$$

and using De Moivre's Theorem, reduces to

$$\frac{i}{2} \int_{-\pi}^{+\pi} \frac{\cos n\theta + i \sin n\theta}{\cos \theta - \cos \theta_1} d\theta \qquad . \qquad . \qquad . \qquad \text{(A,3.1)}$$

The *poles* or *singularities*† of the function $f(z)$ are those points where $f(z)$ is infinite, i.e. in this case where

$$z^2 - 2z \cos \theta_1 + 1 = 0$$

i.e.
$$z = \cos \theta_1 \pm i \sin \theta_1 = e^{\pm i\theta_1} . \qquad . \qquad . \qquad \text{(A,3.2)}$$

In general if a function $f(z)$ has a simple pole at the point $z = c$, then

$$\operatorname*{Lim}_{z \to c} (z - c) \, f(z)$$

is finite and its value is called the *residue* at the pole.

In this case

$$\operatorname*{Lim}_{z \to c} (z - c) \, f(z) = \operatorname*{Lim}_{z \to c} \left(\frac{(z - c)z^n}{z^2 - 2z \cos \theta_1 + 1} \right)$$

which, by L'Hôpital's Theorem,

$$= \left[\frac{\dfrac{d}{dz}\left\{ (z - c)z^n \right\}}{\dfrac{d}{dz}\left\{ z^2 - 2z \cos \theta_1 + 1) \right\}} \right]_{z=c}$$

---

* This section may be omitted at a first reading.
† See p. 277.

Thus differentiating and reducing, and for this case putting $c = e^{\pm i\theta_1}$, from equation (A,3.2) the residues at the two poles are $\dfrac{\sin n\theta_1 \pm i \cos n\theta_1}{2 \sin \theta_1}$ and the sum of the residues is

$$\frac{\sin n\theta_1}{\sin \theta_1} \qquad . \qquad . \qquad . \qquad . \qquad (A,3.3)$$

Now for this case the poles (at the points $z = e^{\pm i\theta_1}$) are *on* the contour of integration and by Cauchy's Residue Theorem the value of the integral eqn. (A,3.1) is equal to $\pi i \times$ (sum of the residues on the contour).

Thus

$$\frac{i}{2} \int_{-\pi}^{+\pi} \frac{\cos n\theta + i \sin n\theta}{\cos \theta - \cos \theta_1} d\theta = \pi i \frac{\sin n\theta_1}{\sin \theta_1} \qquad . \qquad . \qquad (A,3.4)$$

Equating the imaginary parts of this equation,

$$\frac{1}{2} \int_{-\pi}^{+\pi} \frac{\cos n\theta}{\cos \theta - \cos \theta_1} d\theta = \pi \frac{\sin n\theta_1}{\sin \theta_1}$$

while, by the symmetry of the integrand,

$$\int_{0}^{\pi} \frac{\cos n\theta}{\cos \theta - \cos \theta_1} d\theta = \frac{1}{2} \int_{-\pi}^{+\pi} \frac{\cos n\theta}{\cos \theta - \cos \theta_1} d\theta$$

i.e.

$$\int_{0}^{\pi} \frac{\cos n\theta}{\cos \theta - \cos \theta_1} d\theta = \pi \frac{\sin n\theta_1}{\sin \theta_1} \qquad . \qquad . \qquad . \qquad (A,3.5)$$

INDEX